Study Plan

▶ Course Calendar

Legend 🖨 ⑦

Click a chapter below to start practicing, or follow these steps to create a personalized study plan.

① Take a sample test or an assigned test or quiz. Then return to this page.

② Practice the topics you need to study(✐).

③ To prove mastery(🎓), take another sample test or an assigned test or quiz.

▶ Learn More

Show All | ✐ Show What I Need to Study   ➡ Jump to where I worked last

Book Contents for Topics I Need to Study		Correct	Worked	Available Exercises	Time Spent
⊖ Ch 2: Matrices	✐			32	
⊕ 2.1 Solving Systems of Linear Equations, I	✐			6	
⊕ 2.2 Solving Systems of Linear Equations, II	✐			6	
⊕ 2.3 Arithmetic Operations on Matrices	✐			9	
⊕ 2.4 The Inverse of a Matrix	✐			2	
⊕ 2.5 The Gauss-Jordan Method for Calculating Inverses	✐			5	
⊕ 2.6 Input-Output Analysis	✐			4	
Total: All Chapters		0	0	32	

▶ Show results that created this study plan

This course is based on Goldstein: Finite Mathematics and Its Applications, 9e
Copyright 2008 Pearson Education

Test prep when you need it

Take a practice test to gauge your readiness. MyMathLab generates a personalized Study Plan with links to interactive tutorial exercises for those skills you need to review.

D1411000

Pearson
Tutor
Center

Tutors when you need them

MyMathLab users have access to tutoring from the Pearson Math Tutor Center.*
The Tutor Center is staffed by qualified math instructors who provide one-on-one tutoring via toll-free phone, email, and real-time Internet sessions. For more details, visit **www.pearsontutorservices.com**

Proven

Since 2001, more than 3.3 million students at more than 1,800 colleges have used MyMathLab and MathXL. MyMathLab and MathXL provide you with a personalized, interactive learning environment where you can learn at your own pace, measure your progress, and improve your success in this course.

* Pearson Tutor Services are provided by Pearson Higher Education, a division of Pearson Education, for US and Canadian post-secondary students. Pearson's offer of tutoring service is subject to change without notice.

Student Purchasing Options

Talk to your instructor about using MyMathLab or MathXL for this course.

FINITE
MATHEMATICS
& ITS APPLICATIONS

Larry J. Goldstein
David I. Schneider
Martha J. Siegel

Second Custom Edition for Pepperdine University

Taken from:

Finite Mathematics & Its Applications, Tenth Edition
by Larry J. Goldstein, David I. Schneider, and Martha J. Siegel

Brief Calculus & Its Applications, Twelfth Edition
by Larry J. Goldstein, David C. Lay, David I. Schneider, and Nakhlé H. Asmar

Learning Solutions

New York   Boston   San Francisco
London   Toronto   Sydney   Tokyo   Singapore   Madrid
Mexico City   Munich   Paris   Cape Town   Hong Kong   Montreal

Cover Art: Courtesy of PhotoDisc/Getty Images

Taken from:

Finite Mathematics & Its Applications, Tenth Edition
by Larry J. Goldstein, David I. Schneider, and Martha J. Siegel
Copyright © 2010, 2007, 2004, 2001, 1998, 1995, 1991, 1988, 1984, 1980 by Pearson Education, Inc.
Published by Prentice Hall
Upper Saddle River, New Jersey 07458

Brief Calculus & Its Applications, Twelfth Edition
by Larry J. Goldstein, David C. Lay, David I. Schneider, and Nakhlé H. Asmar
Copyright © 2010, 2007, 2004, 2001, 1999, 1996, 1993, 1990, 1987, 1984, 1980, 1977 by Pearson Education, Inc.
Published by Prentice Hall
Upper Saddle River, New Jersey 07458

This special edition published in cooperation with Pearson Learning Solutions.

The information, illustrations, and/or software contained in this book, and regarding the above-mentioned programs, are provided "As Is," without warranty of any kind, express or implied, including without limitation any warranty concerning the accuracy, adequacy, or completeness of such information. Neither the publisher, the authors, nor the copyright holders shall be responsible for any claims attributable to errors, omissions, or other inaccuracies contained in this book. Nor shall they be liable for direct, indirect, special, incidental, or consequential damages arising out of the use of such information or material.

All trademarks, service marks, registered trademarks, and registered service marks are the property of their respective owners and are used herein for identification purposes only.

Pearson Learning Solutions, 501 Boylston Street, Suite 900, Boston, MA 02116
A Pearson Education Company
www.pearsoned.com

Printed in the United States of America

8 9 10 V202 15 14 13

000200010270650818

JH

ISBN 10: 0-558-92541-3
ISBN 13: 978-0-558-92541-3

CONTENTS

The book divides naturally into four parts. The first part consists of linear mathematics: linear equations, matrices, and linear programming (Chapters 1-4); the second part is devoted to probability and statistics (Chapters 5-7); the third part covers topics utilizing the ideas of the other parts (Chapters 8-10); and the fourth part explores key topics from discrete mathematics that are sometimes covered in the modern finite mathematics curriculum (Chapters 11-12).

5 Sets and Counting   205

6 Probability   263

7 Probability and Statistics   331

8 Markov Processes

9 The Theory of Games

From *Brief Calculus & Its Applications*, Twelfth Edition by Larry J. Goldstein, David C. Lay, David I. Schneider, and Nakhlé H. Asmar ISBN: 0321568567

From *Finite Mathematics & Its Applications,* Tenth Edition by Larry J. Goldstein, David I. Schneider, and Martha J. Siegel ISBN: 0321571894

PREFACE

This work is the tenth edition of our text for the traditional finite mathematics course taught to first- and second-year college students, especially those majoring in business and the social and biological sciences. Finite mathematics courses exhibit tremendous diversity with respect to both content and approach. Therefore, in developing this book, we incorporated a wide range of topics from which an instructor may design a curriculum, as well as a high degree of flexibility in the order in which the topics may be presented. For the mathematics of finance, we even allow for flexibility in the approach of the presentation.

The Series

This text is part of a series consisting of three texts: *Finite Mathematics & Its Applications*, *Calculus & Its Applications*, and *Brief Calculus & Its Applications*. All three titles are available for purchase in three formats: printed text, eBook and as an eBook within the MyMathLab online course.

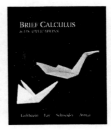

Topics Included

This edition has more material than can be covered in most one-semester courses. Therefore, the instructor can structure the course to the students' needs and interests. The book divides naturally into four parts. The first part consists of linear mathematics: linear equations, matrices, and linear programming (Chapters 1–4); the second part is devoted to probability and statistics (Chapters 5–7); the third part covers topics utilizing the ideas of the other parts (Chapters 8–10); and the fourth part explores key topics from discrete mathematics that are sometimes included in the modern finite mathematics curriculum (Chapters 11 and 12). We prefer to begin with linear mathematics since it makes for a smooth transition from high school mathematics and leads quickly to interesting applications, especially linear programming. Our preference notwithstanding, the instructor may begin this book with Chapter 5 (Sets and Counting) and then do either the linear mathematics or the probability and statistics.

Minimal Prerequisites

Because of great variation in student preparation, we keep formal prerequisites to a minimum. We assume only a first year of high school algebra. Furthermore, we review, as needed, those topics that are typically weak spots for students.

Trusted Features

In this edition, we attempt to maintain our popular student-oriented approach throughout and, in particular, by the following features:

Relevant and Varied Applications

We provide realistic applications that illustrate the uses of finite mathematics in other disciplines. The reader may survey the variety of applications by referring to the Index of Applications. Wherever possible, we attempt to use applications to motivate the mathematics. For example, the concept of linear programming is introduced in Chapter 3 via a discussion of production options for a factory with labor limitations.

Plentiful Examples

We include 353 worked examples, many more than is customary. Furthermore, we include computational details to enhance comprehension by students whose basic skills are weak.

Exercises to Meet All Student Needs

The 3171 exercises comprise about one-quarter of the book, the most important part of the text in our opinion. The exercises at the ends of the sections are usually arranged in the order in which the text proceeds, so that homework assignments may be made easily after only part of a section is discussed. Interesting applications and more challenging problems tend to be located near the ends of the exercise sets. Supplementary exercises at the end of each chapter amplify the other exercise sets and provide cumulative exercises that require skills acquired from earlier chapters. Answers to the odd-numbered exercises are included at the back of the book.

Exercises from Professional Exams

We have included questions similar to those found on CPA and GMAT exams to further illustrate the relevance of the material in the course. These multiple-choice questions are identified with the notation **PE**. Examples of this can be found in Chapter 1, pages 34–35.

Practice Problems

The Practice Problems are a popular and useful feature of the book. They are carefully selected exercises located at the end of each section, just before the exercise set. Complete solutions follow the exercise set. The Practice Problems often focus on points that are potentially confusing or are likely to be overlooked. We recommend that the reader seriously attempt to do the practice problems and study their solutions before moving on to the exercises.

Use of Technology

Although the use of technology is optional for this text, many of the topics can be enhanced with graphing calculators, spreadsheets, and mathematical software. Whenever relevant, we explicitly show the student how to use graphing calculators and spreadsheets effectively to assist in understanding the fundamental concepts of the course. In addition, the text contains appendices on the fundamentals of using graphing calculators and spreadsheets. The powerful mathematical software Explorations in Finite Mathematics is available for download from the Pearson website (www.pearsoned.com/goldstein). Many sections contain specially designed technology exercises intended to be solved with one of these technologies.

In our discussions of graphing calculators, we specifically refer to the TI-83/84 Plus calculators and the TI-89 since these are the most popular graphing calculators. Therefore, most students will have a book customized to their calculator. Students with other graphing calculators can consult their guidebooks to learn how to make adjustments. Had the calculator material been written generically, *every* student would have to make adjustments. For the same reasons, the discussions of electronic spreadsheets refer to Microsoft Excel.

End-of-Chapter Study Aids

Near the end of each chapter is a set of questions labeled Review of Fundamental Concepts that help the student recall the key ideas of the chapter and focus on the relevance of these concepts. Each chapter also contains a detailed summary of the important definitions and results from the chapter. Finally, each chapter has a sample test that can be used by the student to help determine if he or she has mastered the important concepts of the chapter.

Chapter Projects

Each chapter has an extended project that can be used as an in-class or out-of-class group project, or special assignment. These projects develop interesting applications or enhance key concepts of the chapters. For example, the Chapter 2 project, entitled "Population Dynamics," focuses on how logging directly affects the spotted owl population. This environmental application is one that will have relevance for students.

New to This Edition

Among the changes in this edition, the following are the most significant.

1. *Additional Exercises and Updated Data* We have added 217 new exercises and have updated the real-world data appearing in 55 exercises and examples.
2. *Algebra Comments* The steps performed when solving linear equations and inequalities are explained with brief comments.
3. *Transition Diagrams* The discussion of Markov processes has been enhanced by the use of transition diagrams.
4. *Financial Computations* The computations for compound interest, annuities, and mortgages in Chapter 10 (The Mathematics of Finance) are carried out with formulas rather than with tables.
5. *TVM Solver* The use of the TI-83/84 Plus' TVM Solver financial calculator is explained.
6. *More About Mortgages* A discussion of interest-only and adjustable-rate mortgages has been added to Section 10.4 (Personal Financial Decisions). This topic is especially relevant due to the role these mortgages played in precipitating the foreclosure crisis.
7. *Excel Upgrade* Although the use of spreadsheets is optional, many students are familiar with Excel and use it to enhance their understanding of the topics presented in the textbook. The discussion of Excel has been expanded to include Excel 2007.

Program Supplements

For Students

Student's Solutions Manual (ISBN: 0-321-59898-9)
Fully worked solutions to odd-numbered exercises

DVD Lecture Videos (ISBN: 0-321-57734-5)
A comprehensive set of topical videos, in which examples for each topic are worked out by an instructor. The videos provide excellent support for students who require additional assistance, for distance learning and self-paced programs, or for students who missed class.

For Instructors

Instructor's Edition (ISBN: 0-321-60013-4)
This version of the text includes answers to all exercises presented in the book.

Instructor Resource Center
All instructor resources can be downloaded from www.pearsonhighered.com/irc. This is a password-protected site that requires instructors to set up an account or, alternatively, instructor resources can be ordered from your Pearson

Higher Education sales representative. Instructors may use their instructor's log-in from MyMathLab to access the Instructor Resource Center.

Instructor's Solutions Manual (ISBN: 0-321-59897-0)
Fully worked solutions to every textbook exercise.

TestGen®
TestGen (www.pearsonhighered.com/testgen) enables instructors to build, edit, print, and administer tests using a computerized bank of questions developed to cover all of the text objectives. TestGen is algorithmically based, allowing instructors to create multiple but equivalent versions of the same question or test with the click of a button. Instructors can also modify test bank questions or add new ones. Tests can be printed or administered online. The software and testbank are available for download from Pearson Education's online catalog.

PowerPoint Lecture Slides
Fully editable and printable slides that follow the textbook. Use during lecture or post to a Web site in an online course. For download from the Instructor Resource Center and available within MyMathLab.

MyMathLab® Online Course (access code required)
MyMathLab is a series of text-specific, easily customizable online courses for Pearson Education's textbooks in mathematics and statistics. Powered by CourseCompass™ (our online teaching and learning environment) and MathXL® (our online homework, tutorial, and assessment system), MyMathLab gives you the tools you need to deliver all or a portion of your course online, whether students are in a lab setting or working from home. MyMathLab provides a rich and flexible set of course materials, featuring free-response exercises that are algorithmically generated for unlimited practice and mastery. Students can also use online tools, such as video lectures, animations, and a multimedia textbook, to independently improve their understanding and performance. Instructors can use MyMathLab's homework and test managers to select and assign online exercises correlated to the textbook, and they can also create and assign their own online exercises and import TestGen tests for added flexibility. MyMathLab's online gradebook—designed specifically for mathematics and statistics—automatically tracks students' homework and test results and gives the instructor control over how to calculate final grades. Instructors can also add offline (paper-and-pencil) grades to the gradebook. MyMathLab also includes access to the **Pearson Tutor Center** (www.pearsontutorservices.com). The Tutor Center is staffed by qualified mathematics instructors who provide textbook-specific tutoring for students via toll-free phone, fax, email, and interactive Web sessions. MyMathLab is available to qualified adopters. For more information, visit our website at www.mymathlab.com or contact your sales representative.

MathXL® Online Course (access code required)
MathXL® is a powerful online homework, tutorial, and assessment system that accompanies Pearson Education's textbooks in mathematics or statistics. With MathXL, instructors can create, edit, and assign online homework and tests using algorithmically generated exercises correlated to the textbook's objectives. They can also create and assign their own online exercises and import TestGen tests for added flexibility. All student work is tracked in MathXL's online gradebook. Students can take chapter tests in MathXL and receive personalized study plans based on their test results. The study plan diagnoses weaknesses and links students directly to tutorial exercises for the objectives they need to study and retest. Students can also access supplemental animations and video clips directly from selected exercises. MathXL is available to qualified adopters. For more information, visit our website at www.mathxl.com, or contact your Pearson sales representative.

Explorations in Finite Mathematics
Built from the ground up by David Schneider (University of Maryland), *Explorations in Finite Mathematics*, which runs on both Macintosh and PC computers, enhances the understanding of many topics covered in the text through the visualization of said topics. Part One of this software covers linear mathematics topics involving linear equations, linear inequalities, and matrices. Students will be able to perform routines such as Gauss–Jordan elimination, matrix operations and inversions, the simplex method, and Markov chains. Part Two contains routines for Venn diagrams, computation of combinations, permutations and factorials, statistical analysis of data, financial calculations and much more. *Explorations in Finite Mathematics* is available for download from the Website www.pearsoned.com/goldstein.

Acknowledgments

While writing this book, we have received assistance from many persons. And our heartfelt thanks go out to them all. Especially, we should like to thank the following reviewers, who took the time and energy to share their ideas, preferences, and often their enthusiasm, with us.

Reviewers of the Tenth Edition

Michelle DeDeo, *University of North Florida*

Helen M. Doerr, *Syracuse University*

Russell E. Goodman, *Central College*

Barry J. Griffiths, *University of Central Florida*

Klara Grodzinsky, *Georgia Institute of Technology*

Phillip Miller, *Indiana University Southeast*

Erika Miller, *Towson University*

Rennie Mirollo, *Boston College*

Reviewers of Earlier Editions

Josephine Battaglia, *Pennsylvania State University*

Karl A. Beres, *Ripon College*

Larry G. Blaine, *Plymouth State University*

William D. Blair, *Northern Illinois University*

Brenda Bloomgarden, *Chesapeake College*

Paul Boisvert, *Robert Morris College*

Bart Braden, *Northern Kentucky University*

Stephen H. Brown, *Auburn University*

Robert Carmignani, *University of Missouri*

Eric Chandler, *Randolph-Macon College*

James P. Coughlin, *Towson University*

Sam Councilman, *California State University, Long Beach*

D.R. Dunninger, *Michigan State University*

Karen J. Edwards, *Paul Smith's College*

Theodore Faticoni, *Fordham University*

Gary W. Frick, *The College of Southern Maryland*

Robert Gusalnick, *University of South Carolina*

Juan Gatica, *University of Iowa*

Ruthanne Harre, *Missouri Valley College*

Eric Heinz, *Catonsville Community College*

Russell Hendel, *Towson University*

Thomas J. Hill, *University of Oklahoma, Norman*

James F. Hurley, *University of Connecticut*

Ralph James, *California State University at Stanislaus*

Donald A. Jones, *Oregon State University*

Karla Karstens, *University of Vermont*

Philip Kutzko, *University of Iowa*

Peter Majumdar, *Indiana-Purdue University at Fort Wayne*

Manoug Manougian, *University of South Florida*

Joan McCarter, *Arizona State University*

Jeanette L. McGillicuddy, *River College*

Michael McLane, *Purdue University*

Carl D. Meyer, Jr., *North Carolina State University*

Juan Migliore, *University of Notre Dame*

Charles J. Miller, *Foothill Community College*

Donald E. Myers, *University of Arizona, Tempe*

Richard O'Malley, *University of Wisconsin at Milwaukee*

Roger Osborn, *University of Texas, Austin*

Hiram Paley, *Univeristy of Illinois, Urbana-Champaign*

Mary Pearce, *Austin Community College*

Richard Pellerin, *Northern Virginia Community College*

Dennis Pence, *Western Michigan University*

Richard Porter, *Northeastern University*

William Ramaley, *Fort Lewis College*

Henry J. Ricardo, *Medgar Evers College of the City University of New York*

Arthur Rosenthal, *Salem State College*

Linda Schultz, *McHenry County College*

Elisabeth Schuster, *DeVry Institute of Technology*

Randy Schwartz, *Schoolcraft College*

Joseph Stampfli, *Indiana University*

Phil Steitz, *Beloit College*

Robin G. Symonds, *Indiana University at Kokomo*

Martin C. Tangora, *University of Illinois, Chicago*

Elizabeth Teles, *Montgomery College*

James C. Thorpe, *University of Missouri, St. Louis*

David C. Vella, *Skidmore College*

Tan Vovan, *Suffolk University*

Hugh Walters, *Contra Costa College*

Chungkuang Wang, *Fashion Institute of Technology*

Frank Warner, *University of Pennsylvania*

Rebecca Wells, *Henderson Community College*

Peter Williams, *California State University at San Bernardino*

Cynthia Wilson, *Life College*

We also thank the many people at Pearson who have contributed to the success of this book. We appreciate the efforts of the production, art, manufacturing, marketing, and sales departments. We are grateful to Anthony Gagliardi, Damon Demas, Paul Lorczak, Helen Doerr, and Haizhang Zhang for their careful creation and thorough checking of solutions to exercises. Our sincere thanks to Erica O'Leary for her assistance throughout the revision of the book and Peter Rosenbaum for his assistance with the finance chapter. Production editor Bob Walters did a fantastic job keeping the book on schedule. The authors wish to extend special thanks to our editors Christine O'Brien and Chuck Synovec, and our typesetter Dennis Kletzing. Christine and Chuck's help in planning and executing this new edition was greatly appreciated. Dennis' considerable skills and congenial manner made for an uncomplicated and pleasant production process.

If you have comments or suggestions, we would like to hear from you. We hope that you enjoy using this book as much as we have enjoyed writing it.

Larry J. Goldstein
larrygoldstein@comcast.net

David I. Schneider
dis@math.umd.edu

Martha J. Siegel
msiegel@towson.edu

From *Brief Calculus & Its Applications*, Twelfth Edition by Larry J. Goldstein, David C. Lay, David I. Schneider, and Nakhlé H. Asmar ISBN: 0321568567

FUNCTIONS OF SEVERAL VARIABLES

Until now, most of our applications of calculus have involved functions of one variable. In real life, however, a quantity of interest often depends on more than one variable. For instance, the sales level of a product may depend not only on its price, but also on the prices of competing products, the amount spent on advertising, and perhaps the time of year. The total cost of manufacturing the product depends on the cost of raw materials, labor, plant maintenance, and so on.

This chapter introduces the basic ideas of calculus for functions of more than one variable. Section 7.1 presents two examples that will be used throughout the chapter. Derivatives are treated in Section 7.2 and then used in Sections 7.3 and 7.4 to solve optimization problems more general than those in Chapter 2. The final two sections are devoted to least-squares problems and a brief introduction to the integration of functions of two variables.

7.1 Examples of Functions of Several Variables

A function $f(x, y)$ of the two variables x and y is a rule that assigns a number to each pair of values for the variables; for instance,

$$f(x, y) = e^x(x^2 + 2y).$$

An example of a function of three variables is

$$f(x, y, z) = 5xy^2z.$$

EXAMPLE 1   A store sells butter at \$2.50 per pound and margarine at \$1.40 per pound. The revenue from the sale of x pounds of butter and y pounds of margarine is given by the function

$$f(x, y) = 2.50x + 1.40y.$$

Determine and interpret $f(200, 300)$.

Solution $f(200, 300) = 2.50(200) + 1.40(300) = 500 + 420 = 920$. The revenue from the sale of 200 pounds of butter and 300 pounds of margarine is \$920.   ■

A function $f(x, y)$ of two variables may be graphed in a manner analogous to that for functions of one variable. It is necessary to use a three-dimensional coordinate system, where each point is identified by three coordinates (x, y, z). For each choice of x, y, the graph of $f(x, y)$ includes the point $(x, y, f(x, y))$. This graph is usually a surface in three-dimensional space, with equation $z = f(x, y)$. (See Fig. 1.) Three graphs of specific functions are shown in Fig. 2.

Application to Architectural Design   When designing a building, we would like to know, at least approximately, how much heat the building loses per day. The heat loss affects many aspects of the design, such as the size of the heating plant, the size and location of duct work, and so on. A building loses heat through its sides, roof, and floor. How much heat is lost will generally differ for each face of the building and will depend on such factors as insulation, materials used in construction, exposure (north, south, east, or west), and climate. It is possible to estimate how much heat is lost per square foot of each face. Using these data, we can construct a heat-loss function as in the following example.

EXAMPLE 2   A rectangular industrial building of dimensions x, y, and z is shown in Fig. 3(a). In Fig. 3(b) we give the amount of heat lost per day by each side of the building, measured in suitable units of heat per square foot. Let $f(x, y, z)$ be the total daily heat loss for such a building.

(a) Find a formula for $f(x, y, z)$.

(b) Find the total daily heat loss if the building has length 100 feet, width 70 feet, and height 50 feet.

Solution   (a) The total heat loss is the sum of the amount of heat loss through each face of the building. The heat loss through the roof is

[heat loss per square foot of roof] · [area of roof in square feet] $= 10xy$.

Similarly, the heat loss through the east side is $8yz$. Continuing in this way, we see that the total daily heat loss is

$$f(x, y, z) = 10xy + 8yz + 6yz + 10xz + 5xz + 1 \cdot xy.$$

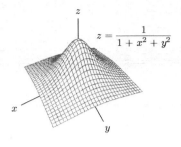

$$z = \frac{1}{1 + x^2 + y^2}$$

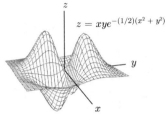

$$z = xye^{-(1/2)(x^2 + y^2)}$$

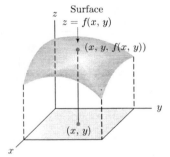

Figure 1. Graph of $f(x, y)$.

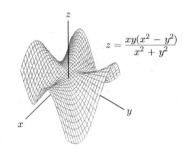

$$z = \frac{xy(x^2 - y^2)}{x^2 + y^2}$$

Figure 2

We collect terms to obtain

$$f(x, y, z) = 11xy + 14yz + 15xz.$$

(b) The amount of heat loss when $x = 100$, $y = 70$, and $z = 50$ is given by $f(100, 70, 50)$, which equals

$$f(100, 70, 50) = 11(100)(70) + 14(70)(50) + 15(100)(50)$$
$$= 77{,}000 + 49{,}000 + 75{,}000 = 201{,}000.$$
 ■

In Section 7.3 we will determine the dimensions x, y, z that minimize the heat loss for a building of specific volume.

Production Functions in Economics The costs of a manufacturing process can generally be classified as one of two types: cost of labor and cost of capital. The meaning of the cost of labor is clear. By the cost of capital, we mean the cost of buildings, tools, machines, and similar items used in the production process. A manufacturer usually has some control over the relative portions of labor and capital utilized in its production process. It can completely automate production so that labor is at a minimum or utilize mostly labor and little capital. Suppose that x units of labor and y units of capital are used.* Let $f(x, y)$ denote the number of units

---

*Economists normally use L and K, respectively, for labor and capital. However, for simplicity, we use x and y.

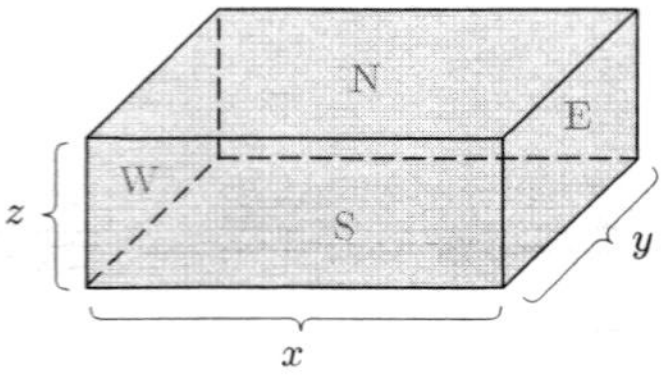

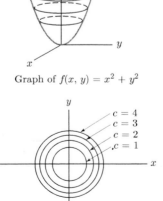

	Roof	East side	West side	North side	South side	Floor
Heat loss (per sq ft)	10	8	6	10	5	1
Area (sq ft)	xy	yz	yz	xz	xz	xy

(a)   (b)

Figure 3. Heat loss from an industrial building.

of finished product that are manufactured. Economists have found that $f(x, y)$ is often a function of the form

$$f(x, y) = Cx^A y^{1-A},$$

where A and C are constants, $0 < A < 1$. Such a function is called a *Cobb–Douglas production function.*

EXAMPLE 3

Production in a firm Suppose that during a certain time period the number of units of goods produced when utilizing x units of labor and y units of capital is $f(x, y) = 60x^{3/4}y^{1/4}$.

(a) How many units of goods will be produced by using 81 units of labor and 16 units of capital?

(b) Show that whenever the amounts of labor and capital being used are doubled so is the production. (Economists say that the production function has "constant returns to scale.")

Solution (a) $f(81, 16) = 60(81)^{3/4} \cdot (16)^{1/4} = 60 \cdot 27 \cdot 2 = 3240$. There will be 3240 units of goods produced.

(b) Utilization of a units of labor and b units of capital results in the production of $f(a, b) = 60a^{3/4}b^{1/4}$ units of goods. Utilizing $2a$ and $2b$ units of labor and capital, respectively, results in $f(2a, 2b)$ units produced. Set $x = 2a$ and $y = 2b$. Then we see that

$$f(2a, 2b) = 60(2a)^{3/4}(2b)^{1/4}$$
$$= 60 \cdot 2^{3/4} \cdot a^{3/4} \cdot 2^{1/4} \cdot b^{1/4}$$
$$= 60 \cdot 2^{(3/4+1/4)} \cdot a^{3/4}b^{1/4}$$
$$= 2^1 \cdot 60a^{3/4}b^{1/4}$$
$$= 2f(a, b). \qquad \blacksquare$$

Graph of $f(x, y) = x^2 + y^2$

$c = 4$
$c = 3$
$c = 2$
$c = 1$

Level curves of $f(x, y) = x^2 + y^2$

Figure 4. Level curves.

Level Curves It is possible graphically to depict a function $f(x, y)$ of two variables using a family of curves called level curves. Let c be any number. Then the graph of the equation $f(x, y) = c$ is a curve in the xy-plane called the *level curve of height c*. This curve describes all points of height c on the graph of the function $f(x, y)$. As c varies, we have a family of level curves indicating the sets of points on which $f(x, y)$ assumes various values c. In Fig. 4 we have drawn the graph and various level curves for the function $f(x, y) = x^2 + y^2$.

Level curves often have interesting physical interpretations. For example, surveyors draw *topographic maps* that use level curves to represent points having equal altitude. Here $f(x, y) =$ the altitude at point (x, y). Figure 5(a) shows the graph of

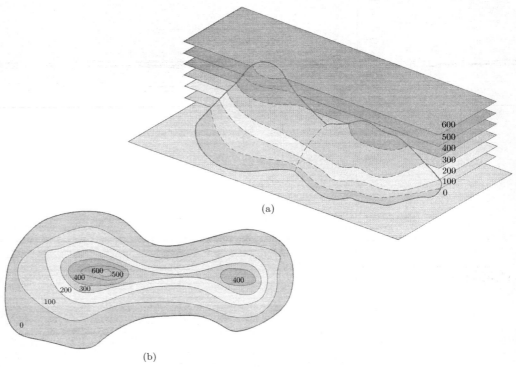

(a)

(b)

Figure 5. Topographic level curves show altitudes.

$f(x, y)$ for a typical hilly region. Figure 5(b) shows the level curves corresponding to various altitudes. Note that when the level curves are closer together the surface is steeper.

EXAMPLE 4   Determine the level curve at height 600 for the production function $f(x, y) = 60x^{3/4}y^{1/4}$ of Example 3.

Solution   The level curve is the graph of $f(x, y) = 600$, or

$$60x^{3/4}y^{1/4} = 600$$

$$y^{1/4} = \frac{10}{x^{3/4}}$$

$$y = \frac{10{,}000}{x^3}.$$

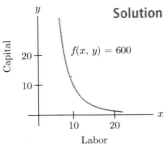

Figure 6. A level curve of a production function.

Of course, since x and y represent quantities of labor and capital, they must both be positive. We have sketched the graph of the level curve in Fig. 6. The points on the curve are precisely those combinations of capital and labor that yield 600 units of production. Economists call this curve an *isoquant* .   ∎

Practice Problems 7.1

1. Let $f(x, y, z) = x^2 + y/(x - z) - 4$. Compute $f(3, 5, 2)$.

2. In a certain country the daily demand for coffee is

given by $f(p_1, p_2) = 16p_1/p_2$ thousand pounds, where p_1 and p_2 are the respective prices of tea and coffee in dollars per pound. Compute and interpret $f(3, 4)$.

EXERCISES 7.1

1. Let $f(x, y) = x^2 - 3xy - y^2$. Compute $f(5, 0)$, $f(5, -2)$, and $f(a, b)$.

2. Let $g(x, y) = \sqrt{x^2 + 2y^2}$. Compute $g(1, 1)$, $g(0, -1)$, and $g(a, b)$.

3. Let $g(x, y, z) = x/(y - z)$. Compute $g(2, 3, 4)$ and $g(7, 46, 44)$.

4. Let $f(x, y, z) = x^2 e^{\sqrt{y^2 + z^2}}$. Compute $f(1, -1, 1)$ and $f(2, 3, -4)$.

5. Let $f(x, y) = xy$. Show that $f(2 + h, 3) - f(2, 3) = 3h$.

6. Let $f(x, y) = xy$. Show that $f(2, 3 + k) - f(2, 3) = 2k$.

7. **Cost** Find a formula $C(x, y, z)$ that gives the cost of materials for the closed rectangular box in Fig. 7(a), with dimensions in feet. Assume that the material for the top and bottom costs \$3 per square foot and the material for the sides costs \$5 per square foot.

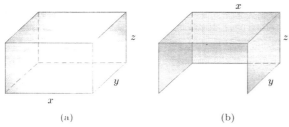

(a)   (b)

Figure 7

8. **Cost** Find a formula $C(x, y, z)$ that gives the cost of material for the rectangular enclosure in Fig. 7(b), with dimensions in feet. Assume that the material for the top costs \$3 per square foot and the material for the back and two sides costs \$5 per square foot.

9. Consider the Cobb–Douglas production function $f(x, y) = 20x^{1/3}y^{2/3}$. Compute $f(8, 1)$, $f(1, 27)$, and $f(8, 27)$. Show that, for any positive constant k, $f(8k, 27k) = kf(8, 27)$.

10. Let $f(x, y) = 10x^{2/5}y^{3/5}$. Show that $f(3a, 3b) = 3f(a, b)$.

11. The present value of A dollars to be paid t years in the future (assuming a 5% continuous interest rate) is $P(A, t) = Ae^{-.05t}$. Find and interpret $P(100, 13.8)$.

12. Refer to Example 3. If labor costs \$100 per unit and capital costs \$200 per unit, express as a function of two variables, $C(x, y)$, the cost of utilizing x units of labor and y units of capital.

13. **Tax and Homeowner Exemption** The value of residential property for tax purposes is usually much lower than its actual market value. If v is the market value, the *assessed value* for real estate taxes might be only 40%

of v. Suppose that the property tax, T, in a community is given by the function

$$T = f(r, v, x) = \frac{r}{100}(.40v - x),$$

where v is the estimated market value of a property (in dollars), x is a *homeowner's exemption* (a number of dollars depending on the type of property), and r is the tax rate (stated in dollars per hundred dollars) of net assessed value.

(a) Determine the real estate tax on a property valued at \$200,000 with a homeowner's exemption of \$5000, assuming a tax rate of \$2.50 per hundred dollars of net assessed value.

(b) Determine the tax due if the tax rate increases by 20% to \$3.00 per hundred dollars of net assessed value. Assume the same property value and homeowner's exemption. Does the tax due also increase by 20%?

14. Let $f(r, v, x)$ be the real estate tax function of Exercise 13.

(a) Determine the real estate tax on a property valued at \$100,000 with a homeowner's exemption of \$5000, assuming a tax rate of \$2.20 per hundred dollars of net assessed value.

(b) Determine the real estate tax when the market value rises 20% to \$120,000. Assume the same homeowner's exemption and a tax rate of \$2.20 per hundred dollars of net assessed value. Does the tax due also increase by 20%?

Draw the level curves of heights 0, 1, and 2 for the functions in Exercises 15 and 16.

15. $f(x, y) = 2x - y$ 16. $f(x, y) = -x^2 + 2y$

17. Draw the level curve of the function $f(x, y) = x - y$ containing the point $(0, 0)$.

18. Draw the level curve of the function $f(x, y) = xy$ containing the point $(\frac{1}{2}, 4)$.

19. Find a function $f(x, y)$ that has the line $y = 3x - 4$ as a level curve.

20. Find a function $f(x, y)$ that has the curve $y = 2/x^2$ as a level curve.

21. Suppose that a topographic map is viewed as the graph of a certain function $f(x, y)$. What are the level curves?

22. A certain production process uses labor and capital. If the quantities of these commodities are x and y, respectively, the total cost is $100x + 200y$ dollars. Draw the level curves of height 600, 800, and 1000 for this function. Explain the significance of these curves. (Economists frequently refer to these lines as *budget lines* or *isocost lines*.)

Match the graphs of the functions in Exercises 23–26 to the systems of level curves shown in Figs. 8(a)–(d).

23.

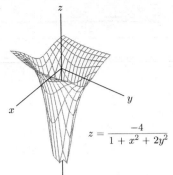

$$z = \frac{-4}{1 + x^2 + 2y^2}$$

24.

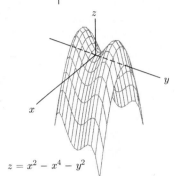

$$z = x^2 - x^4 - y^2$$

25.

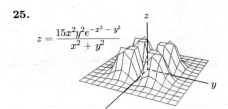

$$z = \frac{15x^2y^2e^{-x^2-y^2}}{x^2 + y^2}$$

26.

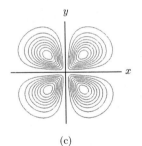

$$z = e^{-x^2} + e^{-4y^2}$$

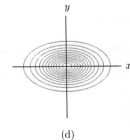

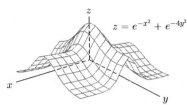

(a)   (b)   (c)   (d)

Figure 8

Solutions to Practice Problems 7.1

1. Substitute 3 for x, 5 for y, and 2 for z.

$$f(3, 5, 2) = 3^2 + \frac{5}{3 - 2} - 4 = 10.$$

2. To compute $f(3, 4)$, substitute 3 for p_1 and 4 for p_2 into $f(p_1, p_2) = 16p_1/p_2$. Thus

$$f(3, 4) = 16 \cdot \tfrac{3}{4} = 12.$$

Therefore, if the price of tea is \$3 per pound and the price of coffee is \$4 per pound, 12,000 pounds of coffee will be sold each day. (Notice that as the price of coffee increases the demand decreases.)

7.2 Partial Derivatives

In Chapter 1 we introduced the notion of a derivative to measure the rate at which a function $f(x)$ is changing with respect to changes in the variable x. Let us now study the analog of the derivative for functions of two (or more) variables.

Let $f(x, y)$ be a function of the two variables x and y. Since we want to know how $f(x, y)$ changes with respect to the changes in both the variable x and the variable y, we shall define two derivatives of $f(x, y)$ (to be called partial derivatives), one with respect to each variable.

> **DEFINITION**   The *partial derivative of $f(x, y)$ with respect to x*, written $\dfrac{\partial f}{\partial x}$, is the derivative of $f(x, y)$, where y is treated as a constant and $f(x, y)$ is considered as a function of x alone. The *partial derivative of $f(x, y)$ with respect to y*, written $\dfrac{\partial f}{\partial y}$, is the derivative of $f(x, y)$, where x is treated as a constant.

EXAMPLE 1   Let $f(x, y) = 5x^3 y^2$. Compute

$$\frac{\partial f}{\partial x} \quad \text{and} \quad \frac{\partial f}{\partial y}.$$

Solution   To compute $\dfrac{\partial f}{\partial x}$, we think of $f(x, y)$ written as

$$f(x, y) = \left[5y^2\right] x^3,$$

where the brackets emphasize that $5y^2$ is to be treated as a constant. Therefore, when differentiating with respect to x, $f(x, y)$ is just a constant times x^3. Recall that if k is any constant then

$$\frac{d}{dx}(kx^3) = 3 \cdot k \cdot x^2.$$

Thus

$$\frac{\partial f}{\partial x} = 3 \cdot \left[5y^2\right] \cdot x^2 = 15x^2 y^2.$$

After some practice, it is unnecessary to place the y^2 in front of the x^3 before differentiating.

Now, to compute $\dfrac{\partial f}{\partial y}$, we think of

$$f(x, y) = \left[5x^3\right] y^2.$$

When differentiating with respect to y, $f(x, y)$ is simply a constant (that is, $5x^3$) times y^2. Hence

$$\frac{\partial f}{\partial y} = 2 \cdot \left[5x^3\right] \cdot y = 10x^3 y. \qquad \blacksquare$$

EXAMPLE 2   Let $f(x, y) = 3x^2 + 2xy + 5y$. Compute

$$\frac{\partial f}{\partial x} \quad \text{and} \quad \frac{\partial f}{\partial y}.$$

Solution To compute $\dfrac{\partial f}{\partial x}$, we think of

$$f(x,y) = 3x^2 + [2y]x + [5y].$$

Now we differentiate $f(x,y)$ as if it were a quadratic polynomial in x:

$$\frac{\partial f}{\partial x} = 6x + [2y] + 0 = 6x + 2y.$$

Note that $5y$ is treated as a constant when differentiating with respect to x, so the partial derivative of $5y$ with respect to x is zero.

To compute $\dfrac{\partial f}{\partial y}$, we think of

$$f(x,y) = \left[3x^2\right] + [2x]y + 5y.$$

Then

$$\frac{\partial f}{\partial y} = 0 + [2x] + 5 = 2x + 5.$$

Note that $3x^2$ is treated as a constant when differentiating with respect to y, so the partial derivative of $3x^2$ with respect to y is zero. ∎

EXAMPLE 3   Compute

$$\frac{\partial f}{\partial x} \quad \text{and} \quad \frac{\partial f}{\partial y}$$

for each of the following.

(a) $f(x,y) = (4x + 3y - 5)^8$ **(b)** $f(x,y) = e^{xy^2}$ **(c)** $f(x,y) = y/(x + 3y)$

Solution (a) To compute $\dfrac{\partial f}{\partial x}$, we think of

$$f(x,y) = (4x + [3y - 5])^8.$$

By the general power rule,

$$\frac{\partial f}{\partial x} = 8 \cdot (4x + [3y - 5])^7 \cdot 4 = 32(4x + 3y - 5)^7.$$

Here we used the fact that the derivative of $4x + 3y - 5$ with respect to x is just 4.

To compute $\dfrac{\partial f}{\partial y}$, we think of

$$f(x,y) = ([4x] + 3y - 5)^8.$$

Then

$$\frac{\partial f}{\partial y} = 8 \cdot ([4x] + 3y - 5)^7 \cdot 3 = 24(4x + 3y - 5)^7.$$

(b) To compute $\dfrac{\partial f}{\partial x}$, we observe that

$$f(x,y) = e^{x[y^2]},$$

so that

$$\frac{\partial f}{\partial x} = \left[y^2\right] e^{x[y^2]} = y^2 e^{xy^2}.$$

To compute $\dfrac{\partial f}{\partial y}$, we think of

$$f(x,y) = e^{[x]y^2}.$$

Thus

$$\frac{\partial f}{\partial y} = e^{[x]y^2} \cdot 2[x]y = 2xye^{xy^2}.$$

(c) To compute $\frac{\partial f}{\partial x}$, we use the general power rule to differentiate $[y](x + [3y])^{-1}$ with respect to x:

$$\frac{\partial f}{\partial x} = (-1) \cdot [y](x + [3y])^{-2} \cdot 1 = -\frac{y}{(x + 3y)^2}.$$

To compute $\frac{\partial f}{\partial y}$, we use the quotient rule to differentiate

$$f(x, y) = \frac{y}{[x] + 3y}$$

with respect to y. We find that

$$\frac{\partial f}{\partial y} = \frac{([x] + 3y) \cdot 1 - y \cdot 3}{([x] + 3y)^2} = \frac{x}{(x + 3y)^2}.$$

The use of brackets to highlight constants is helpful initially to compute partial derivatives. From now on we shall merely form a mental picture of those terms to be treated as constants and dispense with brackets. ■

A partial derivative of a function of several variables is also a function of several variables and hence can be evaluated at specific values of the variables. We write

$$\frac{\partial f}{\partial x}(a, b)$$

for $\frac{\partial f}{\partial x}$ evaluated at $x = a$, $y = b$. Similarly,

$$\frac{\partial f}{\partial y}(a, b)$$

denotes the function $\frac{\partial f}{\partial y}$ evaluated at $x = a$, $y = b$.

EXAMPLE 4   Let $f(x, y) = 3x^2 + 2xy + 5y$.

(a) Calculate $\frac{\partial f}{\partial x}(1, 4)$.   **(b)** Evaluate $\frac{\partial f}{\partial y}$ at $(x, y) = (1, 4)$.

Solution (a) $\frac{\partial f}{\partial x} = 6x + 2y$, $\frac{\partial f}{\partial x}(1, 4) = 6 \cdot 1 + 2 \cdot 4 = 14$.

(b) $\frac{\partial f}{\partial y} = 2x + 5$, $\frac{\partial f}{\partial y}(1, 4) = 2 \cdot 1 + 5 = 7$. ■

Geometric Interpretation of Partial Derivatives   Consider the three-dimensional surface $z = f(x, y)$ in Fig. 1. If y is held constant at b and x is allowed to vary, the equation

$$z = f(x, b)$$
$$\underset{\text{constant}}{\big\uparrow}$$

describes a curve on the surface. [The curve is formed by cutting the surface $z = f(x, y)$ with a vertical plane parallel to the xz-plane.] The value of $\frac{\partial f}{\partial x}(a, b)$ is the slope of the tangent line to the curve at the point where $x = a$ and $y = b$.

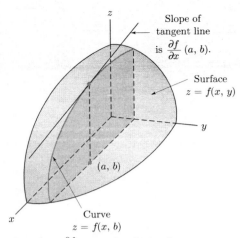

Figure 1. $\frac{\partial f}{\partial x}$ gives the slope of a curve formed by holding y constant.

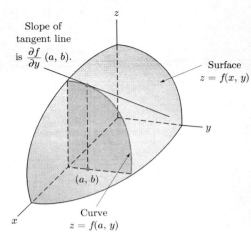

Figure 2. $\frac{\partial f}{\partial y}$ gives the slope of a curve formed by holding x constant.

Likewise, if x is held constant at a and y is allowed to vary, the equation

$$z = f(a, y)$$

constant

describes the curve on the surface $z = f(x, y)$ shown in Fig. 2. The value of the partial derivative $\frac{\partial f}{\partial y}(a, b)$ is the slope of this curve at the point where $x = a$ and $y = b$.

Partial Derivatives and Rates of Change   Since $\frac{\partial f}{\partial x}$ is simply the ordinary derivative with y held constant, $\frac{\partial f}{\partial x}$ gives the rate of change of $f(x, y)$ with respect to x for y held constant. In other words, keeping y constant and increasing x by one (small) unit produces a change in $f(x, y)$ that is approximately given by $\frac{\partial f}{\partial x}$. An analogous interpretation holds for $\frac{\partial f}{\partial y}$.

EXAMPLE 5   Interpret the partial derivatives of $f(x, y) = 3x^2 + 2xy + 5y$ calculated in Example 4.

Solution   We showed in Example 4 that

$$\frac{\partial f}{\partial x}(1, 4) = 14, \qquad \frac{\partial f}{\partial y}(1, 4) = 7.$$

The fact that

$$\frac{\partial f}{\partial x}(1, 4) = 14$$

means that if y is kept constant at 4 and x is allowed to vary near 1, then $f(x, y)$ changes at a rate 14 times the change in x. That is, if x increases by one small unit, $f(x, y)$ increases by approximately 14 units. If x increases by h units (where h is small), $f(x, y)$ increases by approximately $14 \cdot h$ units. That is,

$$f(1 + h, 4) - f(1, 4) \approx 14 \cdot h.$$

Similarly, the fact that

$$\frac{\partial f}{\partial y}(1,4) = 7$$

means that, if we keep x constant at 1 and let y vary near 4, then $f(x,y)$ changes at a rate equal to seven times the change in y. So, for a small value of k, we have

$$f(1, 4 + k) - f(1, 4) \approx 7 \cdot k.$$ ■

We can generalize the interpretations of $\frac{\partial f}{\partial x}$ and $\frac{\partial f}{\partial y}$ given in Example 5 to yield the following general fact:

Let $f(x,y)$ be a function of two variables. Then, if h and k are small, we have

$$f(a + h, b) - f(a, b) \approx \frac{\partial f}{\partial x}(a, b) \cdot h,$$

$$f(a, b + k) - f(a, b) \approx \frac{\partial f}{\partial y}(a, b) \cdot k.$$

Partial derivatives can be computed for functions of any number of variables. When taking the partial derivative with respect to one variable, we treat the other variables as constant.

EXAMPLE 6   Let $f(x, y, z) = x^2 yz - 3z$.

(a) Compute $\frac{\partial f}{\partial x}, \frac{\partial f}{\partial y},$ and $\frac{\partial f}{\partial z}$.   (b) Calculate $\frac{\partial f}{\partial z}(2, 3, 1)$.

Solution (a) $\frac{\partial f}{\partial x} = 2xyz, \frac{\partial f}{\partial y} = x^2 z, \frac{\partial f}{\partial z} = x^2 y - 3.$

(b) $\frac{\partial f}{\partial z}(2, 3, 1) = 2^2 \cdot 3 - 3 = 12 - 3 = 9.$ ■

EXAMPLE 7   Let $f(x, y, z)$ be the heat-loss function computed in Example 2 of Section 7.1. That is, $f(x, y, z) = 11xy + 14yz + 15xz$. Calculate and interpret $\frac{\partial f}{\partial x}(10, 7, 5)$.

Solution We have

$$\frac{\partial f}{\partial x} = 11y + 15z$$

$$\frac{\partial f}{\partial x}(10, 7, 5) = 11 \cdot 7 + 15 \cdot 5 = 77 + 75 = 152.$$

The quantity $\frac{\partial f}{\partial x}$ is commonly referred to as the *marginal heat loss with respect to change in x*. Specifically, if x is changed from 10 by h units (where h is small) and the values of y and z remain fixed at 7 and 5, the amount of heat loss will change by approximately $152 \cdot h$ units.   ■

EXAMPLE 8   **Production**   Consider the production function $f(x, y) = 60x^{3/4}y^{1/4}$, which gives the number of units of goods produced when utilizing x units of labor and y units of capital.

(a) Find $\dfrac{\partial f}{\partial x}$ and $\dfrac{\partial f}{\partial y}$.

(b) Evaluate $\dfrac{\partial f}{\partial x}$ and $\dfrac{\partial f}{\partial y}$ at $x = 81$, $y = 16$.

(c) Interpret the numbers computed in part (b).

Solution (a) $\dfrac{\partial f}{\partial x} = 60 \cdot \dfrac{3}{4} x^{-1/4} y^{1/4} = 45 x^{-1/4} y^{1/4} = 45 \dfrac{y^{1/4}}{x^{1/4}}$,

$\dfrac{\partial f}{\partial y} = 60 \cdot \dfrac{1}{4} x^{3/4} y^{-3/4} = 15 x^{3/4} y^{-3/4} = 15 \dfrac{x^{3/4}}{y^{3/4}}$.

(b) $\dfrac{\partial f}{\partial x}(81, 16) = 45 \cdot \dfrac{16^{1/4}}{81^{1/4}} = 45 \cdot \dfrac{2}{3} = 30$,

$\dfrac{\partial f}{\partial y}(81, 16) = 15 \cdot \dfrac{81^{3/4}}{16^{3/4}} = 15 \cdot \dfrac{27}{8} = \dfrac{405}{8} = 50\tfrac{5}{8}$.

(c) The quantities $\dfrac{\partial f}{\partial x}$ and $\dfrac{\partial f}{\partial y}$ are referred to as the *marginal productivity of labor* and the *marginal productivity of capital*. If the amount of capital is held fixed at $y = 16$ and the amount of labor increases by 1 unit, the quantity of goods produced will increase by approximately 30 units. Similarly, an increase in capital of 1 unit (with labor fixed at 81) results in an increase in production of approximately $50\tfrac{5}{8}$ units of goods. ∎

Just as we formed second derivatives in the case of one variable, we can form second partial derivatives of a function $f(x, y)$ of two variables. Since $\dfrac{\partial f}{\partial x}$ is a function of x and y, we can differentiate it with respect to x or y. The partial derivative of $\dfrac{\partial f}{\partial x}$ with respect to x is denoted by $\dfrac{\partial^2 f}{\partial x^2}$. The partial derivative of $\dfrac{\partial f}{\partial x}$ with respect to y is denoted by $\dfrac{\partial^2 f}{\partial y \, \partial x}$. Similarly, the partial derivative of the function $\dfrac{\partial f}{\partial y}$ with respect to x is denoted by $\dfrac{\partial^2 f}{\partial x \, \partial y}$, and the partial derivative of $\dfrac{\partial f}{\partial y}$ with respect to y is denoted by $\dfrac{\partial^2 f}{\partial y^2}$. Almost all functions $f(x, y)$ encountered in applications [and all functions $f(x, y)$ in this text] have the property that

$$\frac{\partial^2 f}{\partial y \, \partial x} = \frac{\partial^2 f}{\partial x \, \partial y}.$$

When computing $\dfrac{\partial^2 f}{\partial y \, \partial x}$ and $\dfrac{\partial^2 f}{\partial x \, \partial y}$, note that verifying the last equation is a check that you have done the differentiation correctly.

EXAMPLE 9

Let $f(x, y) = x^2 + 3xy + 2y^2$. Calculate

$$\frac{\partial^2 f}{\partial x^2}, \quad \frac{\partial^2 f}{\partial y^2}, \quad \frac{\partial^2 f}{\partial x \, \partial y}, \quad \text{and} \quad \frac{\partial^2 f}{\partial y \, \partial x}.$$

Solution First we compute $\dfrac{\partial f}{\partial x}$ and $\dfrac{\partial f}{\partial y}$.

$$\frac{\partial f}{\partial x} = 2x + 3y, \qquad \frac{\partial f}{\partial y} = 3x + 4y.$$

To compute $\dfrac{\partial^2 f}{\partial x^2}$, we differentiate $\dfrac{\partial f}{\partial x}$ with respect to x:

$$\frac{\partial^2 f}{\partial x^2} = 2.$$

Similarly, to compute $\dfrac{\partial^2 f}{\partial y^2}$, we differentiate $\dfrac{\partial f}{\partial y}$ with respect to y:

$$\frac{\partial^2 f}{\partial y^2} = 4.$$

To compute $\dfrac{\partial^2 f}{\partial x\, \partial y}$, we differentiate $\dfrac{\partial f}{\partial y}$ with respect to x:

$$\frac{\partial^2 f}{\partial x\, \partial y} = 3.$$

Finally, to compute $\dfrac{\partial^2 f}{\partial y\, \partial x}$, we differentiate $\dfrac{\partial f}{\partial x}$ with respect to y:

$$\frac{\partial^2 f}{\partial y\, \partial x} = 3.$$ ■

INCORPORATING TECHNOLOGY

Evaluating Partial Derivatives The function from Example 4 and its first partial derivatives are specified in Fig. 3(a) and evaluated in Fig. 3(b). Recall that the expression $1 \rightarrow X$ is entered with $\boxed{1}$ $\boxed{\text{STO} \triangleright}$ $\boxed{\text{X,T,}\theta\text{,}n}$ and indicates that we are setting $X = 1$. The expression $4 \rightarrow Y$ has a similar meaning, but the variable Y is entered using $\boxed{\text{ALPHA}}$ [Y]. We can also evaluate other partial derivatives. For example, the partial derivative $\dfrac{\partial^2 f}{\partial x\, \partial y}$ in this case could be found by setting $Y_4 = \text{nDeriv}(Y_3, X, X)$. ■

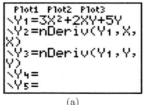
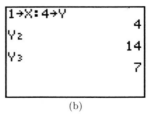

Figure 3   (a)   (b)

Practice Problems 7.2

1. The number of TV sets an appliance store sells per week is given by a function of two variables, $f(x, y)$, where x is the price per TV set and y is the amount of money spent weekly on advertising. Suppose that the current price is $400 per set and that currently $2000 per week is being spent for advertising.

   (a) Would you expect $\dfrac{\partial f}{\partial x}(400, 2000)$ to be positive or negative?

   (b) Would you expect $\dfrac{\partial f}{\partial y}(400, 2000)$ to be positive or negative?

2. The monthly mortgage payment for a house is a function of two variables, $f(A, r)$, where A is the amount of the mortgage and the interest rate is $r\%$. For a 30-year mortgage, $f(92{,}000, 9) = 740.25$ and $\dfrac{\partial f}{\partial r}(92{,}000, 9) = 66.20$. What is the significance of the number 66.20?

EXERCISES 7.2

Find $\dfrac{\partial f}{\partial x}$ and $\dfrac{\partial f}{\partial y}$ for each of the following functions.

1. $f(x,y) = 5xy$

2. $f(x,y) = x^2 - y^2$

3. $f(x,y) = 2x^2 e^y$

4. $f(x,y) = xe^{xy}$

5. $f(x,y) = \dfrac{x}{y} + \dfrac{y}{x}$

6. $f(x,y) = \dfrac{1}{x+y}$

7. $f(x,y) = (2x - y + 5)^2$

8. $f(x,y) = \dfrac{e^x}{1 + e^y}$

9. $f(x,y) = x^2 e^{3x} \ln y$

10. $f(x,y) = \ln(xy)$

11. $f(x,y) = \dfrac{x-y}{x+y}$

12. $f(x,y) = \sqrt{x^2 + y^2}$

13. Let $f(L,K) = 3\sqrt{LK}$. Find $\dfrac{\partial f}{\partial L}$.

14. Let $f(p,q) = 1 - p(1+q)$. Find $\dfrac{\partial f}{\partial q}$ and $\dfrac{\partial f}{\partial p}$.

15. Let $f(x,y,z) = (1 + x^2 y)/z$. Find $\dfrac{\partial f}{\partial x}$, $\dfrac{\partial f}{\partial y}$, and $\dfrac{\partial f}{\partial z}$.

16. Let $f(x,y,z) = ze^{x/y}$. Find $\dfrac{\partial f}{\partial x}$, $\dfrac{\partial f}{\partial y}$, and $\dfrac{\partial f}{\partial z}$.

17. Let $f(x,y,z) = xze^{yz}$. Find $\dfrac{\partial f}{\partial x}$, $\dfrac{\partial f}{\partial y}$, and $\dfrac{\partial f}{\partial z}$.

18. Let $f(x,y,z) = \dfrac{xy}{z}$. Find $\dfrac{\partial f}{\partial x}$, $\dfrac{\partial f}{\partial y}$, and $\dfrac{\partial f}{\partial z}$.

19. Let $f(x,y) = x^2 + 2xy + y^2 + 3x + 5y$. Find $\dfrac{\partial f}{\partial x}(2,-3)$ and $\dfrac{\partial f}{\partial y}(2,-3)$.

20. Let $f(x,y) = (x + y^2)^3$. Evaluate $\dfrac{\partial f}{\partial x}$ and $\dfrac{\partial f}{\partial y}$ at $(x,y) = (1,2)$.

21. Let $f(x,y,z) = xy^2 z + 5$. Evaluate $\dfrac{\partial f}{\partial y}$ at $(x,y,z) = (2,-1,3)$.

22. Let $f(x,y,z) = \dfrac{x}{y-z}$. Compute $\dfrac{\partial f}{\partial y}(2,-1,3)$.

23. Let $f(x,y) = x^3 y + 2xy^2$. Find $\dfrac{\partial^2 f}{\partial x^2}$, $\dfrac{\partial^2 f}{\partial y^2}$, $\dfrac{\partial^2 f}{\partial x\,\partial y}$, and $\dfrac{\partial^2 f}{\partial y\,\partial x}$.

24. Let $f(x,y) = xe^y + x^4 y + y^3$. Find $\dfrac{\partial^2 f}{\partial x^2}$, $\dfrac{\partial^2 f}{\partial y^2}$, $\dfrac{\partial^2 f}{\partial x\,\partial y}$, and $\dfrac{\partial^2 f}{\partial y\,\partial x}$.

25. Production   A farmer can produce $f(x,y) = 200\sqrt{6x^2 + y^2}$ units of produce by utilizing x units of labor and y units of capital. (The capital is used to rent or purchase land, materials, and equipment.)

(a) Calculate the marginal productivities of labor and capital when $x = 10$ and $y = 5$.

(b) Let h be a small number. Use the result of part (a) to determine the approximate effect on production of changing labor from 10 to $10 + h$ units while keeping capital fixed at 5 units.

(c) Use part (b) to estimate the change in production when labor decreases from 10 to 9.5 units and capital stays fixed at 5 units.

26. The productivity of a country is given by $f(x,y) = 300x^{2/3}y^{1/3}$, where x and y are the amount of labor and capital.

(a) Compute the marginal productivities of labor and capital when $x = 125$ and $y = 64$.

(b) Use part (a) to determine the approximate effect on productivity of increasing capital from 64 to 66 units, while keeping labor fixed at 125 units.

(c) What would be the approximate effect of decreasing labor from 125 to 124 units while keeping capital fixed at 64 units?

27. Demand In a certain suburban community, commuters have the choice of getting into the city by bus or train. The demand for these modes of transportation varies with their cost. Let $f(p_1, p_2)$ be the number of people who will take the bus when p_1 is the price of the bus ride and p_2 is the price of the train ride. For example, if $f(4.50, 6) = 7000$, then 7000 commuters will take the bus when the price of a bus ticket is \$4.50 and the price of a train ticket is \$6.00. Explain why $\dfrac{\partial f}{\partial p_1} < 0$ and $\dfrac{\partial f}{\partial p_2} > 0$.

28. Refer to Exercise 27. Let $g(p_1, p_2)$ be the number of people who will take the train when p_1 is the price of the bus ride and p_2 is the price of the train ride. Would you expect $\dfrac{\partial g}{\partial p_1}$ to be positive or negative? How about $\dfrac{\partial g}{\partial p_2}$?

29. Let p_1 be the average price of DVD players, p_2 the average price of DVDs, $f(p_1, p_2)$ the demand for DVD players, and $g(p_1, p_2)$ the demand for DVDs. Explain why $\dfrac{\partial f}{\partial p_2} < 0$ and $\dfrac{\partial g}{\partial p_1} < 0$.

30. The demand for a certain gas-guzzling car is given by $f(p_1, p_2)$, where p_1 is the price of the car and p_2 is the price of gasoline. Explain why $\dfrac{\partial f}{\partial p_1} < 0$ and $\dfrac{\partial f}{\partial p_2} < 0$.

31. The volume (V) of a certain amount of a gas is determined by the temperature (T) and the pressure (P) by the formula $V = .08(T/P)$. Calculate and interpret $\dfrac{\partial V}{\partial P}$ and $\dfrac{\partial V}{\partial T}$ when $P = 20$, $T = 300$.

32. Beer Consumption   Using data collected from 1929 to 1941, Richard Stone* determined that the yearly quantity Q of beer consumed in the United Kingdom was approximately given by the formula $Q = f(m, p, r, s)$, where

$$f(m, p, r, s) = (1.058)m^{.136}p^{-.727}r^{.914}s^{.816}$$

and m is the aggregate real income (personal income after direct taxes, adjusted for retail price changes), p is the average retail price of the commodity (in this case, beer), r is the average retail price level of all other consumer goods and services, and s is a measure of the strength of the beer. Determine which partial derivatives are positive and which are negative and give interpretations. (For example, since $\dfrac{\partial f}{\partial r} > 0$, people buy more beer when the prices of other goods increase and the other factors remain constant.)

33. Richard Stone (see Exercise 32) determined that the yearly consumption of food in the United States was given by

$$f(m, p, r) = (2.186)m^{.595}p^{-.543}r^{.922}.$$

Determine which partial derivatives are positive and which are negative and give interpretations of these facts.

34. Distribution of Revenue   For the production function $f(x, y) = 60x^{3/4}y^{1/4}$ considered in Example 8, think of $f(x, y)$ as the revenue when utilizing x units of labor and y units of capital. Under actual operating conditions, say $x = a$ and $y = b$, $\dfrac{\partial f}{\partial x}(a, b)$ is referred to as the *wage per unit of labor* and $\dfrac{\partial f}{\partial y}(a, b)$ is referred to as the *wage per unit of capital.* Show that

$$f(a, b) = a \cdot \left[\frac{\partial f}{\partial x}(a, b)\right] + b \cdot \left[\frac{\partial f}{\partial y}(a, b)\right].$$

(This equation shows how the revenue is distributed between labor and capital.)

35. Compute $\dfrac{\partial^2 f}{\partial x^2}$, where $f(x, y) = 60x^{3/4}y^{1/4}$, a production function (where x is units of labor). Explain why $\dfrac{\partial^2 f}{\partial x^2}$ is always negative.

36. Compute $\dfrac{\partial^2 f}{\partial y^2}$, where $f(x, y) = 60x^{3/4}y^{1/4}$, a production function (where y is units of capital). Explain why $\dfrac{\partial^2 f}{\partial y^2}$ is always negative.

37. Let $f(x, y) = 3x^2 + 2xy + 5y$, as in Example 5. Show that

$$f(1 + h, 4) - f(1, 4) = 14h + 3h^2.$$

Thus the error in approximating $f(1+h, 4) - f(1, 4)$ by $14h$ is $3h^2$. (If $h = .01$, for instance, the error is only .0003.)

38. Body Surface Area   Physicians, particularly pediatricians, sometimes need to know the body surface area of a patient. For instance, the surface area is used to adjust the results of certain tests of kidney performance. Tables are available that give the approximate body surface area A in square meters of a person who weighs W kilograms and is H centimeters tall. The following empirical formula† is also used:

$$A = .007W^{.425}H^{.725}.$$

Evaluate $\dfrac{\partial A}{\partial W}$ and $\dfrac{\partial A}{\partial H}$ when $W = 54$ and $H = 165$, and give a physical interpretation of your answers. You may use the approximations $(54)^{.425} \approx 5.4$, $(54)^{-.575} \approx .10$, $(165)^{.725} \approx 40.5$, and $(165)^{-.275} \approx .25$.

Solutions to Practice Problems 7.2

1. (a) Negative. $\dfrac{\partial f}{\partial x}(400, 2000)$ is approximately the change in sales due to a $1 increase in x (price). Since raising prices lowers sales, we would expect $\dfrac{\partial f}{\partial x}(400, 2000)$ to be negative.

(b) Positive. $\dfrac{\partial f}{\partial y}(400, 2000)$ is approximately the change in sales due to a $1 increase in advertising. Since spending more money on advertising

brings in more customers, we would expect sales to increase; that is, $\dfrac{\partial f}{\partial y}(400, 2000)$ is most likely positive.

2. If the interest rate is raised from 9% to 10%, the monthly payment will increase by about $66.20. [An increase to $9\frac{1}{2}\%$ causes an increase in the monthly payment of about $\frac{1}{2} \cdot (66.20)$ or $33.10, and so on.]

---

*Richard Stone, "The Analysis of Market Demand," *Journal of the Royal Statistical Society*, 108 (1945), 286–391.

†See J. Routh, *Mathematical Preparation for Laboratory Technicians* (Philadelphia: W. B. Saunders Co., 1971), p. 92.

7.3 Maxima and Minima of Functions of Several Variables

Previously, we studied how to determine the maxima and minima of functions of a single variable. Let us extend that discussion to functions of several variables.

If $f(x, y)$ is a function of two variables, we say that $f(x, y)$ has a *relative maximum* when $x = a$, $y = b$ if $f(x, y)$ is at most equal to $f(a, b)$ whenever x is near a and y is near b. Geometrically, the graph of $f(x, y)$ has a peak at $(x, y) = (a, b)$. [See Fig. 1(a).] Similarly, we say that $f(x, y)$ has a *relative minimum* when $x = a$, $y = b$ if $f(x, y)$ is at least equal to $f(a, b)$ whenever x is near a and y is near b. Geometrically, the graph of $f(x, y)$ has a pit whose bottom occurs at $(x, y) = (a, b)$. [See Fig. 1(b).]

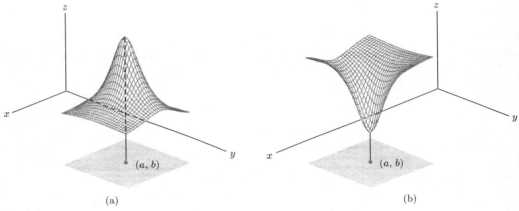

(a)   (b)

Figure 1.   Maximum and minimum points.

Suppose that the function $f(x, y)$ has a relative minimum at $(x, y) = (a, b)$, as in Fig. 2. When y is held constant at b, $f(x, y)$ is a function of x with a relative minimum at $x = a$. Therefore, the tangent line to the curve $z = f(x, b)$ is horizontal at $x = a$ and hence has slope 0. That is,

$$\frac{\partial f}{\partial x}(a, b) = 0.$$

Likewise, when x is held constant at a, then $f(x, y)$ is a function of y with a relative minimum at $y = b$. Therefore, its derivative with respect to y is zero at $y = b$. That

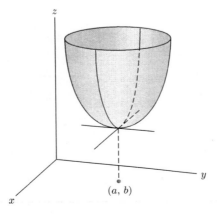

Figure 2.   Horizontal tangent lines at a relative minimum.

is,

$$\frac{\partial f}{\partial y}(a, b) = 0.$$

Similar considerations apply when $f(x, y)$ has a relative maximum at $(x, y) = (a, b)$.

First-Derivative Test for Functions of Two Variables If $f(x, y)$ has either a relative maximum or minimum at $(x, y) = (a, b)$, then

$$\frac{\partial f}{\partial x}(a, b) = 0$$

and

$$\frac{\partial f}{\partial y}(a, b) = 0.$$

A relative maximum or minimum may or may not be an absolute maximum or minimum. However, to simplify matters in this text, the examples and exercises have been chosen so that, if an absolute extremum of $f(x, y)$ exists, it will occur at a point where $f(x, y)$ has a relative extremum.

EXAMPLE 1

The function $f(x, y) = 3x^2 - 4xy + 3y^2 + 8x - 17y + 30$ has the graph pictured in Fig. 2. Find the point (a, b) at which $f(x, y)$ attains its minimum value.

Solution We look for those values of x and y at which both partial derivatives are zero. The partial derivatives are

$$\frac{\partial f}{\partial x} = 6x - 4y + 8,$$

$$\frac{\partial f}{\partial y} = -4x + 6y - 17.$$

Setting $\frac{\partial f}{\partial x} = 0$ and $\frac{\partial f}{\partial y} = 0$, we obtain

$$6x - 4y + 8 = 0 \quad \text{or} \quad y = \frac{6x + 8}{4},$$

$$-4x + 6y - 17 = 0 \quad \text{or} \quad y = \frac{4x + 17}{6}.$$

By equating these two expressions for y, we have

$$\frac{6x + 8}{4} = \frac{4x + 17}{6}.$$

Cross-multiplying, we see that

$$36x + 48 = 16x + 68$$
$$20x = 20$$
$$x = 1.$$

When we substitute this value for x into our first equation for y in terms of x, we obtain

$$y = \frac{6x + 8}{4} = \frac{6 \cdot 1 + 8}{4} = \frac{7}{2}.$$

If $f(x, y)$ has a minimum, it must occur where $\frac{\partial f}{\partial x} = 0$ and $\frac{\partial f}{\partial y} = 0$. We have determined that the partial derivatives are zero only when $x = 1$, $y = \frac{7}{2}$. From Fig. 2 we know that $f(x, y)$ has a minimum, so it must be at $(x, y) = (1, \frac{7}{2})$. ■

EXAMPLE 2

Price discrimination   A monopolist markets a product in two countries and can charge different amounts in each country. Let x be the number of units to be sold in the first country and y the number of units to be sold in the second country. Due to the laws of demand, the monopolist must set the price at $97 - (x/10)$ dollars in the first country and $83 - (y/20)$ dollars in the second country to sell all the units. The cost of producing these units is $20{,}000 + 3(x + y)$. Find the values of x and y that maximize the profit.

Solution   Let $f(x, y)$ be the profit derived from selling x units in the first country and y in the second. Then

$$f(x, y) = [\text{revenue from first country}] + [\text{revenue from second country}] - [\text{cost}]$$

$$= \left(97 - \frac{x}{10}\right) x + \left(83 - \frac{y}{20}\right) y - [20{,}000 + 3(x + y)]$$

$$= 97x - \frac{x^2}{10} + 83y - \frac{y^2}{20} - 20{,}000 - 3x - 3y$$

$$= 94x - \frac{x^2}{10} + 80y - \frac{y^2}{20} - 20{,}000.$$

To find where $f(x, y)$ has its maximum value, we look for those values of x and y at which both partial derivatives are zero.

$$\frac{\partial f}{\partial x} = 94 - \frac{x}{5},$$

$$\frac{\partial f}{\partial y} = 80 - \frac{y}{10}.$$

We set $\dfrac{\partial f}{\partial x} = 0$ and $\dfrac{\partial f}{\partial y} = 0$ to obtain

$$94 - \frac{x}{5} = 0 \quad \text{or} \quad x = 470,$$

$$80 - \frac{y}{10} = 0 \quad \text{or} \quad y = 800.$$

Therefore, the firm should adjust its prices to levels where it will sell 470 units in the first country and 800 units in the second country.   ◼

EXAMPLE 3

Heat loss   Suppose that we want to design a rectangular building having a volume of 147,840 cubic feet. Assuming that the daily loss of heat is given by

$$w = 11xy + 14yz + 15xz,$$

where x, y, and z are, respectively, the length, width, and height of the building, find the dimensions of the building for which the daily heat loss is minimal.

Solution   We must minimize the function

$$w = 11xy + 14yz + 15xz, \tag{1}$$

where x, y, z satisfy the constraint equation (refer to Section 2.5)

$$xyz = 147{,}840.$$

For simplicity, let us denote 147,840 by V. Then $xyz = V$, so $z = V/xy$. We substitute this expression for z into the objective function (1) to obtain a heat-loss function $g(x, y)$ of two variables:

$$g(x, y) = 11xy + 14y\frac{V}{xy} + 15x\frac{V}{xy} = 11xy + \frac{14V}{x} + \frac{15V}{y}.$$

To minimize this function, we first compute the partial derivatives with respect to x and y; then we equate them to zero.

$$\frac{\partial g}{\partial x} = 11y - \frac{14V}{x^2} = 0,$$

$$\frac{\partial g}{\partial y} = 11x - \frac{15V}{y^2} = 0.$$

These two equations yield

$$y = \frac{14V}{11x^2}, \tag{2}$$

$$11xy^2 = 15V. \tag{3}$$

If we substitute the value of y from (2) into (3), we see that

$$11x\left(\frac{14V}{11x^2}\right)^2 = 15V$$

$$\frac{14^2V^2}{11x^3} = 15V$$

$$x^3 = \frac{14^2 \cdot V^2}{11 \cdot 15 \cdot V} = \frac{14^2 \cdot V}{11 \cdot 15}$$

$$= \frac{14^2 \cdot 147,840}{11 \cdot 15}$$

$$= 175,616.$$

Therefore, we see (using a calculator) that

$$x = 56.$$

From equation (2) we find that

$$y = \frac{14 \cdot V}{11x^2} = \frac{14 \cdot 147,840}{11 \cdot 56^2} = 60.$$

Finally,

$$z = \frac{V}{xy} = \frac{147,840}{56 \cdot 60} = 44.$$

Thus the building should be 56 feet long, 60 feet wide, and 44 feet high to minimize the heat loss.* ▪

---

*For further discussion of this heat-loss problem, as well as other examples of optimization in architectural design, see L. March, "Elementary Models of Built Forms," Chapter 3 in *Urban Space and Structures*, L. Martin and L. March, eds. (New York: Cambridge University Press, 1972).

When considering a function of two variables, we find points (x, y) at which $f(x, y)$ has a potential relative maximum or minimum by setting $\dfrac{\partial f}{\partial x}$ and $\dfrac{\partial f}{\partial y}$ equal to zero and solving for x and y. However, if we are given no additional information about $f(x, y)$, it may be difficult to determine whether we have found a maximum or a minimum (or neither). In the case of functions of one variable, we studied concavity and deduced the second-derivative test. There is an analog of the second derivative test for functions of two variables, but it is much more complicated than the one-variable test. We state it without proof.

Second-Derivative Test for Functions of Two Variables Suppose that $f(x, y)$ is a function and (a, b) is a point at which

$$\frac{\partial f}{\partial x}(a, b) = 0 \quad \text{and} \quad \frac{\partial f}{\partial y}(a, b) = 0,$$

and let

$$D(x, y) = \frac{\partial^2 f}{\partial x^2} \cdot \frac{\partial^2 f}{\partial y^2} - \left(\frac{\partial^2 f}{\partial x \, \partial y} \right)^2.$$

1. If

$$D(a, b) > 0 \quad \text{and} \quad \frac{\partial^2 f}{\partial x^2}(a, b) > 0,$$

   then $f(x, y)$ has a relative minimum at (a, b).

2. If

$$D(a, b) > 0 \quad \text{and} \quad \frac{\partial^2 f}{\partial x^2}(a, b) < 0,$$

   then $f(x, y)$ has a relative maximum at (a, b).

3. If

$$D(a, b) < 0,$$

   then $f(x, y)$ has neither a relative maximum nor a relative minimum at (a, b).

4. If $D(a, b) = 0$, no conclusion can be drawn from this test.

The saddle-shaped graph in Fig. 3 illustrates a function $f(x, y)$ for which $D(a, b) < 0$. Both partial derivatives are zero at $(x, y) = (a, b)$, and yet the function has neither a relative maximum nor a relative minimum there. (Observe that the function has a relative maximum with respect to x when y is held constant and a relative minimum with respect to y when x is held constant.)

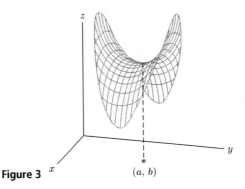

Figure 3

EXAMPLE 4   Let $f(x, y) = x^3 - y^2 - 12x + 6y + 5$. Find all possible relative maximum and minimum points of $f(x, y)$. Use the second-derivative test to determine the nature of each such point.

Solution Since

$$\frac{\partial f}{\partial x} = 3x^2 - 12, \qquad \frac{\partial f}{\partial y} = -2y + 6,$$

we find that $f(x, y)$ has a potential relative extreme point when

$$3x^2 - 12 = 0,$$
$$-2y + 6 = 0.$$

From the first equation, $3x^2 = 12$, $x^2 = 4$, and $x = \pm 2$. From the second equation, $y = 3$. Thus, $\frac{\partial f}{\partial x}$ and $\frac{\partial f}{\partial y}$ are both zero when $(x, y) = (2, 3)$ and when $(x, y) = (-2, 3)$. To apply the second-derivative test, compute

$$\frac{\partial^2 f}{\partial x^2} = 6x, \qquad \frac{\partial^2 f}{\partial y^2} = -2, \qquad \frac{\partial^2 f}{\partial x \, \partial y} = 0,$$

and

$$D(x, y) = \frac{\partial^2 f}{\partial x^2} \cdot \frac{\partial^2 f}{\partial y^2} - \left(\frac{\partial^2 f}{\partial x \, \partial y} \right)^2 = (6x)(-2) - 0^2 = -12x. \qquad (4)$$

Since $D(2, 3) = -12(2) = -24$, which is negative, case 3 of the second-derivative test says that $f(x, y)$ has neither a relative maximum nor a relative minimum at $(2, 3)$. However, $D(-2, 3) = -12(-2) = 24$. Since $D(-2, 3)$ is positive, the function $f(x, y)$ has either a relative maximum or a relative minimum at $(-2, 3)$. To determine which, we compute

$$\frac{\partial^2 f}{\partial x^2}(-2, 3) = 6(-2) = -12 < 0.$$

By case 2 of the second-derivative test, the function $f(x, y)$ has a relative maximum at $(-2, 3)$. ∎

In this section we have restricted ourselves to functions of two variables, but the case of three or more variables is handled in a similar fashion. For instance, here is the first-derivative test for a function of three variables.

If $f(x, y, z)$ has a relative maximum or minimum at $(x, y, z) = (a, b, c)$, then

$$\frac{\partial f}{\partial x}(a, b, c) = 0,$$

$$\frac{\partial f}{\partial y}(a, b, c) = 0,$$

$$\frac{\partial f}{\partial z}(a, b, c) = 0.$$

Practice Problems 7.3

1. Find all points (x, y) where $f(x, y) = x^3 - 3xy + \frac{1}{2}y^2 + 8$ has a possible relative maximum or minimum.

2. Apply the second-derivative test to the function $g(x, y)$ of Example 3 to confirm that a relative minimum actually occurs when $x = 56$ and $y = 60$.

EXERCISES 7.3

Find all points (x, y) where $f(x, y)$ has a possible relative maximum or minimum.

1. $f(x, y) = x^2 - 3y^2 + 4x + 6y + 8$
2. $f(x, y) = \frac{1}{2}x^2 + y^2 - 3x + 2y - 5$
3. $f(x, y) = x^2 - 5xy + 6y^2 + 3x - 2y + 4$
4. $f(x, y) = -3x^2 + 7xy - 4y^2 + x + y$
5. $f(x, y) = x^3 + y^2 - 3x + 6y$
6. $f(x, y) = x^2 - y^3 + 5x + 12y + 1$
7. $f(x, y) = \frac{1}{3}x^3 - 2y^3 - 5x + 6y - 5$
8. $f(x, y) = x^4 - 8xy + 2y^2 - 3$
9. The function $f(x, y) = 2x + 3y + 9 - x^2 - xy - y^2$ has a maximum at some point (x, y). Find the values of x and y where this maximum occurs.
10. The function $f(x, y) = \frac{1}{2}x^2 + 2xy + 3y^2 - x + 2y$ has a minimum at some point (x, y). Find the values of x and y where this minimum occurs.

In Exercises 11–16, both first partial derivatives of the function $f(x, y)$ are zero at the given points. Use the second-derivative test to determine the nature of $f(x, y)$ at each of these points. If the second-derivative test is inconclusive, so state.

11. $f(x, y) = 3x^2 - 6xy + y^3 - 9y$; $(3, 3)$, $(-1, -1)$
12. $f(x, y) = 6xy^2 - 2x^3 - 3y^4$; $(0, 0)$, $(1, 1)$, $(1, -1)$
13. $f(x, y) = 2x^2 - x^4 - y^2$; $(-1, 0)$, $(0, 0)$, $(1, 0)$
14. $f(x, y) = x^4 - 4xy + y^4$; $(0, 0)$, $(1, 1)$, $(-1, -1)$
15. $f(x, y) = ye^x - 3x - y + 5$; $(0, 3)$
16. $f(x, y) = \dfrac{1}{x} + \dfrac{1}{y} + xy$; $(1, 1)$

Find all points (x, y) where $f(x, y)$ has a possible relative maximum or minimum. Then use the second-derivative test to determine, if possible, the nature of $f(x, y)$ at each of these points. If the second-derivative test is inconclusive, so state.

17. $f(x, y) = x^2 - 2xy + 4y^2$
18. $f(x, y) = 2x^2 + 3xy + 5y^2$
19. $f(x, y) = -2x^2 + 2xy - y^2 + 4x - 6y + 5$
20. $f(x, y) = -x^2 - 8xy - y^2$
21. $f(x, y) = x^2 + 2xy + 5y^2 + 2x + 10y - 3$
22. $f(x, y) = x^2 - 2xy + 3y^2 + 4x - 16y + 22$
23. $f(x, y) = x^3 - y^2 - 3x + 4y$
24. $f(x, y) = x^3 - 2xy + 4y$
25. $f(x, y) = 2x^2 + y^3 - x - 12y + 7$
26. $f(x, y) = x^2 + 4xy + 2y^4$
27. Find the possible values of x, y, z at which

$$f(x, y, z) = 2x^2 + 3y^2 + z^2 - 2x - y - z$$

assumes its minimum value.

28. Find the possible values of x, y, z at which

$$f(x, y, z) = 5 + 8x - 4y + x^2 + y^2 + z^2$$

assumes its minimum value.

29. United States postal rules require that the length plus the girth of a package cannot exceed 84 inches. Find the dimensions of the rectangular package of greatest volume that can be mailed. [*Note:* From Fig. 4 we see that $84 = (\text{length}) + (\text{girth}) = l + (2x + 2y)$.]

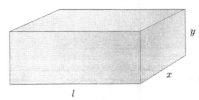

Figure 4

30. Find the dimensions of the rectangular box of least surface area that has a volume of 1000 cubic inches.
31. A company manufactures and sells two products, I and II, that sell for \$10 and \$9 per unit, respectively. The cost of producing x units of product I and y units of product II is

$$400 + 2x + 3y + .01(3x^2 + xy + 3y^2).$$

Find the values of x and y that maximize the company's profits. [*Note:* Profit = (revenue) − (cost).]

32. A monopolist manufactures and sells two competing products, I and II, that cost \$30 and \$20 per unit, respectively, to produce. The revenue from marketing x units of product I and y units of product II is $98x + 112y - .04xy - .1x^2 - .2y^2$. Find the values of x and y that maximize the monopolist's profits.
33. A company manufactures and sells two products, I and II, that sell for \$$p_I$ and \$$p_{II}$ per unit, respectively. Let $C(x, y)$ be the cost of producing x units of product I and y units of product II. Show that if the company's profit is maximized when $x = a$, $y = b$ then

$$\frac{\partial C}{\partial x}(a, b) = p_I \quad \text{and} \quad \frac{\partial C}{\partial y}(a, b) = p_{II}.$$

34. A monopolist manufactures and sells two competing products, I and II, that cost \$$p_I$ and \$$p_{II}$ per unit, respectively, to produce. Let $R(x, y)$ be the revenue from marketing x units of product I and y units of product II. Show that if the monopolist's profit is maximized when $x = a$, $y = b$ then

$$\frac{\partial R}{\partial x}(a, b) = p_I \quad \text{and} \quad \frac{\partial R}{\partial y}(a, b) = p_{II}.$$

Solutions to Practice Problems 7.3

1. Compute the first partial derivatives of $f(x, y)$ and solve the system of equations that results from setting the partials equal to zero.

$$\frac{\partial f}{\partial x} = 3x^2 - 3y = 0,$$

$$\frac{\partial f}{\partial y} = -3x + y = 0.$$

Solve each equation for y in terms of x.

$$\begin{cases} y = x^2 \\ y = 3x. \end{cases}$$

Equate expressions for y and solve for x.

$$x^2 = 3x$$
$$x^2 - 3x = 0$$
$$x(x - 3) = 0$$
$$x = 0 \quad \text{or} \quad x = 3.$$

When $x = 0$, $y = 0^2 = 0$. When $x = 3$, $y = 3^2 = 9$. Therefore, the possible relative maximum or minimum points are $(0, 0)$ and $(3, 9)$.

2. We have

$$g(x, y) = 11xy + \frac{14V}{x} + \frac{15V}{y},$$

$$\frac{\partial g}{\partial x} = 11y - \frac{14V}{x^2}, \quad \text{and} \quad \frac{\partial g}{\partial y} = 11x - \frac{15V}{y^2}.$$

Now,

$$\frac{\partial^2 g}{\partial x^2} = \frac{28V}{x^3}, \quad \frac{\partial^2 g}{\partial y^2} = \frac{30V}{y^3}, \quad \text{and} \quad \frac{\partial^2 g}{\partial x \, \partial y} = 11.$$

Therefore,

$$D(x, y) = \frac{28V}{x^3} \cdot \frac{30V}{y^3} - (11)^2$$

$$D(56, 60) = \frac{28(147,840)}{(56)^3} \cdot \frac{30(147,840)}{(60)^3} - 121$$

$$= 484 - 121 = 363 > 0,$$

and

$$\frac{\partial^2 g}{\partial x^2}(56, 60) = \frac{28(147,840)}{(56)^3} > 0.$$

It follows that $g(x, y)$ has a relative minimum at $x = 56$, $y = 60$.

7.4 Lagrange Multipliers and Constrained Optimization

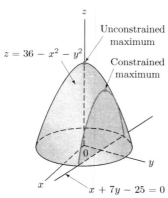

$z = 36 - x^2 - y^2$

Unconstrained maximum

Constrained maximum

$x + 7y - 25 = 0$

Figure 1.   A constrained optimization problem.

We have seen a number of optimization problems in which we were required to minimize (or maximize) an objective function where the variables were subject to a constraint equation. For instance, in Example 4 of Section 2.5, we minimized the cost of a rectangular enclosure by minimizing the objective function $42x + 28y$, where x and y were subject to the constraint equation $600 - xy = 0$. In the preceding section (Example 3) we minimized the daily heat loss from a building by minimizing the objective function $11xy + 14yz + 15xz$, subject to the constraint equation $147,840 - xyz = 0$.

Figure 1 gives a graphical illustration of what happens when an objective function is maximized subject to a constraint. The graph of the objective function is the cone-shaped surface $z = 36 - x^2 - y^2$, and the colored curve on that surface consists of those points whose x- and y-coordinates satisfy the constraint equation $x + 7y - 25 = 0$. The constrained maximum is at the highest point on this curve. Of course, the surface itself has a higher "unconstrained maximum" at $(x, y, z) = (0, 0, 36)$, but these values of x and y do not satisfy the constraint equation.

In this section we introduce a powerful technique for solving problems of this type. Let us begin with the following general problem, which involves two variables.

Problem   Let $f(x, y)$ and $g(x, y)$ be functions of two variables. Find values of x and y that maximize (or minimize) the objective function $f(x, y)$ and that also satisfy the constraint equation $g(x, y) = 0$.

Of course, if we can solve the equation $g(x, y) = 0$ for one variable in terms of the other and substitute the resulting expression into $f(x, y)$, we arrive at a function of a single variable that can be maximized (or minimized) by using the methods of Chapter 2. However, this technique can be unsatisfactory for two reasons. First, it may be difficult to solve the equation $g(x, y) = 0$ for x or for y. For example, if $g(x, y) = x^4 + 5x^3y + 7x^2y^3 + y^5 - 17 = 0$, it is difficult to write y as a function of x or x as a function of y. Second, even if $g(x, y) = 0$ can be solved for one variable in terms of the other, substitution of the result into $f(x, y)$ may yield a complicated function.

One clever idea for handling the preceding problem was discovered by the eighteenth-century mathematician Lagrange, and the technique that he pioneered today bears his name, the method of *Lagrange multipliers*. The basic idea of this method is to replace $f(x, y)$ by an auxiliary function of three variables $F(x, y, \lambda)$, defined as

$$F(x, y, \lambda) = f(x, y) + \lambda g(x, y).$$

The new variable λ (lambda) is called a *Lagrange multiplier* and always multiplies the constraint function $g(x, y)$. The following theorem is stated without proof.

Theorem Suppose that, subject to the constraint $g(x, y) = 0$, the function $f(x, y)$ has a relative maximum or minimum at $(x, y) = (a, b)$. Then there is a value of λ, say $\lambda = c$, such that the partial derivatives of $F(x, y, \lambda)$ all equal zero at $(x, y, \lambda) = (a, b, c)$.

The theorem implies that, if we locate all points (x, y, λ) where the partial derivatives of $F(x, y, \lambda)$ are all zero, among the corresponding points (x, y), we then will find all possible places where $f(x, y)$ may have a constrained relative maximum or minimum. Thus the first step in the method of Lagrange multipliers is to set the partial derivatives of $F(x, y, \lambda)$ equal to zero and solve for x, y, and λ:

$$\frac{\partial F}{\partial x} = 0 \tag{L-1}$$

$$\frac{\partial F}{\partial y} = 0 \tag{L-2}$$

$$\frac{\partial F}{\partial \lambda} = 0. \tag{L-3}$$

From the definition of $F(x, y, \lambda)$, we see that $\dfrac{\partial F}{\partial \lambda} = g(x, y)$. Thus the third equation (L-3) is just the original constraint equation $g(x, y) = 0$. So, when we find a point (x, y, λ) that satisfies (L-1), (L-2), and (L-3), the coordinates x and y will automatically satisfy the constraint equation.

The first example applies this method to the problem described in Fig. 1.

EXAMPLE 1

Maximize $36 - x^2 - y^2$ subject to the constraint $x + 7y - 25 = 0$.

Solution Here $f(x, y) = 36 - x^2 - y^2$, $g(x, y) = x + 7y - 25$, and

$$F(x, y, \lambda) = 36 - x^2 - y^2 + \lambda(x + 7y - 25).$$

Equations (L-1) to (L-3) read

$$\frac{\partial F}{\partial x} = -2x + \lambda = 0, \tag{1}$$

$$\frac{\partial F}{\partial y} = -2y + 7\lambda = 0, \tag{2}$$

$$\frac{\partial F}{\partial \lambda} = x + 7y - 25 = 0. \tag{3}$$

We solve the first two equations for λ:

$$\lambda = 2x$$

$$\lambda = \tfrac{2}{7}y. \tag{4}$$

If we equate these two expressions for λ, we obtain

$$2x = \tfrac{2}{7}y$$

$$x = \tfrac{1}{7}y. \tag{5}$$

Substituting this expression for x into equation (3), we have

$$\tfrac{1}{7}y + 7y - 25 = 0$$

$$\tfrac{50}{7}y = 25$$

$$y = \tfrac{7}{2}.$$

With this value for y, equations (4) and (5) produce the values of x and λ:

$$x = \tfrac{1}{7}y = \tfrac{1}{7}\left(\tfrac{7}{2}\right) = \tfrac{1}{2},$$

$$\lambda = \tfrac{2}{7}y = \tfrac{2}{7}\left(\tfrac{7}{2}\right) = 1.$$

Therefore, the partial derivatives of $F(x, y, \lambda)$ are zero when $x = \tfrac{1}{2}$, $y = \tfrac{7}{2}$, and $\lambda = 1$. So the maximum value of $36 - x^2 - y^2$ subject to the constraint $x + 7y - 25 = 0$ is

$$36 - \left(\tfrac{1}{2}\right)^2 - \left(\tfrac{7}{2}\right)^2 = \tfrac{47}{2}. \qquad \blacksquare$$

The preceding technique for solving three equations in the three variables x, y, and λ can usually be applied to solve Lagrange multiplier problems. Here is the basic procedure.

1. Solve (L-1) and (L-2) for λ in terms of x and y; then equate the resulting expressions for λ.
2. Solve the resulting equation for one of the variables.
3. Substitute the expression so derived into the equation (L-3), and solve the resulting equation of one variable.
4. Use the one known variable and the equations of steps 1 and 2 to determine the other two variables.

In most applications we know that an absolute (constrained) maximum or minimum exists. In the event that the method of Lagrange multipliers produces exactly one possible relative extreme value, we will assume that it is indeed the sought after absolute extreme value. For instance, the statement of Example 1 is meant to imply that there is an absolute maximum value. Since we determined that there was just one possible relative extreme value, we concluded that it was the absolute maximum value.

EXAMPLE 2

Using Lagrange multipliers, minimize $42x + 28y$, subject to the constraint $600 - xy = 0$, where x and y are restricted to positive values. (This problem arose in Example 4 of Section 2.5, where $42x + 28y$ was the cost of building a 600-square-foot enclosure having dimensions x and y.)

Solution   We have $f(x, y) = 42x + 28y$, $g(x, y) = 600 - xy$, and

$$F(x, y, \lambda) = 42x + 28y + \lambda(600 - xy).$$

The equations (L-1) to (L-3), in this case, are

$$\frac{\partial F}{\partial x} = 42 - \lambda y = 0,$$

$$\frac{\partial F}{\partial y} = 28 - \lambda x = 0,$$

$$\frac{\partial F}{\partial \lambda} = 600 - xy = 0.$$

From the first two equations we see that

$$\lambda = \frac{42}{y} = \frac{28}{x}. \qquad \text{(step 1)}$$

Therefore,

$$42x = 28y$$

and

$$x = \frac{2}{3}y. \qquad \text{(step 2)}$$

Substituting this expression for x into the third equation, we derive

$$600 - \left(\frac{2}{3}y\right)y = 0$$

$$y^2 = \frac{3}{2} \cdot 600 = 900$$

$$y = \pm 30. \qquad \text{(step 3)}$$

We discard the case $y = -30$ because we are interested only in positive values of x and y. Using $y = 30$, we find that

$$\left.\begin{array}{r} x = \dfrac{2}{3}(30) = 20 \\[2mm] \lambda = \dfrac{28}{20} = \dfrac{7}{5}. \end{array}\right\} \qquad \text{(step 4)}$$

So the minimum value of $42x + 28y$ with x and y subject to the constraint occurs when $x = 20$, $y = 30$, and $\lambda = \frac{7}{5}$. That minimum value is

$$42 \cdot (20) + 28 \cdot (30) = 1680. \qquad \blacksquare$$

EXAMPLE 3

Production   Suppose that x units of labor and y units of capital can produce $f(x, y) = 60x^{3/4}y^{1/4}$ units of a certain product. Also suppose that each unit of labor costs \$100, whereas each unit of capital costs \$200. Assume that \$30,000 is available to spend on production. How many units of labor and how many units of capital should be utilized to maximize production?

Solution The cost of x units of labor and y units of capital equals $100x + 200y$. Therefore, since we want to use all the available money ($\$30,000$), we must satisfy the constraint equation

$$100x + 200y = 30,000$$

or

$$g(x, y) = 30,000 - 100x - 200y = 0.$$

The objective function is $f(x, y) = 60x^{3/4}y^{1/4}$. In this case, we have

$$F(x, y, \lambda) = 60x^{3/4}y^{1/4} + \lambda(30,000 - 100x - 200y).$$

The equations (L-1) to (L-3) read

$$\frac{\partial F}{\partial x} = 45x^{-1/4}y^{1/4} - 100\lambda = 0, \tag{L-1}$$

$$\frac{\partial F}{\partial y} = 15x^{3/4}y^{-3/4} - 200\lambda = 0, \tag{L-2}$$

$$\frac{\partial F}{\partial \lambda} = 30,000 - 100x - 200y = 0. \tag{L-3}$$

By solving the first two equations for λ, we see that

$$\lambda = \frac{45}{100}x^{-1/4}y^{1/4} = \frac{9}{20}x^{-1/4}y^{1/4},$$

$$\lambda = \frac{15}{200}x^{3/4}y^{-3/4} = \frac{3}{40}x^{3/4}y^{-3/4}.$$

Therefore, we must have

$$\frac{9}{20}x^{-1/4}y^{1/4} = \frac{3}{40}x^{3/4}y^{-3/4}.$$

To solve for y in terms of x, let us multiply both sides of this equation by $x^{1/4}y^{3/4}$:

$$\frac{9}{20}y = \frac{3}{40}x$$

or

$$y = \frac{1}{6}x.$$

Inserting this result in (L-3), we find that

$$100x + 200\left(\frac{1}{6}x\right) = 30,000$$

$$\frac{400x}{3} = 30,000$$

$$x = 225.$$

Hence

$$y = \frac{225}{6} = 37.5.$$

So maximum production is achieved by using 225 units of labor and 37.5 units of capital. ∎

In Example 3 it turns out that, at the optimum values of x and y,

$$\lambda = \frac{9}{20}x^{-1/4}y^{1/4} = \frac{9}{20}(225)^{-1/4}(37.5)^{1/4} \approx .2875,$$

$$\frac{\partial f}{\partial x} = 45x^{-1/4}y^{1/4} = 45(225)^{-1/4}(37.5)^{1/4}, \tag{6}$$

$$\frac{\partial f}{\partial y} = 15x^{3/4}y^{-3/4} = 15(225)^{3/4}(37.5)^{-3/4}. \tag{7}$$

It can be shown that the Lagrange multiplier λ can be interpreted as the *marginal productivity of money*. That is, if 1 additional dollar is available, approximately .2875 additional units of the product can be produced.

Recall that the partial derivatives $\dfrac{\partial f}{\partial x}$ and $\dfrac{\partial f}{\partial y}$ are called the marginal productivity of labor and capital, respectively. From equations (6) and (7) we have

$$\frac{[\text{marginal productivity of labor}]}{[\text{marginal productivity of capital}]} = \frac{45(225)^{-1/4}(37.5)^{1/4}}{15(225)^{3/4}(37.5)^{-3/4}}$$

$$= \frac{45}{15}(225)^{-1}(37.5)^{1}$$

$$= \frac{3(37.5)}{225} = \frac{37.5}{75} = \frac{1}{2}.$$

On the other hand,

$$\frac{[\text{cost per unit of labor}]}{[\text{cost per unit of capital}]} = \frac{100}{200} = \frac{1}{2}.$$

This result illustrates the following law of economics. *If labor and capital are at their optimal levels, the ratio of their marginal productivities equals the ratio of their unit costs.*

The method of Lagrange multipliers generalizes to functions of any number of variables. For instance, we can maximize $f(x, y, z)$, subject to the constraint equation $g(x, y, z) = 0$, by considering the Lagrange function

$$F(x, y, z, \lambda) = f(x, y, z) + \lambda g(x, y, z).$$

The analogs of equations (L-1) to (L-3) are

$$\frac{\partial F}{\partial x} = 0, \quad \frac{\partial F}{\partial y} = 0, \quad \frac{\partial F}{\partial z} = 0, \quad \frac{\partial F}{\partial \lambda} = 0.$$

Let us now show how we can solve the heat-loss problem of Section 7.3 by using this method.

EXAMPLE 4   Use Lagrange multipliers to find the values of x, y, z that minimize the objective function

$$f(x, y, z) = 11xy + 14yz + 15xz,$$

subject to the constraint

$$xyz = 147{,}840.$$

Solution The Lagrange function is

$$F(x, y, z, \lambda) = 11xy + 14yz + 15xz + \lambda(147{,}840 - xyz).$$

The conditions for a relative minimum are

$$\frac{\partial F}{\partial x} = 11y + 15z - \lambda yz = 0,$$

$$\frac{\partial F}{\partial y} = 11x + 14z - \lambda xz = 0,$$

$$\frac{\partial F}{\partial z} = 14y + 15x - \lambda xy = 0,$$

$$\frac{\partial F}{\partial \lambda} = 147{,}840 - xyz = 0. \tag{8}$$

From the first three equations we have

$$\left.\begin{array}{l}\lambda = \dfrac{11y + 15z}{yz} = \dfrac{11}{z} + \dfrac{15}{y} \\[2mm] \lambda = \dfrac{11x + 14z}{xz} = \dfrac{11}{z} + \dfrac{14}{x} \\[2mm] \lambda = \dfrac{14y + 15x}{xy} = \dfrac{14}{x} + \dfrac{15}{y}\end{array}\right\}. \tag{9}$$

Let us equate the first two expression for λ:

$$\frac{11}{z} + \frac{15}{y} = \frac{11}{z} + \frac{14}{x}$$

$$\frac{15}{y} = \frac{14}{x}$$

$$x = \frac{14}{15}y.$$

Next, we equate the second and third expressions for λ in (9):

$$\frac{11}{z} + \frac{14}{x} = \frac{14}{x} + \frac{15}{y}$$

$$\frac{11}{z} = \frac{15}{y}$$

$$z = \frac{11}{15}y.$$

We now substitute the expressions for x and z into the constraint equation (8) and obtain

$$\frac{14}{15}y \cdot y \cdot \frac{11}{15}y = 147{,}840$$

$$y^3 = \frac{(147{,}840)(15)^2}{(14)(11)} = 216{,}000$$

$$y = 60.$$

From this, we find that

$$x = \frac{14}{15}(60) = 56 \quad \text{and} \quad z = \frac{11}{15}(60) = 44.$$

We conclude that the heat loss is minimized when $x = 56$, $y = 60$, and $z = 44$. ∎

In the solution of Example 4, we found that, at the optimal values of x, y, and z,

$$\frac{14}{x} = \frac{15}{y} = \frac{11}{z}.$$

Referring to Example 2 of Section 7.1, we see that 14 is the combined heat loss through the east and west sides of the building, 15 is the heat loss through the north and south sides of the building, and 11 is the heat loss through the floor and roof. Thus we have that under optimal conditions

$$\frac{[\text{heat loss through east and west sides}]}{[\text{distance between east and west sides}]}$$

$$= \frac{[\text{heat loss through north and south sides}]}{[\text{distance between north and south sides}]}$$

$$= \frac{[\text{heat loss through floor and roof}]}{[\text{distance between floor and roof}]}.$$

This is a principle of optimal design: Minimal heat loss occurs when the distance between each pair of opposite sides is some fixed constant times the heat loss from the pair of sides.

The value of λ in Example 4 corresponding to the optimal values of x, y, and z is

$$\lambda = \frac{11}{z} + \frac{15}{y} = \frac{11}{44} + \frac{15}{60} = \frac{1}{2}.$$

We can show that the Lagrange multiplier λ is the marginal heat loss with respect to volume. That is, if a building of volume slightly more than 147,840 cubic feet is optimally designed, $\frac{1}{2}$ unit of additional heat will be lost for each additional cubic foot of volume.

Practice Problems 7.4

1. Let $F(x, y, \lambda) = 2x + 3y + \lambda(90 - 6x^{1/3}y^{2/3})$. Find $\dfrac{\partial F}{\partial x}$.

2. Refer to Exercise 29 of Section 7.3. What is the function $F(x, y, l, \lambda)$ when the exercise is solved using the method of Lagrange multipliers?

EXERCISES 7.4

Solve the following exercises by the method of Lagrange multipliers.

1. Minimize $x^2 + 3y^2 + 10$, subject to the constraint $8 - x - y = 0$.

2. Maximize $x^2 - y^2$, subject to the constraint $2x + y - 3 = 0$.

3. Maximize $x^2 + xy - 3y^2$, subject to the constraint $2 - x - 2y = 0$.

4. Minimize $\frac{1}{2}x^2 - 3xy + y^2 + \frac{1}{2}$, subject to the constraint $3x - y - 1 = 0$.

5. Find the values of x, y that maximize

$$-2x^2 - 2xy - \tfrac{3}{2}y^2 + x + 2y,$$

subject to the constraint $x + y - \frac{5}{2} = 0$.

6. Find the values of x, y that minimize

$$x^2 + xy + y^2 - 2x - 5y,$$

subject to the constraint $1 - x + y = 0$.

7. Find the two positive numbers whose product is 25 and whose sum is as small as possible.

8. Four hundred eighty dollars are available to fence in a rectangular garden. The fencing for the north and south sides of the garden costs $10 per foot and the fencing for the east and west sides costs $15 per foot. Find the dimensions of the largest possible garden.

9. Three hundred square inches of material are available to construct an open rectangular box with a square base. Find the dimensions of the box that maximize the volume.

10. The amount of space required by a particular firm is $f(x, y) = 1000\sqrt{6x^2 + y^2}$, where x and y are, respectively, the number of units of labor and capital utilized. Suppose that labor costs $480 per unit and capital costs $40 per unit and that the firm has $5000 to spend. Determine the amounts of labor and capital that should be utilized in order to minimize the amount of space required.

11. Find the dimensions of the rectangle of maximum area that can be inscribed in the unit circle. [See Fig. 2(a).]

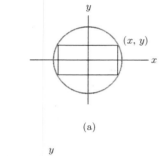

(a)

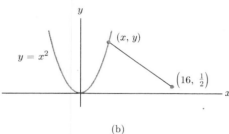

(b)

Figure 2

12. Find the point on the parabola $y = x^2$ that has minimal distance from the point $\left(16, \frac{1}{2}\right)$. [See Fig. 2(b).] [*Suggestion*: If d denotes the distance from (x, y) to $\left(16, \frac{1}{2}\right)$, then $d^2 = (x - 16)^2 + (y - \frac{1}{2})^2$. If d^2 is minimized, then d will be minimized.]

13. Suppose that a firm makes two products A and B that use the same raw materials. Given a fixed amount of raw materials and a fixed amount of manpower, the firm must decide how much of its resources should be allocated to the production of A and how much to B. If x units of A and y units of B are produced, suppose that x and y must satisfy

$$9x^2 + 4y^2 = 18,000.$$

The graph of this equation (for $x \geq 0$, $y \geq 0$) is called a *production possibilities curve* (Fig. 3). A point (x, y) on this curve represents a *production schedule* for the firm, committing it to produce x units of A and y units of B. The reason for the relationship between x and y

involves the limitations on personnel and raw materials available to the firm. Suppose that each unit of A yields a $3 profit, whereas each unit of B yields a $4 profit. Then the profit of the firm is

$$P(x, y) = 3x + 4y.$$

Find the production schedule that maximizes the profit function $P(x, y)$.

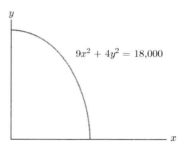

Figure 3. A production possibilities curve.

14. A firm makes x units of product A and y units of product B and has a production possibilities curve given by the equation $4x^2 + 25y^2 = 50,000$ for $x \geq 0$, $y \geq 0$. (See Exercise 13.) Suppose profits are $2 per unit for product A and $10 per unit for product B. Find the production schedule that maximizes the total profit.

15. The production function for a firm is $f(x, y) = 64x^{3/4}y^{1/4}$, where x and y are the number of units of labor and capital utilized. Suppose that labor costs $96 per unit and capital costs $162 per unit and that the firm decides to produce 3456 units of goods.

    (a) Determine the amounts of labor and capital that should be utilized in order to minimize the cost. That is, find the values of x, y that minimize $96x + 162y$, subject to the constraint $3456 - 64x^{3/4}y^{1/4} = 0$.

    (b) Find the value of λ at the optimal level of production.

    (c) Show that, at the optimal level of production, we have

$$\frac{[\text{marginal productivity of labor}]}{[\text{marginal productivity of capital}]}$$
$$= \frac{[\text{unit price of labor}]}{[\text{unit price of capital}]}.$$

16. Consider the monopolist of Example 2, Section 7.3, who sells his goods in two countries. Suppose that he must set the same price in each country. That is, $97 - (x/10) = 83 - (y/20)$. Find the values of x and y that maximize profits under this new restriction.

17. Find the values of x, y, and z that maximize xyz subject to the constraint $36 - x - 6y - 3z = 0$.

18. Find the values of x, y, and z that maximize $xy + 3xz + 3yz$ subject to the constraint $9 - xyz = 0$.

19. Find the values of x, y, z that maximize

$$3x + 5y + z - x^2 - y^2 - z^2,$$

subject to the constraint $6 - x - y - z = 0$.

20. Find the values of x, y, z that minimize

$$x^2 + y^2 + z^2 - 3x - 5y - z,$$

subject to the constraint $20 - 2x - y - z = 0$.

21. The material for a closed rectangular box costs $2 per square foot for the top and $1 per square foot for the sides and bottom. Using Lagrange multipliers, find the dimensions for which the volume of the box is 12 cubic feet and the cost of the materials is minimized. [Referring to Fig. 4(a), the cost will be $3xy + 2xz + 2yz$.]

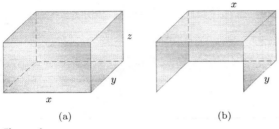

(a)   (b)

Figure 4

22. Use Lagrange multipliers to find the three positive numbers whose sum is 15 and whose product is as large as possible.

23. Find the dimensions of an open rectangular glass tank of volume 32 cubic feet for which the amount of material needed to construct the tank is minimized. [See Fig. 4(a).]

24. A shelter for use at the beach has a back, two sides, and a top made of canvas. [See Fig. 4(b).] Find the dimensions that maximize the volume and require 96 square feet of canvas.

25. Let $f(x, y)$ be any production function where x represents labor (costing a per unit) and y represents capital (costing b per unit). Assuming that c is available, show that, at the values of x, y that maximize production,

$$\frac{\frac{\partial f}{\partial x}}{\frac{\partial f}{\partial y}} = \frac{a}{b}.$$

Note: Let $F(x, y, \lambda) = f(x, y) + \lambda(c - ax - by)$. The result follows from (L-1) and (L-2).

26. By applying the result in Exercise 25 to the production function $f(x, y) = kx^\alpha y^\beta$, show that, for the values of x, y that maximize production, we have

$$\frac{y}{x} = \frac{a\beta}{b\alpha}.$$

(This tells us that the ratio of capital to labor does not depend on the amount of money available nor on the level of production but only on the numbers a, b, α, and β.)

Solutions to Practice Problems 7.4

1. The function can be written as

$$F(x, y, \lambda) = 2x + 3y + \lambda \cdot 90 - \lambda \cdot 6x^{1/3}y^{2/3}.$$

When differentiating with respect to x, both y and λ should be treated as constants (so $\lambda \cdot 90$ and $\lambda \cdot 6$ are also regarded as constants).

$$\frac{\partial F}{\partial x} = 2 - \lambda \cdot 6 \cdot \frac{1}{3}x^{-2/3} \cdot y^{2/3}$$

$$= 2 - 2\lambda x^{-2/3}y^{2/3}.$$

(*Note:* It is not necessary to write out the multiplication by λ as we did. Most people just do this mentally and then differentiate.)

2. The quantity to be maximized is the volume xyl. The constraint is that length plus girth is 84. This translates to $84 = l + 2x + 2y$ or $84 - l - 2x - 2y = 0$. Therefore,

$$F(x, y, l, \lambda) = xyl + \lambda(84 - l - 2x - 2y).$$

7.5 The Method of Least Squares

Today, people can compile graphs of literally thousands of different quantities: the purchasing value of the dollar as a function of time, the pressure of a fixed volume of air as a function of temperature, the average income of people as a function of their years of formal education, or the incidence of strokes as a function of blood pressure. The observed points on such graphs tend to be irregularly distributed due to the complicated nature of the phenomena underlying them, as well as to errors made in observation. (For example, a given procedure for measuring average income may not count certain groups.)

In spite of the imperfect nature of the data, we are often faced with the problem of making assessments and predictions based on them. Roughly speaking, this problem amounts to filtering the sources of errors in the data and isolating the basic underlying trend. Frequently, on the basis of a suspicion or a working hypothesis, we may suspect that the underlying trend is linear; that is, the data should lie on a straight line. But which straight line? This is the problem that the *method of least squares* attempts to answer. To be more specific, let us consider the following problem:

Problem of Fitting a Straight Line to Data   Given observed data points (x_1, y_1), (x_2, y_2), ..., (x_N, y_N) on a graph, find the straight line that best fits these points.

To completely understand the statement of the problem being considered, we must define what it means for a line to "best" fit a set of points. If (x_i, y_i) is one of our observed points, we will measure how far it is from a given line $y = Ax + B$ by the vertical distance from the point to the line. Since the point on the line with x-coordinate x_i is $(x_i, Ax_i + B)$, this vertical distance is the distance between the y-coordinates $Ax_i + B$ and y_i. (See Fig. 1.) If $E_i = (Ax_i + B) - y_i$, either E_i or $-E_i$ is the vertical distance from (x_i, y_i) to the line. To avoid this ambiguity, we work with the square of this vertical distance:

$$E_i^2 = (Ax_i + B - y_i)^2.$$

The total error in approximating the data points $(x_1, y_1), \ldots, (x_N, y_N)$ by the line $y = Ax + B$ is usually measured by the sum E of the squares of the vertical distances from the points to the line,

$$E = E_1^2 + E_2^2 + \cdots + E_N^2.$$

E is called the *least-squares error* of the observed points with respect to the line. If all the observed points lie on the line $y = Ax + B$, all E_i are zero and the error E is zero. If a given observed point is far away from the line, the corresponding E_i^2 is large and hence makes a large contribution to the error E.

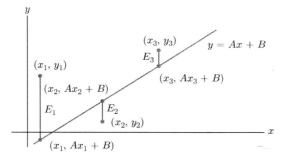

Figure 1. Fitting a line to data points.

In general, we cannot expect to find a line $y = Ax + B$ that fits the observed points so well that the error E is zero. Actually, this situation will occur only if the observed points lie on a straight line. However, we can rephrase our original problem as follows:

Problem   Given observed data points $(x_1, y_1), (x_2, y_2), \ldots, (x_N, y_N)$, find a straight line $y = Ax + B$ for which the error E is as small as possible. This line is called the *least-squares line* or *regression line*.

It turns out that this problem is a minimization problem in the two variables A and B and can be solved by using the methods of Section 7.3. Let us consider an example.

EXAMPLE 1

Find the straight line that minimizes the least-squares error for the points $(1, 4)$, $(2, 5)$, $(3, 8)$.

Solution Let the straight line be $y = Ax + B$. When $x = 1, 2, 3$, the y-coordinate of the corresponding point of the line is $A+B$, $2A+B$, $3A+B$, respectively. Therefore, the squares of the vertical distances from the points $(1, 4)$, $(2, 5)$, $(3, 8)$ are, respectively,

$$E_1^2 = (A + B - 4)^2,$$
$$E_2^2 = (2A + B - 5)^2,$$
$$E_3^2 = (3A + B - 8)^2.$$

(See Fig. 2.) Thus the least-squares error is

$$E = E_1^2 + E_2^2 + E_3^2 = (A + B - 4)^2 + (2A + B - 5)^2 + (3A + B - 8)^2.$$

This error obviously depends on the choice of A and B. Let $f(A, B)$ denote this least-squares error. We want to find values of A and B that minimize $f(A, B)$. To do so, we take partial derivatives with respect to A and B and set the partial derivatives equal to zero:

$$\frac{\partial f}{\partial A} = 2(A + B - 4) + 2(2A + B - 5) \cdot 2 + 2(3A + B - 8) \cdot 3$$
$$= 28A + 12B - 76 = 0,$$

$$\frac{\partial f}{\partial B} = 2(A + B - 4) + 2(2A + B - 5) + 2(3A + B - 8)$$
$$= 12A + 6B - 34 = 0.$$

To find A and B, we must solve the system of simultaneous linear equations

$$28A + 12B = 76$$
$$12A + 6B = 34.$$

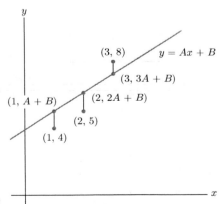

Figure 2

Multiplying the second equation by 2 and subtracting from the first equation, we have $4A = 8$, or $A = 2$. Therefore, $B = \frac{5}{3}$, and the straight line that minimizes the least-squares error is $y = 2x + \frac{5}{3}$. ∎

The minimization process used in Example 1 can be applied to a general set of data points $(x_1, y_1), \ldots, (x_N, y_N)$ to obtain the following algebraic formula for A and B:

$$A = \frac{N \cdot \Sigma\, xy - \Sigma\, x \cdot \Sigma\, y}{N \cdot \Sigma\, x^2 - (\Sigma\, x)^2},$$

$$B = \frac{\Sigma\, y - A \cdot \Sigma\, x}{N},$$

where

$\Sigma\, x = $ sum of the x-coordinates of the data points

$\Sigma\, y = $ sum of the y-coordinates of the data points

$\Sigma\, xy = $ sum of the products of the coordinates of the data points

$\Sigma\, x^2 = $ sum of the squares of the x-coordinates of the data points

$N = $ number of data points.

That is,

$$\Sigma\, x = x_1 + x_2 + \cdots + x_N$$

$$\Sigma\, y = y_1 + y_2 + \cdots + y_N$$

$$\Sigma\, xy = x_1 \cdot y_1 + x_2 \cdot y_2 + \cdots + x_N \cdot y_N$$

$$\Sigma\, x^2 = x_1^2 + x_2^2 + \cdots + x_N^2.$$

EXAMPLE 2

The following table* gives the crude male death rate for lung cancer in 1950 and the per capita consumption of cigarettes in 1930 in various countries.

Country	Cigarette Consumption (Per Capita)	Lung Cancer Deaths (Per Million Males)
Norway	250	95
Sweden	300	120
Denmark	350	165
Australia	470	170

(a) Use the preceding formulas to obtain the straight line that best fits these data.

(b) In 1930 the per capita cigarette consumption in Finland was 1100. Use the straight line found in part (a) to estimate the male lung cancer death rate in Finland in 1950.

Solution (a) The points are plotted in Fig. 3. The sums are calculated in Table 1 and then used to determine the values of A and B.

---

*These data were obtained from *Smoking and Health*, Report of the Advisory Committee to the Surgeon General of the Public Health Service, U.S. Department of Health, Education, and Welfare, Washington, D.C., Public Health Service Publication No. 1103, p. 176.

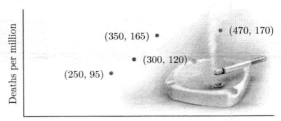

Figure 3. Lung cancer data for least-squares analysis.

TABLE 1	Least-Squares Calculation for Smoking Data		
x	y	xy	x^2
250	95	23,750	62,500
300	120	36,000	90,000
350	165	57,750	122,500
470	170	79,900	220,900
$\Sigma x = 1370$	$\Sigma y = 550$	$\Sigma xy = 197,400$	$\Sigma x^2 = 495,900$

$$A = \frac{4 \cdot 197,400 - 1370 \cdot 550}{4 \cdot 495,900 - 1370^2} = \frac{36,100}{106,700} = \frac{361}{1067} \approx .338,$$

$$B = \frac{550 - \frac{361}{1067} \cdot 1370}{4} = \frac{1067 \cdot 550 - 361 \cdot 1370}{1067 \cdot 4} = \frac{92,280}{4268} \approx 21.621.$$

Therefore, the equation of the least-squares line is $y = .338x + 21.621$.

(b) We use the straight line to estimate the lung cancer death rate in Finland by setting $x = 1100$. Then we get

$$y = .338(1100) + 21.621 = 393.421 \approx 393.$$

Therefore, we estimate the lung cancer death rate in Finland to be 393 deaths per million males. (*Note:* The actual rate was 350 deaths per million males.) ∎

INCORPORATING TECHNOLOGY

Least Squares Method   To implement the least-squares method on your TI-83/84, select $\boxed{\text{SELECT}}$ $\boxed{1}$ for the EDIT screen to obtain a table used for entering the data. If necessary, clear data from columns L_1 and/or L_2 by moving the cursor to the top of the column and pressing $\boxed{\text{CLEAR}}$ $\boxed{\text{ENTER}}$. [See Fig. 4(a).]

After the x- and y-values are placed into lists on a graphing calculator, we use the statistical routine LinReg to calculate the coefficients of the least-squares line. Now press $\boxed{\text{STAT}}$ $\boxed{\triangleright}$ for the CALC menu, and press $\boxed{4}$ to place **LinReg(ax+b)** on the home screen. Press $\boxed{\text{ENTER}}$ to obtain the slope and y-intercept of the least-squares line. [See Fig. 4(b).]

If desired, the equation for the line can automatically be assigned to a function and graphed along with the original points. First, we assign the equation for the least-squares line to a function. Select $\boxed{\text{Y=}}$, move to the function, and press $\boxed{\text{CLEAR}}$ to erase any current expression. Now press $\boxed{\text{VARS}}$ $\boxed{5}$ to select the **Statistics** variables. Move your cursor over to he EQ menu, and press $\boxed{1}$ for **RegEQ** (Regression Equation).

To graph this line, press GRAPH. To graph this line along with the original data points, we proceed as follows. From the Y=, and with only the least-squares line selected, press 2nd [STAT PLOT] ENTER to select **Plot1**, and press ENTER to turn **Plot1 ON**. Now select the first plot from the six icons for the plot **Type**. This corresponds to a scatter plot. Finally, press GRAPH. [See Fig. 4(c).] ■

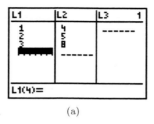

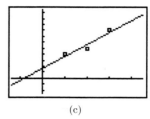

Figure 4   (a)   (b)   (c)

Practice Problems 7.5

1. Let $E = (A + B + 2)^2 + (3A + B)^2 + (6A + B - 8)^2$. What is $\dfrac{\partial E}{\partial A}$?

2. Find the formula (of the type in Problem 1) that gives the least-squares error E for the points $(1, 10)$, $(5, 8)$, and $(7, 0)$.

EXERCISES 7.5

1. Find the least-squares error E for the least-squares line fit to the four points in Fig. 5.

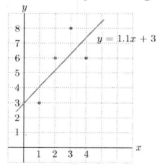

$y = 1.1x + 3$

Figure 5

2. Find the least-squares error E for the least-squares line fit to the five points in Fig. 6.

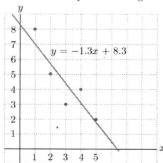

$y = -1.3x + 8.3$

Figure 6

3. Find the formula (of the type in Practice Problem 1) that gives the least-squares error for the points $(2, 6)$, $(5, 10)$, and $(9, 15)$.

4. Find the formula (of the type in Practice Problem 1) that gives the least-squares error for the points $(8, 4)$, $(9, 2)$, and $(10, 3)$.

In Exercises 5–8, use partial derivatives to obtain the formula for the best least-squares fit to the data points.

5. $(1, 2)$, $(2, 5)$, $(3, 11)$

6. $(1, 8)$, $(2, 4)$, $(4, 3)$

7. $(1, 9)$, $(2, 8)$, $(3, 6)$, $(4, 3)$

8. $(1, 5)$, $(2, 7)$, $(3, 6)$, $(4, 10)$

9. Complete Table 2 and find the values of A and B for the straight line that provides the best least-squares fit to the data.

TABLE 2			
x	y	xy	x^2
1	7		
2	6		
3	4		
4	3		
$\Sigma x =$	$\Sigma y =$	$\Sigma xy =$	$\Sigma x^2 =$

10. Complete Table 3 and find the values of A and B for the straight line that provides the best least-squares fit to the data.

TABLE 3

x	y	xy	x^2
1	2		
2	4		
3	7		
4	9		
5	12		
$\Sigma x =$	$\Sigma y =$	$\Sigma xy =$	$\Sigma x^2 =$

In the remaining exercises, use one or more of the three methods discussed in this section (partial derivatives, formulas, or graphing utilities) to obtain the formula for the least-squares line.

11. Table 4* gives the U.S. per capita health care expenditures for the years 1990–1994.

TABLE 4   U.S. Per Capita Health Care Expenditures

Years (after 1990)	Dollars (in thousands)
0	2.688
1	2.902
2	3.144
3	3.331
4	3.510

(a) Find the least-squares line for these data.

(b) Use the least-squares line to predict the per capita health care expenditures for the year 2000.

(c) Use the least-squares line to predict when per capita health care expenditures will reach $6000.

12. Table 5 shows the 1994 price of a gallon of fuel (in U.S. dollars) and the average miles driven per automobile for several countries.[†]

(a) Find the straight line that provides the best least-squares fit to these data.

(b) In 1994, the price of gas in Japan was $4.14 per gallon. Use the straight line of part (a) to estimate the average number of miles automobiles were driven in Japan.

TABLE 5   Effect of Gas Prices on Miles Driven

Country	Price per Gallon	Average Miles per Auto
Canada	$1.57	10,371
England	$2.86	10,186
France	$3.31	8,740
Germany	$3.34	7,674
Sweden	$3.44	7,456
United States	$1.24	11,099

13. Table 6 gives the percent of persons 25 years and over who have completed four or more years of college.[‡]

TABLE 6   College Completion Rates

Year	1970	1975	1980	1985	1990	1995
Percent	10.7	13.9	16.2	19.4	21.3	23.0

(a) Use the method of least squares to obtain the straight line that best fits these data. [*Hint*: First convert *Year* to *Years after 1970*.]

(b) Estimate the percent for the year 1993.

(c) If the trend determined by the straight line in part (a) continues, when will the percent reach 27.1?

14. Table 7 gives the number of cars (in millions) in use in the United States[§] for certain years.

TABLE 7   Automobile Population

Year	Cars	Year	Cars
1980	104.6	1991	123.3
1985	114.7	1992	120.3
1989	122.8	1993	121.1
1990	123.3	1994	122

(a) Use the method of least squares to obtain the straight line that best fits these data. [*Hint*: First convert *Years* to *Years after 1980*.]

(b) Estimate the number of cars in use in 1983.

(c) If the trend determined by the straight line in part (a) continues, when will the number of cars in use reach 130 million?

---

*U.S. Health Care Financing Administration, *Health Care Financing Review*, Spring 1996.

[†]Source: Energy Information Administration, *International Energy Annual*. U.S. Highway Administration, *Highway Statistics*, 1994.

[‡]U.S. Bureau of the Census.

[§]American Automobile Manufacturers Association, Inc., Detroit, Michigan, *Motor Vehicle Facts and Figures*.

15. An ecologist wished to know whether certain species of aquatic insects have their ecological range limited by temperature. He collected the data in Table 8, relating the average daily temperature at different portions of a creek with the elevation (above sea level) of that portion of the creek.*

    (a) Find the straight line that provides the best least-squares fit to these data.

    (b) Use the linear function to estimate the average daily temperature for this creek at altitude 3.2 kilometers.

TABLE 8 Relationship between Elevation and Temperature in a Creek	
Elevation (kilometers)	Average Temperature (degrees Celsius)
2.7	11.2
2.8	10
3.0	8.5
3.5	7.5

Solutions to Practice Problems 7.5

1. $\dfrac{\partial E}{\partial A} = 2(A + B + 2)\cdot 1 + 2(3A + B)\cdot 3$
$\qquad + 2(6A + B - 8)\cdot 6$

$\qquad = (2A + 2B + 4) + (18A + 6B)$
$\qquad\quad + (72A + 12B - 96)$

$\qquad = 92A + 20B - 92.$

(Notice that we used the general power rule when differentiating and so had to always multiply by the derivative of the quantity inside the parentheses. Also, you might be tempted to first square the terms in the expression for E and then differentiate. We recommend that you resist this temptation.)

2. $E = (A + B - 10)^2 + (5A + B - 8)^2 + (7A + B)^2$. In general, E is a sum of squares, one for each point being fitted. The point (a, b) gives rise to the term $(aA + B - b)^2$.

7.6 Double Integrals

Up to this point, our discussion of the calculus of several variables has been confined to the study of differentiation. Let us now take up the topic of the integration of functions of several variables. As has been the case throughout most of this chapter, we restrict our discussion to functions $f(x, y)$ of two variables.

We begin with some motivation. Before we define the concept of an integral for functions of several variables, we review the essential features of the integral in one variable.

Consider the definite integral $\int_a^b f(x)\, dx$. To write down this integral takes two pieces of information. The first is the function $f(x)$. The second is the interval over which the integration is to be performed. In this case, the interval is the portion of the x-axis from $x = a$ to $x = b$. The value of the definite integral is a number. In case the function $f(x)$ is nonnegative throughout the interval from $x = a$ to $x = b$, this number equals the area under the graph of $f(x)$ from $x = a$ to $x = b$. (See Fig. 1.) If $f(x)$ is negative for some values of x in the interval, the integral still equals the area bounded by the graph, but areas below the x-axis are counted as negative.

Let us generalize the foregoing ingredients to a function $f(x, y)$ of two variables. First, we must provide a two-dimensional analog of the interval from $x = a$ to $x = b$. This is easy. We take a two-dimensional region R of the plane, such as the region shown in Fig. 2. As our generalization of $f(x)$, we take a function $f(x, y)$ of two

---

*The authors express their thanks to Dr. J. David Allen, formerly of the Department of Zoology at the University of Maryland, for providing the data for this exercise.

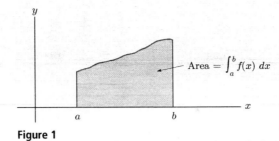

Area $= \int_a^b f(x)\,dx$

Figure 1

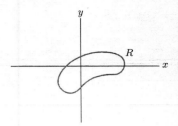

Figure 2. A region in the xy-plane.

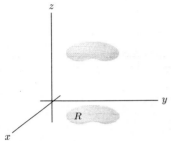

Figure 3. Graph of $f(x,y)$ above the region R.

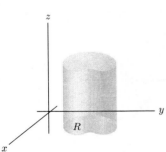

Figure 4. Solid bounded by $f(x,y)$ over R.

variables. Our generalization of the definite integral is denoted

$$\iint\limits_R f(x,y)\,dx\,dy$$

and is called the *double integral of $f(x,y)$ over the region R*. The value of the double integral is a number defined as follows. For the sake of simplicity, let us begin by assuming that $f(x,y) \geq 0$ for all points (x,y) in the region R. [This is the analog of the assumption that $f(x) \geq 0$ for all x in the interval from $x = a$ to $x = b$.] This means that the graph of f lies above the region R in three-dimensional space. (See Fig. 3.) The portion of the graph over R determines a solid figure. (See Fig. 4.) This figure is called the *solid bounded by $f(x,y)$ over the region R*. We define the double integral $\iint_R f(x,y)\,dx\,dy$ to be the volume of this solid. In case the graph of $f(x,y)$ lies partially above the region R and partially below, we define the double integral to be the volume of the solid above the region minus the volume of the solid below the region. That is, we count volumes below the xy-plane as negative.

Now that we have defined the notion of a double integral, we must learn how to calculate its value. To do so, let us introduce the notion of an iterated integral. Let $f(x,y)$ be a function of two variables, let $g(x)$ and $h(x)$ be two functions of x alone, and let a and b be numbers. Then an *iterated integral* is an expression of the form

$$\int_a^b \left(\int_{g(x)}^{h(x)} f(x,y)\,dy \right) dx.$$

To explain the meaning of this collection of symbols, we proceed from the inside out. We evaluate the integral

$$\int_{g(x)}^{h(x)} f(x,y)\,dy$$

by considering $f(x,y)$ as a function of y alone. This is indicated by the dy in the inner integral. We treat x as a constant in this integration. So we evaluate the integral by first finding an antiderivative $F(x,y)$ with respect to y. The integral above is then evaluated as

$$F(x,h(x)) - F(x,g(x)).$$

That is, we evaluate the antiderivative between the limits $y = g(x)$ and $y = h(x)$. This gives us a function of x alone. To complete the evaluation of the integral, we integrate this function from $x = a$ to $x = b$. The next two examples illustrate the procedure for evaluating iterated integrals.

EXAMPLE 1   Evaluate the iterated integral

$$\int_1^2 \left(\int_3^4 (y - x)\, dy \right) dx.$$

Solution Here $g(x)$ and $h(x)$ are constant functions: $g(x) = 3$ and $h(x) = 4$. We evaluate the inner integral first. The variable in this integral is y, so we treat x as a constant.

$$\int_3^4 (y - x)\, dy = \left(\frac{1}{2}y^2 - xy \right) \Big|_3^4$$

$$= \left(\frac{1}{2} \cdot 16 - x \cdot 4 \right) - \left(\frac{1}{2} \cdot 9 - x \cdot 3 \right)$$

$$= 8 - 4x - \frac{9}{2} + 3x$$

$$= \frac{7}{2} - x.$$

Now we carry out the integration with respect to x:

$$\int_1^2 \left(\frac{7}{2} - x \right) dx = \frac{7}{2}x - \frac{1}{2}x^2 \Big|_1^2$$

$$= \left(\frac{7}{2} \cdot 2 - \frac{1}{2} \cdot 4 \right) - \left(\frac{7}{2} - \frac{1}{2} \cdot 1 \right)$$

$$= (7 - 2) - (3) = 2.$$

So the value of the iterated integral is 2. ◼

EXAMPLE 2   Evaluate the iterated integral

$$\int_0^1 \left(\int_{\sqrt{x}}^{x+1} 2xy\, dy \right) dx.$$

Solution We evaluate the inner integral first.

$$\int_{\sqrt{x}}^{x+1} 2xy\, dy = xy^2 \Big|_{\sqrt{x}}^{x+1} = x(x+1)^2 - x(\sqrt{x})^2$$

$$= x(x^2 + 2x + 1) - x \cdot x$$

$$= x^3 + 2x^2 + x - x^2$$

$$= x^3 + x^2 + x.$$

Now we evaluate the outer integral.

$$\int_0^1 (x^3 + x^2 + x)\, dx = \frac{1}{4}x^4 + \frac{1}{3}x^3 + \frac{1}{2}x^2 \Big|_0^1 = \frac{1}{4} + \frac{1}{3} + \frac{1}{2} = \frac{13}{12}$$

So the value of the iterated integral is $\frac{13}{12}$. ◼

Let us now return to the discussion of the double integral $\iint_R f(x, y)\, dx\, dy$. When the region R has a special form, the double integral may be expressed as an iterated integral, as follows: Suppose that R is bounded by the graphs of $y = g(x)$, $y = h(x)$ and by the vertical lines $x = a$ and $x = b$. (See Fig. 5.) In this case, we have the following fundamental result, which we cite without proof.

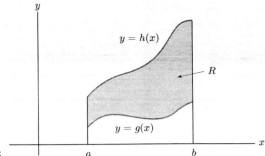

Figure 5

Let R be the region in the xy-plane bounded by the graphs of $y = g(x)$, $y = h(x)$, and the vertical lines $x = a$, $x = b$. Then

$$\iint\limits_{R} f(x, y)\, dx\, dy = \int_a^b \left(\int_{g(x)}^{h(x)} f(x, y)\, dy \right) dx.$$

Since the value of the double integral gives the volume of the solid bounded by the graph of $f(x, y)$ over the region R, the preceding result may be used to calculate volumes, as the next two examples show.

EXAMPLE 3

Calculate the volume of the solid bounded above by the function $f(x, y) = y - x$ and lying over the rectangular region R: $1 \le x \le 2$, $3 \le y \le 4$. (See Fig. 6.)

Solution The desired volume is given by the double integral $\iint\limits_{R} (y - x)\, dx\, dy$. By the result just cited, this double integral is equal to the iterated integral

$$\int_1^2 \left(\int_3^4 (y - x)\, dy \right) dx.$$

The value of this iterated integral was shown in Example 1 to be 2, so the volume of the solid shown in Fig. 6 is 2. ∎

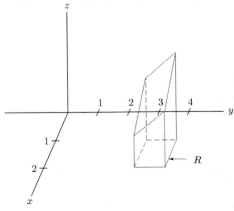

Figure 6

EXAMPLE 4

Calculate $\iint\limits_{R} 2xy\,dx\,dy$, where R is the region shown in Fig. 7.

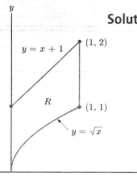

Figure 7

Solution The region R is bounded below by $y = \sqrt{x}$, above by $y = x + 1$, on the left by $x = 0$, and on the right by $x = 1$. Therefore,

$$\iint\limits_{R} 2xy\,dx\,dy = \int_{0}^{1} \left(\int_{\sqrt{x}}^{x+1} 2xy\,dy \right) dx = \frac{13}{12} \quad \text{(by Example 2).} \quad \blacksquare$$

In our discussion, we have confined ourselves to iterated integrals in which the inner integral was with respect to y. In a completely analogous manner, we may treat iterated integrals in which the inner integral is with respect to x. Such iterated integrals may be used to evaluate double integrals over regions R bounded by curves of the form $x = g(y)$, $x = h(y)$, and horizontal lines $y = a$, $y = b$. The computations are analogous to those given in this section.

Practice Problems 7.6

1. Calculate the iterated integral

$$\int_{0}^{2} \left(\int_{0}^{x/2} e^{2y-x}\,dy \right) dx.$$

2. Calculate

$$\iint\limits_{R} e^{2y-x}\,dx\,dy$$

where R is the region in Fig. 8.

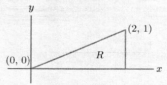

Figure 8

EXERCISES 7.6

Calculate the following iterated integrals.

1. $\int_{0}^{1} \left(\int_{0}^{1} e^{x+y}\,dy \right) dx$

2. $\int_{-1}^{1} \left(\int_{-1}^{1} xy\,dx \right) dy$

3. $\int_{-2}^{0} \left(\int_{-1}^{1} xe^{xy}\,dy \right) dx$

4. $\int_{0}^{1} \left(\int_{-1}^{1} \frac{1}{3}y^3 x\,dy \right) dx$

5. $\int_{1}^{4} \left(\int_{x}^{x^2} xy\,dy \right) dx$

6. $\int_{0}^{3} \left(\int_{x}^{2x} y\,dy \right) dx$

7. $\int_{-1}^{1} \left(\int_{x}^{2x} (x+y)\,dy \right) dx$

8. $\int_{0}^{1} \left(\int_{0}^{x} e^{x+y}\,dy \right) dx$

Let R be the rectangle consisting of all points (x, y) such that $0 \le x \le 2$, $2 \le y \le 3$. Calculate the following double integrals. Interpret each as a volume.

9. $\iint\limits_{R} xy^2\,dx\,dy$

10. $\iint\limits_{R} (xy + y^2)\,dx\,dy$

11. $\iint\limits_{R} e^{-x-y}\,dx\,dy$

12. $\iint\limits_{R} e^{y-x}\,dx\,dy$

Calculate the volumes over the following regions R bounded above by the graph of $f(x, y) = x^2 + y^2$.

13. R is the rectangle bounded by the lines $x = 1$, $x = 3$, $y = 0$, and $y = 1$.

14. R is the region bounded by the lines $x = 0$, $x = 1$ and the curves $y = 0$ and $y = \sqrt[3]{x}$.

Solutions to Practice Problems 7.6

1. $\displaystyle\int_0^2 \left(\int_0^{x/2} e^{2y-x}\, dy \right) dx = \int_0^2 \left(\frac{1}{2}e^{2y-x} \Big|_0^{x/2} \right) dx$

$\displaystyle = \int_0^2 \left(\frac{1}{2}e^{2(x/2)-x} - \frac{1}{2}e^{2(0)-x} \right) dx$

$\displaystyle = \int_0^2 \left(\frac{1}{2} - \frac{1}{2}e^{-x} \right) dx$

$\displaystyle = \frac{1}{2}x + \frac{1}{2}e^{-x} \Big|_0^2$

$\displaystyle = \frac{1}{2}\cdot 2 + \frac{1}{2}e^{-2} - \left(\frac{1}{2}\cdot 0 + \frac{1}{2}e^{-0} \right)$

$\displaystyle = 1 + \frac{1}{2}e^{-2} - 0 - \frac{1}{2}$

$\displaystyle = \frac{1}{2} + \frac{1}{2}e^{-2}.$

2. The line passing through the points $(0,0)$ and $(2,1)$ has equation $y = x/2$. Hence the region R is bounded below by $y = 0$, above by $y = x/2$, on the left by $x = 0$, and on the right by $x = 2$. Therefore,

$$\iint_R e^{2y-x}\, dx\, dy = \int_0^2 \left(\int_0^{x/2} e^{2y-x}\, dy \right) dx$$

$$= \frac{1}{2} + \frac{1}{2}e^{-2}$$

by Problem 1.

REVIEW OF FUNDAMENTAL CONCEPTS

1. Give an example of a level curve of a function of two variables.

2. Explain how to find a first partial derivative of a function of two variables.

3. Explain how to find a second partial derivative of a function of two variables.

4. What expression involving a partial derivative gives an approximation to $f(a+h,b) - f(a,b)$?

5. Interpret $\dfrac{\partial f}{\partial y}(2,3)$ as a rate of change.

6. Give an example of a Cobb–Douglas production function. What is the marginal productivity of labor? Of capital?

7. Explain how to find possible relative extreme points for a function of several variables.

8. State the second-derivative test for functions of two variables.

9. Outline how the method of Lagrange multipliers is used to solve an optimization problem.

10. What is the least-squares line approximation to a set of data points? How is the line determined?

11. Give a geometric interpretation for $\iint_R f(x,y)\, dx\, dy$, where $f(x,y) \geq 0$.

12. Give a formula for evaluating a double integral in terms of an iterated integral.

SUPPLEMENTARY EXERCISES

1. Let $f(x,y) = x\sqrt{y}/(1+x)$. Compute $f(2,9)$, $f(5,1)$, and $f(0,0)$.

2. Let $f(x,y,z) = x^2 e^{y/z}$. Compute $f(-1,0,1)$, $f(1,3,3)$, and $f(5,-2,2)$.

3. If A dollars are deposited in a bank at a 6% continuous interest rate, the amount in the account after t years is $f(A,t) = Ae^{.06t}$. Find and interpret $f(10,11.5)$.

4. Let $f(x,y,\lambda) = xy + \lambda(5 - x - y)$. Find $f(1,2,3)$.

5. Let $f(x,y) = 3x^2 + xy + 5y^2$. Find $\dfrac{\partial f}{\partial x}$ and $\dfrac{\partial f}{\partial y}$.

6. Let $f(x,y) = 3x - \frac{1}{2}y^4 + 1$. Find $\dfrac{\partial f}{\partial x}$ and $\dfrac{\partial f}{\partial y}$.

7. Let $f(x,y) = e^{x/y}$. Find $\dfrac{\partial f}{\partial x}$ and $\dfrac{\partial f}{\partial y}$.

8. Let $f(x,y) = x/(x - 2y)$. Find $\dfrac{\partial f}{\partial x}$ and $\dfrac{\partial f}{\partial y}$.

9. Let $f(x,y,z) = x^3 - yz^2$. Find $\dfrac{\partial f}{\partial x}$, $\dfrac{\partial f}{\partial y}$, and $\dfrac{\partial f}{\partial z}$.

10. Let $f(x,y,\lambda) = xy + \lambda(5 - x - y)$. Find $\dfrac{\partial f}{\partial x}$, $\dfrac{\partial f}{\partial y}$, and $\dfrac{\partial f}{\partial \lambda}$.

11. Let $f(x,y) = x^3 y + 8$. Compute $\dfrac{\partial f}{\partial x}(1,2)$ and $\dfrac{\partial f}{\partial y}(1,2)$.

12. Let $f(x, y, z) = (x + y)z$. Evaluate $\dfrac{\partial f}{\partial y}$ at $(x, y, z) = (2, 3, 4)$.

13. Let $f(x, y) = x^5 - 2x^3y + \frac{1}{2}y^4$. Find $\dfrac{\partial^2 f}{\partial x^2}, \dfrac{\partial^2 f}{\partial y^2}, \dfrac{\partial^2 f}{\partial x\, \partial y}$, and $\dfrac{\partial^2 f}{\partial y\, \partial x}$.

14. Let $f(x, y) = 2x^3 + x^2y - y^2$. Compute $\dfrac{\partial^2 f}{\partial x^2}, \dfrac{\partial^2 f}{\partial y^2}$, and $\dfrac{\partial^2 f}{\partial x\, \partial y}$ at $(x, y) = (1, 2)$.

15. A dealer in a certain brand of electronic calculator finds that (within certain limits) the number of calculators she can sell per week is given by $f(p, t) = -p + 6t - .02pt$, where p is the price of the calculator and t is the number of dollars spent on advertising. Compute $\dfrac{\partial f}{\partial p}(25, 10{,}000)$ and $\dfrac{\partial f}{\partial t}(25, 10{,}000)$ and interpret these numbers.

16. The crime rate in a certain city can be approximated by a function $f(x, y, z)$, where x is the unemployment rate, y is the amount of social services available, and z is the size of the police force. Explain why $\dfrac{\partial f}{\partial x} > 0$, $\dfrac{\partial f}{\partial y} < 0$, and $\dfrac{\partial f}{\partial z} < 0$.

In Exercises 17–20, find all points (x, y) where $f(x, y)$ has a possible relative maximum or minimum.

17. $f(x, y) = -x^2 + 2y^2 + 6x - 8y + 5$

18. $f(x, y) = x^2 + 3xy - y^2 - x - 8y + 4$

19. $f(x, y) = x^3 + 3x^2 + 3y^2 - 6y + 7$

20. $f(x, y) = \frac{1}{2}x^2 + 4xy + y^3 + 8y^2 + 3x + 2$

In Exercises 21–23, find all points (x, y) where $f(x, y)$ has a possible relative maximum or minimum. Then use the second-derivative test to determine, if possible, the nature of $f(x, y)$ at each of these points. If the second-derivative test is inconclusive, so state.

21. $f(x, y) = x^2 + 3xy + 4y^2 - 13x - 30y + 12$

22. $f(x, y) = 7x^2 - 5xy + y^2 + x - y + 6$

23. $f(x, y) = x^3 + y^2 - 3x - 8y + 12$

24. Find the values of x, y, z at which

$$f(x, y, z) = x^2 + 4y^2 + 5z^2 - 6x + 8y + 3$$

assumes its minimum value.

Use the method of Lagrange multipliers to:

25. Maximize $3x^2 + 2xy - y^2$, subject to the constraint $5 - 2x - y = 0$.

26. Find the values of x, y that minimize $-x^2 - 3xy - \frac{1}{2}y^2 + y + 10$, subject to the constraint $10 - x - y = 0$.

27. Find the values of x, y, z that minimize $3x^2 + 2y^2 + z^2 + 4x + y + 3z$, subject to the constraint $4 - x - y - z = 0$.

28. Find the dimensions of a rectangular box of volume 1000 cubic inches for which the sum of the dimensions is minimized.

29. A person wants to plant a rectangular garden along one side of a house and put a fence on the other three sides. (See Fig. 1.) Using the method of Lagrange multipliers, find the dimensions of the garden of greatest area that can be enclosed by using 40 feet of fencing.

Figure 9. A garden.

30. The solution to Exercise 29 is $x = 10$, $y = 20$, $\lambda = 10$. If 1 additional foot of fencing becomes available, compute the new optimal dimensions and the new area. Show that the increase in area (compared with the area in Exercise 29) is approximately equal to 10 (the value of λ).

In Exercises 31–33, find the straight line that best fits the following data points, where "best" is meant in the sense of least squares.

31. $(1, 1)$, $(2, 3)$, $(3, 6)$

32. $(1, 1)$, $(3, 4)$, $(5, 7)$

33. $(0, 1)$, $(1, -1)$, $(2, -3)$, $(3, -5)$

In Exercises 34 and 35, calculate the iterated integral.

34. $\displaystyle\int_0^1 \left(\int_0^4 (x\sqrt{y} + y)\, dy \right) dx$

35. $\displaystyle\int_0^5 \left(\int_1^4 (2xy^4 + 3)\, dy \right) dx$

In Exercises 36 and 37, let R be the rectangle consisting of all points (x, y) such that $0 \le x \le 4$, $1 \le y \le 3$, and calculate the double integral.

36. $\displaystyle\iint_R (2x + 3y)\, dx\, dy$ **37.** $\displaystyle\iint_R 5\, dx\, dy$

38. The present value of y dollars after x years at 15% continuous interest is $f(x, y) = ye^{-.15x}$. Sketch some sample level curves. (Economists call this collection of level curves a *discount system*.)

MATRICES

We begin this chapter by developing a method for solving systems of linear equations in any number of variables. Our discussion of this method will lead naturally into the study of mathematical objects called *matrices*. The arithmetic and applications of matrices are the main topics of the chapter. We discuss in detail the application of matrix arithmetic to input–output analysis, which can be (and is) used to make production decisions for large businesses and entire economies.

2.1 Solving Systems of Linear Equations, I

In Chapter 1 we presented a method for solving systems of linear equations in two variables. The method of Chapter 1 is very efficient for determining the solutions. Unfortunately, it works only for systems of linear equations having *two* variables. In many applications we meet systems having more than two variables, as the following example illustrates.

EXAMPLE 1

Manufacturing The Upside Down company specializes in making down jackets, ski vests, and comforters. The requirements for down and labor and the profits earned are given in the following chart.

	Down (pounds)	Time (labor-hours)	Profit ($)
Jacket	3	2	6
Vest	2	1	6
Comforter	4	1	2

Each week the company has available 600 pounds of down and 275 labor-hours. It wants to earn a weekly profit of $1150. How many of each item should the company make each week?

Solution The requirements and earnings can be expressed by a system of equations. Let x be the number of jackets, y the number of vests, and z the number of comforters. If 600 pounds of down are used, then

$$[\text{down in jackets}] + [\text{down in vests}] + [\text{down in comforters}] = 600$$
$$3\,[\text{no. jackets}] \;\; + \;\; 2\,[\text{no. vests}] \;\; + \;\; 4\,[\text{no. comforters}] \;\; = 600.$$

That is,

$$3x + 2y + 4z = 600.$$

Similarly, the equation for labor is

$$2x + y + z = 275,$$

and the equation for the profit is

$$6x + 6y + 2z = 1150.$$

The numbers x, y, and z must simultaneously satisfy a system of three linear equations in three variables.

$$\begin{cases} 3x + 2y + 4z = 600 \\ 2x + y + z = 275 \\ 6x + 6y + 2z = 1150. \end{cases} \tag{1}$$

Later we present a method for determining the solution to this system. This method yields the solution $x = 50$, $y = 125$, and $z = 50$. It is easy to confirm that these values of x, y, and z satisfy all three equations:

$$3(50) + 2(125) + 4(50) = 600$$
$$2(50) + (125) + (50) = 275$$
$$6(50) + 6(125) + 2(50) = 1150.$$

Thus, the Upside Down company can make a profit of $1150 by producing 50 jackets, 125 vests, and 50 comforters. ∎

In this section we develop a step-by-step procedure for solving systems of linear equations such as (1). The procedure, called the **Gauss–Jordan elimination method**, consists of repeatedly simplifying the system, using so-called elementary row operations, until the solution stares us in the face!

In the system of linear equations (1) the equations have been written in such a way that the x-terms, the y-terms, and the z-terms lie in different columns. We shall always be careful to display systems of equations with separate columns for each variable. One of the key ideas of the Gauss–Jordan elimination method is to think of the solution as a system of linear equations in its own right. For example, we can write the solution of system (1) as

$$\begin{cases} x & = 50 \\ y & = 125 \\ z = & 50. \end{cases} \tag{2}$$

This is just a system of linear equations in which the coefficients of most terms are zero! Since the only terms with nonzero coefficients are arranged on a diagonal, such a system is said to be in **diagonal form**.

Our method for solving a system of linear equations consists of repeatedly using three operations that alter the system but do not change the solutions. The operations are used to transform the system into a system in diagonal form. Since the operations involve only elementary arithmetic and are applied to entire equations (i.e., rows of the system), they are called **elementary row operations**. Let us begin our study of the Gauss–Jordan elimination method by introducing these operations.

Elementary Row Operation 1   Interchange any two equations.

This operation is harmless enough. It certainly does not change the solutions of the system.

Elementary Row Operation 2   Multiply an equation by a nonzero number.

For example, if we are given the system of linear equations

$$\begin{cases} 2x - 3y + 4z = 11 \\ 4x - 19y + z = 31 \\ 5x + 7y - z = 12, \end{cases}$$

then we may replace it by a new system obtained by leaving the last two equations unchanged and multiplying the first equation by 3. To accomplish this, multiply each term of the first equation by 3. The transformed system is

$$\begin{cases} 6x - 9y + 12z = 33 \\ 4x - 19y + z = 31 \\ 5x + 7y - z = 12. \end{cases}$$

The operation of multiplying an equation by a nonzero number does not change the solutions of the system. For if a particular set of values of the variables satisfies the original equation, it satisfies the resulting equation, and vice versa.

Elementary row operation 2 may be used to make the coefficient of a particular variable 1.

EXAMPLE 2

Demonstrating elementary row operation 2   Replace the system

$$\begin{cases} -5x + 10y + 20z = 4 \\ x \qquad - 12z = 1 \\ x + y + z = 0 \end{cases}$$

by an equivalent system in which the coefficient of x in the first equation is 1.

Solution The coefficient of x in the first equation is -5, so we use elementary row operation 2 to multiply the first equation by $-\frac{1}{5}$. Multiplying each term of the first equation by $-\frac{1}{5}$ gives

$$\begin{cases} x - 2y - 4z = -\frac{4}{5} \\ x \qquad - 12z = \quad 1 \\ x + y + z = \quad 0. \end{cases}$$

Now Try Exercise 1

■

Another operation that can be performed on a system without changing its solutions is to replace one equation by its sum with some other equation. For example, consider this system of equations:

$$A: \quad \begin{cases} x + y - 2z = 3 \\ x + 2y - 5z = 4 \\ 5x + 8y - 18z = 14. \end{cases}$$

We can replace the second equation by the sum of the first and the second. Since

$$\begin{array}{r} x + y - 2z = 3 \\ + \quad x + 2y - 5z = 4 \\ \hline 2x + 3y - 7z = 7, \end{array}$$

the resulting system is

$$B: \quad \begin{cases} x + y - 2z = 3 \\ 2x + 3y - 7z = 7 \\ 5x + 8y - 18z = 14. \end{cases}$$

If a particular choice of x, y, and z satisfies system A, it also satisfies system B. This is because system B results from adding equations. Similarly, system A can be derived from system B by subtracting equations. So any particular solution of system A is a solution of system B, and vice versa.

The operation of adding equations is usually used in conjunction with elementary row operation 2. That is, an equation is changed by adding to it a nonzero multiple of another equation. For example, consider the system

$$\begin{cases} x + y - 2z = 3 \\ x + 2y - 5z = 4 \\ 5x + 8y - 18z = 14. \end{cases}$$

Let us change the second equation by adding to it twice the first. Since

$$\begin{array}{rr} 2(\text{first}) & 2x + 2y - 4z = 6 \\ + (\text{second}) & x + 2y - 5z = 4 \\ \hline & 3x + 4y - 9z = 10, \end{array}$$

the new second equation is

$$3x + 4y - 9z = 10$$

and the transformed system is

$$\begin{cases} x + y - 2z = 3 \\ 3x + 4y - 9z = 10 \\ 5x + 8y - 18z = 14. \end{cases}$$

Since addition of equations and elementary row operation 2 are often used together, let us define a third elementary row operation.

> **Elementary Row Operation 3**   Change an equation by adding to it a multiple of another equation.

For reference, let us summarize the elementary row operations we have just defined.

> **Elementary Row Operations**
>
> **1.** Interchange any two equations.
>
> **2.** Multiply an equation by a nonzero number.
>
> **3.** Change an equation by adding to it a multiple of another equation.

The idea of the Gauss–Jordan elimination method is to transform an arbitrary system of linear equations into diagonal form by repeated applications of the three elementary row operations. To see how the method works, consider the following example.

EXAMPLE 3

Solving a system of equations using Gauss–Jordan elimination   Solve the following system by the Gauss–Jordan elimination method:

$$\begin{cases} x - 3y = 7 \\ -3x + 4y = -1. \end{cases}$$

Solution   Let us transform this system into diagonal form by examining one column at a time, starting from the left. Examine the first column:

$$\begin{array}{c} x \\ -3x \end{array}$$

The coefficient of the top x is 1, which is exactly what it should be for the system to be in diagonal form. So we do nothing to this term. Now examine the next term in the column, $-3x$. In diagonal form this term must be absent. In order to accomplish this, we add a multiple of the first equation to the second. Since the coefficient of x in the second is -3, we add three times the first equation to the second equation in order to cancel the x-term. (Abbreviation: $R_2 + 3R_1$. The R_2 refers to the second equation; that is, the equation in the second row of the system of equations. The expression $R_2 + 3R_1$ means that we are replacing the second equation by the original equation plus 3 times the first equation.)

$$\begin{cases} x - 3y = 7 \\ -3x + 4y = -1 \end{cases} \xrightarrow{\;R_2 + 3R_1\;} \begin{cases} x - 3y = 7 \\ \quad\; -5y = 20. \end{cases}$$

The first column now has the proper form, so we proceed to the second column. In diagonal form that column will have one nonzero term, namely the second, and the coefficient of y in that term must be 1. To bring this about, multiply the second equation by $-\frac{1}{5}$ (abbreviation: $(-\frac{1}{5})R_2$):

$$\begin{cases} x - 3y = 7 \\ \quad\; -5y = 20 \end{cases} \xrightarrow{\;(-\frac{1}{5})R_2\;} \begin{cases} x - 3y = 7 \\ \qquad\; y = -4. \end{cases}$$

The second column still does not have the correct form. We must get rid of the $-3y$-term in the first equation. We do this by adding a multiple of the second equation to the first. Since the coefficient of the term to be canceled is -3, we add three times the second equation to the first:

$$\begin{cases} x - 3y = 7 \\ \phantom{x - {}} y = -4 \end{cases} \quad \xrightarrow{R_1 + 3R_2} \quad \begin{cases} x \phantom{{}- 3y} = -5 \\ \phantom{x - {}} y = -4. \end{cases}$$

The system is now in diagonal form and the solution can be read off: $x = -5$, $y = -4$.

Now Try Exercise 37   ■

NOTE ▶ The abbreviation for interchanging the first and second equation is $R_1 \leftrightarrow R_2$.   ■

EXAMPLE 4   **Solving a system of equations using Gauss–Jordan elimination**   Use the Gauss–Jordan elimination method to solve the system

$$\begin{cases} 2x - 6y = -8 \\ -5x + 13y = 1. \end{cases}$$

Solution   We can perform the calculations in a mechanical way, proceeding column by column from the left:

$$\begin{cases} 2x - 6y = -8 \\ -5x + 13y = 1 \end{cases} \quad \xrightarrow{\frac{1}{2}R_1} \quad \begin{cases} x - 3y = -4 \\ -5x + 13y = 1 \end{cases}$$

$$\xrightarrow{R_2 + 5R_1} \quad \begin{cases} x - 3y = -4 \\ - 2y = -19 \end{cases}$$

$$\xrightarrow{(-\frac{1}{2})R_2} \quad \begin{cases} x - 3y = -4 \\ y = \frac{19}{2} \end{cases}$$

$$\xrightarrow{R_1 + 3R_2} \quad \begin{cases} x \phantom{{}- 3y} = \frac{49}{2} \\ y = \frac{19}{2}. \end{cases}$$

Now Try Exercise 45   So the solution of the system is $x = \frac{49}{2}$, $y = \frac{19}{2}$.   ■

The calculation becomes easier to follow if we omit writing down the variables at each stage and work only with the coefficients. At each stage of the computation, the system is represented by a rectangular array of numbers. For instance, the original system is written[1]

$$\begin{bmatrix} 2 & -6 & | & -8 \\ -5 & 13 & | & 1 \end{bmatrix}.$$

The elementary row operations are performed on the rows of this rectangular array just as if the variables were there. So, for example, the first step in the above solution is to multiply the first equation by $\frac{1}{2}$. This corresponds to multiplying the first row of the array by $\frac{1}{2}$ to get

$$\begin{bmatrix} 1 & -3 & | & -4 \\ -5 & 13 & | & 1 \end{bmatrix}.$$

The diagonal form just corresponds to the array

$$\begin{bmatrix} 1 & 0 & | & \frac{49}{2} \\ 0 & 1 & | & \frac{19}{2} \end{bmatrix}.$$

---

[1] The vertical line between the second and third columns is a placemarker that separates the data obtained from the left- and right-hand sides of the equations. It is inserted for visual convenience.

Note that this array has ones down the diagonal and zeros everywhere else on the left. The solution of the system appears on the right.

A rectangular array of numbers is called a **matrix** (plural: *matrices*). In the next example, we use matrices to carry out the Gauss–Jordan elimination method.

EXAMPLE 5

Solving a system of equations using Gauss–Jordan elimination   Use the Gauss–Jordan elimination method to solve the system

$$\begin{cases} 3x - 6y + 9z = 0 \\ 4x - 6y + 8z = -4 \\ -2x - y + z = 7. \end{cases}$$

Solution   The initial array corresponding to the system is

$$\left[\begin{array}{ccc|c} 3 & -6 & 9 & 0 \\ 4 & -6 & 8 & -4 \\ -2 & -1 & 1 & 7 \end{array}\right].$$

We must use elementary row operations to transform this array into diagonal form— that is, with ones down the diagonal and zeros everywhere else on the left:

$$\left[\begin{array}{ccc|c} 1 & 0 & 0 & * \\ 0 & 1 & 0 & * \\ 0 & 0 & 1 & * \end{array}\right].$$

We proceed one column at a time.

$$\left[\begin{array}{ccc|c} 3 & -6 & 9 & 0 \\ 4 & -6 & 8 & -4 \\ -2 & -1 & 1 & 7 \end{array}\right] \xrightarrow{\frac{1}{3}R_1} \left[\begin{array}{ccc|c} 1 & -2 & 3 & 0 \\ 4 & -6 & 8 & -4 \\ -2 & -1 & 1 & 7 \end{array}\right] \xrightarrow{R_2 + (-4)R_1}$$

$$\left[\begin{array}{ccc|c} 1 & -2 & 3 & 0 \\ 0 & 2 & -4 & -4 \\ -2 & -1 & 1 & 7 \end{array}\right] \xrightarrow{R_3 + 2R_1} \left[\begin{array}{ccc|c} 1 & -2 & 3 & 0 \\ 0 & 2 & -4 & -4 \\ 0 & -5 & 7 & 7 \end{array}\right] \xrightarrow{\frac{1}{2}R_2}$$

$$\left[\begin{array}{ccc|c} 1 & -2 & 3 & 0 \\ 0 & 1 & -2 & -2 \\ 0 & -5 & 7 & 7 \end{array}\right] \xrightarrow{R_1 + 2R_2} \left[\begin{array}{ccc|c} 1 & 0 & -1 & -4 \\ 0 & 1 & -2 & -2 \\ 0 & -5 & 7 & 7 \end{array}\right] \xrightarrow{R_3 + 5R_2}$$

$$\left[\begin{array}{ccc|c} 1 & 0 & -1 & -4 \\ 0 & 1 & -2 & -2 \\ 0 & 0 & -3 & -3 \end{array}\right] \xrightarrow{\left(-\frac{1}{3}\right)R_3} \left[\begin{array}{ccc|c} 1 & 0 & -1 & -4 \\ 0 & 1 & -2 & -2 \\ 0 & 0 & 1 & 1 \end{array}\right] \xrightarrow{R_1 + 1R_3}$$

$$\left[\begin{array}{ccc|c} 1 & 0 & 0 & -3 \\ 0 & 1 & -2 & -2 \\ 0 & 0 & 1 & 1 \end{array}\right] \xrightarrow{R_2 + 2R_3} \left[\begin{array}{ccc|c} 1 & 0 & 0 & -3 \\ 0 & 1 & 0 & 0 \\ 0 & 0 & 1 & 1 \end{array}\right]$$

The last array is in diagonal form, so we just put back the variables and read off the solution:

$$x = -3, \qquad y = 0, \qquad z = 1.$$

Because so much arithmetic has been performed, it is a good idea to check the solution by substituting the values for x, y, and z into each of the equations of the original system. This will uncover any arithmetic errors that may have occurred.

$$\begin{cases} 3x - 6y + 9z = 0 \\ 4x - 6y + 8z = -4 \\ -2x - y + z = 7 \end{cases} \qquad \begin{cases} 3(-3) - 6(0) + 9(1) = 0 \\ 4(-3) - 6(0) + 8(1) = -4 \\ -2(-3) - (0) + (1) = 7 \end{cases}$$

$$\begin{cases} -9 - 0 + 9 = 0 \\ -12 - 0 + 8 = -4 \\ 6 - 0 + 1 = 7 \end{cases}$$

$$\begin{cases} 0 = 0 \\ -4 = -4 \\ 7 = 7 \end{cases}$$

Now Try Exercise 43   So we have indeed found a solution of the system.   ∎

REMARK   Note that so far we have not had to use elementary row operation 1, which allows interchange of equations. But in some examples it is definitely needed.

Consider this system:

$$\begin{cases} y + z = 0 \\ 3x - y + z = 6 \\ 6x - z = 3. \end{cases}$$

The first step of the Gauss–Jordan elimination method consists of making the x-coefficient 1 in the first equation. But we cannot do this, since the first equation does not involve x. To remedy this difficulty, just interchange the first two equations to guarantee that the first equation involves x. Now proceed as before. Of course, in terms of the matrix of coefficients, interchanging equations corresponds to interchanging rows of the matrix.   ∎

INCORPORATING TECHNOLOGY

GC   Graphing utilities can perform many operations with matrices, including elementary row operations.

TI-83/84 Plus   Pressing 2ND [MATRX] or 2ND [MATRIX] presents the three menus shown in Fig. 1. You define a new matrix or alter an existing matrix with the EDIT menu. You place the name of an existing matrix on the home screen with the NAMES menu. You perform operations on existing matrices with the MATH menu.

With the EDIT menu, you first select one of the names **[A]**, **[B]**, **[C]**, ... for the matrix and then specify the size and fill in the entries as shown in Fig. 2. The three elementary row operations are carried out with commands of the following forms from the MATRX/MATH menu.

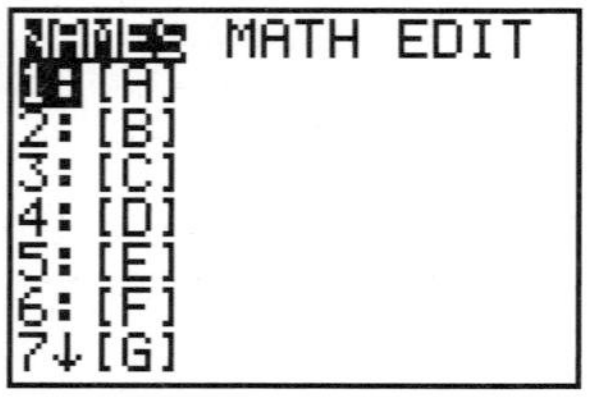

rowSwap(*matrix*, *rowA*, *rowB*)	Interchange *rowA* and *rowB* of *matrix*
***row**(*value*, *matrix*, *row*)	Multiply *row* of *matrix* by *value*
***row+**(*value*, *matrix*, *rowA*, *rowB*)	Add *value*∗*rowA* to *rowB* of *matrix*

When one of these commands is carried out, the resulting matrix is displayed but the stored matrix is not changed. Therefore, when a sequence of commands is executed to carry out the Gauss–Jordan elimination method, each command should be followed with STO ► *matrix* to change the stored matrix. (*Note*: To display the name of a matrix, press 2nd[MATRX], cursor down to the matrix, and press ENTER.)

```
NAMES MATH EDIT
1:[A]
2:[B]
3:[C]
4:[D]
5:[E]
6:[F]
7↓[G]
```
Figure 1

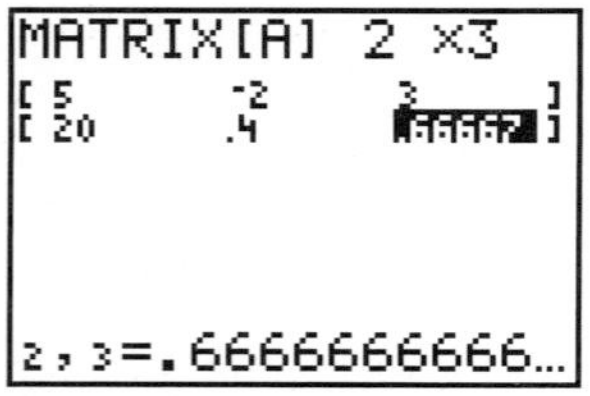

```
MATRIX[A]  2 ×3
[ 5     -2    3  ]
[ 20    .4    .6666]

2,3=.6666666666...
```
Figure 2

For instance, if in Example 5 the original matrix is named [A], then the first three row operations are carried out with

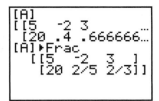

Figure 3

$$*\texttt{row(1/3,[A],1)}\boxed{\text{STO}}\blacktriangleright\texttt{[A]}$$

$$*\texttt{row+(-4,[A],1,2)}\boxed{\text{STO}}\blacktriangleright\texttt{[A]}$$

$$*\texttt{row+(2,[A],1,3)}\boxed{\text{STO}}\blacktriangleright\texttt{[A]}.$$

Matrix entries are normally displayed on the calculator as decimals. From the home screen you can display the entries as fractions with a command such as **[A]** ▶**Frac** or **Ans**▶**Frac**. (▶**Frac** is displayed by pressing MATH **1**.) See Fig. 3.

TI-89 Matrices are created and altered with the Data/Matrix editor that is accessed through the APPS key. See Appendix D for details.   ∎

ES[2] The systems of linear equations presented in this section can be solved with a device called **Solver**. The steps below use Solver to find the solution to Example 5.

NOTE A cell is most easily used in formulas if it has been given a name such as **x**, **y**, or **z**. To name a cell, select it, click on the Name box (located just above the upper-left corner of the spreadsheet), type the name, and press Enter. Single letter names can consist of any letter other than C or R.   ∎

1. Give the cells A1, A2, and A3 the names x, y, and z, respectively. (There is no need to place any values into these cells.)

2. In the cells B1, B2, and B3, place the formulas consisting of the left sides of the three equations. For instance, type the formula **=3*x-6*y+9*z** into cell B1.

3. (Excel 2007) On the **Data** tab, in the **Analysis** group, click on **Solver**. (Excel 97-2003) Click on Solver in the Tools menu. A window titled Solver Parameters will appear. (*Note*: If Solver is not present on your computer, see Appendix C for instructions on installing Solver.)

4. Clear the contents, if any, of the Set Target Cell box. (Ignore any entries appearing in the "Equal To" line.)

5. Type **x**, **y**, **z** into the By Changing Cells box.

6. Click the Add button. An Add Constraint dialog box will appear.
   (a) Enter **B1,=,** and **0** into the three boxes and then press the Add button.
   (b) Enter **B2,=,** and **-4** into the three boxes and then press the Add button.
   (c) Enter **B3,=,** and **7** into the three boxes and then press the OK button. The Solver Parameters window will reappear as shown in Fig. 4 on the next page. *Note*: The entries 0, -4, and 7 are the numbers on the right sides of the equations.

7. Click the Solve button. A window titled Solver Results will appear.

8. Click the OK button. The solution to the system of linear equations will appear in the x, y, and z cells. *Note*: The values may differ slightly from the true values due to rounding errors. For instance, the value for y may appear as something like 2.72E-15 (that is, 2.72×10^{-15}) instead of 0.

---

[2]ES is an abbreviation for "Excel Spreadsheet."

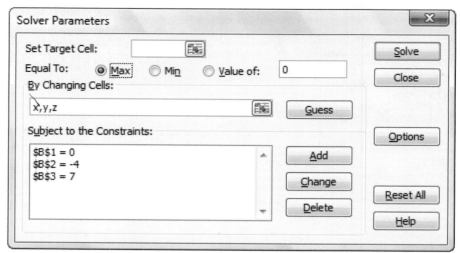

Figure 4

Practice Problems 2.1

1. Determine whether the following systems of linear equations are in diagonal form.

(a) $\begin{cases} x \quad\ + z = 3 \\ \quad\ y \qquad = 2 \\ \qquad\quad z = 7 \end{cases}$ (b) $\begin{cases} x \qquad\qquad = -1 \\ \quad\ y \qquad = 0 \\ \qquad\quad 3z = 4 \end{cases}$

2. Perform the indicated elementary row operation.

(a) $\begin{cases} x - 3y = 2 \\ 2x + 3y = 5 \end{cases} \xrightarrow{R_2 + (-2)R_1}$

(b) $\begin{cases} x + y = 3 \\ -x + 2y = 5 \end{cases} \xrightarrow{R_2 + 1R_1}$

3. State the next elementary row operation that should be performed when applying the Gauss–Jordan elimination method.

(a) $\begin{bmatrix} 0 & 2 & 4 & 1 \\ 0 & 3 & -7 & 0 \\ 3 & 6 & -3 & 3 \end{bmatrix}$

(b) $\begin{bmatrix} 1 & -3 & 4 & 5 \\ 0 & 2 & 3 & 4 \\ -6 & 5 & -7 & 0 \end{bmatrix}$

EXERCISES 2.1

In Exercises 1–8, perform the indicated elementary row operations and give their abbreviations.

1. Operation 2: Multiply the first equation by 2.
$$\begin{cases} \tfrac{1}{2}x - 3y = 2 \\ 5x + 4y = 1 \end{cases}$$

2. Operation 2: Multiply the second equation by -1.
$$\begin{cases} x + 4y = 6 \\ \quad\ -y = 2 \end{cases}$$

3. Operation 3: Change the second equation by adding to it 5 times the first equation.
$$\begin{cases} x + 2y = 3 \\ -5x + 4y = 1 \end{cases}$$

4. Operation 3: Change the second equation by adding to it $\left(-\tfrac{1}{2}\right)$ times the first equation.
$$\begin{cases} x - 6y = 4 \\ \tfrac{1}{2}x + 2y = 1 \end{cases}$$

5. Operation 3: Change the third equation by adding to it (-4) times the first equation.
$$\begin{cases} x - 2y + z = 0 \\ \qquad\ y - 2z = 4 \\ 4x + y + 3z = 5 \end{cases}$$

6. Operation 3: Change the third equation by adding to it 3 times the second equation.
$$\begin{cases} x + 6y - 4z = 1 \\ \qquad\ y + 3z = 1 \\ \quad\ -3y + 7z = 2 \end{cases}$$

7. Operation 3: Change the first row by adding to it $\frac{1}{2}$ times the second row.

$$\begin{bmatrix} 1 & -\frac{1}{2} & 3 \\ 0 & 1 & 4 \end{bmatrix}$$

8. Operation 3: Change the third row by adding to it (-4) times the second row.

$$\begin{bmatrix} 1 & 0 & 7 & 9 \\ 0 & 1 & -2 & 3 \\ 0 & 4 & 8 & 5 \end{bmatrix}$$

In Exercises 9–12, write the matrix corresponding to the system of linear equations.

9. $\begin{cases} -3x + 4y = -2 \\ x - 7y = 8 \end{cases}$

10. $\begin{cases} \frac{2}{3}x - 3y = 4 \\ y = -5 \end{cases}$

11. $\begin{cases} x + 13y - 2z = 0 \\ 2x \quad\quad - z = 3 \\ y \quad\quad = 5 \end{cases}$

12. $\begin{cases} y - z = 22 \\ 2x \quad\quad = 17 \\ x - 3y \quad = 12 \end{cases}$

In Exercises 13–16, write the system of linear equations corresponding to the matrix.

13. $\begin{bmatrix} 0 & -2 & 3 \\ 1 & 7 & -4 \end{bmatrix}$

14. $\begin{bmatrix} -5 & \frac{2}{3} & 3 \\ 1 & 7 & -\frac{5}{8} \end{bmatrix}$

15. $\begin{bmatrix} 3 & 2 & 0 & -3 \\ 0 & 1 & -6 & 4 \\ -5 & -1 & 7 & 0 \end{bmatrix}$

16. $\begin{bmatrix} \frac{6}{5} & -1 & 12 & -\frac{2}{3} \\ -1 & 0 & 0 & 5 \\ 0 & 2 & -1 & 6 \end{bmatrix}$

In Exercises 17–22, describe in your own words the meaning of the notation with respect to a matrix.

17. $\frac{1}{3}R_2$

18. $R_2 + (-4)R_1$

19. $R_1 + 3R_2$

20. $(-1)R_1$

21. $R_2 \leftrightarrow R_3$

22. $R_1 \leftrightarrow R_2$

In Exercises 23–28, carry out the indicated elementary row operation.

23. $\begin{bmatrix} 1 & 2 & 0 \\ -3 & 4 & 5 \end{bmatrix} \xrightarrow{R_2 + 3R_1} \begin{bmatrix} & & \\ & & \end{bmatrix}$

24. $\begin{bmatrix} -\frac{1}{2} & 2 & \frac{3}{4} \\ -3 & 4 & 9 \end{bmatrix} \xrightarrow{(-2)R_1} \begin{bmatrix} & & \\ & & \end{bmatrix}$

25. $\begin{bmatrix} \frac{1}{7} & \frac{2}{7} & \frac{3}{7} \\ 3 & -2 & 0 \end{bmatrix} \xrightarrow{7R_1} \begin{bmatrix} & & \\ & & \end{bmatrix}$

26. $\begin{bmatrix} 1 & 3 & -2 \\ 4 & 4 & 5 \end{bmatrix} \xrightarrow{R_2 + (-4)R_1} \begin{bmatrix} & & \\ & & \end{bmatrix}$

27. $\begin{bmatrix} 0 & 1 & 7 \\ 1 & 3 & -5 \end{bmatrix} \xrightarrow{R_1 \leftrightarrow R_2} \begin{bmatrix} & & \\ & & \end{bmatrix}$

28. $\begin{bmatrix} 4 & 5 & 6 \\ -3 & 2 & 0 \end{bmatrix} \xrightarrow{R_1 + 1R_2} \begin{bmatrix} & & \\ & & \end{bmatrix}$

In Exercises 29–36, state the next elementary row operation that should be performed in order to put the matrix into diagonal form. Do not perform the operation.

29. $\begin{bmatrix} 1 & -5 & 1 \\ -2 & 4 & 6 \end{bmatrix}$

30. $\begin{bmatrix} 1 & 3 & 4 \\ 0 & 2 & 6 \end{bmatrix}$

31. $\begin{bmatrix} 1 & 2 & 3 \\ 0 & 1 & 4 \end{bmatrix}$

32. $\begin{bmatrix} 1 & -2 & 5 & 7 \\ 0 & -3 & 6 & 9 \\ 4 & 5 & -6 & 7 \end{bmatrix}$

33. $\begin{bmatrix} 0 & 5 & -3 & 6 \\ 2 & -3 & 4 & 5 \\ 4 & 1 & -7 & 8 \end{bmatrix}$

34. $\begin{bmatrix} 1 & 4 & -2 & 5 \\ 0 & -3 & 6 & 9 \\ 0 & 4 & 3 & 1 \end{bmatrix}$

35. $\begin{bmatrix} 1 & 0 & 3 & 4 \\ 0 & 1 & 2 & 5 \\ 0 & 0 & 1 & 6 \end{bmatrix}$

36. $\begin{bmatrix} 1 & 2 & 4 & 5 \\ 0 & 0 & 3 & 6 \\ 0 & 1 & 1 & 7 \end{bmatrix}$

In Exercises 37–50, solve the linear system by using the Gauss–Jordan elimination method.

37. $\begin{cases} x + 9y = 8 \\ 2x + 8y = 6 \end{cases}$

38. $\begin{cases} \frac{1}{3}x + 2y = 1 \\ -2x - 4y = 6 \end{cases}$

39. $\begin{cases} x - 3y + 4z = 1 \\ 4x - 10y + 10z = 4 \\ -3x + 9y - 5z = -6 \end{cases}$

40. $\begin{cases} \frac{1}{2}x + y = 4 \\ -4x - 7y + 3z = -31 \\ 6x + 14y + 7z = 50 \end{cases}$

41. $\begin{cases} 2x - 2y + 4 = 0 \\ 3x + 4y - 1 = 0 \end{cases}$

42. $\begin{cases} 2x + 3y = 4 \\ -x + 2y = -2 \end{cases}$

43. $\begin{cases} 4x - 4y + 4z = -8 \\ x - 2y - 2z = -1 \\ 2x + y + 3z = 1 \end{cases}$

44. $\begin{cases} x + 2y + 2z - 11 = 0 \\ x - y - z + 4 = 0 \\ 2x + 5y + 9z - 39 = 0 \end{cases}$

45. $\begin{cases} .2x + .3y = 4 \\ .6x + 1.1y = 15 \end{cases}$

46. $\begin{cases} \frac{3}{2}x + 6y = 9 \\ \frac{1}{2}x - \frac{2}{3}y = 11 \end{cases}$

47. $\begin{cases} x + y + 4z = 3 \\ 4x + y - 2z = -6 \\ -3x + 2z = 1 \end{cases}$

48. $\begin{cases} -2x - 3y + 2z = -2 \\ x + y = 3 \\ -x - 3y + 5z = 8 \end{cases}$

49. $\begin{cases} -x + y = -1 \\ x + z = 4 \\ 6x - 3y + 2z = 10 \end{cases}$

50. $\begin{cases} x + 2z = 9 \\ y + z = 1 \\ 3x - 2y = 9 \end{cases}$

51. **PE** A baked potato smothered with cheddar cheese weighs 180 grams and contains 10.5 grams of protein. If cheddar cheese contains 25% protein and a baked potato contains 2% protein, how many grams of cheddar cheese are there?

    (a) 25   (b) 30   (c) 35   (d) 40   (e) 45

52. **PE** A high school math department purchased brand A calculators for $80 each and brand B calculators for $95 each. It purchased a total of 20 calculators at a total cost of $1780. How many brand A calculators did the department purchase?

    (a) 7   (b) 8   (c) 9   (d) 10   (e) 11

Exercises 53 and 54 are multiple choice exercises with five possible choices. Each exercise consists of a question and two statements that may or may not provide sufficient information to answer the question. Select the response below that best describes the situation.

(a) *Statement I alone is sufficient to answer the question, but statement II is not sufficient.*

(b) *Statement II alone is sufficient to answer the question, but statement I is not sufficient.*

(c) *Both statements together are sufficient to answer the question, but neither alone is sufficient.*

(d) *Each statement alone is sufficient to answer the question.*

(e) *Both statements together are not sufficient to answer the question.*

53. **PE** A box of golf balls and a golf glove cost a total of $20. How much does the box of balls cost?

    Statement I: The golf glove costs three times as much as the box of golf balls.

    Statement II: The golf glove costs $15.

54. **PE** I have four nickels and three pennies in my pocket. What is the total weight of these coins?

    Statement I: A nickel weighs twice as much as a penny.

    Statement II: The total weight of a nickel and two pennies is 10 grams.

55. **Sales** A street vendor has a total of 350 short and long sleeve T-shirts. If she sells the short sleeve shirts for $10 each and the long sleeve shirts for $14 each, how many of each did she sell if she sold all of her stock for $4300?

56. **Sales** A grocery store carries two brands of bleach. A 96-ounce bottle of the national brand sells for $1.99, while the same size bottle of the store brand sells for $1.79. How many bottles of each brand were sold if a total of 82 bottles were sold for $158.98?

57. **Movie Tickets** A 350-seat movie theater charges $9.25 admission for adults and $6.25 for children. If the theater is full and $2973.50 is collected, how many adults and how many children are in the audience?

58. **Batting Average** A baseball player's batting average is determined by dividing the number of hits by the number of times at bat and multiplying by 1000. (Batting averages are usually, but not necessarily, rounded to the nearest whole number.) For instance, if a player gets 2 hits in 5 times at bat, his batting average is 400: $\left(\frac{2}{5} \times 1000 = 400\right)$. Partway through the season, a player thinks to himself, "If I get a hit in my next time at bat, my average will go up to 250; if I don't get a hit, it will drop to 187.5." How many times has this player batted, how many hits has he had, and what is his current batting average?

59. **Investment Planning** A bank wishes to invest a $100,000 trust fund in three sources: bonds paying 8%; certificates of deposit paying 7%; and first mortgages paying 10%. The bank wishes to realize an $8000 annual income from the investment. A condition of the trust is that the total amount invested in bonds and certificates of deposit must be triple the amount invested in mortgages. How much should the bank invest in each possible category? Let x, y, and z, respectively, be the amounts invested in bonds, certificates of deposit, and first mortgages. Solve the system of equations by the Gauss–Jordan elimination method.

60. **Nutrition Planning** A dietitian wishes to plan a meal around three foods. Each ounce of food I contains 10% of the daily requirements for carbohydrates, 10% for protein, and 15% for vitamin C. Each ounce of food II contains 10% of the daily requirements for carbohydrates, 5% for protein, and 0% for vitamin C. Each ounce of food III contains 10% of the daily requirements for carbohydrates, 25% for protein, and 10% for vitamin C. How many ounces of each food should be served in order to supply exactly the daily requirements for each nutrient? Let x, y, and z, respectively, be the number of ounces of foods I, II, and III.

61. **Candy Assortments** A small candy store makes three types of party mixes. The first type contains 40% nonpareils and 60% peanut clusters, while the second type contains 30% peanut clusters and 70% chocolate covered raisins. The third type consists of 40% nonpareils, 30% peanut clusters, and 30% chocolate covered raisins. If the store has 90 pounds of nonpareils, 100 pounds of peanut clusters, and 120 pounds of chocolate covered raisins available, how many pounds of each type of party mix should be made?

62. **Investment Planning** New parents Jim and Lucy want to start saving for their son's college education. They have $5000 to invest in three different types of plans. A traditional savings account pays 1% annual interest, a certificate of deposit pays 3.6% annual interest, and a prepaid college plan pays 5.5% annual interest. If they want to invest the same amount in the prepaid college fund as in the other two plans together, how much should they invest in each plan to realize an interest income of $195 for the first year?

Exercises 63–68 require the use of a graphing calculator or spreadsheet.

63. Enter the matrix corresponding to the equations in Exercise 3, and change the second row by adding to it 5 times the first row.

64. Enter the matrix from Exercise 5, and change the third row by adding to it (-4) times the first row.

65. Enter the matrix in Exercise 7, and interchange the rows.

66. Enter the matrix corresponding to the linear system in Exercise 45, and multiply the first row by 5.

67. Use technology to solve the system of linear equations in Exercise 47.

68. Use technology to solve the system of linear equations in Exercise 48.

Solutions to Practice Problems 2.1

1. (a) Not in diagonal form, since the first equation contains both x and z.

(b) Not in diagonal form, since the coefficient of z is not 1.

2. (a) Change the system into another system in which the second equation is altered by having (-2)(first equation) added to it. The new system is

$$\begin{cases} x - 3y = 2 \\ 9y = 1. \end{cases}$$

The equation $9y = 1$ was obtained as follows:

$$\begin{array}{ll} (-2)(\text{first equation}) & -2x + 6y = -4 \\ + \text{ (second equation)} & \underline{2x + 3y = 5} \\ & 9y = 1. \end{array}$$

(b) Change the second equation by adding to it 1 times the first equation. The result is

$$\begin{cases} x + y = 3 \\ 3y = 8. \end{cases}$$

In general, notation of the form $R_i + kR_j$ specifies that the first row mentioned, R_i, be changed by adding to it a multiple, k, of the second row mentioned, R_j. The row R_j is not changed by the operation.

3. (a) The first row should contain a nonzero number as its first entry. This can be accomplished by interchanging the first and third rows. The notation for this operation is

$$R_1 \leftrightarrow R_3$$

(b) The first column can be put into proper form by eliminating the -6. To accomplish this, multiply the first row by 6 and add this product to the third row. The notation for this operation is

$$R_3 + 6R_1$$

2.2 Solving Systems of Linear Equations, II

In this section we introduce the operation of pivoting and consider systems of linear equations that do not have exactly one solution.

Roughly speaking, the Gauss–Jordan elimination method applied to a matrix proceeds as follows: Consider the columns one at a time, from left to right. For each column use the elementary row operations to transform the appropriate entry to a one and the remaining entries in the column to zeros. (The "appropriate" entry is the first entry in the first column, the second entry in the second column, and so forth.) This sequence of elementary row operations performed for each column is called **pivoting**. More precisely,

Method   To pivot a matrix about a given nonzero entry,

1. Transform the given entry into a one.

2. Transform all other entries in the same column into zeros.

Pivoting is used in solving problems other than systems of linear equations. As we shall see in Chapter 4, it is the basis for the simplex method of solving linear programming problems.

EXAMPLE 1

Pivoting Pivot the matrix about the circled element.

$$\begin{bmatrix} 18 & \boxed{-6} & | & 15 \\ 5 & -2 & | & 4 \end{bmatrix}$$

Solution The first step is to transform the -6 to a 1. We do this by multiplying the first row by $-\frac{1}{6}$:

$$\begin{bmatrix} 18 & -6 & | & 15 \\ 5 & -2 & | & 4 \end{bmatrix} \xrightarrow{\left(-\frac{1}{6}\right) R_1} \begin{bmatrix} -3 & 1 & | & -\frac{5}{2} \\ 5 & -2 & | & 4 \end{bmatrix}.$$

Next, we transform the -2 (the only remaining entry in column 2) into a 0:

$$\begin{bmatrix} -3 & 1 & | & -\frac{5}{2} \\ 5 & -2 & | & 4 \end{bmatrix} \xrightarrow{R_2 + 2R_1} \begin{bmatrix} -3 & 1 & | & -\frac{5}{2} \\ -1 & 0 & | & -1 \end{bmatrix}.$$

The last matrix is the result of pivoting the original matrix about the circled entry.

Now Try Exercise 1

In terms of pivoting, we can give the following summary of the Gauss–Jordan elimination method.

Gauss–Jordan Elimination Method to Transform a System of Linear Equations into Diagonal Form

1. Write down the matrix corresponding to the linear system.
2. Make sure that the first entry in the first column is nonzero. Do this by interchanging the first row with one of the rows below it, if necessary.
3. Pivot the matrix about the first entry in the first column.
4. Make sure that the second entry in the second column is nonzero. Do this by interchanging the second row with one of the rows below it, if necessary.
5. Pivot the matrix about the second entry in the second column.
6. Continue in this manner.

All the systems considered in the preceding section had only a single solution. In this case we say that the solution is **unique**. Let us now use the Gauss–Jordan elimination method to study the various possibilities other than a unique solution.

EXAMPLE 2

A system of equations that has no solution Find all solutions of the system

$$\begin{cases} x - y + z = 3 \\ x + y - z = 5 \\ -2x + 4y - 4z = 1. \end{cases}$$

Solution We apply the Gauss–Jordan elimination method to the matrix of the system.

$$
\begin{bmatrix}
\textcircled{1} & -1 & 1 & 3 \\
1 & 1 & -1 & 5 \\
-2 & 4 & -4 & 1
\end{bmatrix}
\xrightarrow[\;R_3 + 2R_1\;]{R_2 + (-1)R_1}
\begin{bmatrix}
1 & -1 & 1 & 3 \\
0 & \textcircled{2} & -2 & 2 \\
0 & 2 & -2 & 7
\end{bmatrix}
$$

$$
\xrightarrow[\;R_3 + (-2)R_2\;]{\begin{array}{c}\frac{1}{2}R_2 \\ R_1 + 1R_2\end{array}}
\begin{bmatrix}
1 & 0 & 0 & 4 \\
0 & 1 & -1 & 1 \\
0 & 0 & 0 & 5
\end{bmatrix}
$$

We cannot pivot about the last zero in the third column, so we have carried the method as far as we can. Let us write out the equations corresponding to the last matrix:

$$
\begin{cases}
x & = 4 \\
y - z & = 1 \\
0 & = 5.
\end{cases}
$$

Note that the last equation is a built-in contradiction. The last equation can never be satisfied, no matter what the values of x, y, and z. Thus, the original system has no solution. Systems with no solution can always be detected by the presence of a matrix row of the form $\begin{bmatrix} 0 & 0 & \cdots & 0 \mid a \end{bmatrix}$, where a is a nonzero number. ∎

Now Try Exercise 13

EXAMPLE 3   **Solving a system of equations that has infinitely many solutions**   Determine all solutions of the system

$$
\begin{cases}
2x + 2y + 4z = 8 \\
x - y + 2z = 2 \\
-x + 5y - 2z = 2.
\end{cases}
$$

Solution We set up the matrix corresponding to the system and perform the appropriate pivoting operations. (The elements pivoted about are circled.)

$$
\begin{bmatrix}
\textcircled{2} & 2 & 4 & 8 \\
1 & -1 & 2 & 2 \\
-1 & 5 & -2 & 2
\end{bmatrix}
\xrightarrow[\;R_3 + 1R_1\;]{\begin{array}{c}\frac{1}{2}R_1 \\ R_2 + (-1)R_1\end{array}}
\begin{bmatrix}
1 & 1 & 2 & 4 \\
0 & \textcircled{-2} & 0 & -2 \\
0 & 6 & 0 & 6
\end{bmatrix}
$$

$$
\xrightarrow[\;R_3 + (-6)R_2\;]{\begin{array}{c}\left(-\frac{1}{2}\right)R_2 \\ R_1 + (-1)R_2\end{array}}
\begin{bmatrix}
1 & 0 & 2 & 3 \\
0 & 1 & 0 & 1 \\
0 & 0 & 0 & 0
\end{bmatrix}
$$

Note that our method must terminate here, since there is no way to transform the third entry in the third column into a 1 without disturbing the columns already in appropriate form. The equations corresponding to the last matrix read

$$
\begin{cases}
x & + 2z = 3 \\
y & = 1 \\
0 & = 0.
\end{cases}
$$

The last equation does not involve any of the variables and so may be omitted. This leaves the two equations

$$\begin{cases} x & + 2z = 3 \\ & y & = 1. \end{cases}$$

Now, taking the $2z$-term in the first equation to the right side, we can write the equations

$$\begin{cases} x = 3 - 2z \\ y = 1. \end{cases}$$

The value of y is given: $y = 1$. The value of x is given in terms of z. To find a solution to this system, assign any value to z. Then the first equation gives a value for x and thereby a specific solution to the system. For example, if we take $z = 1$, then the corresponding specific solution is

$$z = 1$$
$$x = 3 - 2(1) = 1$$
$$y = 1.$$

If we take $z = -3$, the corresponding specific solution is

$$z = -3$$
$$x = 3 - 2(-3) = 9$$
$$y = 1.$$

Thus, we see that the original system has infinitely many specific solutions, corresponding to the infinitely many possible different choices for z.

We say that the **general solution** of the system is

$$z = \text{any value}$$
$$x = 3 - 2z$$
$$y = 1.$$

Now Try Exercise 15

Gauss–Jordan Elimination Method for the Matrix of a Linear System that Cannot be Transformed into Diagonal Form

1. Apply the Gauss–Jordan elimination method to put as many columns as possible into proper form. (A column is in proper form if one entry is 1 and the other entries are 0.) Proceed from left to right, but do not disturb columns that have already been put into proper form. As much as possible, each row should have a 1 in its leftmost nonzero entry. (Such a 1 is called a *leading 1*.) The column for each leading 1 should be to the right of the columns for the leading 1s in the rows above it.

2. If at any time one or more of the rows is of the form $\begin{bmatrix} 0 & 0 & \cdots & 0 \mid a \end{bmatrix}$, where a is a nonzero number, then the linear system has no solution.

3. Otherwise there are infinitely many solutions. Variables corresponding to columns not in proper form can assume any value. The other variables can then be expressed in terms of these variables.

EXAMPLE 4   **Solving a system of equations that has infinitely many solutions**   Find all solutions of the linear system

$$\begin{cases} x + 2y - z + 3w = 5 \\ y + 2z + w = 7. \end{cases}$$

Solution The Gauss–Jordan elimination method proceeds as follows:

$$\begin{bmatrix} 1 & 2 & -1 & 3 & | & 5 \\ 0 & ① & 2 & 1 & | & 7 \end{bmatrix} \quad \text{(The first column is already in proper form.)}$$

$$\xrightarrow{R_1 + (-2)R_2} \begin{bmatrix} 1 & 0 & -5 & 1 & | & -9 \\ 0 & 1 & 2 & 1 & | & 7 \end{bmatrix}.$$

We cannot do anything further with the third and fourth columns (without disturbing the first two columns), so the corresponding variables, z and w, can assume any values. Writing down the equations corresponding to the last matrix yields

$$\begin{cases} x & - 5z + w = -9 \\ & y + 2z + w = 7 \end{cases}$$

or

$$z = \text{any value}$$
$$w = \text{any value}$$
$$x = -9 + 5z - w$$
$$y = 7 - 2z - w$$

To determine a specific solution, let, for example, $z = 1$ and $w = 2$. Then a specific solution of the original system is

$$z = 1$$
$$w = 2$$
$$x = -9 + 5(1) - (2) = -6$$
$$y = 7 - 2(1) - (2) = 3$$

Now Try Exercise 19

EXAMPLE 5

Solving a system of equations that has infinitely many solutions Find all solutions of the system of equations

$$\begin{cases} x - 7y + z = 3 \\ 2x - 14y + 3z = 4. \end{cases}$$

Solution The first pivot operation is routine:

$$\begin{bmatrix} ① & -7 & 1 & | & 3 \\ 2 & -14 & 3 & | & 4 \end{bmatrix} \xrightarrow{R_2 + (-2)R_1} \begin{bmatrix} 1 & -7 & 1 & | & 3 \\ 0 & 0 & 1 & | & -2 \end{bmatrix}.$$

However, it is impossible to pivot about the zero in the second column. So skip the second column and pivot about the second entry in the third column to get

$$\begin{bmatrix} 1 & -7 & 0 & | & 5 \\ 0 & 0 & 1 & | & -2 \end{bmatrix}.$$

This is as far as we can go. The variable corresponding to the second column, namely y, can assume any value, and the general solution of the system is obtained from the equations

$$\begin{cases} x - 7y = 5 \\ z = -2. \end{cases}$$

Therefore, the general solution of the system is

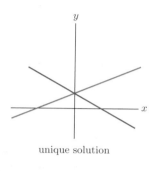

$$y = \text{any value}$$
$$x = 5 + 7y$$
$$z = -2.$$

Now Try Exercise 23

At first it might seem strange that some systems have no solution, some have one, and yet others have infinitely many. The reason for the difference can be explained geometrically. For simplicity, consider the case of systems of two equations in two variables. Each equation in this case has a graph in the xy-plane, and the graph is a straight line. As we have seen, solving the system corresponds to finding the points lying on both lines. There are three possibilities. First, the two lines may intersect. In this case the solution is unique. Second, the two lines may be parallel. Then the two lines do not intersect, and the system has no solution. Finally, the two equations may represent the same line, as, for example, the equations $2x + 3y = 1$ and $4x + 6y = 2$ do. In this case every point on the line is a solution of the system; that is, there are infinitely many solutions (Fig. 1).

unique solution

no solution

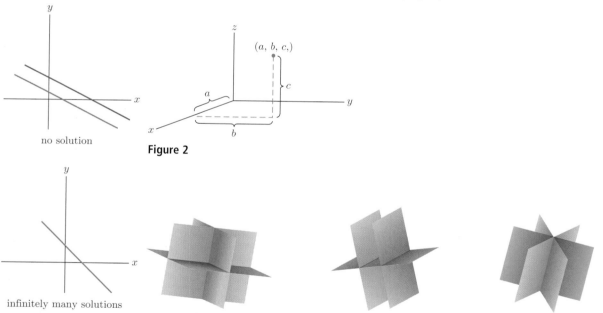

Figure 2

infinitely many solutions

Figure 1

unique solution

no solution

infinitely many solutions

Figure 3

Systems of three equations in three variables can be examined in an analogous way using a 3-dimensional coordinate system. The point having coordinates (a, b, c) is obtained by starting at the origin, moving a units in the x-direction, b units in the y-direction, and then c units in the z-direction (up if c is positive, down if c is negative). See Fig. 2. The collection of points that satisfy a specific linear equation in three variables form a plane. Therefore, the solution of a system of linear equations in three variables consists of all points that are simultaneously on the planes corresponding to each equation. Figure 3 shows some possible configurations for these planes.

INCORPORATING TECHNOLOGY

GC The complete Gauss–Jordan elimination method can be carried out in one step as shown in Figs. 4 and 5 for the matrix of Example 5. The command **rref** is found in the MATRX/MATH menu of the TI-83/84 Plus and in the MATH/Matrix menu of the TI-89. (*Note*: **rref** stands for "reduced row echelon form," the name given to the final form of a matrix that has been completely row reduced.) ∎

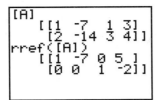

Figure 4. TI-83/84 Plus   **Figure 5.** TI-89

ES When Solver is used with a system of linear equations having infinitely many solutions, only one solution is given. When Solver is used with a system of linear equations having no solution, the sentence "Solver could not find a feasible solution." is displayed.

Practice Problems 2.2

1. Find a specific solution to a system of linear equations whose general solution is

$$w = \text{any value}$$
$$y = \text{any value}$$
$$z = 7 + 6w$$
$$x = 26 - 2y + 14w.$$

2. Find all solutions of this system of linear equations.

$$\begin{cases} 2x + 4y - 4z - 4w = 24 \\ -3x - 6y + 10z - 18w = -8 \\ -x - 2y + 4z - 10w = 2 \end{cases}$$

EXERCISES 2.2

In Exercises 1–8, pivot each matrix about the circled element.

1. $\begin{bmatrix} ② & -4 & 6 \\ 3 & 7 & 1 \end{bmatrix}$

2. $\begin{bmatrix} 1 & 2 & 3 \\ 4 & ⑧ & -12 \end{bmatrix}$

3. $\begin{bmatrix} 7 & 1 & 4 & 5 \\ -1 & 1 & ② & 6 \\ 4 & 0 & 2 & 3 \end{bmatrix}$

4. $\begin{bmatrix} 5 & 10 & -10 & 12 \\ 4 & 3 & 6 & 12 \\ 4 & ㋴ & 4 & -16 \end{bmatrix}$

5. $\begin{bmatrix} ② & 3 \\ 6 & 0 \\ 1 & 5 \end{bmatrix}$

6. $\begin{bmatrix} 2 & 1 \\ ㋮ & 0 \end{bmatrix}$

7. $\begin{bmatrix} 4 & 3 & 0 \\ \frac{2}{3} & 0 & -2 \\ 1 & 3 & ⑥ \end{bmatrix}$

8. $\begin{bmatrix} 1 & 0 & 2 \\ -1 & 1 & ㋛ \\ 1 & 2 & 6 \end{bmatrix}$

In Exercises 9–22, use the Gauss–Jordan elimination method to find all solutions of the systems of linear equations.

9. $\begin{cases} 2x - 4y = 6 \\ -x + 2y = -3 \end{cases}$

10. $\begin{cases} -\frac{1}{2}x + y = \frac{3}{2} \\ -3x + 6y = 10 \end{cases}$

11. $\begin{cases} x + 2y = 5 \\ 3x - y = 1 \\ -x + 3y = 5 \end{cases}$

12. $\begin{cases} x - 6y = 12 \\ -\frac{1}{2}x + 3y = -6 \\ \frac{1}{3}x - 2y = 4 \end{cases}$

13. $\begin{cases} x - y + 3z = 3 \\ -2x + 3y - 11z = -4 \\ x - 2y + 8z = 6 \end{cases}$

14. $\begin{cases} x - 3y + z = 5 \\ -2x + 7y - 6z = -9 \\ x - 2y - 3z = 6 \end{cases}$

15. $\begin{cases} x + y + z = -1 \\ 2x + 3y + 2z = 3 \\ 2x + y + 2z = -7 \end{cases}$

16. $\begin{cases} x - 3y + 2z = 10 \\ -x + 3y - z = -6 \\ -x + 3y + 2z = 6 \end{cases}$

17. $\begin{cases} x + 2y + 3z = 4 \\ 5x + 6y + 7z = 8 \\ x + 2y + 3z = 5 \end{cases}$

18. $\begin{cases} x + 3y = 7 \\ x + 2y = 5 \\ -x + y = 2 \end{cases}$

19. $\begin{cases} x + y - 2z + 2w = 5 \\ 2x + y - 4z + w = 5 \\ 3x + 4y - 6z + 9w = 20 \\ 4x + 4y - 8z + 8w = 20 \end{cases}$

20. $\begin{cases} 2y + z - w = 1 \\ x - y + z + w = 14 \\ -x - 9y - z + 4w = 11 \\ x + y + z = 9 \end{cases}$

21. $\begin{cases} 6x - 4y = 2 \\ -3x + 3y = 6 \\ 5x + 2y = 39 \end{cases}$

22. $\begin{cases} 3x + 2y = 5 \\ -x + 3y = 2 \\ 5x + 2y = 6 \\ 6x + y = 39 \end{cases}$

In Exercises 23–25, find three solutions to the systems of equations.

23. $\begin{cases} x + 2y + z = 5 \\ y + 3z = 9 \end{cases}$

24. $\begin{cases} x + 5y + 3z = 9 \\ 2x + 9y + 7z = 5 \end{cases}$

25. $\begin{cases} x + 7y - 3z = 8 \\ z = 5 \end{cases}$

26. Triathlon An out-of-shape athlete runs 6 miles per hour, swims 1 mile per hour, and bikes 10 miles per hour. He entered a triathlon, which requires all three events, and finished 5 hours and 40 minutes later. A friend who runs 8 miles per hour, swims 2 miles per hour, and bikes 15 miles per hour finished the same course in 3 hours and 35 minutes. The total course was 32 miles long. How many miles was each segment (running, swimming, and biking)?

27. Nutrition Planning In a laboratory experiment, a researcher wants to provide a rabbit with exactly 1000 units of vitamin A, exactly 1600 units of vitamin C, and exactly 2400 units of vitamin E. The rabbit is fed a mixture of three foods. Each gram of food 1 contains 2 units of vitamin A, 3 units of vitamin C, and 5 units of vitamin E. Each gram of food 2 contains 4 units of vitamin A, 7 units of vitamin C, and 9 units of vitamin E. Each gram of food 3 contains 6 units of vitamin A, 10 units of vitamin C, and 14 units of vitamin E. How many grams of each food should the rabbit be fed?

28. Nutrition Planning Rework Exercise 27 with the requirement for vitamin E changed to 2000 units.

29. Quilting Granny's Custom Quilts receives an order for a patchwork quilt made from square patches of three types: solid green, solid blue, and floral. The quilt is to be 8 squares by 12 squares, and there must be 15 times as many solid squares as floral squares. If Granny's charges $3 per solid square and $5 per floral square, and if the customer wishes to spend exactly $300, how many of each type of square may be used in the quilt?

30. Purchasing Options Amanda is decorating her new home and wants to buy some house plants. She is interested in three types of plants costing $7, $10, and $13. If she has budgeted exactly $150 for the plants and wants to buy exactly 15 of them, what are her options?

31. Find all solutions to the following system of equations.

$$\begin{cases} x^2 + y^2 + z^2 = 14 \\ x^2 - y^2 + 2z^2 = 15 \\ x^2 + 2y^2 + 3z^2 = 36 \end{cases}$$

32. For what value of k will the following system of linear equations have a solution?

$$\begin{cases} 2x + 6y = 4 \\ x + 7y = 10 \\ kx + 8y = 4 \end{cases}$$

33. For what values(s) of k will the following system of linear equations have no solution? Infinitely many solutions?

$$\begin{cases} 2x - 3y = 4 \\ -6x + 9y = k \end{cases}$$

34. Suppose that after the Gauss–Jordan elimination method has been applied to a matrix corresponding to a system of linear equations, the matrix has a row of all zeros. Must the system have infinitely many solutions?

35. Figure 6 shows the graphs of the equations from a system of three linear equations in two variables. How many solutions does the system have?

(a) three **(b)** none

(c) infinitely many **(d)** one

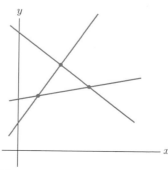

Figure 6

In Exercises 36–40, use a graphing calculator to carry out the tasks.

In Exercises 36–39, graph the three equations together, and determine the number of solutions (exactly one, none, or infinitely many). If there is exactly one solution, estimate the solution.

36. $\begin{cases} 2x + 3y = 5 \\ -3x + 5y = 22 \\ 2x + y = -1 \end{cases}$ 37. $\begin{cases} x + y = 10 \\ 2x - 3y = 5 \\ -x + 3y = 2 \end{cases}$

38. $\begin{cases} 3x - 2y = 3 \\ -2x + 4y = 14 \\ x + y = 11 \end{cases}$ 39. $\begin{cases} 2x + y = 12 \\ 3x - y = 2 \\ x + 2y = 16 \end{cases}$

40. If your calculator has **rref** or an analogous command, apply the command to the matrix in Example 2. How does the final matrix differ from the one appearing in the text?

Solutions to Practice Problems 2.2

1. Since w and y can each assume any value, select any numbers, say $w = 1$ and $y = 2$. Then $z = 7 + 6(1) = 13$ and $x = 26 - 2(2) + 14(1) = 36$. So $x = 36$, $y = 2$, $z = 13$, $w = 1$ is a specific solution. There are infinitely many different specific solutions since there are infinitely many different choices for w and y.

2. We apply the Gauss–Jordan elimination method to the matrix of the system.

$$\left[\begin{array}{cccc|c} ② & 4 & -4 & -4 & 24 \\ -3 & -6 & 10 & -18 & -8 \\ -1 & -2 & 4 & -10 & 2 \end{array}\right]$$

$$\begin{array}{c} \frac{1}{2}R_1 \\ R_2 + 3R_1 \\ \hline R_3 + 1R_1 \end{array} \left[\begin{array}{cccc|c} 1 & 2 & -2 & -2 & 12 \\ 0 & 0 & ④ & -24 & 28 \\ 0 & 0 & 2 & -12 & 14 \end{array}\right]$$

$$\begin{array}{c} \frac{1}{4}R_2 \\ R_1 + 2R_2 \\ \hline R_3 + (-2)R_2 \end{array} \left[\begin{array}{cccc|c} 1 & 2 & 0 & -14 & 26 \\ 0 & 0 & 1 & -6 & 7 \\ 0 & 0 & 0 & 0 & 0 \end{array}\right]$$

The corresponding system of equations is

$$\begin{cases} x + 2y \quad - 14w = 26 \\ \quad\quad z - 6w = 7. \end{cases}$$

The general solution is

$$w = \text{any value}$$
$$y = \text{any value}$$
$$z = 7 + 6w$$
$$x = 26 - 2y + 14w$$

2.3 Arithmetic Operations on Matrices

We introduced matrices in Sections 2.1 and 2.2 to display the coefficients of a system of linear equations. For example, the linear system

$$\begin{cases} 5x - 3y = \frac{1}{2} \\ 4x + 2y = -1 \end{cases}$$

is represented by the matrix

$$\left[\begin{array}{cc|c} 5 & -3 & \frac{1}{2} \\ 4 & 2 & -1 \end{array}\right].$$

After we have become accustomed to using such matrices in solving linear systems, we may omit the vertical line that separates the left and right sides of the equations.

We need only remember that the right side of the equations is recorded in the right column. So, for example, we would write the preceding matrix in the form

$$\begin{bmatrix} 5 & -3 & \frac{1}{2} \\ 4 & 2 & -1 \end{bmatrix}.$$

A matrix is *any* rectangular array of numbers and may be of any size. Here are some examples of matrices of various sizes:

$$\begin{bmatrix} 3 & 7 \\ 0 & -1 \end{bmatrix}, \quad \begin{bmatrix} 1 \\ 2 \end{bmatrix}, \quad \begin{bmatrix} 2 & 1 \end{bmatrix}, \quad \begin{bmatrix} 6 \end{bmatrix}, \quad \begin{bmatrix} 5 & 7 & -1 \\ 0 & 3 & 5 \\ 6 & 0 & 5 \end{bmatrix}.$$

Examples of matrices abound in everyday life. For example, the newspaper stock market report is a large matrix with several thousand rows, one for each listed stock. The columns of the matrix give the various data about each stock, such as opening and closing price, number of shares traded, and so on. Another example of a matrix is a mileage chart on a road map. The rows and columns are labeled with the names of cities. The number at a given row and column gives the distance between the corresponding cities.

In these everyday examples, matrices are used only to display data. However, the most important applications involve arithmetic operations on matrices—namely, addition, subtraction, and multiplication of matrices. The major goal of this section is to discuss these operations. Before we can do so, however, we need some vocabulary with which to describe matrices.

A matrix is described by its **size**; that is, the number of rows and columns it contains. For example, the matrix

$$\begin{bmatrix} 7 & 5 \\ \frac{1}{2} & -2 \\ 2 & -11 \end{bmatrix}$$

has three rows and two columns and is referred to as a *3 × 2* (read: "three-by-two") *matrix*. The matrix $\begin{bmatrix} 4 & 5 & 0 \end{bmatrix}$ has one row and three columns and is a *1 × 3 matrix*. A matrix with only one row is called a **row matrix**. A matrix, such as

$$\begin{bmatrix} 2 \\ 7 \end{bmatrix},$$

that has only one column is called a **column matrix**. If a matrix has the same number of rows and columns, it is called a **square matrix**. Here are some square matrices of various sizes:

$$\begin{bmatrix} 5 \end{bmatrix}, \quad \begin{bmatrix} 1 & 2 \\ 3 & 4 \end{bmatrix}, \quad \begin{bmatrix} 2 & -1 & 0 \\ 3 & 5 & 4 \\ 0 & 3 & -7 \end{bmatrix}.$$

The rows of a matrix are numbered from the top down, and the columns are numbered from left to right. For example, the first row of the matrix

$$A = \begin{bmatrix} 1 & -1 & 0 \\ 2 & 1 & 7 \\ -3 & 2 & 4 \end{bmatrix}$$

is $\begin{bmatrix} 1 & -1 & 0 \end{bmatrix}$, and its third column is

$$\begin{bmatrix} 0 \\ 7 \\ 4 \end{bmatrix}.$$

The numbers in a matrix, called **entries**, may be identified in terms of the row and column containing the entry in question. For example, the entry in the first row, third column of matrix A is 0:

$$\begin{bmatrix} 1 & -1 & \boxed{0} \\ 2 & 1 & 7 \\ -3 & 2 & 4 \end{bmatrix};$$

the entry in the second row, first column is 2:

$$\begin{bmatrix} 1 & -1 & 0 \\ \boxed{2} & 1 & 7 \\ -3 & 2 & 4 \end{bmatrix};$$

and the entry in the third row, third column is 4:

$$\begin{bmatrix} 1 & -1 & 0 \\ 2 & 1 & 7 \\ -3 & 2 & \boxed{4} \end{bmatrix}.$$

We use double-subscripted lowercase letters to indicate the locations of the entries of a matrix. We denote the entry in the ith row, jth column of the matrix A by a_{ij}. For instance, we have $a_{13} = 0$, $a_{21} = 2$, and $a_{33} = 4$.

We say that two matrices A and B are **equal**, denoted $A = B$, provided that they have the same size and that all their corresponding entries are equal.

Addition and Subtraction of Matrices We define the sum $A + B$ of two matrices A and B only if A and B are two matrices of the same size—that is, if A and B have the same number of rows and the same number of columns. In this case $A + B$ is the matrix formed by adding the corresponding entries of A and B. For example,

$$\begin{bmatrix} 2 & 0 \\ 1 & 1 \\ 5 & 3 \end{bmatrix} + \begin{bmatrix} 5 & 4 \\ 0 & 2 \\ 2 & 6 \end{bmatrix} = \begin{bmatrix} 2+5 & 0+4 \\ 1+0 & 1+2 \\ 5+2 & 3+6 \end{bmatrix} = \begin{bmatrix} 7 & 4 \\ 1 & 3 \\ 7 & 9 \end{bmatrix}.$$

We subtract matrices of the same size by subtracting corresponding entries. Thus, we have

$$\begin{bmatrix} 7 \\ 1 \end{bmatrix} - \begin{bmatrix} 3 \\ 2 \end{bmatrix} = \begin{bmatrix} 7-3 \\ 1-2 \end{bmatrix} = \begin{bmatrix} 4 \\ -1 \end{bmatrix}.$$

Multiplication of Matrices It might seem that to define the product of two matrices, one would start with two matrices of like size and multiply the corresponding entries. But this definition is not useful, since the calculations that arise in applications require a somewhat more complex multiplication. In the interests of simplicity, we start by defining the product of a row matrix times a column matrix.

If A is a row matrix and B is a column matrix, then we can form the product $A \cdot B$ provided that the two matrices have the same length. The product $A \cdot B$ is the 1×1 matrix obtained by multiplying corresponding entries of A and B and then forming the sum.

We may put this definition into algebraic terms as follows. Suppose that A is the row matrix

$$A = \begin{bmatrix} a_1 & a_2 & \cdots & a_n \end{bmatrix},$$

and B is the column matrix

$$B = \begin{bmatrix} b_1 \\ b_2 \\ \vdots \\ b_n \end{bmatrix}.$$

Note that A and B are both of the same length, namely n. Then

$$A \cdot B = \begin{bmatrix} a_1 & a_2 & \cdots & a_n \end{bmatrix} \cdot \begin{bmatrix} b_1 \\ b_2 \\ \vdots \\ b_n \end{bmatrix}$$

is calculated by multiplying corresponding entries of A and B and forming the sum; that is,

$$A \cdot B = \begin{bmatrix} a_1 b_1 + a_2 b_2 + \cdots + a_n b_n \end{bmatrix}.$$

Notice that the product is a 1×1 matrix, namely a single number in brackets.

Here are some examples of the product of a row matrix times a column matrix:

$$\begin{bmatrix} 3 & \frac{1}{2} \end{bmatrix} \cdot \begin{bmatrix} 1 \\ 4 \end{bmatrix} = \begin{bmatrix} 3 \cdot 1 + \frac{1}{2} \cdot 4 \end{bmatrix} = \begin{bmatrix} 5 \end{bmatrix};$$

$$\begin{bmatrix} 2 & 0 & -1 \end{bmatrix} \cdot \begin{bmatrix} 6 \\ 5 \\ 3 \end{bmatrix} = \begin{bmatrix} 2 \cdot 6 + 0 \cdot 5 + (-1) \cdot 3 \end{bmatrix} = \begin{bmatrix} 9 \end{bmatrix}.$$

In multiplying a row matrix times a column matrix, it helps to use both of your hands. Use your left index finger to point to the first element of the row matrix and your right to point to the first element of the column. Multiply the elements you are pointing to and keep a running total of the products in your head. After each multiplication move your fingers to the next elements of each matrix. With a little practice you should be able to multiply a row times a column quickly and accurately.

The preceding definition of multiplication may seem strange. But products of this sort occur in many down-to-earth problems. Consider, for instance, the next example.

EXAMPLE 1

Total revenue as a matrix product A dairy farm produces three items—milk, eggs, and cheese. The prices of the three items are $1.50 per gallon, $0.80 per dozen, and $2.00 per pound, respectively. In a certain week the dairy farm sells 30,000 gallons of milk, 2000 dozen eggs, and 5000 pounds of cheese. Represent its total revenue as a matrix product.

Solution The total revenue equals

$$(1.50)(30{,}000) + (.80)(2000) + (2)(5000).$$

This suggests that we define two matrices: The first displays the prices of the various items:

$$\begin{bmatrix} 1.50 & .80 & 2 \end{bmatrix}.$$

The second represents the production:

$$\begin{bmatrix} 30{,}000 \\ 2000 \\ 5000 \end{bmatrix}.$$

Then the revenue for the week, when placed in a 1×1 matrix, equals

$$\begin{bmatrix} 1.50 & .80 & 2 \end{bmatrix} \begin{bmatrix} 30,000 \\ 2000 \\ 5000 \end{bmatrix} = \begin{bmatrix} 56,600 \end{bmatrix}.$$

Now Try Exercise 71

The principle behind Example 1 is this: Any sum of products of the form $a_1b_1 + a_2b_2 + \cdots + a_nb_n$, when placed in a 1×1 matrix, can be written as the matrix product

$$\begin{bmatrix} a_1b_1 + a_2b_2 + \cdots + a_nb_n \end{bmatrix} = \begin{bmatrix} a_1 & a_2 & \cdots & a_n \end{bmatrix} \cdot \begin{bmatrix} b_1 \\ b_2 \\ \vdots \\ b_n \end{bmatrix}.$$

Let us illustrate the procedure for multiplying more general matrices by working out a typical product:

$$\begin{bmatrix} 2 & 1 \\ 0 & 1 \\ 1 & 0 \end{bmatrix} \cdot \begin{bmatrix} 1 & 1 \\ 4 & 2 \end{bmatrix}.$$

To obtain the entries of the product, we multiply the rows of the left matrix by the columns of the right matrix, taking care to arrange the products in a specific way to yield a matrix, as follows. Start with the first row on the left, $\begin{bmatrix} 2 & 1 \end{bmatrix}$, and the first column on the right, $\begin{bmatrix} 1 \\ 4 \end{bmatrix}$. Their product is $\begin{bmatrix} 6 \end{bmatrix}$, so we enter 6 as the element in the first row, first column of the product:

$$\begin{bmatrix} 2 & 1 \\ 0 & 1 \\ 1 & 0 \end{bmatrix} \cdot \begin{bmatrix} 1 & 1 \\ 4 & 2 \end{bmatrix} = \begin{bmatrix} 6 & \\ & \\ & \end{bmatrix}.$$

The product of the first row of the left matrix and the second column of the right matrix is $\begin{bmatrix} 4 \end{bmatrix}$, so we put a 4 in the first row, second column of the product:

$$\begin{bmatrix} 2 & 1 \\ 0 & 1 \\ 1 & 0 \end{bmatrix} \cdot \begin{bmatrix} 1 & 1 \\ 4 & 2 \end{bmatrix} = \begin{bmatrix} 6 & 4 \\ & \\ & \end{bmatrix}.$$

There are no more columns that can be multiplied by the first row, so let us move to the second row and shift back to the first column. Correspondingly, we move down one row in the product:

$$\begin{bmatrix} 2 & 1 \\ 0 & 1 \\ 1 & 0 \end{bmatrix} \cdot \begin{bmatrix} 1 & 1 \\ 4 & 2 \end{bmatrix} = \begin{bmatrix} 6 & 4 \\ 4 & \\ & \end{bmatrix};$$

$$\begin{bmatrix} 2 & 1 \\ 0 & 1 \\ 1 & 0 \end{bmatrix} \cdot \begin{bmatrix} 1 & 1 \\ 4 & 2 \end{bmatrix} = \begin{bmatrix} 6 & 4 \\ 4 & 2 \\ & \end{bmatrix}.$$

We have now exhausted the second row of the left matrix, so we shift to the third row and correspondingly move down one row in the product:

$$\begin{bmatrix} 2 & 1 \\ 0 & 1 \\ 1 & 0 \end{bmatrix} \cdot \begin{bmatrix} 1 & 1 \\ 4 & 2 \end{bmatrix} = \begin{bmatrix} 6 & 4 \\ 4 & 2 \\ 1 & \end{bmatrix};$$

$$\begin{bmatrix} 2 & 1 \\ 0 & 1 \\ 1 & 0 \end{bmatrix} \cdot \begin{bmatrix} 1 & 1 \\ 4 & 2 \end{bmatrix} = \begin{bmatrix} 6 & 4 \\ 4 & 2 \\ 1 & 1 \end{bmatrix}.$$

Note that we have now multiplied every row of the left matrix by every column of the right matrix. This completes the computation of the product:

$$\begin{bmatrix} 2 & 1 \\ 0 & 1 \\ 1 & 0 \end{bmatrix} \cdot \begin{bmatrix} 1 & 1 \\ 4 & 2 \end{bmatrix} = \begin{bmatrix} 6 & 4 \\ 4 & 2 \\ 1 & 1 \end{bmatrix}.$$

EXAMPLE 2   **Matrix multiplication** Calculate the following product:

$$\begin{bmatrix} 1 & 5 \\ 3 & 2 \end{bmatrix} \cdot \begin{bmatrix} 1 & 2 \\ 1 & 0 \end{bmatrix}.$$

Solution

$$\begin{bmatrix} 1 & 5 \\ 3 & 2 \end{bmatrix} \cdot \begin{bmatrix} 1 & 2 \\ 1 & 0 \end{bmatrix} = \begin{bmatrix} 6 & \\ & \end{bmatrix}$$

$$\begin{bmatrix} 1 & 5 \\ 3 & 2 \end{bmatrix} \cdot \begin{bmatrix} 1 & 2 \\ 1 & 0 \end{bmatrix} = \begin{bmatrix} 6 & 2 \\ & \end{bmatrix}$$

$$\begin{bmatrix} 1 & 5 \\ 3 & 2 \end{bmatrix} \cdot \begin{bmatrix} 1 & 2 \\ 1 & 0 \end{bmatrix} = \begin{bmatrix} 6 & 2 \\ 5 & \end{bmatrix}$$

$$\begin{bmatrix} 1 & 5 \\ 3 & 2 \end{bmatrix} \cdot \begin{bmatrix} 1 & 2 \\ 1 & 0 \end{bmatrix} = \begin{bmatrix} 6 & 2 \\ 5 & 6 \end{bmatrix}$$

Thus,

$$\begin{bmatrix} 1 & 5 \\ 3 & 2 \end{bmatrix} \cdot \begin{bmatrix} 1 & 2 \\ 1 & 0 \end{bmatrix} = \begin{bmatrix} 6 & 2 \\ 5 & 6 \end{bmatrix}.$$

Now Try Exercise 25   ■

Notice that we cannot use the preceding method to compute the product $A \cdot B$ of *any* matrices A and B. For the procedure to work, it is crucial that the number of entries of each row of A be the same as the number of entries of each column of B. (Or, to put it another way, the number of columns of the left matrix must equal the number of rows of the right matrix.) Therefore, in order for us to form the product $A \cdot B$, the sizes of A and B must match up in a special way. If A is $m \times n$ and B is $p \times q$, then the product $A \cdot B$ is defined only in case the "inner" dimensions n and p are equal. In that case, the size of the product is determined by the "outer" dimensions m and q. It is an $m \times q$ matrix:

$$A \quad \cdot \quad B \quad = \quad C.$$
$$m \times n \quad p \times q \quad m \times q$$

equal

So, for example,

$$\begin{bmatrix} \end{bmatrix}_{3 \times 4} \begin{bmatrix} \end{bmatrix}_{4 \times 2} = \begin{bmatrix} \end{bmatrix}_{3 \times 2}$$

$$\begin{bmatrix} \end{bmatrix}_{2 \times 2} \begin{bmatrix} \end{bmatrix}_{2 \times 1} = \begin{bmatrix} \end{bmatrix}_{2 \times 1}.$$

If the sizes of A and B do not match up in the way just described, the product $A \cdot B$ is not defined.

EXAMPLE 3

Matrix multiplication   Calculate the following products, if defined.

(a) $\begin{bmatrix} 3 & -1 \\ 2 & 0 \\ 1 & 5 \end{bmatrix} \begin{bmatrix} 1 & 0 \\ 5 & -4 \\ 2 & -1 \end{bmatrix}$ (b) $\begin{bmatrix} 3 & -1 \\ 2 & 0 \\ 1 & 5 \end{bmatrix} \begin{bmatrix} 5 & 4 \\ -2 & 3 \end{bmatrix}$

Solution (a) The matrices to be multiplied are 3×2 and 3×2. The inner dimensions do not match, so the product is undefined.

(b) We are asked to multiply a 3×2 matrix times a 2×2 matrix. The inner dimensions match, so the product is defined and has size determined by the outer dimensions, that is, 3×2.

$$\begin{bmatrix} 3 & -1 \\ 2 & 0 \\ 1 & 5 \end{bmatrix} \begin{bmatrix} 5 & 4 \\ -2 & 3 \end{bmatrix} = \begin{bmatrix} 3 \cdot 5 + (-1) \cdot (-2) & 3 \cdot 4 + (-1) \cdot 3 \\ 2 \cdot 5 + 0 \cdot (-2) & 2 \cdot 4 + 0 \cdot 3 \\ 1 \cdot 5 + 5 \cdot (-2) & 1 \cdot 4 + 5 \cdot 3 \end{bmatrix}$$

$$= \begin{bmatrix} 17 & 9 \\ 10 & 8 \\ -5 & 19 \end{bmatrix}$$

Now Try Exercise 27   ■

Multiplication of matrices has many properties in common with multiplication of ordinary numbers. However, there is at least one important difference. With matrix multiplication, the order of the factors is usually important. For example, the product of a 2×3 matrix times a 3×2 matrix is defined: The product is a 2×2 matrix. If the order is reversed to a 3×2 matrix times a 2×3 matrix, the product is a 3×3 matrix. So reversing the order may change the size of the product. Even when it does not, reversing the order may still change the entries in the product, as the following two products demonstrate:

$$\begin{bmatrix} 1 & 5 \\ 3 & 2 \end{bmatrix} \begin{bmatrix} 1 & 2 \\ 1 & 0 \end{bmatrix} = \begin{bmatrix} 6 & 2 \\ 5 & 6 \end{bmatrix}; \qquad \begin{bmatrix} 1 & 2 \\ 1 & 0 \end{bmatrix} \begin{bmatrix} 1 & 5 \\ 3 & 2 \end{bmatrix} = \begin{bmatrix} 7 & 9 \\ 1 & 5 \end{bmatrix}.$$

EXAMPLE 4   **Investment earnings** An investment trust has investments in three states. Its deposits in each state are divided among bonds, mortgages, and consumer loans. On January 1 the amount (in millions of dollars) of money invested in each category by state is given by the matrix

$$
\begin{array}{c}
\\
\text{State A} \\
\text{State B} \\
\text{State C}
\end{array}
\begin{array}{ccc}
\text{Bonds} & \text{Mortgages} & \begin{array}{c}\text{Consumer} \\ \text{loans}\end{array}
\end{array}
\begin{bmatrix}
10 & 5 & 20 \\
30 & 12 & 10 \\
15 & 6 & 25
\end{bmatrix}.
$$

The current average yields are 7% for bonds, 9% for mortgages, and 15% for consumer loans. Determine the earnings of the trust from its investments in each state.

Solution Define the matrix of investment yields by

$$
\begin{bmatrix} .07 \\ .09 \\ .15 \end{bmatrix}
\begin{array}{l}
\text{Bonds} \\
\text{Mortgages} \\
\text{Consumer loans.}
\end{array}
$$

The amount earned in state A, for instance, is

[amount of bonds][yield of bonds]

+ [amount of mortgages][yield of mortgages]

+ [amount of consumer loans][yield of consumer loans]

$$= (10)(.07) + (5)(.09) + (20)(.15).$$

And this is just the first entry of the product:

$$
\begin{bmatrix}
10 & 5 & 20 \\
30 & 12 & 10 \\
15 & 6 & 25
\end{bmatrix}
\begin{bmatrix}
.07 \\
.09 \\
.15
\end{bmatrix}.
$$

Similarly, the earnings for the other states are the second and third entries of the product. Carrying out the arithmetic, we find that

$$
\begin{bmatrix}
10 & 5 & 20 \\
30 & 12 & 10 \\
15 & 6 & 25
\end{bmatrix}
\begin{bmatrix}
.07 \\
.09 \\
.15
\end{bmatrix}
=
\begin{bmatrix}
4.15 \\
4.68 \\
5.34
\end{bmatrix}.
$$

Therefore, the trust earns $4.15 million in state A, $4.68 million in state B, and $5.34 million in state C.

Now Try Exercise 51(a)

EXAMPLE 5   **Manufacturing revenue** A clothing manufacturer has factories in Los Angeles, San Antonio, and Newark. Sales (in thousands) during the first quarter of last year are summarized in the production matrix

$$
\begin{array}{c}
\\
\text{Coats} \\
\text{Shirts} \\
\text{Sweaters} \\
\text{Ties}
\end{array}
\begin{array}{ccc}
\text{Los Angeles} & \text{San Antonio} & \text{Newark}
\end{array}
\begin{bmatrix}
12 & 13 & 38 \\
25 & 5 & 26 \\
11 & 8 & 8 \\
5 & 0 & 12
\end{bmatrix}.
$$

During this period the selling price of a coat was $100, of a shirt $10, of a sweater $25, and of a tie $5.

(a) Use a matrix calculation to determine the total revenue produced by each of the factories.

(b) Suppose that the prices had been $110, $8, $20, and $10, respectively. How would this have affected the revenue of each factory?

Solution (a) For each factory, we wish to multiply the price of each item by the number produced to arrive at revenue. Since the production figures for the various items of clothing are arranged down the columns, we arrange the prices in a row matrix, ready for multiplication. The price matrix is

$$\begin{bmatrix} 100 & 10 & 25 & 5 \end{bmatrix}.$$

The revenues of the various factories are then the entries of the product

$$\begin{bmatrix} 100 & 10 & 25 & 5 \end{bmatrix} \begin{bmatrix} 12 & 13 & 38 \\ 25 & 5 & 26 \\ 11 & 8 & 8 \\ 5 & 0 & 12 \end{bmatrix} = \begin{bmatrix} \text{Los Angeles} & \text{San Antonio} & \text{Newark} \\ 1750 & 1550 & 4320 \end{bmatrix}.$$

Since the production figures are in thousands, the revenue figures are in thousands of dollars. That is, the Los Angeles factory has revenues of $1,750,000, the San Antonio factory $1,550,000, and the Newark factory $4,320,000.

(b) In a similar way, we determine the revenue of each factory if the price matrix had been $\begin{bmatrix} 110 & 8 & 20 & 10 \end{bmatrix}$.

$$\begin{bmatrix} 110 & 8 & 20 & 10 \end{bmatrix} \begin{bmatrix} 12 & 13 & 38 \\ 25 & 5 & 26 \\ 11 & 8 & 8 \\ 5 & 0 & 12 \end{bmatrix} = \begin{bmatrix} \text{Los Angeles} & \text{San Antonio} & \text{Newark} \\ 1790 & 1630 & 4668 \end{bmatrix}.$$

The change in revenue at each factory can be read from the difference of the revenue matrices:

$$\begin{bmatrix} 1790 & 1630 & 4668 \end{bmatrix} - \begin{bmatrix} 1750 & 1550 & 4320 \end{bmatrix} = \begin{bmatrix} 40 & 80 & 348 \end{bmatrix}.$$

If prices had been as given in (b), revenues of the Los Angeles factory would have increased by $40,000, revenues at San Antonio would have increased by $80,000, and revenues at Newark would have increased by $348,000. ■

Now Try Exercise 55

There are special matrices analogous to the number 1. Such matrices are called *identity matrices*.

DEFINITION The **identity matrix** I_n is the $n \times n$ square matrix with all zeros except for ones down the upper-left-to-lower-right diagonal.

Here are the identity matrices of sizes 2, 3, and 4:

$$I_2 = \begin{bmatrix} 1 & 0 \\ 0 & 1 \end{bmatrix}; \qquad I_3 = \begin{bmatrix} 1 & 0 & 0 \\ 0 & 1 & 0 \\ 0 & 0 & 1 \end{bmatrix}; \qquad I_4 = \begin{bmatrix} 1 & 0 & 0 & 0 \\ 0 & 1 & 0 & 0 \\ 0 & 0 & 1 & 0 \\ 0 & 0 & 0 & 1 \end{bmatrix}.$$

The characteristic property of an identity matrix is that it plays the role of the number 1; that is,

$$I_n \cdot A = A \cdot I_n = A$$

for all $n \times n$ matrices A.

One of the principal uses of matrices is in dealing with systems of linear equations. Matrices provide a compact way of writing systems, as the next example shows.

EXAMPLE 6

Representing a system of equations as a matrix equation Write the system of linear equations

$$\begin{cases} -2x + 4y = 2 \\ -3x + 7y = 7 \end{cases}$$

as a matrix equation.

Solution The system of equations can be written in the form

$$\begin{bmatrix} -2x + 4y \\ -3x + 7y \end{bmatrix} = \begin{bmatrix} 2 \\ 7 \end{bmatrix}.$$

So consider the matrices

$$A = \begin{bmatrix} -2 & 4 \\ -3 & 7 \end{bmatrix}, \qquad X = \begin{bmatrix} x \\ y \end{bmatrix}, \qquad B = \begin{bmatrix} 2 \\ 7 \end{bmatrix}.$$

Notice that

$$AX = \begin{bmatrix} -2 & 4 \\ -3 & 7 \end{bmatrix} \begin{bmatrix} x \\ y \end{bmatrix} = \begin{bmatrix} -2x + 4y \\ -3x + 7y \end{bmatrix}.$$

Thus, AX is a 2×1 column matrix whose entries correspond to the left side of the given system of linear equations. Since the entries of B correspond to the right side of the system of equations, we can rewrite the given system in the form

$$AX = B$$

—that is,

$$\begin{bmatrix} -2 & 4 \\ -3 & 7 \end{bmatrix} \begin{bmatrix} x \\ y \end{bmatrix} = \begin{bmatrix} 2 \\ 7 \end{bmatrix}.$$

Now Try Exercise 39

The matrix A of the preceding example displays the coefficients of the variables x and y, and so it is called the **coefficient matrix** of the system.

INCORPORATING TECHNOLOGY

GC   The arithmetic operations $+$, $-$, and $*$ can be applied to matrices in much the same way as to numbers, as Figs. 1, 2, 4, and 5 show. (*Note*: With the TI-83/84 Plus **[A]*[B]** also can be written as **[A][B]**.) Identity matrices are placed on the home screen with the command **identity** (in the MATRIX/MATH menu of the TI-83/84 Plus and in the MATH/Matrix menu of the TI-89), as shown in Figures 3 and 6. The value in the ith row, jth column of the matrix **[A]** can be displayed with **[A](i,j)** on the TI-83/84 Plus and with **a[i,j]** on the TI-89. ■

ES   The entries of an $m \times n$ matrix can be typed directly into an m by n range of cells. (In order to insert a fraction, type in a formula such as **=2/3**. A matrix is most easily used in calculations if it has been given a name, such as **A** or **B**. To name a matrix, select it, click on the Name box, type the name, and press Enter. Single-letter names can consist of any letter other than C or R.

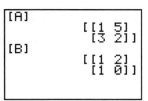

Figure 1

Figure 2

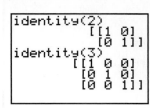

Figure 3

Figure 4

Figure 5

Figure 6

Matrices are added, subtracted, and multiplied with the + operator, the − operator, and the MMULT function, respectively. The following steps carry out these operations on the matrices A and B:

1. Highlight a range of cells having the size of the matrix to be computed.
2. Type **=A+B**, **=A−B**, or **=MMULT(A,B)**.
3. Press Ctrl+Shift+Enter. (*Note*: The plus signs indicate that the three keys should be held down together.) The computed matrix will be displayed in the highlighted block.

Practice Problems 2.3

1. Compute

$$\begin{bmatrix} 3 & 1 & 2 \\ -1 & 0 & \frac{1}{2} \\ 0 & 4 & 1 \end{bmatrix} \begin{bmatrix} 7 & -1 & 0 \\ 5 & 4 & 2 \\ -6 & 0 & 4 \end{bmatrix}.$$

2. Give the system of linear equations that is equivalent to the matrix equation

$$\begin{bmatrix} 3 & -6 \\ 2 & 1 \end{bmatrix} \begin{bmatrix} x \\ y \end{bmatrix} = \begin{bmatrix} 5 \\ 0 \end{bmatrix}.$$

3. Give a matrix equation equivalent to this system of equations:

$$\begin{cases} 8x + 3y = 7 \\ 9x - 2y = -5. \end{cases}$$

EXERCISES 2.3

In Exercises 1–6, give the size and special characteristics of the given matrix (such as square, column, row, identity).

1. $\begin{bmatrix} 3 & 2 & 4 \\ \frac{1}{2} & 0 & 6 \end{bmatrix}$

2. $\begin{bmatrix} 3 \\ -1 \end{bmatrix}$

3. $\begin{bmatrix} 2 & \frac{1}{3} & 0 \end{bmatrix}$

4. $\begin{bmatrix} 1 & 0 \\ 0 & 1 \end{bmatrix}$

5. $\begin{bmatrix} 1 & 0 \\ 0 & 0 \end{bmatrix}$

6. $\begin{bmatrix} 5 \end{bmatrix}$

Exercises 7–10 refer to the 2×3 matrix $A = \begin{bmatrix} 2 & -4 & 6 \\ 0 & 3 & -1 \end{bmatrix}$.

7. Find a_{12} and a_{21}.

8. Find a_{23} and a_{11}.

9. For what values of i and j does $a_{ij} = 6$?

10. For what values of i and j does $a_{ij} = 3$?

In Exercises 11–18, perform the indicated matrix calculations.

11. $\begin{bmatrix} 4 & -2 \\ 3 & 0 \end{bmatrix} + \begin{bmatrix} 5 & 5 \\ 4 & -1 \end{bmatrix}$ **12.** $\begin{bmatrix} 8 \\ -3 \end{bmatrix} + \begin{bmatrix} 5 \\ 6 \end{bmatrix}$

13. $\begin{bmatrix} 2 & 8 \\ \frac{4}{3} & 4 \\ 1 & -2 \end{bmatrix} - \begin{bmatrix} 1 & 5 \\ \frac{1}{3} & 2 \\ -3 & 0 \end{bmatrix}$

14. $\begin{bmatrix} 1 & 0 \\ 0 & 1 \end{bmatrix} - \begin{bmatrix} .8 & .5 \\ .2 & .5 \end{bmatrix}$

15. $\begin{bmatrix} 5 & 3 \end{bmatrix} \begin{bmatrix} 1 \\ 2 \end{bmatrix}$ **16.** $\begin{bmatrix} 1 & 0 & 0 \end{bmatrix} \begin{bmatrix} \frac{1}{2} \\ 6 \\ 2 \end{bmatrix}$

17. $\begin{bmatrix} 6 & 1 & 5 \end{bmatrix} \begin{bmatrix} \frac{1}{2} \\ -3 \\ 2 \end{bmatrix}$ **18.** $\begin{bmatrix} 0 & 0 \end{bmatrix} \begin{bmatrix} 5 \\ -3 \end{bmatrix}$

In Exercises 19–24, the sizes of two matrices are given. Tell whether or not the product AB is defined. If so, give its size.

19. A, 3×4; B, 4×5 **20.** A, 3×3; B, 3×4

21. A, 3×2; B, 3×2 **22.** A, 1×1; B, 1×1

23. A, 3×3; B, 3×1 **24.** A, 4×2; B, 3×4

In Exercises 25–34, perform the multiplication.

25. $\begin{bmatrix} 3 & 1 \\ 0 & 2 \end{bmatrix} \begin{bmatrix} 1 & 4 \\ 3 & 5 \end{bmatrix}$ **26.** $\begin{bmatrix} 4 & -1 \\ 2 & \frac{1}{2} \end{bmatrix} \begin{bmatrix} 3 \\ 2 \end{bmatrix}$

27. $\begin{bmatrix} 4 & 1 & 0 \\ -2 & 0 & 3 \\ 1 & 5 & -1 \end{bmatrix} \begin{bmatrix} 5 \\ 1 \\ 2 \end{bmatrix}$ **28.** $\begin{bmatrix} 0 & 0 \\ 0 & 0 \\ 0 & 0 \end{bmatrix} \begin{bmatrix} 1 & 2 \\ 3 & 4 \end{bmatrix}$

29. $\begin{bmatrix} 1 & 0 \\ 0 & 1 \end{bmatrix} \begin{bmatrix} 5 & 6 \\ 7 & 8 \end{bmatrix}$ **30.** $\begin{bmatrix} 1 & 2 \\ 1 & 3 \end{bmatrix} \begin{bmatrix} 3 & -2 \\ -1 & 1 \end{bmatrix}$

31. $\begin{bmatrix} .6 & .3 \\ .4 & .7 \end{bmatrix} \begin{bmatrix} .6 & .3 \\ .4 & .7 \end{bmatrix}$

32. $\begin{bmatrix} 0 & 1 & 2 \\ -1 & 4 & \frac{1}{2} \\ 1 & 3 & 0 \end{bmatrix} \begin{bmatrix} 3 & -1 & 5 \\ 0 & 2 & 2 \\ 4 & -6 & 0 \end{bmatrix}$

33. $\begin{bmatrix} 2 & -1 & 4 \\ 0 & 1 & 0 \\ \frac{1}{2} & 3 & -2 \end{bmatrix} \begin{bmatrix} 4 & 8 & 0 \\ 3 & -1 & 2 \\ 5 & 0 & 1 \end{bmatrix}$

34. $\begin{bmatrix} 1 & 0 & 0 \\ 0 & 1 & 0 \\ 0 & 0 & 1 \end{bmatrix} \begin{bmatrix} 1 \\ 2 \\ 3 \end{bmatrix}$

In Exercises 35–38, give the system of linear equations that is equivalent to the matrix equation. Do not solve.

35. $\begin{bmatrix} 2 & 3 \\ 4 & 5 \end{bmatrix} \begin{bmatrix} x \\ y \end{bmatrix} = \begin{bmatrix} 6 \\ 7 \end{bmatrix}$ **36.** $\begin{bmatrix} -3 & 4 \\ 0 & 1 \end{bmatrix} \begin{bmatrix} x \\ y \end{bmatrix} = \begin{bmatrix} 1 \\ 1 \end{bmatrix}$

37. $\begin{bmatrix} 1 & 2 & 3 \\ 4 & 5 & 6 \\ 7 & 8 & 9 \end{bmatrix} \begin{bmatrix} x \\ y \\ z \end{bmatrix} = \begin{bmatrix} 10 \\ 11 \\ 12 \end{bmatrix}$

38. $\begin{bmatrix} 1 & 0 & 0 \\ 0 & 1 & 0 \\ 0 & 0 & 1 \end{bmatrix} \begin{bmatrix} x \\ y \\ z \end{bmatrix} = \begin{bmatrix} 1 \\ 2 \\ 3 \end{bmatrix}$

In Exercises 39–42, write the given system of linear equations in matrix form.

39. $\begin{cases} 3x + 2y = -1 \\ 7x - y = 2 \end{cases}$ **40.** $\begin{cases} 5x - 2y = 6 \\ -2x + 4y = 0 \end{cases}$

41. $\begin{cases} x - 2y + 3z = 5 \\ y + z = 6 \\ z = 2 \end{cases}$ **42.** $\begin{cases} -2x + 4y - z = 5 \\ x + 6y + 3z = -1 \\ 7x + 4z = 8 \end{cases}$

The distributive law says that $(A+B)C = AC+BC$. That is, adding A and B and then multiplying on the right by C gives the same result as first multiplying each of A and B on the right by C and then adding. In Exercises 43 and 44, verify the distributive law for the given matrices.

43. $A = \begin{bmatrix} 1 & 2 \\ 0 & 3 \end{bmatrix}$, $B = \begin{bmatrix} 3 & -2 \\ 4 & 5 \end{bmatrix}$, $C = \begin{bmatrix} 1 & 6 \\ 2 & 0 \end{bmatrix}$

44. $A = \begin{bmatrix} 1 & 0 & 0 \\ 0 & 1 & 0 \\ 0 & 0 & 1 \end{bmatrix}$, $B = \begin{bmatrix} 2 & 1 & 3 \\ 0 & 5 & -1 \\ 3 & 6 & 0 \end{bmatrix}$, $C = \begin{bmatrix} 0 \\ 3 \\ -4 \end{bmatrix}$

Two $n \times n$ matrices A and B are called inverses (of one another) if both products AB and BA equal I_n. Check that the pairs of matrices in Exercises 45 and 46 are inverses.

45. $\begin{bmatrix} 3 & -1 \\ -1 & \frac{1}{2} \end{bmatrix}$, $\begin{bmatrix} 1 & 2 \\ 2 & 6 \end{bmatrix}$

46. $\begin{bmatrix} 2 & 8 & -11 \\ -1 & -5 & 7 \\ 1 & 2 & -3 \end{bmatrix}$, $\begin{bmatrix} 1 & 2 & 1 \\ 4 & 5 & -3 \\ 3 & 4 & -2 \end{bmatrix}$

47. Wardrobe Costs The quantities of pants, shirts, and jackets owned by Mike and Don are given by the matrix A, and the costs of these items are given by matrix B.

$$\begin{array}{c} \\ \text{Mike} \\ \text{Don} \end{array} \begin{array}{ccc} \text{Pants} & \text{Shirts} & \text{Jackets} \\ \begin{bmatrix} 6 & 8 & 2 \\ 2 & 5 & 3 \end{bmatrix} \end{array} = A$$

$$\begin{array}{c} \text{Pants} \\ \text{Shirts} \\ \text{Jackets} \end{array} \begin{bmatrix} 20 \\ 15 \\ 50 \end{bmatrix} = B$$

(a) Calculate the matrix AB.

(b) Interpret the entries of the matrix AB.

48. Retail Sales Two stores sell the exact same brand and style of a dresser, a nightstand, and a bookcase. Matrix A gives the retail prices (in dollars) for the items. Matrix B gives the number of each item sold at each store in one month.

$$A = \begin{bmatrix} \underset{250}{\text{Dresser}} & \underset{80}{\text{Nightstand}} & \underset{60}{\text{Bookcase}} \end{bmatrix}$$

$$B = \begin{bmatrix} \overset{\text{Store 1}}{40} & \overset{\text{Store 2}}{35} \\ 30 & 35 \\ 50 & 75 \end{bmatrix} \begin{matrix} \text{Dresser} \\ \text{Nightstand} \\ \text{Bookcase} \end{matrix}$$

(a) Calculate AB.

(b) Interpret the entries of AB.

49. Retail Sales A candy shop sells various items for the price per pound (in dollars) indicated in matrix A. Matrix B gives the number of pounds of peanuts, raisins, and espresso beans used in a week. Matrix C gives the total number of pounds of plain, milk chocolate-covered, and dark chocolate-covered items sold each week.

$$A = \begin{bmatrix} \overset{\text{Plain}}{3} & \overset{\text{Milk}}{3} & \overset{\text{Dark}}{5.8} \\ 2.5 & 3.5 & 6 \\ 9 & 8 & 9.5 \end{bmatrix} \begin{matrix} \text{Peanuts} \\ \text{Raisins} \\ \text{Espresso beans} \end{matrix}$$

$$B = \begin{bmatrix} \overset{\text{Peanuts}}{210} & \overset{\text{Raisins}}{175} & \overset{\text{Espresso beans}}{135} \end{bmatrix}$$

$$C = \begin{bmatrix} 105 \\ 390 \\ 285 \end{bmatrix} \begin{matrix} \text{Plain} \\ \text{Milk} \\ \text{Dark} \end{matrix}$$

Determine and interpret the following matrices.

(a) BA (b) AC

50. Wholesale and Retail Sales A company has three appliance stores that sell washers, dryers, and stoves. Matrices A and B give the wholesale and retail prices of these items, respectively. Matrices C and D give the quantities of these items sold by the three stores in September and October, respectively.

$$A = \begin{bmatrix} \overset{\text{Washers}}{300} & \overset{\text{Dryers}}{250} & \overset{\text{Stoves}}{450} \end{bmatrix}$$

$$B = \begin{bmatrix} \overset{\text{Washers}}{500} & \overset{\text{Dryers}}{450} & \overset{\text{Stoves}}{750} \end{bmatrix}$$

$$C = \begin{bmatrix} \overset{\text{Store 1}}{30} & \overset{\text{Store 2}}{40} & \overset{\text{Store 3}}{20} \\ 20 & 30 & 10 \\ 10 & 5 & 35 \end{bmatrix} \begin{matrix} \text{Washers} \\ \text{Dryers} \\ \text{Stoves} \end{matrix}$$

$$D = \begin{bmatrix} \overset{\text{Store 1}}{20} & \overset{\text{Store 2}}{50} & \overset{\text{Store 3}}{30} \\ 30 & 10 & 20 \\ 10 & 20 & 30 \end{bmatrix} \begin{matrix} \text{Washers} \\ \text{Dryers} \\ \text{Stoves} \end{matrix}$$

Determine and interpret the following matrices.

(a) AC (b) AD
(c) BC (d) BD
(e) $B - A$ (f) $(B - A)C$
(g) $(B - A)D$ (h) $C + D$
(i) $(B - A)(C + D)$

51. Course Grades Three professors teaching the same course have entirely different grading policies. The percentage of students given each grade by the professors is summarized in the following matrix:

	Grade				
	A	B	C	D	F
Prof. I	25	35	30	10	0
Prof. II	10	20	40	20	10
Prof. III	5	10	20	40	25

(a) The point values of the grades are A = 4, B = 3, C = 2, D = 1, and F = 0. Use matrix multiplication to determine the average grade given by each professor.

(b) Professor I has 240 students, professor II has 120 students, and professor III has 40 students. Use matrix multiplication to determine the numbers of A's, B's, C's, D's, and F's given.

52. Semester Grades A professor bases semester grades on four 100-point items: homework, quizzes, a midterm exam, and a final exam. Students may choose one of three schemes summarized in the following matrix for weighting the points from the four items. Use matrix multiplication to determine the most advantageous weighting scheme for a student who earned 97 points on homework, 72 points on the quizzes, 83 points on the midterm exam, and 75 points on the final exam.

	Items			
	Hw	Qu	ME	FE
Scheme I	.10	.10	.30	.50
Scheme II	.10	.20	.30	.40
Scheme III	.15	.15	.35	.35

53. Voter Analysis In a certain town the proportions of voters voting Democratic and Republican by various age groups is summarized by this matrix:

$$
\begin{array}{c}
\\
\text{Under 30} \\
\text{30--50} \\
\text{Over 50}
\end{array}
\begin{array}{cc}
\text{Dem.} & \text{Rep.} \\
\left[\begin{array}{cc}
.65 & .35 \\
.55 & .45 \\
.45 & .55
\end{array}\right] & = A.
\end{array}
$$

The population of voters in the town by age group is given by the matrix

$$
B = \left[\begin{array}{ccc} 6000 & 8000 & 4000 \end{array}\right].
$$
$$
\underbrace{}_{\substack{\text{Under}\\30}} \quad \underbrace{}_{\text{30--50}} \quad \underbrace{}_{\substack{\text{Over}\\50}}
$$

Interpret the entries of the matrix product BA.

54. Voter Analysis Refer to Exercise 53.

(a) Using the given data, which party would win and what would be the percentage of the winning vote?

(b) Suppose that the population of the town shifted toward older residents as reflected in the population matrix $B = \left[\begin{array}{ccc} 2000 & 4000 & 12{,}000 \end{array}\right]$. What would be the result of the election now?

55. Labor Costs Suppose that a contractor employs carpenters, bricklayers, and plumbers, working three shifts per day. The number of labor-hours employed in each of the shifts is summarized in the following matrix:

$$
\begin{array}{c}
\\
\\
\text{Carpenters} \\
\text{Bricklayers} \\
\text{Plumbers}
\end{array}
\begin{array}{c}
\text{Shift} \\
\hline
\begin{array}{ccc}
1 & 2 & 3
\end{array} \\
\left[\begin{array}{ccc}
50 & 20 & 10 \\
30 & 30 & 15 \\
20 & 20 & 5
\end{array}\right].
\end{array}
$$

Labor in shift 1 costs $10 per hour, in shift 2 $15 per hour, and in shift 3 $20 per hour. Use matrix multiplication to compute the amount spent on each type of labor.

56. Epidemiology A flu epidemic hits a large city. Each resident of the city is either sick, well, or a carrier. The proportion of people in each of the categories is expressed by the following matrix:

$$
\begin{array}{c}
\\
\text{Well} \\
\text{Sick} \\
\text{Carrier}
\end{array}
\begin{array}{c}
\text{Age} \\
\hline
\begin{array}{ccc}
\text{0--10} & \text{10--30} & \text{Over 30}
\end{array} \\
\left[\begin{array}{ccc}
.70 & .70 & .60 \\
.10 & .20 & .30 \\
.20 & .10 & .10
\end{array}\right] = A.
\end{array}
$$

The population of the city is distributed by age and sex as follows:

$$
\text{Age}\left|
\begin{array}{c}
\begin{array}{cc}
\text{Male} & \text{Female}
\end{array} \\
\begin{array}{c}
\text{0--10} \\
\text{10--30} \\
\text{Over 30}
\end{array}
\left[\begin{array}{cc}
60{,}000 & 65{,}000 \\
100{,}000 & 110{,}000 \\
200{,}000 & 230{,}000
\end{array}\right] = B.
\end{array}
\right.
$$

(a) Compute AB.

(b) How many sick males are there?

(c) How many female carriers are there?

57. Nutrition Analysis Mikey's diet consists of food X and food Y. The matrix N represents the number of units of nutrients 1, 2, and 3 per ounce for each of the foods.

$$
N = \begin{array}{c}
\begin{array}{ccc}
1 & 2 & 3
\end{array} \\
\left[\begin{array}{ccc}
60 & 50 & 38 \\
42 & 50 & 67
\end{array}\right]
\begin{array}{c}
X \\
Y
\end{array}
\end{array}
$$

The matrices B, L, and D represent the number of ounces of each food that Mikey eats each day for breakfast, lunch, and dinner, respectively.

$$
B = \begin{array}{c}\begin{array}{cc}X & Y\end{array}\\\left[\begin{array}{cc}2 & 1\end{array}\right]\end{array} \quad
L = \begin{array}{c}\begin{array}{cc}X & Y\end{array}\\\left[\begin{array}{cc}1 & 3\end{array}\right]\end{array} \quad
D = \begin{array}{c}\begin{array}{cc}X & Y\end{array}\\\left[\begin{array}{cc}2 & 4\end{array}\right]\end{array}
$$

Calculate and interpret the following.

(a) BN (b) LN (c) DN

(d) $B + L + D$ (e) $(B + L + D)N$

58. Bakery Sales A bakery makes three types of cookies, I, II, and III. Each type of cookie is made from the four ingredients A, B, C, and D. The number of units of each ingredient used in each type of cookie is given by the matrix M. The cost per unit of each of the four ingredients (in cents) is given by the matrix N. The selling price for each of the cookies (in cents) is given by the matrix S. The baker receives an order for 10 type I cookies, 20 type II cookies, and 15 type III cookies, as represented by the matrix R.

$$
M = \begin{array}{c}
\begin{array}{cccc} A & B & C & D \end{array} \\
\left[\begin{array}{cccc}
1 & 0 & 2 & 4 \\
3 & 2 & 1 & 1 \\
2 & 5 & 3 & 1
\end{array}\right]
\begin{array}{c} \text{I} \\ \text{II} \\ \text{III} \end{array}
\end{array}
\qquad
N = \left[\begin{array}{c}
10 \\ 20 \\ 15 \\ 17
\end{array}\right]
\begin{array}{c} A \\ B \\ C \\ D \end{array}
$$

$$
S = \left[\begin{array}{c}
175 \\ 150 \\ 225
\end{array}\right]
\begin{array}{c} \text{I} \\ \text{II} \\ \text{III} \end{array}
\qquad
R = \begin{array}{c}
\begin{array}{ccc} \text{I} & \text{II} & \text{III} \end{array} \\
\left[\begin{array}{ccc} 10 & 20 & 15 \end{array}\right]
\end{array}
$$

Calculate and interpret the following.

(a) RM (b) MN (c) RMN

(d) $S - MN$ (e) $R(S - MN)$ (f) RS

59. Revenue A community fitness center has a pool and a weight room. The admission prices (in dollars) for residents and nonresidents are given by the matrix

$$
P = \left[\begin{array}{c}
4.50 \\ 5.00
\end{array}\right]
\begin{array}{c} \text{Residents} \\ \text{Nonresidents.} \end{array}
$$

The average daily numbers of customers for the fitness center are given by the matrix

$$
A = \begin{array}{c}
\begin{array}{cc} \text{Residents} & \text{Nonresidents} \end{array} \\
\left[\begin{array}{cc}
90 & 63 \\
78 & 59
\end{array}\right]
\begin{array}{c} \text{Pool} \\ \text{Weight room.} \end{array}
\end{array}
$$

(a) Compute AP.

(b) What is the average amount of money taken in by the pool each day?

60. Production Planning A company makes radios and TV sets. Each radio requires 3 hours of assembly and $\frac{1}{2}$ hour of packaging, while each TV set requires 5 hours of assembly and 1 hour of packaging.

(a) Write a matrix T representing the required time for assembly and packaging of radios and TV sets.

(b) The company receives an order from a retail outlet for 30 radios and 20 TV sets. Find a matrix S so that either ST or TS gives the total assembly time and the total packaging time required to fill the order. What is the total assembly time? What is the total packaging time?

61. Production Planning A bakery sells Boston cream pies and carrot cakes. Each Boston cream pie requires 30 minutes preparation time, 30 minutes baking time, and 15 minutes for finishing. Each carrot cake requires 45 minutes preparation time, 50 minutes baking time, and 10 minutes for finishing.

(a) Write a matrix T representing the required time for preparation, baking, and finishing for the Boston cream pies and the carrot cakes.

(b) The bakery receives an order for 20 Boston cream pies and 8 carrot cakes for a large party. Find a matrix S so that either ST or TS gives the total preparation, baking, and finishing times required to fill this order.

(c) What is the total baking time? What is the total finishing time?

62. Time Requirements A beauty salon offers manicures and pedicures. A manicure requires 20 minutes for preparation, 5 minutes for lacquering, and 15 minutes for drying. A pedicure requires 30 minutes for preparation, 5 minutes for lacquering, and 20 minutes for drying.

(a) Construct a matrix T representing the time required for preparation, lacquering, and drying for manicures and pedicures.

(b) Suppose the salon will be giving manicures and pedicures to a large wedding party. If 15 members of the wedding party want manicures and 9 want pedicures, find a matrix S so that either ST or TS gives the total amount of time required for each of the three steps.

(c) What is the total time required for drying?

63. Production and Revenue The J.E. Carrying Company makes two types of backpacks. The larger Huge One backpack requires 2 hours for cutting, 3 hours for sewing, and 2 hours for finishing, and sells for $32. The smaller Regular Joe backpack requires 1.5 hours for cutting, 2 hours for sewing, and 1 hour for finishing, and sells for $24.

(a) Construct a matrix T representing the time required for each of the three steps in making the backpacks.

(b) Construct a matrix S representing the sales prices for the two types of backpacks.

(c) Suppose the J.E. Carrying Company receives an order for 27 Huge One backpacks and 56 Regular Joe backpacks. Construct a matrix A so that either AT or TA gives the total time required to construct the backpacks in this order, and either AS or SA gives the total revenue generated by this order.

(d) How much total time is needed for sewing to fill this order?

(e) What is the total revenue for this order?

64. MP3 Sales A store sells three types of MP3 players. Matrix A contains information about size (in gigabytes), battery life (in hours), and weight (in ounces) of the three MP3 players. Matrix B contains the sales prices (in dollars) of the MP3 players, while matrix C contains the number of each type of player sold in one week.

$$A = \begin{bmatrix} \overset{\text{Type I}}{4} & \overset{\text{Type II}}{8} & \overset{\text{Type III}}{2} \\ 33 & 20 & 15 \\ 2 & 1.7 & .9 \end{bmatrix} \begin{matrix} \text{Size} \\ \text{Battery Life} \\ \text{Weight} \end{matrix}$$

$$B = \begin{bmatrix} \overset{\text{Type I}}{100} & \overset{\text{Type II}}{180} & \overset{\text{Type III}}{60} \end{bmatrix}$$

$$C = \begin{bmatrix} 25 \\ 16 \\ 32 \end{bmatrix} \begin{matrix} \text{Type I} \\ \text{Type II} \\ \text{Type III} \end{matrix}$$

Calculate and interpret the following

(a) BC (b) AC

(c) the row 2, column 1 entry of AC

65. Make up an application whose answer is that the total cost is given by

$$\begin{bmatrix} 20 & 30 \end{bmatrix} \begin{bmatrix} 600 \\ 700 \end{bmatrix}.$$

66. Find the values of a and b for which $A \cdot B = I_3$, where

$$A = \begin{bmatrix} 3 & 2 & 0 \\ 1 & 1 & 0 \\ 0 & 0 & 1 \end{bmatrix} \quad \text{and} \quad B = \begin{bmatrix} a & b & 0 \\ -1 & 3 & 0 \\ 0 & 0 & 1 \end{bmatrix}.$$

In Exercises 67 and 68, determine the matrix B based on the screen shown.

67.

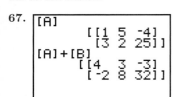

```
[A]
            [[1  5  -4]
             [3  2  25]]
[A]+[B]
            [[4  3  -3]
             [-2 8  32]]
```

68.

```
[A]
            [[1  5  -4]
             [3  2  25]]
[A]-[B]
            [[-4 1  -1]
             [3  3  23]]
```

69. If A is a 3×4 matrix and $A(BB)$ is defined, what is the size of matrix B?

70. If B is a 3×5 matrix and $(AA)B$ is defined, what is the size of matrix A?

71. School Enrollments Table 1 gives the number of public school teachers (elementary and secondary) and the average number of pupils per teacher for three mid-Atlantic states in 2006. Set up a product of two matrices that gives the total number of pupils in the three states.

TABLE 1 Teachers and Pupils

	Delaware	Maryland	Virginia
Teachers	7998	56,685	96,158
Pupils per teacher	15.1	15.2	12.6

72. Population Table 2 gives the area and 2008 population density for three West-Coast states. Set up a product of two matrices that gives total population of the three states.

TABLE 2 State Areas and Densities

	California	Oregon	Washington
Land Area (sq. mi.)	155,959	95,997	66,544
Pop. Density (per sq. mile)	234.4	39.0	97.2

In Exercises 73–80, use a graphing calculator or spreadsheet to carry out the matrix operations.

In Exercises 73–80, calculate the given expression, where

$$A = \begin{bmatrix} .4 & 7 & -3 \\ 19 & .5 & 1.6 \\ -9 & 11 & 2 \end{bmatrix}, \qquad B = \begin{bmatrix} 6 & -9 & .3 \\ 1.5 & 22 & -4 \\ -5 & 6.6 & 14 \end{bmatrix},$$

and

$$C = \begin{bmatrix} 2.4 & 8 & -.2 \\ -11 & .3 & 6 \\ 7 & -4 & 5.1 \end{bmatrix}.$$

73. AB

74. BA

75. $A(B+C)$

76. $AB + AC$

77. A^2 (that is, AA)

78. A^3 (that is, AAA)

79. Calculate $[A]^{\wedge}2$ and $[A]^{\wedge}3$. Compare your results with your answers in Exercises 77 and 78.

80. Try multiplying matrices A and B, where the number of columns of A differs from the number of rows of B. How does your calculator or spreadsheet respond?

Solutions to Practice Problems 2.3

1. Answer:

$$\begin{bmatrix} 3 & 1 & 2 \\ -1 & 0 & \frac{1}{2} \\ 0 & 4 & 1 \end{bmatrix} \begin{bmatrix} 7 & -1 & 0 \\ 5 & 4 & 2 \\ -6 & 0 & 4 \end{bmatrix}$$

$$= \begin{bmatrix} 14 & 1 & 10 \\ -10 & 1 & 2 \\ 14 & 16 & 12 \end{bmatrix}.$$

The systematic steps to be taken are as follows:

(a) Determine the size of the product matrix. Since we have a

$$③ \times 3 \quad \text{times a} \quad 3 \times ③,$$
$$\llcorner \text{ outer dimensions } \lrcorner$$

the size of the product is given by the outer dimensions or 3×3. Begin by drawing a 3×3 rectangular array.

(Continued)

(b) Find the entries one at a time. To find the entry in the first row, first column of the product, look at the first row of the left matrix and the first column of the right matrix and form their product.

$$\begin{bmatrix} 3 & 1 & 2 \\ -1 & 0 & \frac{1}{2} \\ 0 & 4 & 1 \end{bmatrix} \begin{bmatrix} 7 & -1 & 0 \\ 5 & 4 & 2 \\ -6 & 0 & 4 \end{bmatrix}$$

$$= \begin{bmatrix} 14 & & \\ & & \\ & & \end{bmatrix}$$

since $3 \cdot 7 + 1 \cdot 5 + 2(-6) = 14$. In general, to find the entry in the ith row, jth column of the product, put one finger on the ith row of the left matrix and another finger on the jth column of the right matrix. Then multiply the row matrix times the column matrix to get the desired entry.

2. Denote the three matrices by A, X, and B, respectively. Since b_{11} (the entry of the first row, first col-

umn of B) is 5, this means that

$$\begin{bmatrix} \text{first row of } A \end{bmatrix} \begin{bmatrix} \text{first} \\ \text{column} \\ \text{of } X \end{bmatrix} = \begin{bmatrix} b_{11} \end{bmatrix}.$$

That is,

$$\begin{bmatrix} 3 & -6 \end{bmatrix} \begin{bmatrix} x \\ y \end{bmatrix} = \begin{bmatrix} 5 \end{bmatrix} \quad \text{or} \quad 3x - 6y = 5.$$

Similarly, $b_{21} = 0$ says that $2x + y = 0$. Therefore, the corresponding system of linear equations is

$$\begin{cases} 3x - 6y = 5 \\ 2x + y = 0. \end{cases}$$

3. The coefficient matrix is

$$\begin{bmatrix} 8 & 3 \\ 9 & -2 \end{bmatrix}.$$

So the system is equivalent to the matrix equation

$$\begin{bmatrix} 8 & 3 \\ 9 & -2 \end{bmatrix} \begin{bmatrix} x \\ y \end{bmatrix} = \begin{bmatrix} 7 \\ -5 \end{bmatrix}.$$

2.4 The Inverse of a Matrix

In Section 2.3 we introduced the operations of addition, subtraction, and multiplication of matrices. In this section let us pursue the algebra of matrices a bit further and consider equations involving matrices. Specifically, we consider equations of the form

$$AX = B, \tag{1}$$

where A and B are given matrices and X is an unknown matrix whose entries are to be determined. Such equations among matrices are intimately bound up with the theory of systems of linear equations. Indeed, we described the connection in a special case in Example 6 of Section 2.3. In that example we wrote the system of linear equations

$$\begin{cases} -2x + 4y = 2 \\ -3x + 7y = 7 \end{cases}$$

as a matrix equation of the form (1), where

$$A = \begin{bmatrix} -2 & 4 \\ -3 & 7 \end{bmatrix}, \qquad B = \begin{bmatrix} 2 \\ 7 \end{bmatrix}, \qquad X = \begin{bmatrix} x \\ y \end{bmatrix}.$$

Note that by determining the entries (x and y) of the unknown matrix X, we solve the system of linear equations. We will return to this example after we have made a complete study of the matrix equation (1).

As motivation for our solution of equation (1), let us consider the analogous equation among numbers:

$$ax = b,$$

where a and b are given numbers[1] and x is to be determined. Let us examine its solution in great detail. Multiply both sides by $1/a$. (Note that $1/a$ makes sense, since $a \neq 0$.)

$$\left(\frac{1}{a}\right) \cdot (ax) = \frac{1}{a} \cdot b$$

$$\left(\frac{1}{a} \cdot a\right) \cdot x = \frac{1}{a} \cdot b$$

$$1 \cdot x = \frac{1}{a} \cdot b$$

$$x = \frac{1}{a} \cdot b$$

Let us model our solution of equation (1) on the preceding calculation. To do so, we need to multiply both sides of the equation by a matrix that plays the same role in matrix arithmetic as $1/a$ plays in ordinary arithmetic. Our first task then will be to introduce this matrix and study its properties.

The number $1/a$ has the following relationship to the number a:

$$\frac{1}{a} \cdot a = a \cdot \frac{1}{a} = 1. \tag{2}$$

The matrix analog of the number 1 is an identity matrix I. This prompts us to generalize equation (2) to matrices as follows. Suppose that we are given a square matrix A. Then the **inverse** of A, denoted A^{-1}, is a square matrix with the property

$$A^{-1}A = I \quad \text{and} \quad AA^{-1} = I, \tag{3}$$

where I is an identity matrix of the same size as A. The matrix A^{-1} is the matrix analog of the number $1/a$. It can be shown that a matrix A has at most one inverse. (However, A may not have an inverse at all; see Example 3.)

If we are given a matrix A, then it is easy to determine whether or not a given matrix is its inverse. Merely check equation (3) with the given matrix substituted for A^{-1}. For example, if

$$A = \begin{bmatrix} -2 & 4 \\ -3 & 7 \end{bmatrix}, \quad \text{then} \quad A^{-1} = \begin{bmatrix} -\frac{7}{2} & 2 \\ -\frac{3}{2} & 1 \end{bmatrix}.$$

Indeed, we have

$$\underbrace{\begin{bmatrix} -\frac{7}{2} & 2 \\ -\frac{3}{2} & 1 \end{bmatrix}}_{A^{-1}} \underbrace{\begin{bmatrix} -2 & 4 \\ -3 & 7 \end{bmatrix}}_{A} = \begin{bmatrix} 7-6 & -14+14 \\ 3-3 & -6+7 \end{bmatrix} = \underbrace{\begin{bmatrix} 1 & 0 \\ 0 & 1 \end{bmatrix}}_{I_2}$$

and

$$\underbrace{\begin{bmatrix} -2 & 4 \\ -3 & 7 \end{bmatrix}}_{A} \underbrace{\begin{bmatrix} -\frac{7}{2} & 2 \\ -\frac{3}{2} & 1 \end{bmatrix}}_{A^{-1}} = \begin{bmatrix} 7-6 & -4+4 \\ \frac{21}{2}-\frac{21}{2} & -6+7 \end{bmatrix} = \underbrace{\begin{bmatrix} 1 & 0 \\ 0 & 1 \end{bmatrix}}_{I_2}.$$

The inverse of a matrix can be calculated using Gauss–Jordan elimination, as the next example illustrates.

---

[1] We may as well assume that $a \neq 0$. Otherwise, x does not occur.

EXAMPLE 1

Finding the inverse of a matrix   Let

$$A = \begin{bmatrix} 3 & 1 \\ 5 & 2 \end{bmatrix}.$$

Determine A^{-1}.

Solution   Since A is a 2×2 matrix, A^{-1} is also a 2×2 matrix and satisfies

$$AA^{-1} = I_2 \quad \text{and} \quad A^{-1}A = I_2, \qquad (4)$$

where $I_2 = \begin{bmatrix} 1 & 0 \\ 0 & 1 \end{bmatrix}$ is the 2×2 identity matrix. Suppose that

$$A^{-1} = \begin{bmatrix} x & y \\ z & w \end{bmatrix}.$$

Then the first equation of (4) reads

$$\begin{bmatrix} 3 & 1 \\ 5 & 2 \end{bmatrix} \begin{bmatrix} x & y \\ z & w \end{bmatrix} = \begin{bmatrix} 1 & 0 \\ 0 & 1 \end{bmatrix}.$$

Multiplying out the matrices on the left gives

$$\begin{bmatrix} 3x + z & 3y + w \\ 5x + 2z & 5y + 2w \end{bmatrix} = \begin{bmatrix} 1 & 0 \\ 0 & 1 \end{bmatrix}.$$

Now equate corresponding elements in the two matrices to obtain the equations

$$\begin{cases} 3x + z = 1 \\ 5x + 2z = 0, \end{cases} \qquad \begin{cases} 3y + w = 0 \\ 5y + 2w = 1. \end{cases}$$

Notice that the equations break up into two pairs of linear equations, each pair involving only two variables. Solving these two systems of linear equations yields $x = 2$, $z = -5$, $y = -1$, and $w = 3$. Therefore,

$$A^{-1} = \begin{bmatrix} 2 & -1 \\ -5 & 3 \end{bmatrix}.$$

Indeed, we may readily verify that

$$\begin{bmatrix} 3 & 1 \\ 5 & 2 \end{bmatrix} \begin{bmatrix} 2 & -1 \\ -5 & 3 \end{bmatrix} = \begin{bmatrix} 1 & 0 \\ 0 & 1 \end{bmatrix}$$

$$\begin{bmatrix} 2 & -1 \\ -5 & 3 \end{bmatrix} \begin{bmatrix} 3 & 1 \\ 5 & 2 \end{bmatrix} = \begin{bmatrix} 1 & 0 \\ 0 & 1 \end{bmatrix}.$$

Now Try Exercise 3   ∎

The preceding method can be used to calculate the inverse of matrices of any size, although it involves considerable calculation. We provide a rather efficient computational method for calculating A^{-1} in the next section. For now, however, let us be content with the above method. Using it, we can derive a general formula for A^{-1} in the case where A is a 2×2 matrix.

To determine the inverse of a 2×2 matrix, let

$$A = \begin{bmatrix} a & b \\ c & d \end{bmatrix}.$$

Let $D = ad - bc$, and assume that $D \neq 0$. Then A^{-1} is given by the formula

$$A^{-1} = \begin{bmatrix} \dfrac{d}{D} & -\dfrac{b}{D} \\ -\dfrac{c}{D} & \dfrac{a}{D} \end{bmatrix}. \tag{5}$$

We will omit the derivation of this formula. It proceeds along lines similar to those of Example 1. Notice that formula (5) involves division by D. Since division by 0 is not permissible, it is necessary that $D \neq 0$ for formula (5) to be applied. We discuss the case $D = 0$ in Example 3.

Obtaining equation (5) can be reduced to a simple step-by-step procedure.

To determine the inverse of $\begin{bmatrix} a & b \\ c & d \end{bmatrix}$ if $D = ad - bc \neq 0$,

1. Interchange a and d to get $\begin{bmatrix} d & b \\ c & a \end{bmatrix}$.

2. Change the signs of b and c to get $\begin{bmatrix} d & -b \\ -c & a \end{bmatrix}$.

3. Divide all entries by D to get $\begin{bmatrix} \dfrac{d}{D} & -\dfrac{b}{D} \\ -\dfrac{c}{D} & \dfrac{a}{D} \end{bmatrix}$.

EXAMPLE 2   **Using the formula for the inverse of a 2 x 2 matrix**   Calculate the inverse of

$$\begin{bmatrix} -2 & 4 \\ -3 & 7 \end{bmatrix}.$$

Solution $D = (-2) \cdot 7 - 4 \cdot (-3) = -2$, so $D \neq 0$, and we may use the preceding computation.

1. Interchange a and d:

$$\begin{bmatrix} 7 & 4 \\ -3 & -2 \end{bmatrix}.$$

2. Change the signs of b and c:

$$\begin{bmatrix} 7 & -4 \\ 3 & -2 \end{bmatrix}.$$

3. Divide all entries by $D = -2$:

$$\begin{bmatrix} -\dfrac{7}{2} & 2 \\ -\dfrac{3}{2} & 1 \end{bmatrix}.$$

Thus

$$\begin{bmatrix} -2 & 4 \\ -3 & 7 \end{bmatrix}^{-1} = \begin{bmatrix} -\frac{7}{2} & 2 \\ -\frac{3}{2} & 1 \end{bmatrix}.$$

Now Try Exercise 5   ■

Not every square matrix has an inverse. Indeed, it may be impossible to satisfy equation (3) for any choice of A^{-1}. This phenomenon can even occur in the case of 2×2 matrices. Here one can show that *if $D = 0$, then the matrix does not have an inverse*. The next example illustrates this phenomenon in a special case.

EXAMPLE 3   **Showing that a 2 x 2 matrix does not have an inverse** Show that

$$\begin{bmatrix} 1 & 1 \\ 1 & 1 \end{bmatrix}$$

does not have an inverse.

Solution Note first that $D = 1 \cdot 1 - 1 \cdot 1 = 0$, so the inverse cannot be computed via equation (5). Suppose that the given matrix did have an inverse, say

$$\begin{bmatrix} s & t \\ u & v \end{bmatrix}.$$

Then the following equation would hold:

$$\begin{bmatrix} s & t \\ u & v \end{bmatrix} \begin{bmatrix} 1 & 1 \\ 1 & 1 \end{bmatrix} = \begin{bmatrix} 1 & 0 \\ 0 & 1 \end{bmatrix}.$$

On multiplying out the two matrices on the left, we get the equation

$$\begin{bmatrix} s + t & s + t \\ u + v & u + v \end{bmatrix} = \begin{bmatrix} 1 & 0 \\ 0 & 1 \end{bmatrix},$$

so that, on equating entries in the first row:

$$s + t = 1, \qquad s + t = 0.$$

Now Try Exercise 23 But $s + t$ cannot equal both 1 and 0. So we reach a contradiction, and therefore the original matrix cannot have an inverse.   ■

We were led to introduce the inverse of a matrix from a discussion of the matrix equation $AX = B$. Let us now return to that discussion. Suppose that A and B are given matrices and that we wish to solve the matrix equation

$$AX = B$$

for the unknown matrix X. Suppose further that A has an inverse A^{-1}. Multiply both sides of the equation on the left by A^{-1} to obtain

$$A^{-1} \cdot AX = A^{-1}B.$$

Because $A^{-1} \cdot A = I$, we have

$$IX = A^{-1}B$$
$$X = A^{-1}B.$$

Thus the matrix X is found by simply multiplying B on the left by A^{-1}, and we can summarize our findings as follows:

> **Solving a Matrix Equation**   If the matrix A has an inverse, then the solution of the matrix equation
>
> $$AX = B \quad \text{is given by} \quad X = A^{-1}B.$$

Matrix equations can be used to solve systems of linear equations, as illustrated in the next example.

EXAMPLE 4

Using a matrix inverse to solve a system of equations   Use a matrix equation to solve the system of linear equations

$$\begin{cases} -2x + 4y = 2 \\ -3x + 7y = 7. \end{cases}$$

Solution   In Example 6 of Section 2.3 we saw that the system could be written as a matrix equation:

$$\underset{A}{\begin{bmatrix} -2 & 4 \\ -3 & 7 \end{bmatrix}} \underset{X}{\begin{bmatrix} x \\ y \end{bmatrix}} = \underset{B}{\begin{bmatrix} 2 \\ 7 \end{bmatrix}}.$$

We happen to know A^{-1} from Example 2, namely

$$A^{-1} = \begin{bmatrix} -\frac{7}{2} & 2 \\ -\frac{3}{2} & 1 \end{bmatrix}.$$

So we may compute the matrix $X = A^{-1}B$:

$$X = \begin{bmatrix} x \\ y \end{bmatrix} = \begin{bmatrix} -\frac{7}{2} & 2 \\ -\frac{3}{2} & 1 \end{bmatrix} \begin{bmatrix} 2 \\ 7 \end{bmatrix} = \begin{bmatrix} 7 \\ 4 \end{bmatrix}.$$

Now Try Exercise 11   Thus, the solution of the system is $x = 7$, $y = 4$. ∎

EXAMPLE 5

Analyzing marriage trends   Let x and y denote the number of married and single adults in a certain town as of January 1. Let m and s denote the corresponding numbers for the following year. A statistical survey shows that x, y, m, and s are related by the equations

$$.9x + .2y = m$$
$$.1x + .8y = s.$$

In a given year there were found to be 490,000 married adults and 147,000 single adults.

(a) How many married adults were there in the preceding year?

(b) How many married adults were there two years ago?

Solution   **(a)** The given equations can be written in the matrix form

$$AX = B,$$

where

$$A = \begin{bmatrix} .9 & .2 \\ .1 & .8 \end{bmatrix}, \qquad X = \begin{bmatrix} x \\ y \end{bmatrix}, \qquad B = \begin{bmatrix} m \\ s \end{bmatrix}.$$

We are given that $B = \begin{bmatrix} 490{,}000 \\ 147{,}000 \end{bmatrix}$. So, since

$$X = A^{-1}B \quad \text{and} \quad A^{-1} = \begin{bmatrix} \frac{8}{7} & -\frac{2}{7} \\ -\frac{1}{7} & \frac{9}{7} \end{bmatrix},$$

we have

$$X = \begin{bmatrix} \frac{8}{7} & -\frac{2}{7} \\ -\frac{1}{7} & \frac{9}{7} \end{bmatrix} \begin{bmatrix} 490{,}000 \\ 147{,}000 \end{bmatrix} = \begin{bmatrix} 518{,}000 \\ 119{,}000 \end{bmatrix}.$$

Thus last year there were 518,000 married adults and 119,000 single adults.

(b) We deduce x and y for two years ago from the values of m and s for last year, namely $m = 518{,}000$, $s = 119{,}000$.

$$X = A^{-1}B = \begin{bmatrix} \frac{8}{7} & -\frac{2}{7} \\ -\frac{1}{7} & \frac{9}{7} \end{bmatrix} \begin{bmatrix} 518{,}000 \\ 119{,}000 \end{bmatrix} = \begin{bmatrix} 558{,}000 \\ 79{,}000 \end{bmatrix}.$$

That is, two years ago there were 558,000 married adults and 79,000 single adults.

Now Try Exercise 17 ∎

EXAMPLE 6

Using a matrix inverse to solve systems of equations In Section 2.5 we will show that if

$$A = \begin{bmatrix} 4 & -2 & 3 \\ 8 & -3 & 5 \\ 7 & -2 & 4 \end{bmatrix}, \quad \text{then} \quad A^{-1} = \begin{bmatrix} -2 & 2 & -1 \\ 3 & -5 & 4 \\ 5 & -6 & 4 \end{bmatrix}.$$

(a) Use this fact to solve the system of linear equations

$$\begin{cases} 4x - 2y + 3z = 1 \\ 8x - 3y + 5z = 4 \\ 7x - 2y + 4z = 5. \end{cases}$$

(b) Solve the system of equations

$$\begin{cases} 4x - 2y + 3z = 4 \\ 8x - 3y + 5z = 7 \\ 7x - 2y + 4z = 6. \end{cases}$$

Solution **(a)** The system can be written in the matrix form

$$\underset{A}{\begin{bmatrix} 4 & -2 & 3 \\ 8 & -3 & 5 \\ 7 & -2 & 4 \end{bmatrix}} \underset{X}{\begin{bmatrix} x \\ y \\ z \end{bmatrix}} = \underset{B}{\begin{bmatrix} 1 \\ 4 \\ 5 \end{bmatrix}}.$$

The solution of this matrix equation is $X = A^{-1}B$, or

$$\begin{bmatrix} x \\ y \\ z \end{bmatrix} = \begin{bmatrix} -2 & 2 & -1 \\ 3 & -5 & 4 \\ 5 & -6 & 4 \end{bmatrix} \begin{bmatrix} 1 \\ 4 \\ 5 \end{bmatrix} = \begin{bmatrix} 1 \\ 3 \\ 1 \end{bmatrix}.$$

Thus the solution of the system is $x = 1$, $y = 3$, $z = 1$.

(b) This system has the same left-hand side as the preceding system, so its solution is

$$\begin{bmatrix} x \\ y \\ z \end{bmatrix} = \begin{bmatrix} -2 & 2 & -1 \\ 3 & -5 & 4 \\ 5 & -6 & 4 \end{bmatrix} \begin{bmatrix} 4 \\ 7 \\ 6 \end{bmatrix} = \begin{bmatrix} 0 \\ 1 \\ 2 \end{bmatrix}.$$

Now Try Exercise 19

That is, the solution of the system is $x = 0$, $y = 1$, $z = 2$. ∎

Using the method of matrix equations to solve a system of linear equations is especially efficient if one wishes to solve a number of systems all having the same left-hand sides but different right-hand sides. For then A^{-1} must be computed only once for all the systems under consideration. (This point is useful in Exercises 19–22.)

INCORPORATING TECHNOLOGY

GC (TI-83/84 Plus) The inverse of a square matrix can be obtained directly with the inverse key $\boxed{x^{-1}}$. See Fig. 1. (*Note*: Do not use [A]^-1.)

```
[A]
            [[-2 4]
             [-3 7]]
[A]-1
            [[-3.5 2]
             [-1.5 1]]
```

Figure 1

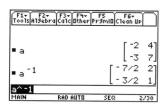

Figure 2

(TI-89) The inverse of a square matrix can be obtained directly by raising the matrix to the -1 power. See Fig. 2. ∎

ES To obtain the inverse of the $n \times n$ matrix named A, select an n by n square of cells where you would like the inverse matrix to be displayed, type **=MINVERSE(A)**, and press Crtl+Shift+Enter.

Practice Problems 2.4

1. Show that the inverse of

$$\begin{bmatrix} -4 & 1 & 2 \\ 7 & -1 & -4 \\ -\frac{1}{2} & 0 & \frac{1}{2} \end{bmatrix} \quad \text{is} \quad \begin{bmatrix} 1 & 1 & 4 \\ 3 & 2 & 4 \\ 1 & 1 & 6 \end{bmatrix}.$$

2. Use the method of this section to solve the system of linear equations

$$\begin{cases} .8x + .6y = 5 \\ .2x + .4y = 2. \end{cases}$$

EXERCISES 2.4

In Exercises 1 and 2, use the fact that

$$\begin{bmatrix} 2 & 2 \\ \frac{1}{2} & 1 \end{bmatrix}^{-1} = \begin{bmatrix} 1 & -2 \\ -\frac{1}{2} & 2 \end{bmatrix}.$$

1. Solve $\begin{cases} 2x + 2y = 4 \\ \frac{1}{2}x + y = 1. \end{cases}$

2. Solve $\begin{cases} 2x + 2y = 14 \\ \frac{1}{2}x + y = 4. \end{cases}$

In Exercises 3–10, find the inverse of the given matrix.

3. $\begin{bmatrix} 7 & 2 \\ 3 & 1 \end{bmatrix}$

4. $\begin{bmatrix} 2 & 3 \\ 5 & 7 \end{bmatrix}$

5. $\begin{bmatrix} 6 & 2 \\ 5 & 2 \end{bmatrix}$

6. $\begin{bmatrix} 1 & .5 \\ 0 & .5 \end{bmatrix}$

7. $\begin{bmatrix} .7 & .2 \\ .3 & .8 \end{bmatrix}$

8. $\begin{bmatrix} 0 & 1 \\ 1 & 0 \end{bmatrix}$

9. $\begin{bmatrix} 3 \end{bmatrix}$

10. $\begin{bmatrix} .2 \end{bmatrix}$

In Exercises 11–14, use the method of this section to solve the system of linear equations.

11. $\begin{cases} x + 2y = 3 \\ 2x + 6y = 5 \end{cases}$

12. $\begin{cases} 5x + 3y = 1 \\ 7x + 4y = 2 \end{cases}$

13. $\begin{cases} \frac{1}{2}x + 2y = 4 \\ 3x + 16y = 0 \end{cases}$

14. $\begin{cases} .8x + .6y = 2 \\ .2x + .4y = 1 \end{cases}$

15. Marriage Trends It is found that the number of married and single adults in a certain town are subject to the following statistics. Suppose that x and y denote the number of married and single adults, respectively, in a given year (say as of January 1) and let m, s denote the corresponding numbers for the following year. Then

$$.8x + .3y = m$$
$$.2x + .7y = s.$$

(a) Write this system of equations in matrix form.

(b) Solve the resulting matrix equation for $X = \begin{bmatrix} x \\ y \end{bmatrix}$.

(c) Suppose that in a given year there were found to be 100,000 married adults and 50,000 single adults. How many married (respectively, single) adults were there the preceding year?

(d) How many married (respectively, single) adults were there two years ago?

16. Epidemiology A flu epidemic is spreading through a town of 48,000 people. It is found that if x and y denote the numbers of people sick and well in a given week, respectively, and if s and w denote the corresponding numbers for the following week, then

$$\tfrac{1}{3}x + \tfrac{1}{4}y = s$$
$$\tfrac{2}{3}x + \tfrac{3}{4}y = w.$$

(a) Write this system of equations in matrix form.

(b) Solve the resulting matrix equation for $X = \begin{bmatrix} x \\ y \end{bmatrix}$.

(c) Suppose that 13,000 people are sick in a given week. How many were sick the preceding week?

(d) Same question as part (c), except assume that 14,000 are sick.

17. Housing Trends Statistics show that at a certain university, 70% of the students who live on campus during a given semester will remain on campus the following semester, and 90% of students living off campus during a given semester will remain off campus the following semester. Let x and y denote the number of students who live on and off campus this semester, and let u and

v be the corresponding numbers for the next semester. Then

$$.7x + .1y = u$$
$$.3x + .9y = v.$$

(a) Write this system of equations in matrix form.

(b) Solve the resulting matrix equation for $\begin{bmatrix} x \\ y \end{bmatrix}$.

(c) Suppose that out of a group of 9000 students, 6000 currently live on campus and 3000 live off campus. How many lived on campus last semester? How many will live off campus next semester?

18. Performance on Tests A teacher estimates that of the students who pass a test, 80% will pass the next test, while of the students who fail a test, 50% will pass the next test. Let x and y denote the number of students who pass and fail a given test, and let u and v be the corresponding numbers for the following test.

(a) Write a matrix equation relating $\begin{bmatrix} x \\ y \end{bmatrix}$ to $\begin{bmatrix} u \\ v \end{bmatrix}$.

(b) Suppose that 25 of the teacher's students pass the third test and 8 fail the third test. How many students will pass the fourth test? Approximately how many passed the second test?

In Exercises 19 and 20, use the fact that

$$\begin{bmatrix} 1 & 2 & 2 \\ 1 & 3 & 2 \\ 1 & 2 & 3 \end{bmatrix}^{-1} = \begin{bmatrix} 5 & -2 & -2 \\ -1 & 1 & 0 \\ -1 & 0 & 1 \end{bmatrix}.$$

19. Solve $\begin{cases} x + 2y + 2z = 1 \\ x + 3y + 2z = -1 \\ x + 2y + 3z = -1. \end{cases}$

20. Solve $\begin{cases} x + 2y + 2z = 1 \\ x + 3y + 2z = 0 \\ x + 2y + 3z = 0. \end{cases}$

In Exercises 21 and 22, use the fact that

$$\begin{bmatrix} 9 & 0 & 2 & 0 \\ -20 & -9 & -5 & 5 \\ 4 & 0 & 1 & 0 \\ -4 & -2 & -1 & 1 \end{bmatrix}^{-1} = \begin{bmatrix} 1 & 0 & -2 & 0 \\ 0 & 1 & 0 & -5 \\ -4 & 0 & 9 & 0 \\ 0 & 2 & 1 & -9 \end{bmatrix}.$$

21. Solve $\begin{cases} 9x \qquad\ + 2z \qquad\quad = 1 \\ -20x - 9y - 5z + 5w = 0 \\ 4x \qquad\ + z \qquad\quad = 0 \\ -4x - 2y - z + w = -1. \end{cases}$

22. Solve $\begin{cases} 9x \qquad\ + 2z \qquad\quad = 2 \\ -20x - 9y - 5z + 5w = 1 \\ 4x \qquad\ + z \qquad\quad = 3 \\ -4x - 2y - z + w = 0. \end{cases}$

23. Without computing D, show that the matrix $\begin{bmatrix} 6 & 3 \\ 2 & 1 \end{bmatrix}$ does not have an inverse.

24. If $A^{-1} = \begin{bmatrix} 2 & 7 \\ 1 & -3 \end{bmatrix}$, what is the matrix A?

25. Age Distribution There are two age groups for a particular species of organism. Group I consists of all organisms aged under 1 year, while group II consists of all organisms aged from 1 to 2 years. No organism survives more than 2 years. The average number of offspring per year born to each member of group I is 1, while the average number of organisms per year born to each member of group II is 2. Nine-tenths of group I survive to enter group II each year.

(a) Let x and y represent the initial number of organisms in groups I and II, respectively. Let a and b represent the number of organisms in groups I and II, respectively, after one year. Write a matrix equation relating $\begin{bmatrix} x \\ y \end{bmatrix}$ to $\begin{bmatrix} a \\ b \end{bmatrix}$.

(b) If there are initially 450,000 organisms in group I and 360,000 organisms in group II, calculate the number of organisms in each of the groups after 1 year and after 2 years.

(c) Suppose that at a certain time there were 810,000 organisms in group I and 630,000 organisms in group II. Determine the population of each group 1 year earlier.

26. If $A^2 = \begin{bmatrix} -2 & -1 \\ 2 & -1 \end{bmatrix}$ and $A^3 = \begin{bmatrix} -2 & 1 \\ -2 & -3 \end{bmatrix}$, what is A?

27. Show that if AB is a matrix of all zeros and A has an inverse, then B is a matrix of all zeros.

28. Consider the matrices $A = \begin{bmatrix} 3 & 1 \\ 5 & 2 \end{bmatrix}$ and $B = \begin{bmatrix} 6 & 2 \\ 5 & 2 \end{bmatrix}$. Show that $(AB)^{-1} = B^{-1}A^{-1}$.

29. Find a 2×2 matrix A and a 2×1 column matrix B for which $AX = B$ has no solution.

30. Find a 2×2 matrix A and a 2×1 column matrix B for which $AX = B$ has infinitely many solutions.

In Exercises 31–39 use a graphing calculator or spreadsheet.

In Exercises 31–34, use the inverse operation to find the inverse of the given matrix. Display the entries as fractions.

31. $\begin{bmatrix} .2 & 3 \\ 4 & 1.6 \end{bmatrix}$

32. $\begin{bmatrix} -12 & 3.3 \\ 6 & .4 \end{bmatrix}$

33. $\begin{bmatrix} .6 & 3 & -7 \\ 2.5 & -1 & 4 \\ -2 & .3 & 9 \end{bmatrix}$

34. $\begin{bmatrix} 5 & 2.3 & 6 \\ 1.2 & 5 & -7 \\ -3 & -4 & 6.5 \end{bmatrix}$

In Exercises 35–38, calculate the answer using $[A]^{-1} * [B]$ and give the answer using fractions.

35. $\begin{cases} 2x - 4y + 7z = 11 \\ x + 3y - 5z = -9 \\ 3x - y + 3z = 7 \end{cases}$

36. $\begin{cases} 5x + 2y - 3z = 1 \\ 4x - y + z = 22 \\ -x + 5y - 6z = 4 \end{cases}$

37. $\begin{cases} 2x + 7z + 5w = 10 \\ 5x - y + 3z = -2 \\ x + 2y - 2w = 0 \\ 3x - 4y + 2z - 5w = -18 \end{cases}$

38. $\begin{cases} x + 4y - z + 2w = 9 \\ 3x - 8y + 2z + 4w = -2 \\ -x - 3y + 7z - 6w = 10 \\ 4x + 2y - 3z + w = -6 \end{cases}$

39. Try finding the inverse of a matrix that does not have an inverse. How does your calculator or spreadsheet respond?

Solutions to Practice Problems 2.4

1. To see if this matrix is indeed the inverse, multiply it by the original matrix and find out if the products are identity matrices.

$$\begin{bmatrix} 1 & 1 & 4 \\ 3 & 2 & 4 \\ 1 & 1 & 6 \end{bmatrix} \begin{bmatrix} -4 & 1 & 2 \\ 7 & -1 & -4 \\ -\frac{1}{2} & 0 & \frac{1}{2} \end{bmatrix} = \begin{bmatrix} 1 & 0 & 0 \\ 0 & 1 & 0 \\ 0 & 0 & 1 \end{bmatrix},$$

(an identity matrix)

$$\begin{bmatrix} -4 & 1 & 2 \\ 7 & -1 & -4 \\ -\frac{1}{2} & 0 & \frac{1}{2} \end{bmatrix} \begin{bmatrix} 1 & 1 & 4 \\ 3 & 2 & 4 \\ 1 & 1 & 6 \end{bmatrix} = \begin{bmatrix} 1 & 0 & 0 \\ 0 & 1 & 0 \\ 0 & 0 & 1 \end{bmatrix}.$$

(Continued)

2. The matrix form of this system is

$$\begin{bmatrix} .8 & .6 \\ .2 & .4 \end{bmatrix} \begin{bmatrix} x \\ y \end{bmatrix} = \begin{bmatrix} 5 \\ 2 \end{bmatrix}.$$

Therefore, the solution is

$$\begin{bmatrix} x \\ y \end{bmatrix} = \begin{bmatrix} .8 & .6 \\ .2 & .4 \end{bmatrix}^{-1} \begin{bmatrix} 5 \\ 2 \end{bmatrix}.$$

To compute the inverse of the 2×2 matrix, first compute D.

$$D = ad - bc = (.8)(.4) - (.6)(.2) = .32 - .12 = .2$$

Thus,

$$\begin{bmatrix} .8 & .6 \\ .2 & .4 \end{bmatrix}^{-1} = \begin{bmatrix} .4/.2 & -.6/.2 \\ -.2/.2 & .8/.2 \end{bmatrix} = \begin{bmatrix} 2 & -3 \\ -1 & 4 \end{bmatrix}.$$

Therefore,

$$\begin{bmatrix} x \\ y \end{bmatrix} = \begin{bmatrix} 2 & -3 \\ -1 & 4 \end{bmatrix} \begin{bmatrix} 5 \\ 2 \end{bmatrix} = \begin{bmatrix} 4 \\ 3 \end{bmatrix},$$

so the solution is $x = 4$, $y = 3$.

2.5 The Gauss–Jordan Method for Calculating Inverses

Of the several popular methods for finding the inverse of a matrix, the **Gauss–Jordan method** is probably the easiest to describe. It can be used on square matrices of any size. Also, the mechanical nature of the computations allows this method to be programmed for a computer with relative ease. We shall illustrate the procedure with a 2×2 matrix, whose inverse can also be calculated using the method of the previous section. Let

$$A = \begin{bmatrix} \frac{1}{2} & 1 \\ 1 & 3 \end{bmatrix}.$$

It is simple to check that

$$A^{-1} = \begin{bmatrix} 6 & -2 \\ -2 & 1 \end{bmatrix}.$$

Let us now derive this result using the Gauss–Jordan method.

> **Step 1**   Write down the matrix A, and on its right append an identity matrix of the same size.

This is most conveniently done by placing I_2 beside A in a single matrix.

$$\left[\begin{array}{cc|cc} \frac{1}{2} & 1 & 1 & 0 \\ 1 & 3 & 0 & 1 \end{array} \right]$$

$$\underbrace{}_{A} \quad \underbrace{}_{I_2}$$

> **Step 2**   Perform elementary row operations on the left-hand matrix so as to transform it into an identity matrix. Each operation performed on the left-hand matrix is also performed on the right-hand matrix.

This step proceeds exactly like the Gauss–Jordan elimination method and may be most conveniently expressed in terms of pivoting.

$$\left[\begin{array}{cc|cc} \boxed{\frac{1}{2}} & 1 & 1 & 0 \\ 1 & 3 & 0 & 1 \end{array}\right], \quad \left[\begin{array}{cc|cc} 1 & 2 & 2 & 0 \\ 0 & \boxed{1} & -2 & 1 \end{array}\right], \quad \left[\begin{array}{cc|cc} 1 & 0 & 6 & -2 \\ 0 & 1 & -2 & 1 \end{array}\right]$$

Step 3   When the matrix on the left becomes an identity matrix, the matrix on the right is the desired inverse.

So, from the last matrix of our calculation above, we have

$$A^{-1} = \left[\begin{array}{cc} 6 & -2 \\ -2 & 1 \end{array}\right].$$

This is the same result obtained earlier.

We will demonstrate why the preceding method works after some further examples.

EXAMPLE 1

Finding the inverse of a matrix using the Gauss–Jordan method Find the inverse of the matrix

$$A = \left[\begin{array}{ccc} 4 & -2 & 3 \\ 8 & -3 & 5 \\ 7 & -2 & 4 \end{array}\right].$$

Solution

$$\left[\begin{array}{ccc|ccc} \boxed{4} & -2 & 3 & 1 & 0 & 0 \\ 8 & -3 & 5 & 0 & 1 & 0 \\ 7 & -2 & 4 & 0 & 0 & 1 \end{array}\right]$$

$$\left[\begin{array}{ccc|ccc} 1 & -\frac{1}{2} & \frac{3}{4} & \frac{1}{4} & 0 & 0 \\ 0 & \boxed{1} & -1 & -2 & 1 & 0 \\ 0 & \frac{3}{2} & -\frac{5}{4} & -\frac{7}{4} & 0 & 1 \end{array}\right]$$

$$\left[\begin{array}{ccc|ccc} 1 & 0 & \frac{1}{4} & -\frac{3}{4} & \frac{1}{2} & 0 \\ 0 & 1 & -1 & -2 & 1 & 0 \\ 0 & 0 & \boxed{\frac{1}{4}} & \frac{5}{4} & -\frac{3}{2} & 1 \end{array}\right]$$

$$\left[\begin{array}{ccc|ccc} 1 & 0 & 0 & -2 & 2 & -1 \\ 0 & 1 & 0 & 3 & -5 & 4 \\ 0 & 0 & 1 & 5 & -6 & 4 \end{array}\right]$$

Therefore,

$$A^{-1} = \left[\begin{array}{ccc} -2 & 2 & -1 \\ 3 & -5 & 4 \\ 5 & -6 & 4 \end{array}\right].$$

Now Try Exercise 7

Not all square matrices have inverses. If a matrix does not have an inverse, this will become apparent when applying the Gauss–Jordan method. At some point there will be no way to continue transforming the left-hand matrix into an identity matrix. This is illustrated in the next example.

EXAMPLE 2   **Demonstrating that a matrix does not have an inverse**   Find the inverse of the matrix

$$A = \begin{bmatrix} 1 & 3 & 2 \\ 0 & 1 & 4 \\ 1 & 5 & 10 \end{bmatrix}.$$

Solution

$$\left[\begin{array}{ccc|ccc} \boxed{1} & 3 & 2 & 1 & 0 & 0 \\ 0 & 1 & 4 & 0 & 1 & 0 \\ 1 & 5 & 10 & 0 & 0 & 1 \end{array}\right]$$

$$\left[\begin{array}{ccc|ccc} 1 & 3 & 2 & 1 & 0 & 0 \\ 0 & \boxed{1} & 4 & 0 & 1 & 0 \\ 0 & 2 & 8 & -1 & 0 & 1 \end{array}\right]$$

$$\left[\begin{array}{ccc|ccc} 1 & 0 & -10 & 1 & -3 & 0 \\ 0 & 1 & 4 & 0 & 1 & 0 \\ 0 & 0 & 0 & -1 & -2 & 1 \end{array}\right]$$

Since the third row of the left-hand matrix has only zero entries, it is impossible to complete the Gauss–Jordan method. Therefore, the matrix A has no inverse matrix.   ■

Now Try Exercise 9

Verification of the Gauss–Jordan Method for Calculating Inverses   In Section 2.4 we showed how to calculate the inverse by solving several systems of linear equations. Actually, the Gauss–Jordan method is just an organized way of going about the calculation. To see why, let us consider a concrete example:

$$A = \begin{bmatrix} 4 & -2 & 3 \\ 8 & -3 & 5 \\ 7 & -2 & 4 \end{bmatrix}.$$

We wish to determine A^{-1}, so regard it as a matrix of unknowns:

$$A^{-1} = \begin{bmatrix} x_1 & x_2 & x_3 \\ y_1 & y_2 & y_3 \\ z_1 & z_2 & z_3 \end{bmatrix}.$$

The statement $AA^{-1} = I_3$ is

$$\begin{bmatrix} 4 & -2 & 3 \\ 8 & -3 & 5 \\ 7 & -2 & 4 \end{bmatrix} \begin{bmatrix} x_1 & x_2 & x_3 \\ y_1 & y_2 & y_3 \\ z_1 & z_2 & z_3 \end{bmatrix} = \begin{bmatrix} 1 & 0 & 0 \\ 0 & 1 & 0 \\ 0 & 0 & 1 \end{bmatrix}.$$

Multiplying out the matrices on the left and comparing the result with the matrix on the right give us nine equations, namely

$$\begin{cases} 4x_1 - 2y_1 + 3z_1 = 1 \\ 8x_1 - 3y_1 + 5z_1 = 0 \\ 7x_1 - 2y_1 + 4z_1 = 0 \end{cases}$$

$$\begin{cases} 4x_2 - 2y_2 + 3z_2 = 0 \\ 8x_2 - 3y_2 + 5z_2 = 1 \\ 7x_2 - 2y_2 + 4z_2 = 0 \end{cases}$$

$$\begin{cases} 4x_3 - 2y_3 + 3z_3 = 0 \\ 8x_3 - 3y_3 + 5z_3 = 0 \\ 7x_3 - 2y_3 + 4z_3 = 1. \end{cases}$$

Notice that each system of equations corresponds to one column of unknowns in A^{-1}. More precisely, if we set

$$X_1 = \begin{bmatrix} x_1 \\ y_1 \\ z_1 \end{bmatrix}, \qquad X_2 = \begin{bmatrix} x_2 \\ y_2 \\ z_2 \end{bmatrix}, \qquad X_3 = \begin{bmatrix} x_3 \\ y_3 \\ z_3 \end{bmatrix},$$

then the preceding three systems have the respective matrix forms

$$AX_1 = \begin{bmatrix} 1 \\ 0 \\ 0 \end{bmatrix}, \qquad AX_2 = \begin{bmatrix} 0 \\ 1 \\ 0 \end{bmatrix}, \qquad AX_3 = \begin{bmatrix} 0 \\ 0 \\ 1 \end{bmatrix}.$$

Now imagine the process of applying Gauss–Jordan elimination to solve these three systems. We apply elementary row operations to the matrices

$$\left[\begin{array}{c|c} A & \begin{matrix} 1 \\ 0 \\ 0 \end{matrix} \end{array} \right], \qquad \left[\begin{array}{c|c} A & \begin{matrix} 0 \\ 1 \\ 0 \end{matrix} \end{array} \right], \qquad \left[\begin{array}{c|c} A & \begin{matrix} 0 \\ 0 \\ 1 \end{matrix} \end{array} \right].$$

The process ends when we convert A into the identity matrix, at which point the solutions may be read off the right column. So the procedure ends with the matrices

$$\begin{bmatrix} I_3 & | & X_1 \end{bmatrix}, \qquad \begin{bmatrix} I_3 & | & X_2 \end{bmatrix}, \qquad \begin{bmatrix} I_3 & | & X_3 \end{bmatrix}.$$

Realize, however, that at each step of the three Gauss–Jordan eliminations we are performing the same operations, since all three start with the matrix A on the left. So, in order to save calculations, perform the three Gauss–Jordan eliminations simultaneously by performing the row operations on the composite matrix

$$\left[\begin{array}{c|ccc} A & 1 & 0 & 0 \\ & 0 & 1 & 0 \\ & 0 & 0 & 1 \end{array} \right] = \begin{bmatrix} A & | & I_3 \end{bmatrix}.$$

The procedure ends when this matrix is converted into

$$\begin{bmatrix} I_3 & | & X_1 & X_2 & X_3 \end{bmatrix}.$$

That is, since $A^{-1} = \begin{bmatrix} X_1 & X_2 & X_3 \end{bmatrix}$, the procedure ends with A^{-1} on the right. This is the reasoning behind the Gauss–Jordan method of calculating inverses. ∎

1. Use the Gauss–Jordan method to calculate the inverse of the matrix

$$\begin{bmatrix} 1 & 0 & 2 \\ 0 & 1 & -4 \\ 0 & 0 & 2 \end{bmatrix}.$$

2. Solve the system of linear equations

$$\begin{cases} x & + 2z = 4 \\ & y - 4z = 6 \\ & 2z = 9. \end{cases}$$

EXERCISES 2.5

In Exercises 1–12, use the Gauss–Jordan method to compute the inverse of the matrix.

1. $\begin{bmatrix} 7 & 3 \\ 5 & 2 \end{bmatrix}$

2. $\begin{bmatrix} 5 & -2 \\ 6 & 2 \end{bmatrix}$

3. $\begin{bmatrix} 2 & 3 \\ -4 & -7 \end{bmatrix}$

4. $\begin{bmatrix} 1 & -3 \\ 0 & 1 \end{bmatrix}$

5. $\begin{bmatrix} 2 & -4 \\ -1 & 2 \end{bmatrix}$

6. $\begin{bmatrix} 1 & 3 & 1 \\ -1 & 2 & 0 \\ 2 & 11 & 3 \end{bmatrix}$

7. $\begin{bmatrix} 1 & 2 & -2 \\ 1 & 1 & 1 \\ 0 & 0 & 1 \end{bmatrix}$

8. $\begin{bmatrix} 2 & 2 & 0 \\ 0 & -2 & 0 \\ 3 & 0 & 1 \end{bmatrix}$

9. $\begin{bmatrix} -2 & 5 & 2 \\ 1 & -3 & -1 \\ -1 & 2 & 1 \end{bmatrix}$

10. $\begin{bmatrix} 1 & 0 & 0 \\ 2 & 1 & -2 \\ -1 & 2 & 1 \end{bmatrix}$

11. $\begin{bmatrix} 1 & 6 & 0 & 0 \\ 1 & 5 & 0 & 0 \\ 0 & 0 & 4 & 2 \\ 0 & 0 & 50 & 2 \end{bmatrix}$

12. $\begin{bmatrix} 6 & 0 & 2 & 0 \\ -6 & 1 & 0 & 1 \\ 1 & 0 & 1 & 0 \\ -9 & 0 & -1 & 1 \end{bmatrix}$

In Exercises 13–16, use matrix inversion to solve the systems of linear equations.

13. $\begin{cases} x + y + 2z = 3 \\ 3x + 2y + 2z = 4 \\ x + y + 3z = 5 \end{cases}$

14. $\begin{cases} x + 2y + 3z = 4 \\ 3x + 5y + 5z = 3 \\ 2x + 4y + 2z = 4 \end{cases}$

15. $\begin{cases} x & - 2z - 2w = 0 \\ y & - 5w = 1 \\ -4x & + 9z + 9w = 2 \\ 2y + z - 8w = 3 \end{cases}$

16. $\begin{cases} y + 2z = 1 \\ 2x + y + 3z = 2 \\ x + y + 2z = 3 \end{cases}$

17. If $A^{-1} = \begin{bmatrix} 2 & 7 \\ 1 & 3 \end{bmatrix}$, what is the matrix A?

18. Find the 2×2 matrix C for which $AC = B$, where

$$A = \begin{bmatrix} 3 & 2 \\ 4 & 3 \end{bmatrix} \quad \text{and} \quad B = \begin{bmatrix} 5 & 6 \\ 1 & 7 \end{bmatrix}.$$

19. Find a 2×2 matrix A for which

$$A \begin{bmatrix} 2 \\ 1 \end{bmatrix} = \begin{bmatrix} -1 \\ 4 \end{bmatrix} \quad \text{and} \quad A \begin{bmatrix} 5 \\ 3 \end{bmatrix} = \begin{bmatrix} 0 \\ 2 \end{bmatrix}.$$

20. Let

$$A = \begin{bmatrix} 7 & 4 \\ 3 & 2 \end{bmatrix} \quad \text{and} \quad B = \begin{bmatrix} 1 & 5 \\ -3 & 4 \end{bmatrix}.$$

Each of the equations $AX = B$ and $XA = B$ has a 2×2 matrix X as a solution. Find X in each case and explain why the two answers are different.

1. First write the given matrix beside an identity matrix of the same size

$$\begin{bmatrix} 1 & 0 & 2 & | & 1 & 0 & 0 \\ 0 & 1 & -4 & | & 0 & 1 & 0 \\ 0 & 0 & 2 & | & 0 & 0 & 1 \end{bmatrix}.$$

The object is to use elementary row operations to transform the 3×3 matrix on the left into the identity matrix. The first two columns are already in the correct form.

(Continued)

$$\left[\begin{array}{ccc|ccc} 1 & 0 & 2 & 1 & 0 & 0 \\ 0 & 1 & -4 & 0 & 1 & 0 \\ 0 & 0 & 2 & 0 & 0 & 1 \end{array}\right]$$

$$\xrightarrow{\frac{1}{2}R_3}\left[\begin{array}{ccc|ccc} 1 & 0 & 2 & 1 & 0 & 0 \\ 0 & 1 & -4 & 0 & 1 & 0 \\ 0 & 0 & 1 & 0 & 0 & \frac{1}{2} \end{array}\right]$$

$$\xrightarrow{R_1 + (-2)R_3}\left[\begin{array}{ccc|ccc} 1 & 0 & 0 & 1 & 0 & -1 \\ 0 & 1 & -4 & 0 & 1 & 0 \\ 0 & 0 & 1 & 0 & 0 & \frac{1}{2} \end{array}\right]$$

$$\xrightarrow{R_2 + (4)R_3}\left[\begin{array}{ccc|ccc} 1 & 0 & 0 & 1 & 0 & -1 \\ 0 & 1 & 0 & 0 & 1 & 2 \\ 0 & 0 & 1 & 0 & 0 & \frac{1}{2} \end{array}\right]$$

Thus the inverse of the given matrix is

$$\left[\begin{array}{ccc} 1 & 0 & -1 \\ 0 & 1 & 2 \\ 0 & 0 & \frac{1}{2} \end{array}\right].$$

2. The matrix form of this system of equations is $AX = B$, where A is the matrix whose inverse was found in Problem 1, and

$$B = \left[\begin{array}{c} 4 \\ 6 \\ 9 \end{array}\right].$$

Therefore, $X = A^{-1}B$, so that

$$\left[\begin{array}{c} x \\ y \\ z \end{array}\right] = \left[\begin{array}{ccc} 1 & 0 & -1 \\ 0 & 1 & 2 \\ 0 & 0 & \frac{1}{2} \end{array}\right]\left[\begin{array}{c} 4 \\ 6 \\ 9 \end{array}\right] = \left[\begin{array}{c} -5 \\ 24 \\ \frac{9}{2} \end{array}\right].$$

So the solution of the system is $x = -5$, $y = 24$, $z = \frac{9}{2}$.

2.6 Input–Output Analysis

In recent years matrix arithmetic has played an ever-increasing role in economics, especially in that branch of economics called **input–output analysis**. Pioneered by the Harvard economist Vassily Leontieff, input–output analysis is used to analyze an economy in order to meet given consumption and export demands. As we shall see, such analysis leads to matrix calculations and in particular to inverses. Input–output analysis has been of such great significance that Leontieff was awarded the 1973 Nobel Prize in economics for his fundamental work in the subject.

Suppose that we divide an economy into a number of industries—transportation, agriculture, steel, and so on. Each industry produces a certain output using certain raw materials (or input). The input of each industry is made up in part by the outputs of other industries. For example, in order to produce food, agriculture uses as input the output of many industries, such as transportation (tractors and trucks) and oil (gasoline and fertilizers). This interdependence among the industries of the economy is summarized in a matrix—an **input–output matrix**. There is one column for each industry's input requirements. The entries in the column reflect the amount of input required from each of the industries. A typical input–output matrix looks like this:

		Input requirements of:		
		Industry 1	Industry 2	Industry 3 . . .
	Industry 1			
	Industry 2			
From	Industry 3			
	⋮			

It is most convenient to express the entries of this matrix in monetary terms. That is, each column gives the dollar values of the various inputs needed by an industry in order to produce $1 worth of output.

There are consumers (other than the industries themselves) who want to purchase some of the output of these industries. The quantity of goods that these consumers want (or demand) is called the **final demand** on the economy. The final demand can be represented by a column matrix, with one entry for each industry, indicating the amount of consumable output demanded from the industry:

$$\left[\text{final demand}\right] = \begin{bmatrix} \text{amount from industry 1} \\ \text{amount from industry 2} \\ \vdots \end{bmatrix}.$$

We shall consider the situation in which the final-demand matrix is given and it is necessary to determine how much output should be produced by each industry in order to provide the needed inputs of the various industries and also to satisfy the final demand. The proper level of output can be computed using matrix calculations, as illustrated in the next example.

EXAMPLE 1

Determining industrial production Suppose that an economy is composed of only three industries—coal, steel, and electricity. Each of these industries depends on the others for some of its raw materials. Suppose that to make $1 of coal, it takes no coal, but $.02 of steel and $.01 of electricity; to make $1 of steel, it takes $.15 of coal, $.03 of steel, and $.08 of electricity; and to make $1 of electricity, it takes $.43 of coal, $.20 of steel, and $.05 of electricity. How much should each industry produce to allow for consumption (not used for production) at these levels: $2 billion coal, $1 billion steel, $3 billion electricity?

Solution Put all the data indicating the interdependence of the industries in a matrix. In each industry's column, put the amount of input from each of the industries needed to produce $1 of output in that particular industry:

$$\begin{array}{c} \\ \text{Coal} \\ \text{Steel} \\ \text{Electricity} \end{array} \begin{array}{ccc} \text{Coal} & \text{Steel} & \text{Electricity} \end{array} \\ \begin{bmatrix} 0 & .15 & .43 \\ .02 & .03 & .20 \\ .01 & .08 & .05 \end{bmatrix} = A.$$

This matrix is the input–output matrix corresponding to the economy. Let D denote the final-demand matrix. Then, letting the numbers in D stand for billions of dollars, we have

$$D = \begin{bmatrix} 2 \\ 1 \\ 3 \end{bmatrix}.$$

Suppose that the coal industry produces x billion dollars of output, the steel industry y billion dollars, and the electrical industry z billion dollars. Our problem is to determine the x, y, and z that yield the desired amounts left over from the production process. As an example, consider coal. The amount of coal that can be consumed or exported is just

$$x - \left[\text{amount of coal used in production}\right].$$

To determine the amount of coal used in production, refer to the input–output matrix. Production of x billion dollars of coal takes $0 \cdot x$ billion dollars of coal; production of y billion dollars of steel takes $.15y$ billion dollars of coal; and production of z billion dollars of electricity takes $.43z$ billion dollars of coal. Thus,

$$[\text{amount of coal used in production}] = 0 \cdot x + .15y + .43z.$$

This quantity should be recognized as the first entry of a matrix product. Namely, if we let

$$X = \begin{bmatrix} x \\ y \\ z \end{bmatrix},$$

then

$$\begin{bmatrix} \text{coal} \\ \text{steel} \\ \text{electricity} \end{bmatrix}_{\text{used in production}} = \begin{bmatrix} 0 & .15 & .43 \\ .02 & .03 & .20 \\ .01 & .08 & .05 \end{bmatrix} \begin{bmatrix} x \\ y \\ z \end{bmatrix} = AX.$$

The equations for the amounts of steel and electricity used in production are obtained in a manner similar to the equation for coal. But then the amount of each output available for purposes other than production is $X - AX$. That is, we have the matrix equation

$$X - AX = D.$$

To solve this equation for X, proceed as follows. Since $IX = X$, write the equation in the form

$$IX - AX = D$$

$$(I - A)X = D$$

$$X = (I - A)^{-1}D. \tag{1}$$

So, in other words, X may be found by multiplying D on the left by $(I - A)^{-1}$. Let us now do the arithmetic.

$$I - A = \begin{bmatrix} 1 & 0 & 0 \\ 0 & 1 & 0 \\ 0 & 0 & 1 \end{bmatrix} - \begin{bmatrix} 0 & .15 & .43 \\ .02 & .03 & .20 \\ .01 & .08 & .05 \end{bmatrix} = \begin{bmatrix} 1 & -.15 & -.43 \\ -.02 & .97 & -.20 \\ -.01 & -.08 & .95 \end{bmatrix}$$

Applying the Gauss–Jordan method, we find that

$$(I - A)^{-1} = \begin{bmatrix} 1.01 & .20 & .50 \\ .02 & 1.05 & .23 \\ .01 & .09 & 1.08 \end{bmatrix},$$

where all figures are carried to two decimal places (Exercise 9). Therefore,

$$X = (I - A)^{-1}D = \begin{bmatrix} 1.01 & .20 & .50 \\ .02 & 1.05 & .23 \\ .01 & .09 & 1.08 \end{bmatrix} \begin{bmatrix} 2 \\ 1 \\ 3 \end{bmatrix} = \begin{bmatrix} 3.72 \\ 1.78 \\ 3.35 \end{bmatrix}.$$

In other words, coal should produce $3.72 billion worth of output, steel $1.78 billion, and electricity $3.35 billion. This output will meet the required final demands from each industry. ∎

Now Try Exercise 5

The preceding analysis is useful in studying not only entire economies but also segments of economies and even individual companies.

EXAMPLE 2

Determining production for a conglomerate A conglomerate has three divisions, which produce computers, semiconductors, and business forms. For each $1 of output, the computer division needs $.02 worth of computers, $.20 worth of semiconductors, and $.10 worth of business forms. For each $1 of output, the semiconductor division needs $.02 worth of computers, $.01 worth of semiconductors, and $.02 worth of business forms. For each $1 of output, the business forms division requires $.10 worth of computers and $.01 worth of business forms. The conglomerate estimates the sales demand to be $300,000,000 for the computer division, $100,000,000 for the semiconductor division, and $200,000,000 for the business forms division. At what level should each division produce in order to satisfy this demand?

Solution The conglomerate can be viewed as a miniature economy and its sales as the final demand. The input–output matrix for this "economy" is

$$
\begin{array}{c}
\\
\text{Computers} \\
\text{Semiconductors} \\
\text{Business forms}
\end{array}
\begin{array}{ccc}
\text{Computers} & \text{Semiconductors} & \begin{array}{c}\text{Business}\\\text{forms}\end{array} \\
\left[\begin{array}{ccc}
.02 & .02 & .10 \\
.20 & .01 & 0 \\
.10 & .02 & .01
\end{array}\right] & & = A.
\end{array}
$$

The final-demand matrix is

$$
D = \begin{bmatrix} 3 \\ 1 \\ 2 \end{bmatrix},
$$

where the demand is expressed in hundreds of millions of dollars. By equation (1) the matrix X, giving the desired levels of production for the various divisions, is given by

$$
X = (I - A)^{-1}D.
$$

But

$$
I - A = \begin{bmatrix}
.98 & -.02 & -.10 \\
-.20 & .99 & 0 \\
-.10 & -.02 & .99
\end{bmatrix},
$$

so that (Exercise 10)

$$
(I - A)^{-1} = \begin{bmatrix}
1.04 & .02 & .10 \\
.21 & 1.01 & .02 \\
.11 & .02 & 1.02
\end{bmatrix} \quad \text{and} \quad (I - A)^{-1}D = \begin{bmatrix} 3.34 \\ 1.68 \\ 2.39 \end{bmatrix}.
$$

Therefore,

$$
X = \begin{bmatrix} 3.34 \\ 1.68 \\ 2.39 \end{bmatrix}.
$$

That is, the computer division should produce $334,000,000, the semiconductor division $168,000,000, and the business forms division $239,000,000. ■

Now Try Exercise 7

Input–output analysis is usually applied to the entire economy of a country having hundreds of industries. The resulting matrix equation $(I - A)X = D$ could be solved by the Gauss–Jordan elimination method. However, it is best to find the inverse of $I - A$ and solve for X as we have done in the examples of this section. Over a short period, D might change but A is unlikely to change. Therefore, the proper outputs to satisfy the new demand can easily be determined by using the already computed inverse of $I - A$.

The Closed Leontieff Model The foregoing description of an economy is usually called the **open Leontieff model** since it views exports as an activity that takes place external to the economy. However, it is possible to consider exports as yet another industry in the economy. Instead of describing exports by a demand column D, we describe it by a column in the input–output matrix. That is, the export column describes how each dollar of exports is divided among the various industries. Since exports are now regarded as another industry, each of the original columns has an additional entry, namely the amount of output from the export industry (that is, imports) used to produce \$1 of goods (of the industry corresponding to the column). If A denotes the expanded input–output matrix and X the production matrix (as before), then AX is the matrix describing the total demand experienced by each of the industries. In order for the economy to function efficiently, the total amount demanded by the various industries should equal the amount produced. That is, the production matrix must satisfy the equation

$$AX = X.$$

By studying the solutions to this equation, it is possible to determine the equilibrium states of the economy—that is, the production matrices X for which the amounts produced exactly equal the amounts needed by the various industries. The model just described is called the **closed Leontieff model**.

We may expand the closed Leontieff model to include the effects of labor and monetary phenomena by considering labor and banking as yet further industries to be incorporated in the input–output matrix.

INCORPORATING TECHNOLOGY

GC With a graphing calculator, the matrix $(I - A)^{-1}D$ can be calculated with a single press of the $\boxed{\text{ENTER}}$ key. Figures 1 and 2 show the calculation for the matrices of Example 2. ∎

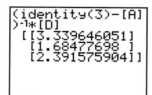

Figure 1

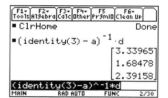

Figure 2

ES To display the matrix $(I - A)^{-1}D$ on an Excel spreadsheet, select a column of n cells, type the formula **=MMULT(MINVERSE(I-A),D)** and press Ctrl+Shift+Enter. (Here D is an $n \times 1$ matrix, I is the $n \times n$ identity matrix, and A is an $n \times n$ square matrix.)

Practice Problems 2.6

1. Let

$$I = \begin{bmatrix} 1 & 0 & 0 \\ 0 & 1 & 0 \\ 0 & 0 & 1 \end{bmatrix}, \quad A = \begin{bmatrix} .1 & 0 & .1 \\ .2 & .1 & .1 \\ .1 & .2 & 0 \end{bmatrix},$$

$$X = \begin{bmatrix} x \\ y \\ z \end{bmatrix}, \quad D = \begin{bmatrix} 100 \\ 200 \\ 50 \end{bmatrix}.$$

Solve the matrix equation

$$(I - A)X = D.$$

2. Let I, A, and X be as in Problem 1, but let

$$D = \begin{bmatrix} 300 \\ 100 \\ 100 \end{bmatrix}.$$

Solve the matrix equation $(I - A)X = D$.

EXERCISES 2.6

Three-Sector Economy *In Exercises 1–4, suppose a simplified economy consisting of the three sectors Manufacturing, Energy, and Services has the input-output matrix*

$$\begin{array}{c} \\ M \\ E \\ S \end{array} \begin{array}{ccc} M & E & S \\ \begin{bmatrix} .3 & .1 & .2 \\ .2 & .25 & .15 \\ .1 & .2 & .15 \end{bmatrix}. \end{array}$$

1. How many cents of energy are required to produce $1 worth of manufactured goods?

2. How many cents of energy are required to produce $1 worth of services?

3. Which sector of the economy requires the greatest amount of services in order to produce $1 worth of output?

4. What is the dollar amount of the energy costs needed to produce 10 million dollars worth of goods from each sector?

5. Industrial Production Suppose that in the economy of Example 1 the demand for electricity triples and the demand for coal doubles, whereas the demand for steel increases only by 50%. At what levels should the various industries produce in order to satisfy the new demand?

6. Conglomerate Suppose that the conglomerate of Example 2 is faced with an increase of 50% in demand for computers, a doubling in demand for semiconductors, and a decrease of 50% in demand for business forms. At what levels should the various divisions produce in order to satisfy the new demand?

7. Conglomerate Suppose that the conglomerate of Example 2 experiences a doubling in the demand for business forms. At what levels should the computer and semiconductor divisions produce?

8. Multinational Corporation A multinational corporation does business in the United States, Canada, and England. Its branches in one country purchase goods from the branches in other countries according to the matrix

	Branch in:		
Purchase from:	United States	Canada	England
United States	.02	0	.02
Canada	.01	.03	.01
England	.03	0	.01

where the entries in the matrix represent proportions of total sales by the respective branch. The external sales by each of the offices are $800,000,000 for the U.S. branch, $300,000,000 for the Canadian branch, and $1,400,000,000 for the English branch. At what level should each of the branches produce in order to satisfy the total demand?

9. Show that to two decimal places

$$\begin{bmatrix} 1 & -.15 & -.43 \\ -.02 & .97 & -.20 \\ -.01 & -.08 & .95 \end{bmatrix}^{-1} = \begin{bmatrix} 1.01 & .20 & .50 \\ .02 & 1.05 & .23 \\ .01 & .09 & 1.08 \end{bmatrix}.$$

10. Show that to two decimal places

$$\begin{bmatrix} .98 & -.02 & -.10 \\ -.20 & .99 & 0 \\ -.10 & -.02 & .99 \end{bmatrix}^{-1} = \begin{bmatrix} 1.04 & .02 & .10 \\ .21 & 1.01 & .02 \\ .11 & .02 & 1.02 \end{bmatrix}.$$

11. Two-Sector Economy A simplified economy consists of the two sectors Transportation and Energy. For each $1 worth of output, the transportation sector requires $.25 worth of input from the transportation sector and $.20 of input from the energy sector. For each $1 worth of output, the energy sector requires $.30 from the transportation sector and $.15 from the energy sector.

(a) Give the input-output matrix A for this economy.

(b) Determine the matrix $(I - A)^{-1}$. (Round entries to two decimal places.)

(c) At what level of output should each sector produce to meet a demand for $5 billion worth of transportation and $3 billion worth of energy?

12. Three-Sector Economy An economy consists of the three sectors agriculture, energy, and manufacturing. For each $1 worth of output, the agriculture sector requires $.08 worth of input from the agriculture sector, $.10 worth of input from the energy sector, and $.20 worth of input from the manufacturing sector. For each $1 worth of output, the energy sector requires $.15 worth of input from the agriculture sector, $.14 worth of input from the energy sector, and $.10 worth of input from the manufacturing sector. For each $1 worth of output, the manufacturing sector requires $.25 worth of input from the agriculture sector, $.12 worth of input from the energy sector, and $.05 worth of input from the manufacturing sector.

(a) Give the input-output matrix A for this economy.

(b) Determine the matrix $(I - A)^{-1}$. (Round entries to two decimal places.)

(c) At what level of output should each sector produce to meet a demand for $4 billion worth of agriculture, $3 billion worth of energy, and $2 billion worth of manufacturing?

13. Two-Product Corporation A corporation has a plastics division and an industrial equipment division. For each $1 worth of output, the plastics division needs $.02 worth of plastics and $.10 worth of equipment. For each $1 worth of output, the industrial equipment division needs $.01 worth of plastics and $.05 worth of equipment. At what level should the divisions produce to meet a demand for $930,000 worth of plastics and $465,000 worth of industrial equipment?

14. Two-Product Corporation Rework Exercise 13 under the condition that the demand for plastics is $1,860,000 and the demand for industrial equipment is $2,790,000.

15. Three-Sector Industry An industrial system involves manufacturing, transportation, and agriculture. The interdependence of the three industries is given by the input–output matrix

$$
\begin{array}{ccc}
M & T & A \\
\end{array}
$$
$$
\begin{bmatrix}
.4 & .3 & .1 \\
.2 & .2 & .2 \\
.1 & .1 & .4
\end{bmatrix}
\begin{array}{c}
M \\
T \\
A
\end{array}
$$

At what levels must the industries produce to satisfy a demand for $100 million worth of manufactured goods,

$80 million of transportation, and $200 million worth of agricultural products?

16. Localized Economy A town has a merchant, a baker, and a farmer. To produce $1 worth of output, the merchant requires $.30 worth of baked goods and $.40 worth of the farmer's products. To produce $1 worth of output, the baker requires $.50 worth of the merchant's goods, $.10 worth of his own goods, and $.30 worth of the farmer's goods. To produce $1 worth of output, the farmer requires $.30 worth of the merchant's goods, $.20 worth of baked goods, and $.30 worth of his own products. How much should the merchant, baker, and farmer produce to meet a demand for $20,000 worth of output from the merchant, $15,000 worth of output from the baker, and $18,000 worth of output from the farmer?

17. The matrix $(I - A)^{-1}$ from Example 1 is given in Exercise 9. Show that if the final demand for coal is increased by one billion dollars, then the additional amounts (in billions of dollars) that must be produced by each of the three industries is given by the first column of $(I - A)^{-1}$.

Hint: $(I - A)^{-1} \begin{bmatrix} 3 \\ 1 \\ 3 \end{bmatrix} = (I - A)^{-1} \left(\begin{bmatrix} 2 \\ 1 \\ 3 \end{bmatrix} + \begin{bmatrix} 1 \\ 0 \\ 0 \end{bmatrix} \right).$

18. Refer to Exercise 17. Interpret the significance of the second and third columns of $(I - A)^{-1}$.

In the following exercises, use a graphing calculator or a spreadsheet to carry out the matrix operations.

In Exercises 19 and 20, use the input–output matrix A and the final-demand matrix D to find the production matrix X for the open Leontieff model. Round your answers to two decimal places.

19. $A = \begin{bmatrix} .1 & .2 & .4 \\ .05 & .3 & .25 \\ .15 & .1 & .2 \end{bmatrix}$, $D = \begin{bmatrix} 3 \\ 7 \\ 4 \end{bmatrix}$.

20. $A = \begin{bmatrix} .2 & .35 & .15 & .05 \\ .1 & .1 & .3 & .2 \\ .075 & .2 & .05 & .1 \\ .3 & .04 & .1 & .15 \end{bmatrix}$, $D = \begin{bmatrix} 5 \\ 2 \\ 1 \\ 7 \end{bmatrix}$

Solutions to Practice Problems 2.6

1. The equation $(I - A)X = D$ has the form $CX = D$, where C is the matrix $I - A$. From Section 2.4 we know that $X = C^{-1}D$. That is, $X = (I - A)^{-1}D$. Now

$$I - A = \begin{bmatrix} 1 & 0 & 0 \\ 0 & 1 & 0 \\ 0 & 0 & 1 \end{bmatrix} - \begin{bmatrix} .1 & 0 & .1 \\ .2 & .1 & .1 \\ .1 & .2 & 0 \end{bmatrix}$$

$$= \begin{bmatrix} .9 & 0 & -.1 \\ -.2 & .9 & -.1 \\ -.1 & -.2 & 1 \end{bmatrix}.$$

Using the Gauss–Jordan method to find the inverse of this matrix, we have (to two decimal places)

$$(I - A)^{-1} = \begin{bmatrix} 1.13 & .03 & .12 \\ .27 & 1.14 & .14 \\ .17 & .23 & 1.04 \end{bmatrix}.$$

Therefore, rounding to the nearest integer, we have

$$X = (I - A)^{-1}D = \begin{bmatrix} 1.13 & .03 & .12 \\ .27 & 1.14 & .14 \\ .17 & .23 & 1.04 \end{bmatrix} \begin{bmatrix} 100 \\ 200 \\ 50 \end{bmatrix}$$

$$= \begin{bmatrix} 125 \\ 262 \\ 115 \end{bmatrix}.$$

2. We have $X = (I - A)^{-1}D$, where $(I - A)^{-1}$ is as computed in Problem 1. So

$$X = (I - A)^{-1}D = \begin{bmatrix} 1.13 & .03 & .12 \\ .27 & 1.14 & .14 \\ .17 & .23 & 1.04 \end{bmatrix} \begin{bmatrix} 300 \\ 100 \\ 100 \end{bmatrix}$$

$$= \begin{bmatrix} 354 \\ 209 \\ 178 \end{bmatrix}.$$

CHAPTER SUMMARY

1. The three elementary row operations for a system of linear equations (or a matrix) are as follows:
   (a) Interchange any two equations (rows).
   (b) Multiply an equation (row) by a nonzero number.
   (c) Change an equation (row) by adding to it a multiple of another equation (row).

2. When an elementary row operation is applied to a system of linear equations the solutions remain the same. The Gauss–Jordan elimination method is a systematic process that applies a sequence of elementary row operations until the solutions can be easily obtained.

3. The process of pivoting on a specific element of a matrix is to apply a sequence of elementary row operations so that the specific element becomes 1 and the other elements in its column become 0. To apply the Gauss–Jordan elimination method, proceed from left to right and perform pivots on as many columns to the left of the vertical line as possible, with the specific elements for the pivots coming from different rows.

4. After a matrix corresponding to a system of linear equations has been completely reduced with the Gauss–Jordan elimination method, all the solutions to the system of linear equations can be obtained. If the matrix on the left of the vertical line is an identity matrix, then there is a unique solution. If one row of the matrix is of the form $0\ \ 0\ \ 0\ \cdots\ 0 \mid a$, where a is a nonzero number, then there is no solution. Other-

wise, there are infinitely many solutions. In this case, variables corresponding to columns that have not been pivoted can assume any values, and the values of the other variables can be expressed in terms of those variables.

5. A matrix of size $m \times n$ has m rows and n columns.

6. Matrices of the same size can be added (or subtracted) by adding (or subtracting) corresponding elements.

7. The product of an $m \times n$ matrix and an $n \times r$ matrix is the $m \times r$ matrix whose ijth element is obtained by multiplying the ith row of the first matrix by the jth column of the second matrix. (The product of each row and column is calculated as the sum of the products of successive entries.)

8. The inverse of a square matrix A is a square matrix A^{-1} with the property that $A^{-1}A = I$ and $AA^{-1} = I$, where I is an identity matrix.

9. A 2×2 matrix $\begin{bmatrix} a & b \\ c & d \end{bmatrix}$ has an inverse if $D = ad - bc \neq 0$. If so, the inverse matrix is

$$\begin{bmatrix} \dfrac{d}{D} & -\dfrac{b}{D} \\ -\dfrac{c}{D} & \dfrac{a}{D} \end{bmatrix}.$$

10. A system of linear equations can be written in the form $AX = B$, where A is a rectangular matrix of coefficients of the variables, X is a column of variables, and

B is a column matrix of the constants from the right side of the system. If the matrix A has an inverse, then the solution of the equation is given by $X = A^{-1}B$.

11. To calculate the inverse of a matrix by the Gauss–Jordan method, append an identity matrix to the right of the original matrix and perform pivots to reduce the original matrix to an identity matrix. The matrix on the right will then be the inverse of the original matrix. (If the original matrix cannot be reduced to an identity matrix, then the original matrix does not have an inverse.)

12. An input–output matrix has rows and columns labeled with the different industries in an economy. The ijth entry of the matrix gives the cost of the input from the industry in row i used in the production of \$1 worth of the output of industry in column j.

13. If A is an input–output matrix and D is a demand matrix giving the dollar values of the outputs from the various industries to be supplied to outside customers, then the matrix $X = (I - A)^{-1}D$ gives the amounts that must be produced by the various industries in order to meet the demand.

REVIEW OF FUNDAMENTAL CONCEPTS

1. What is meant by a solution to a system of linear equations?

2. What is a matrix?

3. State the three elementary row operations on equations or matrices.

4. What does it mean for a system of equations or a matrix to be in diagonal form?

5. What is meant by pivoting a matrix about a nonzero entry?

6. State the Gauss–Jordan elimination method for transforming a system of linear equations into diagonal form.

7. What is a row matrix? Column matrix? Square matrix? Identity matrix, I_n?

8. What is meant by a_{ij}, the ijth entry of a matrix?

9. Define the sum and difference of two matrices.

10. Define the product of two matrices.

11. Define the inverse of a matrix, A^{-1}.

12. Give the formula for the inverse of a 2×2 matrix.

13. Explain how to use the inverse of a matrix to solve a system of linear equations.

14. Describe the steps of the Gauss–Jordan method for calculating the inverse of a matrix.

15. What is an input–output matrix and a final-demand matrix?

16. Explain how to solve an input–output analysis problem.

KEY FORMULAS

Inverse of $\begin{bmatrix} a & b \\ c & d \end{bmatrix}$ is $\begin{bmatrix} \dfrac{d}{D} & -\dfrac{b}{D} \\ -\dfrac{c}{D} & \dfrac{a}{D} \end{bmatrix}$, where $D = ad - bc \neq 0$.

Solution of $AX = B$, where A has an inverse is $X = A^{-1}B$. If A is the input–output matrix for an economy and D is the demand matrix, then the proper production amounts for each sector are given by $X = (I - A)^{-1}D$.

SUPPLEMENTARY EXERCISES

In Exercises 1 and 2, pivot each matrix around the circled element.

1. $\begin{bmatrix} ③ & -6 & 1 \\ 2 & 4 & 6 \end{bmatrix}$

2. $\begin{bmatrix} -5 & -3 & 1 \\ 4 & ② & 0 \\ 0 & 6 & 7 \end{bmatrix}$

3. $\begin{cases} \frac{1}{2}x - y = -3 \\ 4x - 5y = -9 \end{cases}$

4. $\begin{cases} 3x \quad\quad + 9z = \quad 42 \\ 2x + y + 6z = \quad 30 \\ -x + 3y - 2z = -20 \end{cases}$

5. $\begin{cases} 3x - 6y + 6z = -5 \\ -2x + 3y - 5z = \frac{7}{3} \\ x + y + 10z = \quad 3 \end{cases}$

6. $\begin{cases} 3x + 6y - 9z = 1 \\ 2x + 4y - 6z = 1 \\ 3x + 4y + 5z = 0 \end{cases}$

In Exercises 3–8, use the Gauss–Jordan elimination method to find all solutions of the systems of linear equations.

7. $\begin{cases} x + 2y - 5z + 3w = 16 \\ -5x - 7y + 13z - 9w = -50 \\ -x + y - 7z + 2w = 9 \\ 3x + 4y - 7z + 6w = 33 \end{cases}$

8. $\begin{cases} 5x - 10y = 5 \\ 3x - 8y = -3 \\ -3x + 7y = 0 \end{cases}$

In Exercises 9 and 10, perform the indicated matrix operations.

9. $\begin{bmatrix} 2 \\ -1 \\ 0 \end{bmatrix} + \begin{bmatrix} 3 \\ 4 \\ 7 \end{bmatrix}$ 10. $\begin{bmatrix} 1 & 3 & -2 \\ 4 & 0 & -1 \end{bmatrix} \begin{bmatrix} 3 & 5 \\ 1 & 0 \\ 0 & -6 \end{bmatrix}$

11. Find the inverse of the appropriate matrix, and use it to solve the system of equations

$$\begin{cases} 3x + 2y = 0 \\ 5x + 4y = 2. \end{cases}$$

12. The matrices

$$\begin{bmatrix} 4 & -2 & 3 \\ 8 & -3 & 5 \\ 7 & -2 & 4 \end{bmatrix} \text{ and } \begin{bmatrix} -2 & 2 & -1 \\ 3 & -5 & 4 \\ 5 & -6 & 4 \end{bmatrix}$$

are inverses of each other. Use these matrices to solve the following systems of linear equations.

(a) $\begin{cases} -2x + 2y - z = 1 \\ 3x - 5y + 4z = 0 \\ 5x - 6y + 4z = 3 \end{cases}$

(b) $\begin{cases} 4x - 2y + 3z = 0 \\ 8x - 3y + 5z = -1 \\ 7x - 2y + 4z = 2 \end{cases}$

In Exercises 13 and 14, use the Gauss–Jordan method to calculate the inverses of the following matrices.

13. $\begin{bmatrix} 2 & 6 \\ 1 & 2 \end{bmatrix}$ 14. $\begin{bmatrix} 1 & 1 & 1 \\ 3 & 4 & 3 \\ 1 & 1 & 2 \end{bmatrix}$

15. **Crop Allocation** Farmer Brown has 1000 acres of land on which he plans to grow corn, wheat, and soybeans. The cost of cultivating these crops is $206 per acre for corn, $85 per acre for wheat, and $97 per acre for soybeans. If Farmer Brown wishes to use all his available land and his entire budget of $151,500, and if he wishes to plant the same number of acres of corn as wheat and soybeans combined, how many acres of each crop can he grow?

16. **Equipment Sales** A company makes backyard playground equipment like swing sets, slides, and play sets. The cost (in dollars) to make a specific style of each piece is given in matrix C. The sales price (in dollars) for each piece is given in matrix S. Two stores sell these specific pieces and matrix A gives the quantities sold during one month.

$$C = \begin{bmatrix} 165 \\ 65 \\ 210 \end{bmatrix} \begin{matrix} \text{Swing set} \\ \text{Slide} \\ \text{Play set} \end{matrix}$$

$$S = \begin{bmatrix} 200 \\ 80 \\ 250 \end{bmatrix} \begin{matrix} \text{Swing set} \\ \text{Slide} \\ \text{Play set} \end{matrix}$$

$$A = \begin{bmatrix} \overset{\text{Swing set}}{15} & \overset{\text{Slide}}{20} & \overset{\text{Play set}}{8} \\ 10 & 17 & 12 \end{bmatrix}$$

Determine and interpret the following matrices.

(a) AC (b) AS (c) $S - C$ (d) $A(S - C)$

17. **Investment Earnings** Teresa and Patrick want to invest money in three different college savings plans. Matrix A contains the percentages (in decimal form) invested in bonds, stocks, and a conservative fixed income fund for each of the three different plans. Matrix B gives the total amount invested in each of the three savings plans and matrix C gives the rates of return (in decimal form) for one year and for five years.

$$A = \begin{bmatrix} \overset{\text{Bonds}}{.50} & \overset{\text{Stocks}}{.43} & \overset{\text{Fixed Income}}{.07} \\ .45 & .26 & .29 \\ .40 & .40 & .20 \end{bmatrix} \begin{matrix} \text{Plan 1} \\ \text{Plan 2} \\ \text{Plan 3} \end{matrix}$$

$$B = \begin{bmatrix} \overset{\text{Plan 1}}{5000} & \overset{\text{Plan 2}}{8000} & \overset{\text{Plan 3}}{10{,}000} \end{bmatrix}$$

$$C = \begin{bmatrix} \overset{\text{One Year}}{.0032} & \overset{\text{Five Year}}{.1119} \\ .0233 & .0976 \\ .0320 & .0467 \end{bmatrix} \begin{matrix} \text{Plan 1} \\ \text{Plan 2} \\ \text{Plan 3} \end{matrix}$$

Calculate and interpret the following

(a) BA (b) BC
(c) the row 1, column 2 entry of BA
(d) the row 1, column 1 entry of BC

18. **Job Earnings** Sara, Quinn, Tamia, and Zack are working at the pool this summer. One week they spend the following amounts of time at three different tasks.

$$A = \begin{bmatrix} \overset{\text{Concessions}}{11} & \overset{\text{Front Desk}}{7} & \overset{\text{Cleaning}}{12} \\ 9 & 5 & 16 \\ 13 & 8 & 9 \\ 13 & 7 & 10 \end{bmatrix} \begin{matrix} \text{Sara} \\ \text{Quinn} \\ \text{Tamia} \\ \text{Zack} \end{matrix}$$

The hourly pay (in dollars) for the three different tasks is given by

$$B = \begin{bmatrix} 8 \\ 6 \\ 9 \end{bmatrix} \begin{matrix} \text{Concessions} \\ \text{Front Desk} \\ \text{Cleaning} \end{matrix}$$

(a) Calculate and interpret the matrix AB.

(b) Who earned the most that week? Who earned the least?

(c) If the hourly pay for concessions is changed to $9 and the hourly pay for cleaning is changed to $8, who earns the most that week?

(d) How many hours did Sara work that week?

19. **Fruit Baskets** The produce department at a grocery store makes fruit baskets of apples, bananas, and oranges. The cost for each apple is $.85, for each banana is $.20, and for each orange is $.76. Suppose each basket needs to have 18 pieces of fruit and costs $9 to make. How many apples, bananas, and oranges are in each basket if the number of bananas in each basket is the same as the number of apples and oranges together?

20. **Nuclear Disarmament** In an arms race between two superpowers, each nation takes stock of its own and its enemy's nuclear arsenal each year. Each nation has the policy of dismantling a certain percentage of its stockpile each year and adding that same percentage of its competitor's stockpile. Nation A dismantles 20% and nation B dismantles 10%. Suppose that the current stockpiles of nations A and B are 10,000 and 7000 weapons, respectively.

(a) What will the stockpiles be in each of the next two years?

(b) What were the stockpiles in each of the preceding two years?

(c) Show that the "missile gap" between the superpowers decreases by 30% each year under these policies. Show that the total number of weapons decreases each year if nation A begins with the most weapons, and the total number of weapons increases if nation B begins with the most weapons.

21. **Two-Sector Economy** The economy of a small country can be regarded as consisting of two industries, I and II, whose input–output matrix is

$$A = \begin{bmatrix} .4 & .2 \\ .1 & .3 \end{bmatrix}.$$

How many units should be produced by each industry in order to meet a demand for 8 units from industry I and 12 units from industry II?

22. **Coins PE** Joe has $3.30 in his pocket made up of nickels, dimes, and quarters. There are 30 coins and there are five times as many dimes as quarters. How many quarters does Joe have?

(a) 4   (b) 5   (c) 6   (d) 7   (e) 8

Conceptual Exercises

23. Identify each statement as true or false.

(a) If a system of linear equations has two different solutions, it must have infinitely many solutions.

(b) If a system of linear equations has more equations than variables, it cannot have a unique solution.

(c) If a system of linear equations has more variables than equations, then it must have infinitely many solutions.

24. Make up a system of two linear equations that has infinitely many solutions. No solution.

25. If the product of two numbers is zero, then one of the numbers must be zero. If the two matrices A and B are such that AB is a matrix of all zeros, must A or B be a matrix of all zeros?

26. Suppose that we try to solve the matrix equation $AX = B$ by using matrix inversion but find that even though the matrix A is a square matrix, it has no inverse. What can be said about the outcome from solving the associated system of linear equations by the Gauss–Jordan elimination method?

27. Why should the numbers in a single column of an input–output matrix have a sum that is less than 1?

CHAPTER TEST

1. Solve the following system of linear equations by using the Gauss–Jordan elimination method.

$$\begin{cases} x + 2y + z = 5 \\ 2x - y + z = -5 \\ -3x + y - 2z = 8 \end{cases}$$

2. Each of the following is the final matrix of a Gauss–Jordan elimination process. Give the solutions to the corresponding systems of linear equations.

(a) $\begin{bmatrix} 1 & 0 & 0 & | & 4 \\ 0 & 1 & 0 & | & -3 \\ 0 & 0 & 1 & | & 6 \end{bmatrix}$ (b) $\begin{bmatrix} 1 & 0 & 0 & | & 2 \\ 0 & 1 & 0 & | & 3 \\ 0 & 0 & 1 & | & 5 \end{bmatrix}$

(c) $\begin{bmatrix} 1 & 0 & 0 & | & 1 \\ 0 & 1 & 0 & | & -3 \\ 0 & 0 & 1 & | & 4 \\ 0 & 0 & 0 & | & 2 \end{bmatrix}$ (d) $\begin{bmatrix} 1 & 0 & -1 & | & 2 \\ 0 & 1 & 2 & | & 2 \end{bmatrix}$

(e) $\begin{bmatrix} 1 & 2 & 0 & | & 0 \\ 0 & 0 & 1 & | & 0 \\ 0 & 0 & 0 & | & 0 \end{bmatrix}$

3. The following is the general solution to a system of linear equations. Find a *specific* solution.

$$\begin{cases} w = \text{any value} \\ z = \text{any value} \\ y = 2x + w - z \\ x = w + z \end{cases}$$

4. Find three solutions to the system

$$\begin{cases} x + y - 2z = 15 \\ \quad\;\; y + 4z = \;\; 6. \end{cases}$$

5. Let matrices A, B, and C be defined as shown. Calculate the following matrices whenever they are defined: $A + B$, $A + C$, AB, AC, BC.

$$A = \begin{bmatrix} 2 & 1 & 0 \\ 3 & 2 & 1 \end{bmatrix} \quad B = \begin{bmatrix} -1 & 1 \\ 0 & 1 \\ 1 & -1 \end{bmatrix} \quad C = \begin{bmatrix} 0 & 1 & 2 \\ -1 & 1 & 1 \end{bmatrix}$$

6. Resource Allocation Making a large decorative plate for retail sale takes $\frac{1}{2}$ hour molding time, 3 hours oven time, and 4 hours painting time. Vases require 1 hour molding time, 2.5 hours oven time, and 3 hours painting time. Bowls require 1 hour molding time, 2 hours oven time, and 2 hours painting time. We intend to produce x plates, y vases, and z bowls.

(a) Write three equations expressing molding time (m), oven time (v), and painting time (p) needed in terms of x, y, and z.

(b) Write the system as a matrix equation.

(c) Determine the number of hours each of molding time, oven time, and painting time to produce 100 plates, 300 vases, and 200 bowls.

7. Find A^{-1} if it exists, where

$$A = \begin{bmatrix} 1 & 2 & 1 \\ 0 & 1 & 1 \\ 1 & -1 & 0 \end{bmatrix}.$$

8. College Tuition The freshman class at State University has 1500 students. Out-of-state students pay $10,000 tuition, while in-state students are charged $4500 for tuition. The school collected $12,800,000 in tuition. How many students are in-state?

9. Three-Sector Economy In an economic system, each of three industries depends on the others for raw materials. To make $1 of processed wood requires 30¢ wood, 20¢ steel, and 10¢ coal. To make $1 of steel requires no wood, 30¢ steel, and 20¢ coal. To make $1 of coal requires 10¢ wood, 20¢ steel, and 5¢ coal. To allow for $1 consumption in wood, $4 consumption in steel, and $2 consumption in coal, what levels of production for wood, steel, and coal are required?

CHAPTER 2 | PROJECT

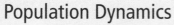

Population Dynamics

In 1991 the U.S. Fish and Wildlife Service proposed logging restrictions on nearly 12 million acres of Pacific Northwest forest to help save the endangered northern spotted owl. This decision caused considerable controversy between the logging industry and environmentalists.

Mathematical ecologists created a mathematical model to analyze the population dynamics of the spotted owl.[1] They divided the female owl population into three categories—juvenile (up to one year old), subadult (1 to 2 years old), and adult (over 2 years old). Suppose that in a certain region there are currently 2950 female spotted owls made up of 650 juveniles, 200 subadults, and 2100 adults. The ecologists used matrices to project the changes in the population from year to year. The original numbers can be displayed in the column matrix

$$X_0 = \begin{bmatrix} 650 \\ 200 \\ 2100 \end{bmatrix}_0 .$$

The populations after one year are given by the column matrix

$$X_1 = \begin{bmatrix} 693 \\ 117 \\ 2116 \end{bmatrix}_1 .$$

The subscript 1 tells us that the matrix gives the population after one year. The column matrices for subsequent years will have subscripts 2, 3, 4, etc.

1. How many subadult females are there after one year?

2. Did the total population of females increase or decrease during the year?

Let A denote the matrix

$$\begin{bmatrix} 0 & 0 & .33 \\ .18 & 0 & 0 \\ 0 & .71 & .94 \end{bmatrix} .$$

According to the mathematical model, subsequent population distributions are generated by multiplication on the left by A. That is,

$$A \cdot X_0 = X_1, \quad A \cdot X_1 = X_2, \quad A \cdot X_2 = X_3, \ldots .$$

If the population distribution at any time is given by $\begin{bmatrix} j \\ s \\ a \end{bmatrix}$, then the distribution one year later is $A \cdot \begin{bmatrix} j \\ s \\ a \end{bmatrix}$.

3. Fill in the blanks in the following statements.
   (a) Each year _____ juvenile females are born for each 100 adult females.
   (b) Each year _____% of the juvenile females survive to become subadults.
   (c) Each year _____% of the subadults survive to become adults and _____% of the adults survive.

---

[1]Lamberson, R. H., R. McKelvey, B. R. Noon, and C. Voss, "A Dynamic Analysis of Northern Spotted Owl Viability in a Fragmented Forest Landscape," *Conservation Biology*, Vol. 6, No. 4, December 1992; 505–512.

4. Calculate the column matrices X_2, X_3, X_4, and X_5. (*Note*: With a graphing calculator you can specify matrix **[A]** to be the 3×3 matrix A and specify **[B]** to be the initial 3×1 population matrix X_0. Display **[B]** in the home screen and then enter the command **[A]∗Ans**. Each press of the ENTER key will generate the next population distribution matrix. *Tip*: Prior to generating the matrices invoke the MODE list and set Float to 0 so that all numbers in the population matrices will be rounded to whole numbers.)

5. Refer to item 4. Is the total female population increasing, decreasing, or neither during the first five years?

6. Explain why calculating **[A]**$^\wedge$**50∗[B]** gives the column matrix for the population distribution after 50 years.

7. Find the projected population matrix after 50 years; after 100 years; after 150 years. Based on this mathematical model, what do you conclude about the prospects for the northern spotted owl?

In this model, the main impediment to the survival of the owl is the number .18 in the second row of matrix A. This number is low for two reasons. The first year of life is precarious for most animals living in the wild. In addition, juvenile owls must eventually leave the nest and establish their own territory. If much of the forest near their original home has been cleared, then they are vulnerable to predators while searching for a new home.

8. Suppose that due to better forest management, the number .18 can be increased to .26. Find the total female population for the first five years under this new assumption. Repeat item 7 and determine if extinction will be avoided under the new assumption.

SETS AND COUNTING

In this chapter we introduce some ideas useful in the study of probability (Chapter 6). Our first topic, the theory of sets, will provide a convenient language and notation in which to discuss probability. Using set theory, we develop a number of counting principles that can also be applied to computing probabilities.

5.1 Sets

In many applied problems one must consider collections of various sorts of objects. For example, a survey of unemployment might consider the collection of all U.S. cities with current unemployment greater than 7%. A study of birthrates might consider the collection of countries with a current birthrate less than 20 per 1000 population. Such collections are examples of sets. A **set** is any collection of objects. The objects, which may be countries, cities, years, numbers, letters, or anything else, are called the **elements** of the set. A set is often specified by a listing of its elements inside a pair of braces. For example, the set whose elements are the first six letters of the alphabet is written

$$\{a, b, c, d, e, f\}.$$

Similarly, the set whose elements are the even numbers between 1 and 11 is written

$$\{2, 4, 6, 8, 10\}.$$

We can also specify a set by giving a description of its elements (without actually listing the elements). For example, the set $\{a, b, c, d, e, f\}$ can also be written

$$\{\text{the first six letters of the alphabet}\},$$

and the set $\{2, 4, 6, 8, 10\}$ can be written

$$\{\text{all even numbers between 1 and 11}\}.$$

For convenience, we usually denote sets by capital letters, A, B, C, and so on. The great diversity of sets is illustrated by the following examples.

1. Let $C = \{\text{possible sequences of outcomes of tossing a coin three times}\}$. If we let H denote "heads" and T denote "tails," the various sequences can be easily described:

$$C = \{\text{HHH}, \text{THH}, \text{HTH}, \text{HHT}, \text{TTH}, \text{THT}, \text{HTT}, \text{TTT}\},$$

where, for instance, THH means "first toss tails, second toss heads, third toss heads."

2. Let $B = \{\text{license plate numbers consisting of three letters followed by three digits}\}$. Some typical elements of B are

$$\text{SBG 602}, \qquad \text{GXZ 179}, \qquad \text{YHJ 006}.$$

The number of elements in B is sufficiently large so that listing all of them is impractical. However, in this chapter we develop a technique that allows us to calculate the number of elements of B.

3. The graph of the equation $y = x^2$ is the set of all points (a, b) in the plane for which $b = a^2$. This set has infinitely many elements.

Sets arise in many practical contexts, as the next example shows.

EXAMPLE 1

Listing the elements of a set Table 1 gives the rate of inflation, as measured by the percentage change in the consumer price index, for the years from 1988 to 2007. Let

$$A = \{\text{years from 1988 to 2007 in which inflation was above 4\%}\}$$
$$B = \{\text{years from 1988 to 2007 in which inflation was below 3\%}\}.$$

Determine the elements of A and B.

Solution By reading Table 1, we see that

$$A = \{1988, 1989, 1990, 1991\}$$

Now Try Exercises 9(a) and (b)

$$B = \{1994, 1995, 1997, 1998, 1999, 2001, 2002, 2003, 2004, 2007\}. \qquad \blacksquare$$

Suppose that we are given two sets, A and B. Then it is possible to form new sets from A and B.

DEFINITION Union and Intersection of Two Sets The **union** of A and B, written $A \cup B$ and pronounced "A union B," is defined as follows:

$A \cup B$ is the set of all elements that belong to either A or B (or both).

The **intersection** of A and B, written $A \cap B$ and pronounced "A intersection B," is defined as follows:

$A \cap B$ is the set of all elements that belong to both A and B.

TABLE 1

Year	Inflation (%)	Year	Inflation (%)
1988	4.1	1998	1.6
1989	4.8	1999	2.2
1990	5.4	2000	3.4
1991	4.2	2001	2.8
1992	3.0	2002	1.6
1993	3.0	2003	2.3
1994	2.6	2004	2.7
1995	2.8	2005	3.4
1996	3.0	2006	3.2
1997	2.3	2007	2.8

For example, let $A = \{1, 2, 3, 4\}$ and $B = \{1, 3, 5, 7, 11\}$. Then

$$A \cup B = \{1, 2, 3, 4, 5, 7, 11\}$$
$$A \cap B = \{1, 3\}.$$

EXAMPLE 2

The intersection and union of sets   Table 2 on the next page gives the rates of unemployment and inflation for the years from 1994 to 2007. Let

$A = \{$years from 1994 to 2007 in which unemployment is at least 5%$\}$

$B = \{$years from 1994 to 2007 in which the inflation rate is at least 3%$\}$.

(a) Describe the sets $A \cap B$ and $A \cup B$.

(b) Determine the elements of A, B, $A \cap B$, and $A \cup B$.

Solution **(a)** From the descriptions of A and B, we have

$A \cap B = \{$years from 1994 to 2007 in which unemployment is at least 5% and inflation is at least 3%$\}$

$A \cup B = \{$years from 1994 to 2007 in which either unemployment is at least 5% or inflation is at least 3% (or both)$\}$.

(b) From the table we see that

$$A = \{1994, 1995, 1996, 2002, 2003, 2004, 2005\}$$

$$B = \{1996, 2000, 2005, 2006\}$$

$$A \cap B = \{1996, 2005\}$$

$$A \cup B = \{1994, 1995, 1996, 2000, 2002, 2003, 2004, 2005, 2006\}. \qquad \blacksquare$$

Now Try Exercises 9(c) and (d)

We have defined the union and the intersection of two sets. In a similar manner, we can define the union and intersection of any number of sets. For example, if A, B, and C are three sets, then their union, denoted $A \cup B \cup C$, is the set whose elements are precisely those that belong to at least one of the sets A, B, and C. Similarly, the intersection of A, B, and C, denoted $A \cap B \cap C$, is the set consisting of those elements that belong to all the sets A, B, and C. In a similar way, we may define the union and intersection of more than three sets.

Suppose we are given a set A. We may form new sets by selecting elements from A. Sets formed in this way are called *subsets* of A.

TABLE 2		
Year	Unemployment (%)	Inflation (%)
1994	6.1	2.6
1995	5.6	2.8
1996	5.4	3.0
1997	4.9	2.3
1998	4.5	1.6
1999	4.2	2.2
2000	4.0	3.4
2001	4.7	2.8
2002	5.8	1.6
2003	6.0	2.3
2004	5.5	2.7
2005	5.1	3.4
2006	4.6	3.2
2007	4.6	2.8

DEFINITION Subset of a Set The set B is a **subset** of the set A, written $B \subseteq A$ and pronounced "B is a subset of A," provided every element of B is an element of A.

For example, $\{1, 3\} \subseteq \{1, 2, 3\}$.

One set that is considered very often is the set that contains no elements at all. This set is called the **empty set** (or *null set*) and is written $\emptyset$. The empty set is a subset of every set.[1]

EXAMPLE 3

Listing the subsets of a set Let $A = \{a, b, c\}$. Find all subsets of A.

Solution Since A contains three elements, every subset of A has at most three elements. We look for subsets according to the number of elements:

Number of elements in subset	Possible subsets
0	$\emptyset$
1	$\{a\}, \{b\}, \{c\}$
2	$\{a, b\}, \{a, c\}, \{b, c\}$
3	$\{a, b, c\}$

Thus we see that A has eight subsets, namely those listed on the right. (Note that we count A as a subset of itself.)

Now Try Exercise 5

It is usually convenient to regard all sets involved in a particular discussion as subsets of a single larger set. Thus, for example, if a problem involves the sets $\{a, b, c\}, \{e, f\}, \{g\}, \{b, x, y\}$, then we can regard all of these as subsets of the set

$$U = \{\text{all letters of the alphabet}\}.$$

---

[1]Here is why: Let A be any set. Every element of $\emptyset$ also belongs to A. If you do not agree, then you must produce an element of $\emptyset$ that does not belong to A. But you cannot, since $\emptyset$ has no elements. So $\emptyset \subseteq A$.

Since U contains all elements being discussed, it is called a **universal set** (for the particular problem). In this book we shall specify the particular universal set we have in mind or it will be clearly defined by the context.

The set A contained in the universal set U has a counterpart, called its complement.

DEFINITION Complement of a Set The **complement** of A, written A' and pronounced "A complement," is defined as follows:

A' is the set of all elements in the universal set U that do not belong to A.

For example, let $U = \{1, 2, 3, 4, 5, 6, 7, 8, 9\}$ and $A = \{2, 4, 6, 8\}$. Then

$$A' = \{1, 3, 5, 7, 9\}.$$

EXAMPLE 4

Finding the complement of a set Let $U = \{a, b, c, d, e, f, g\}$, $S = \{a, b, c\}$, and $T = \{a, c, d\}$. List the elements of the following sets.

(a) S' **(b)** T' **(c)** $(S \cap T)'$ **(d)** $S' \cap T'$ **(e)** $S' \cup T'$

Solution **(a)** S' consists of those elements of U that are not in S, so $S' = \{d, e, f, g\}$.

(b) Similarly, $T' = \{b, e, f, g\}$.

(c) To determine $(S \cap T)'$, we must first determine $S \cap T$:

$$S \cap T = \{a, c\}.$$

Then we determine the complement of this set:

$$(S \cap T)' = \{b, d, e, f, g\}.$$

(d) We determined S' and T' in parts (a) and (b). The set $S' \cap T'$ consists of the elements that belong to both S' and T'. Therefore, referring to parts (a) and (b), we have

$$S' \cap T' = \{e, f, g\}.$$

(e) Since $S' \cup T'$ consists of the elements that belong to S' or T' (or both),

$$S' \cup T' = \{b, d, e, f, g\}.$$

Now Try Exercises 9(e) and (f)

NOTE ▶ The results of parts (c) and (d) show that in general $(S \cap T)'$ *is not* the same as $S' \cap T'$. In the next section, we show that $(S \cap T)'$ *is* the same as $S' \cup T'$. ■

The Greek letter $\in$ (epsilon) is commonly used with sets as a shorthand for "is an element of." For instance, if $S = \{H, T\}$, then $H \in S$. The letter $\in$ should not be confused with the symbol $\subseteq$. For instance, $H \in S$, but $\{H\} \subseteq S$. The symbol $\notin$ is shorthand for "is not an element of." The letter $\in$ can be used to define union, intersection, complement, and subset.

DEFINITION

$A \cup B$ is the set of all x such that $x \in A$ or $x \in B$.

$A \cap B$ is the set of all x such that $x \in A$ and $x \in B$.

A' is the set of all $x \in U$ such that $x \notin A$.

$B \subseteq A$ if $x \in A$ whenever $x \in B$.

Practice Problems 5.1

1. Let $U = \{a, b, c, d, e, f, g\}$, $R = \{a, b, c, d\}$, $S = \{c, d, e\}$, and $T = \{c, e, g\}$. List the elements of the following sets.

   (a) R' (b) $R \cap S$

   (c) $(R \cap S) \cap T$ (d) $R \cap (S \cap T)$

2. Let $U = \{$all Nobel Prize winners$\}$, $W = \{$women who have won Nobel Prizes$\}$, $A = \{$Americans who have won Nobel Prizes$\}$, $L = \{$winners of the Nobel Prize in literature$\}$. Describe the following sets.

   (a) W' (b) $A \cap L'$ (c) $W \cap A \cap L'$

3. Refer to Problem 2. Use set-theoretic notation to describe $\{$Nobel Prize winners who are American men or recipients of the Nobel Prize in literature$\}$.

EXERCISES 5.1

1. Let $U = \{1, 2, 3, 4, 5, 6, 7\}$, $S = \{1, 2, 3, 4\}$, and $T = \{1, 3, 5, 7\}$. List the elements of the following sets.
   (a) S' (b) $S \cup T$ (c) $S \cap T$ (d) $S' \cap T$

2. Let $U = \{1, 2, 3, 4, 5\}$, $S = \{1, 2, 3\}$, and $T = \{5\}$. List the elements of the following sets.
   (a) S' (b) $S \cup T$ (c) $S \cap T$ (d) $S' \cap T$

3. Let $U = \{$all letters of the alphabet$\}$, $R = \{a, b, c\}$, $S = \{c, d, e, f\}$, and $T = \{x, y, z\}$. List the elements of the following sets.
   (a) $R \cup S$ (b) $R \cap S$ (c) $S \cap T$

4. Let $U = \{a, b, c, d, e, f, g\}$, $R = \{a\}$, $S = \{a, b\}$, and $T = \{b, d, e, f, g\}$. List the elements of the following sets.
   (a) $R \cup S$ (b) $R \cap S$ (c) T' (d) $T' \cup S$

5. List all subsets of the set $\{1, 2\}$.

6. List all subsets of the set $\{1\}$.

7. **College Students** Let $U = \{$all college students$\}$, $M = \{$all male college students$\}$, and $F = \{$all college students who like football$\}$. Describe the elements of the following sets.
   (a) $M \cap F$ (b) M' (c) $M' \cap F'$ (d) $M \cup F$

8. **Corporations** Let $U = \{$all corporations$\}$, $S = \{$all corporations with headquarters in New York City$\}$, and $T = \{$all privately owned corporations$\}$. Describe the elements of the following sets.
   (a) S' (b) T' (c) $S \cap T$ (d) $S \cap T'$

9. **S&P Index** The Standard and Poor's Index measures the price of a certain collection of 500 stocks. Table 3 compares the percentage change in the index during the first 5 business days of certain years with the per-centage change for the entire year. Let $U = \{$all years from 1980 to 2007$\}$, $S = \{$all years during which the in-dex increased by 2% or more during the first 5 days$\}$, and $T = \{$all years for which the index increased by 16% or more during the entire year$\}$. List the elements of the following sets.
   (a) S (b) T (c) $S \cap T$
   (d) $S \cup T$ (e) $S' \cap T$ (f) $S \cap T'$

10. **S&P Index** Refer to Table 3. Let $U = \{$all years from 1980 to 2007$\}$, $A = \{$all years during which the index declined during the first 5 days$\}$, and $B = \{$all years during which the index declined for the entire year$\}$. List the elements of the following sets.
    (a) A (b) B (c) $A \cap B$
    (d) $A' \cap B$ (e) $A \cap B'$

11. **S&P Index** Refer to Exercise 9. Describe verbally the fact that $S \cap T'$ has three elements.

12. **S&P Index** Refer to Exercise 10. Describe verbally the fact that $A \cap B'$ has nine elements.

13. Let $U = \{a, b, c, d, e, f\}$, $R = \{a, b, c\}$, $S = \{a, c, e\}$, and $T = \{e, f\}$. List the elements of the following sets.
    (a) $(R \cup S)'$ (b) $R \cup S \cup T$
    (c) $R \cap S \cap T$ (d) $R \cap S \cap T'$
    (e) $R' \cap S \cap T$ (f) $S \cup T$
    (g) $(R \cup S) \cap (R \cup T)$
    (h) $(R \cap S) \cup (R \cap T)$
    (i) $R' \cap T'$

14. Let $U = \{1, 2, 3, 4, 5\}$, $R = \{1, 3, 5\}$, $S = \{3, 4, 5\}$, and $T = \{2, 4\}$. List the elements of the following sets.
    (a) $R \cap S \cap T$ (b) $R \cap S \cap T'$ (c) $R \cap S' \cap T$
    (d) $R' \cap T$ (e) $R \cup S$ (f) $R' \cup R$
    (g) $(S \cap T)'$ (h) $S' \cup T'$

In Exercises 15–20, simplify the given expression.

15. $(S')'$ 16. $S \cap S'$ 17. $S \cup S'$
18. $S \cap \emptyset$ 19. $T \cap S \cap T'$ 20. $S \cup \emptyset$

Corporation *A large corporation classifies its many divisions by their performance in the preceding year. Let $P = \{$divisions that made a profit$\}$, $L = \{$divisions that had an increase in labor costs$\}$, and $T = \{$divisions whose total revenue increased$\}$. Describe the sets in Exercises 21–26 using set-theoretic notation.*

21. $\{$divisions that had increases in labor costs or total revenue$\}$

22. $\{$divisions that did not make a profit$\}$

TABLE 3 Percentage change in the Standard and Poor's index

Year	Percent change for first 5 days	Percent change for year	Year	Percent change for first 5 days	Percent change for year
2007	−0.4	3.5	1993	−1.5	7.1
2006	3.0	13.6	1992	0.2	4.5
2005	−2.1	3.0	1991	−4.6	26.3
2004	1.8	9.0	1990	0.1	−6.6
2003	3.4	26.4	1989	1.2	27.3
2002	1.1	−23.4	1988	−1.5	12.4
2001	−1.9	−13.0	1987	6.2	2.0
2000	−1.9	−10.1	1986	−1.6	14.6
1999	3.7	19.5	1985	−1.9	26.3
1998	−1.5	26.7	1984	2.4	1.4
1997	1.0	31.0	1983	3.3	17.3
1996	0.4	20.3	1982	−2.4	14.8
1995	0.3	34.1	1981	−2.0	−9.7
1994	0.7	−1.5	1980	0.9	25.8

23. {divisions that made a profit despite an increase in labor costs}

24. {divisions that had an increase in labor costs and either were unprofitable or did not increase their total revenue}

25. {profitable divisions with increases in labor costs and total revenue}

26. {divisions that were unprofitable or did not have increases in either labor costs or total revenue}

Automobile Insurance *An automobile insurance company classifies applicants by their driving records for the previous three years. Let S = {applicants who have received speeding tickets}, A = {applicants who have caused accidents}, and D = {applicants who have been arrested for driving while intoxicated}. Describe the sets in Exercises 27–32 using set-theoretic notation.*

27. {applicants who have not received speeding tickets}

28. {applicants who have caused accidents and been arrested for drunk driving}

29. {applicants who have received speeding tickets, caused accidents, or been arrested for drunk driving}

30. {applicants who have not been arrested for drunk driving but have received speeding tickets or have caused accidents}

31. {applicants who have not both caused accidents and received speeding tickets but who have been arrested for drunk driving}

32. {applicants who have not caused accidents or have not been arrested for drunk driving}

College Teachers and Students *Let U = {people at Mount College}, A = {students at Mount College}, B = {teachers at Mount College}, C = {females at Mount College}, and D = {males at Mount College}. Describe verbally the sets in Exercises 33–40.*

33. $A \cap D$ **34.** $B \cap C$ **35.** $A \cap B$ **36.** $B \cup C$

37. $A \cup C'$ **38.** $(A \cap D)'$ **39.** D' **40.** $D \cap U$

Ice Cream Preferences *Let U = {all people}, S = {people who like strawberry ice cream}, V = {people who like vanilla ice cream}, and C = {people who like chocolate ice cream}. Describe the sets in Exercises 41–46 using set-theoretic notation.*

41. {people who don't like strawberry ice cream}

42. {people who like vanilla but not chocolate ice cream}

43. {people who like vanilla or chocolate but not strawberry ice cream}

44. {people who don't like any of the three flavors of ice cream}

45. {people who like neither chocolate nor vanilla ice cream}

46. {people who like only strawberry ice cream}

47. Let U be the set of vertices in Fig. 1 on the next page. Let R = {vertices (x, y) with $x > 0$}, S = {vertices (x, y) with $y > 0$}, and T = {vertices (x, y) with $x \leq y$}. List the elements of the following sets.
  (a) R **(b)** S **(c)** T
  (d) $R' \cup S$ **(e)** $R' \cap T$ **(f)** $R \cap S \cap T$

T.C.S

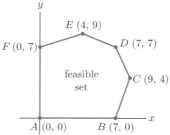

Figure 1

48. Topping Choices Sam ordered a baked potato at a restaurant. The waitress offered him butter, cheese, and chives as toppings. How many different ways could he have his potato? List them.

49. Let $S = \{1, 3, 5, 7\}$ and $T = \{2, 5, 7\}$. Give an example of a subset of T that is not a subset of S.

50. Suppose that S and T are subsets of the set U. Under what circumstance will $S \cap T = T$?

51. Suppose that S and T are subsets of the set U. Under what circumstance will $S \cup T = T$?

52. Find three subsets of the set of integers from 1 through 10, R, S, and T, such that $R \cup (S \cap T)$ is different from $(R \cup S) \cap T$.

In Exercises 53–60, determine if the statement is true or false.

53. $5 \in \{3, 5, 7\}$ **54.** $\{1, 3\} \subseteq \{1, 2, 3\}$

55. $\{b\} \subseteq \{b, c\}$ **56.** $0 \in \{1, 2, 3\}$

57. $0 \in \varnothing$ **58.** $\varnothing \subseteq \{a, b, c\}$

59. $\{b, c\} \subseteq \{b, c\}$ **60.** $1 \notin \{1\}$

Solutions to Practice Problems 5.1

1. **(a)** $\{e, f, g\}$ **(b)** $\{c, d\}$

(c) $\{c\}$. This problem asks for the intersection of two sets. The first set is $R \cap S = \{c, d\}$ and the second set is $T = \{c, e, g\}$. The intersection of these sets is $\{c\}$.

(d) $\{c\}$. Here again the problem asks for the intersection of two sets. However, now the first set is $R = \{a, b, c, d\}$ and the second set is $S \cap T = \{c, e\}$. The intersection of these sets is $\{c\}$.
[*Note:* It should be expected that the set $(R \cap S) \cap T$ is the same as the set $R \cap (S \cap T)$, for each set consists of those elements that are in all three sets. Therefore, each of these sets equals the set $R \cap S \cap T$.]

2. **(a)** $W' = \{$men who have won Nobel Prizes$\}$. This is so since W' consists of those elements of U that are not in W—that is, those Nobel Prize winners who are not women.

(b) $A \cap L' = \{$Americans who have received Nobel Prizes in fields other than literature$\}$.

(c) $W \cap A \cap L' = \{$American women who have received Nobel Prizes in fields other than literature$\}$. This is so since to qualify for $W \cap A \cap L'$, a Nobel Prize winner must simultaneously be in W, in A, and in L'—that is, a woman, an American, and not a winner of the Nobel Prize in literature.

3. $(A \cap W') \cup L$

5.2 A Fundamental Principle of Counting

A counting problem is one that requires us to determine the number of elements in a set S. Counting problems arise in many applications of mathematics and comprise the mathematical field of **combinatorics**. We shall study a number of different sorts of counting problems in the remainder of this chapter.

If S is any set, we will denote the number of elements in S by $n(S)$. For example, if $S = \{1, 7, 11\}$, then $n(S) = 3$, and if $S = \{a, b, c, d, e, f, g, h, i\}$, then $n(S) = 9$. Of course, if $S = \varnothing$, the empty set, then $n(S) = 0$. (The empty set contains no elements.)

Let us begin by stating one of the fundamental principles of counting, the *inclusion–exclusion principle*.

Inclusion–Exclusion Principle Let S and T be sets. Then

$$n(S \cup T) = n(S) + n(T) - n(S \cap T). \qquad (1)$$

Notice that formula (1) connects the four quantities $n(S \cup T)$, $n(S)$, $n(T)$, and $n(S \cap T)$. Given any three, the remaining quantity can be determined by using this formula.

To test the plausibility of the inclusion–exclusion principle, consider this example. Let $S = \{a, b, c, d, e\}$ and $T = \{a, c, g, h\}$. Then

$$S \cup T = \{a, b, c, d, e, g, h\} \qquad n(S \cup T) = 7$$
$$S \cap T = \{a, c\} \qquad n(S \cap T) = 2.$$

In this case the inclusion–exclusion principle reads

$$n(S \cup T) = n(S) + n(T) - n(S \cap T)$$
$$7 \quad = \quad 5 \quad + \quad 4 \quad - \quad 2,$$

which is correct.

Here is the reason for the validity of the inclusion–exclusion principle: The left side of formula (1) is $n(S \cup T)$, the number of elements in either S or T (or both). As a first approximation to this number, add the number of elements in S to the number of elements in T, obtaining $n(S) + n(T)$. However, if an element lies in both S and T, it is counted twice—once in $n(S)$ and again in $n(T)$. To make up for this double counting we must subtract the number of elements counted twice, namely $n(S \cap T)$. So doing gives us $n(S) + n(T) - n(S \cap T)$ as the number of elements in $S \cup T$.

When S and T have no elements in common, the inclusion–exclusion principle reduces to a simple sum.

Special Case of the Inclusion–Exclusion Principle If $S \cap T = \emptyset$, then

$$n(S \cup T) = n(S) + n(T).$$

The next example illustrates a typical use of the inclusion–exclusion principle in an applied problem.

EXAMPLE 1

Using the inclusion–exclusion principle In the year 2007, *Executive* magazine surveyed the presidents of the 500 largest corporations in the United States. Of these 500 people, 310 had degrees (of any sort) in business, 238 had undergraduate degrees in business, and 184 had graduate degrees in business. How many presidents had both undergraduate and graduate degrees in business?

Solution Let

$$S = \{\text{presidents with an undergraduate degree in business}\}$$
$$T = \{\text{presidents with a graduate degree in business}\}.$$

Then

$$S \cup T = \{\text{presidents with at least one degree in business}\}$$
$$S \cap T = \{\text{presidents with both undergraduate and graduate degrees in business}\}.$$

From the data given we have

$$n(S) = 238 \qquad n(T) = 184 \qquad n(S \cup T) = 310.$$

The problem asks for $n(S \cap T)$. By the inclusion–exclusion principle we have

$$n(S \cup T) = n(S) + n(T) - n(S \cap T)$$

$$310 = 238 + 184 - n(S \cap T)$$

$$n(S \cap T) = 112.$$

That is, exactly 112 of the presidents had both undergraduate and graduate degrees in business.

Now Try Exercise 9

It is possible to visualize sets geometrically by means of drawings known as **Venn diagrams**. Such graphical representations of sets are very useful tools in solving counting problems. In order to describe Venn diagrams, let us begin with a single set S contained in a universal set U. Draw a rectangle and view its points as the elements of U [Fig. 1(a)]. To show that S is a subset of U, we draw a circle inside the rectangle and view S as the set of points in the circle [Fig. 1(b)]. The resulting diagram is called a Venn diagram of S. It illustrates the proper relationship between S and U. Since S' consists of those elements of U that are not in S, we may view the portion of the rectangle that is outside of the circle as representing S' [Fig. 1(c)].

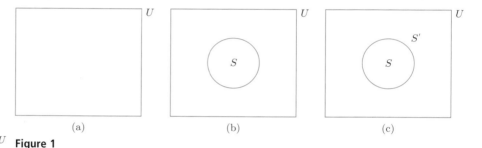

(a)   (b)   (c)

Figure 1

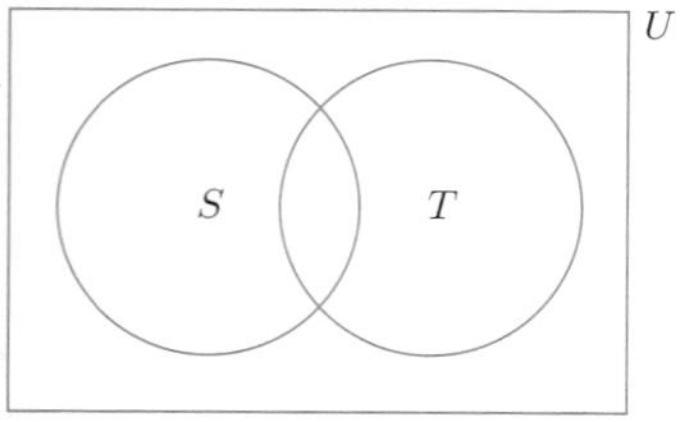

Venn diagrams are particularly useful for visualizing the relationship between two or three sets. Suppose that we are given two sets S and T in a universal set U. As before, we represent each of the sets by means of a circle inside the rectangle (Fig. 2).

We can now illustrate a number of sets by shading in appropriate regions of the rectangle. For instance, in Fig. 3 we have shaded the regions corresponding to T, $S \cup T$, and $S \cap T$, respectively.

Figure 2

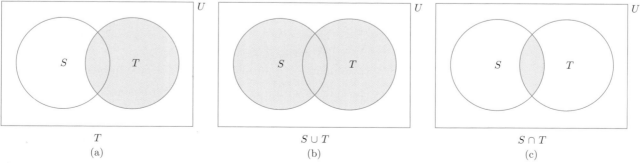

T $S \cup T$ $S \cap T$
(a)   (b)   (c)

Figure 3

EXAMPLE 2   **Shading portions of a Venn diagram** Shade the portions of the rectangle corresponding to the sets

(a) $S \cap T'$ (b) $(S \cap T')'$

Solution **(a)** $S \cap T'$ consists of the points in S and in T', that is, the points in S and not in T. So we shade the points that are in the circle S but are not in the circle T [Fig. 4(a)].

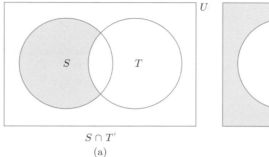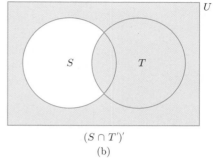

$S \cap T'$
(a)

$(S \cap T')'$
(b)

Figure 4

Now Try Exercises 15 and 19

(b) $(S \cap T')'$ is the complement of the set $S \cap T'$. Therefore, it consists of exactly those points not shaded in Fig. 4(a). [See Fig. 4(b).]   ■

In a similar manner, Venn diagrams can illustrate intersections and unions of three sets. Some representative regions are shaded in Fig. 5.

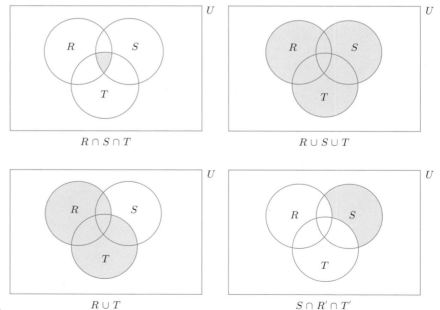

$R \cap S \cap T$

$R \cup S \cup T$

$R \cup T$

$S \cap R' \cap T'$

Figure 5

There are many formulas expressing relationships between intersections and unions of sets. Possibly the most fundamental are the two formulas known as *De Morgan's laws.*

De Morgan's Laws   Let S and T be sets. Then

$$(S \cup T)' = S' \cap T' \quad \text{and} \quad (S \cap T)' = S' \cup T'. \tag{2}$$

In other words, De Morgan's laws state that to form the complement of a union (or intersection), form the complements of the individual sets and change unions to intersections (or intersections to unions).

Verification of De Morgan's Laws   Let us use Venn diagrams to describe $(S \cup T)'$. In Fig. 6(a) we have shaded the region corresponding to $S \cup T$. In Fig. 6(b) we have shaded the region corresponding to $(S \cup T)'$. On the other hand, in Fig. 6(c) we have shaded the region corresponding to S' and in Fig. 6(d) the region corresponding to T'. By considering the common shaded regions of Fig. 6(c) and (d), we arrive at the shaded region corresponding to $S' \cap T'$ [Fig. 6(e)]. Note that this is the same region as shaded in Fig. 6(b). Therefore,

$$(S \cup T)' = S' \cap T'.$$

This verifies the first of De Morgan's laws. The proof of the second law is similar. ∎

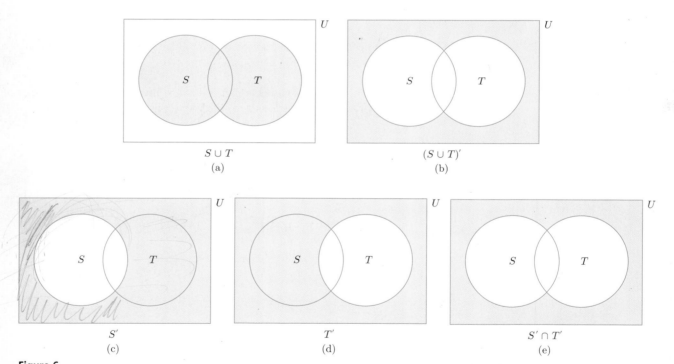

$S \cup T$
(a)

$(S \cup T)'$
(b)

S'
(c)

T'
(d)

$S' \cap T'$
(e)

Figure 6

Practice Problems 5.2

1. Draw a two-circle Venn diagram and shade the portion corresponding to the set $(S \cap T') \cup (S \cap T)$.

2. What does the inclusion–exclusion principle conclude when T is a subset of S?

EXERCISES 5.2

1. Find $n(S \cup T)$, given that $n(S) = 5$, $n(T) = 4$, and $n(S \cap T) = 2$.

2. Find $n(S \cup T)$, given that $n(S) = 17$, $n(T) = 13$, and $n(S \cap T) = 9$.

3. Find $n(S \cap T)$, given that $n(S) = 7$, $n(T) = 8$, and $n(S \cup T) = 15$.

4. Find $n(S \cap T)$, given that $n(S) = 4$, $n(T) = 12$, and $n(S \cup T) = 15$.

5. Find $n(S)$, given that $n(T) = 7$, $n(S \cap T) = 5$, and $n(S \cup T) = 13$.

6. Find $n(T)$, given that $n(S) = 14$, $n(S \cap T) = 6$, and $n(S \cup T) = 14$.

7. If $n(S) = n(S \cap T)$, what can you conclude about S and T?

8. If $n(S) = n(S \cup T)$, what can you conclude about S and T?

9. **Languages** Suppose that each of the 245 million adults in South America is fluent in Portuguese or Spanish. If 134 million are fluent in Portuguese and 130 million are fluent in Spanish, how many are fluent in both languages?

10. **Course Enrollments** Suppose that all of the 1000 first-year students at a certain college are enrolled in a math or an English course. Suppose that 400 are taking both math and English and 600 are taking English. How many are taking a math course?

11. **Symmetry of Letters** Of the 26 capital letters of the alphabet, 11 have vertical symmetry (for instance, A, M, and T), 9 have horizontal symmetry (such as B, C, and D), and 4 have both (H, I, O, X). How many letters have no symmetry?

12. **Magazine Subscriptions** A survey of employees in a certain company revealed that 300 people subscribe to *Newsweek*, 200 subscribe to *Time*, and 50 subscribe to both. How many people subscribe to at least one of these magazines?

13. **Automobile Options** Motors Inc. manufactured 325 cars with automatic transmissions, 216 with power steering, and 89 with both of these options. How many cars were manufactured with at least one of the two options?

14. **Investments** A survey of 100 investors in stocks and bonds revealed that 80 investors owned stocks and 70 owned bonds. How many investors owned both stocks and bonds?

In Exercises 15–26, draw a two-circle Venn diagram and shade the portion corresponding to the set.

15. $S' \cap T$

16. $S' \cap T'$

17. $S \cup T'$

18. $S' \cup T'$

19. $(S' \cap T)'$

20. $(S \cap T)'$

21. $(S \cap T') \cup (S' \cap T)$

22. $(S \cap T) \cup (S' \cap T')$

23. $S \cup (S \cap T)$

24. $S \cup (T' \cup S)$

25. $S \cup S'$

26. $S \cap S'$

In Exercises 27–38, draw a three-circle Venn diagram and shade the portion corresponding to the set.

27. $R \cap S \cap T'$

28. $R' \cap S' \cap T$

29. $R \cup (S \cap T)$

30. $R \cap (S \cup T)$

31. $R \cap (S' \cup T)$

32. $R' \cup (S \cap T')$

33. $R \cap T$

34. $S \cap T'$

35. $R' \cap S' \cap T'$

36. $(R \cup S \cup T)'$

37. $(R \cap T) \cup (S \cap T')$

38. $(R \cup S') \cap (R \cup T')$

In Exercises 39–44, use De Morgan's laws to simplify the given expression.

39. $S' \cup (S \cap T)'$

40. $T \cap (S \cup T)'$

41. $(S' \cup T)'$

42. $(S' \cap T')'$

43. $T \cup (S \cap T)'$

44. $(S' \cap T)' \cup S$

In Exercises 45–50, give a set-theoretic expression that describes the shaded portion of the Venn diagram.

45.
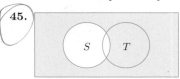

46.
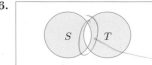

47.
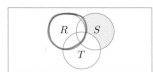

48.
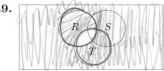

49.
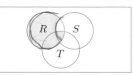

50.

By drawing a Venn diagram, replace each of the expressions in Exercises 51–53 with one involving at most one union and the complement symbol applied only to R, S, and T.

51. $(T \cap S) \cup (T \cap R) \cup (R \cap S') \cup (T \cap R' \cap S')$
52. $(R \cap S) \cup (S \cap T) \cup (R \cap S' \cap T')$
53. $((R \cap S') \cup (S \cap T') \cup (T \cap R'))'$

Citizenship *Assume the universal set U is the set of all people living in the United States. Let A be the set of all citizens, B be the set of all legal aliens, and C be the set of all illegal aliens. Let D be the set of all children under 5 years of age, E be the set of children from 5 to 18 years old, and F be the set of everyone over the age of 18. Let G be the set of all people who are employed. Describe in words the sets in Exercises 54–59.*

54. $E \cap G \cap B$ **55.** $C' \cup (G \cap F)$ **56.** $A \cap (F \cup G)$

57. $F \cap G'$ **58.** $A \cap B$ **59.** $(A' \cup B) \cap G'$

Solutions to Practice Problems 5.2

1. $(S \cap T') \cup (S \cap T)$ is given as a union of two sets, $S \cap T'$ and $S \cap T$. The Venn diagrams for these two sets are given in Fig. 7(a) and (b). The desired set consists of the elements that are in one or the other (or both) of the two sets. Therefore, its Venn diagram is obtained by shading everything that is shaded in either Fig. 7(a) or (b) [see Fig. 7(c)]. [*Note:* Looking at Fig. 7(c) reveals that $(S \cap T') \cup (S \cap T)$ and S are the same set. Often Venn diagrams can be used to simplify complicated set-theoretic expressions.]

2. Not much. When $T \subseteq S$, $S \cup T = S$ and $S \cap T = T$. The inclusion–exclusion principle becomes

$$n(S \cup T) = n(S) + n(T) - n(S \cap T)$$
$$n(S) = n(S) + n(T) - n(T)$$
$$n(S) = n(S)$$

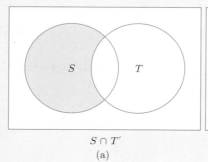

$S \cap T'$
(a)

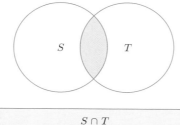

$S \cap T$
(b)

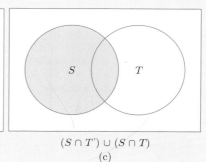

$(S \cap T') \cup (S \cap T)$
(c)

Figure 7

5.3 Venn Diagrams and Counting

In this section we discuss the use of Venn diagrams in solving counting problems. The techniques developed are especially useful in analyzing survey data.

Each Venn diagram divides the universal set U into a certain number of regions. For example, the Venn diagram for a single set divides U into two regions—the inside and outside of the circle [Fig. 1(a)]. The Venn diagram for two sets divides U into four regions [Fig. 1(b)]. And the Venn diagram for three sets divides U into eight regions [Fig. 1(c)]. Each of the regions is called a **basic region** for the Venn diagram. Knowing the number of elements in each basic region is of great use in many applied problems. As an illustration consider the following example.

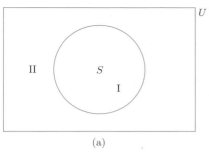

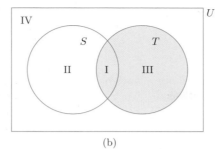

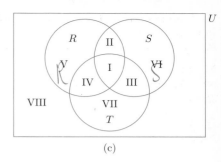

(a)   (b)   (c)

Figure 1

EXAMPLE 1

Nobel prize laureates   Let

$$U = \{\text{Nobel Prize laureates during the period 1901–2007}\}$$
$$A = \{\text{American Nobel Prize laureates during the period 1901–2007}\}$$
$$C = \{\text{Chemistry Nobel Prize laureates during the period 1901–2007}\}$$
$$P = \{\text{Nobel Peace Prize laureates during the period 1901–2007}\}.$$

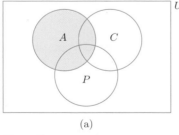

Figure 2

These sets are illustrated in the Venn diagram of Fig. 2 in which each basic region has been labeled with the number of elements in it.

(a) How many Americans received a Nobel Prize during the period 1901–2007?

(b) How many Americans received Nobel Prizes in fields other than chemistry and peace during this period?

(c) How many Americans received the Nobel Peace Prize during this period?

(d) How many people received Nobel Prizes during this period?

Solution **(a)** The number of Americans who received a Nobel Prize is the total contained in the circle A, which is

$$223 + 25 + 1 + 56 = 305 \quad [\text{Fig. 3(a)}].$$

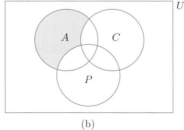

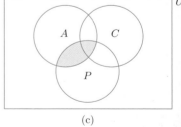

(a)   (b)   (c)

Figure 3

(b) The question asks for the number of Nobel laureates in A but not in C and not in P. So start with the A circle and eliminate those basic regions belonging to C or P [Fig. 3(b)]. There remains a single basic region with 223 Nobel laureates. Note that this region corresponds to $A \cap C' \cap P'$.

(c) The question asks for the number of elements in both A and P—that is, $n(A \cap P)$. But $A \cap P$ comprises two basic regions [Fig. 3(c)]. Thus, to compute $n(A \cap P)$ we add the numbers in these basic regions to obtain $25 + 1 = 26$ Americans who have received the Nobel Peace Prize.

(d) The number of recipients is just $n(U)$, and we obtain it by adding together the numbers corresponding to the basic regions. We obtain

$$310 + 223 + 56 + 1 + 25 + 93 + 0 + 89 = 797.$$ ■

One need not always be given the number of elements in each of the basic regions of a Venn diagram. Very often these data can be deduced from given information.

EXAMPLE 2

Corporate presidents Consider the set of 500 corporate presidents of Example 1, Section 5.2.

(a) Draw a Venn diagram displaying the given data, and determine the number of elements in each basic region.

(b) Determine the number of presidents having exactly one degree (graduate or undergraduate) in business.

Solution **(a)** Recall that we defined the following sets:

$$S = \{\text{presidents with an undergraduate degree in business}\}$$
$$T = \{\text{presidents with a graduate degree in business}\}.$$

We were given the following data:

$$n(S) = 238 \qquad n(T) = 184 \qquad n(S \cup T) = 310.$$

We draw a Venn diagram corresponding to S and T (Fig. 4). Notice that none of the given information corresponds to a basic region of the Venn diagram. So we must use our wits to determine the number of presidents in each of the regions I–IV. Region I is the complement of $S \cup T$, so it contains

$$n(U) - n(S \cup T) = 500 - 310 = 190$$

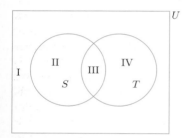

Figure 4

presidents. Region III is just $S \cap T$. By using the inclusion–exclusion principle, in Example 1, Section 5.2, we determined that $n(S \cap T) = 112$. Now the total number of presidents in II and III combined equals $n(S)$, or 238. Therefore, the number of presidents in II is

$$238 - 112 = 126.$$

Similarly, the number of presidents in IV is

$$184 - 112 = 72.$$

Thus we may fill in the data to obtain a completed Venn diagram (Fig. 5).

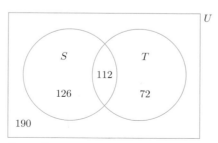

Figure 5

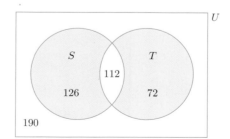

Figure 6

(b) The number of people with exactly one business degree corresponds to the shaded region in Fig. 6. Adding together the number of presidents in each of these regions gives $126 + 72 = 198$ presidents with exactly one business degree.   ■

Now Try Exercise 23

Here is another example illustrating the procedure for determining the number of elements in each of the basic regions of a Venn diagram.

EXAMPLE 3

Advertising media An advertising agency finds that the media use of its 170 clients is as follows:

115 use television (T) 95 use radio and magazines
100 use radio (R) 85 use television and magazines
130 use magazines (M) 70 use all three.
75 use television and radio

Use these data to complete the Venn diagram in Fig. 7 to display the clients' use of mass media.

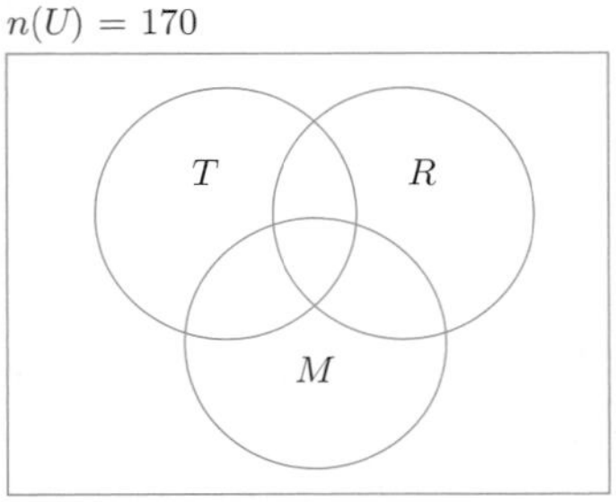

Solution Of the various data given, only the last item corresponds to one of the eight basic regions of the Venn diagram, namely the "70" corresponding to the use of all three media. So we begin by entering this number in the diagram [Fig. 8(a)]. We can fill in the rest of the Venn diagram by working with the remaining information one piece at a time in the reverse order that it is given. Since 85 clients advertise in television and magazines, $85 - 70 = 15$ advertise in television and magazines but not on radio. The appropriate region is labeled in Fig. 8(b). In Fig. 8(c) the next two pieces of information have been used in the same way to fill in two more basic regions. In Fig. 8(c) we observe that three of the four basic regions comprising M have been filled in. Since $n(M) = 130$, we deduce that the number of clients advertising only in magazines is $130 - (15 + 70 + 25) = 130 - 110 = 20$ [Fig. 9(a)]. By similar reasoning the number of clients using only radio advertising and the number using only television advertising can be determined [Fig. 9(b)]. Adding together the numbers in the three circles gives the number of clients utilizing television, radio, or magazines as $25 + 5 + 0 + 15 + 70 + 25 + 20 = 160$. Since there were 170 clients in total, the remainder—or $170 - 160 = 10$ clients—use none of these media. Figure 9(c) gives a complete display of the data. ■

$n(U) = 170$

Figure 7

Now Try Exercise 31(a)

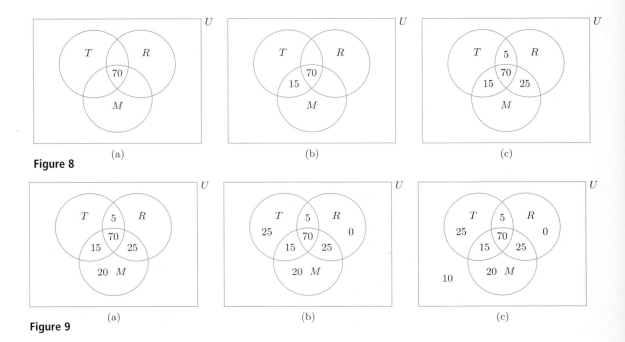

(a)   (b)   (c)

Figure 8

(a)   (b)   (c)

Figure 9

Practice Problems 5.3

1. Of the 1000 first-year students at a certain college, 700 take mathematics courses, 300 take mathematics and economics courses, and 200 do not take any mathematics or economics courses. Represent these data in a Venn diagram.

2. Refer to the Venn diagram from Problem 1.

   (a) How many of the first-year students take an economics course?

   (b) How many take an economics course but not a mathematics course?

EXERCISES 5.3

Family Library *The Venn diagram in Fig. 10 classifies the 100 books in a family's library as Hardback, Fiction, and Children's. Exercises 1–10 refer to this Venn diagram.*

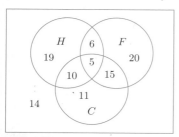

Figure 10

1. How many books are hardback fiction?

2. How many books are paperback fiction?

3. How many books are fiction?

4. How many books are nonfiction?

5. How many books are paperback nonfiction children's books?

6. How many books are adult hardback nonfiction?

7. How many books are either hardback or fiction?

8. How many hardback books are either fiction or children's books?

9. How many children's books are either hardback or fiction?

10. How many books are either hardback, fiction, or children's books?

In Exercises 11–22, let R, S, and T be subsets of the universal set U. Draw an appropriate Venn diagram and use the given data to determine the number of elements in each basic region.

11. $n(U) = 14$, $n(S) = 5$, $n(T) = 6$, $n(S \cap T) = 2$.

12. $n(U) = 20$, $n(S) = 11$, $n(T) = 7$, $n(S \cap T) = 7$.

13. $n(U) = 20$, $n(S) = 12$, $n(T) = 14$, $n(S \cup T) = 18$.

14. $n(S') = 6$, $n(S \cup T) = 10$, $n(S \cap T) = 5$, $n(T) = 7$.

15. $n(U) = 75$, $n(S) = 15$, $n(T) = 25$, $n(S' \cap T') = 40$.

16. $n(S) = 9$, $n(T) = 11$, $n(S \cap T) = 5$, $n(S') = 13$.

17. $n(S) = 3$, $n(S \cup T) = 6$, $n(T) = 4$, $n(S' \cup T') = 9$.

18. $n(U) = 15$, $n(S) = 8$, $n(T) = 9$, $n(S \cup T) = 14$.

19. $n(U) = 44$, $n(R) = 17$, $n(S) = 17$, $n(T) = 17$, $n(R \cap S) = 7$, $n(R \cap T) = 6$, $n(S \cap T) = 5$, $n(R \cap S \cap T) = 2$.

20. $n(U) = 29$, $n(R) = 10$, $n(S) = 12$, $n(T) = 10$, $n(R \cap S) = 1$, $n(R \cap T) = 5$, $n(S \cap T) = 4$, $n(R \cap S \cap T) = 1$.

21. $n(R') = 22$, $n(R \cup S) = 21$, $n(S) = 14$, $n(T) = 22$, $n(R \cap S) = 7$, $n(S \cap T) = 9$, $n(R \cap T) = 11$, $n(R \cap S \cap T) = 5$.

22. $n(U) = 64$, $n(R \cup S \cup T) = 45$, $n(R) = 22$, $n(T) = 26$, $n(R \cap S) = 4$, $n(S \cap T) = 6$, $n(R \cap T) = 8$, $n(R \cap S \cap T) = 1$.

23. **Music Preferences** A survey of 70 high school students revealed that 35 like rock music, 15 like hip-hop music, and 5 like both. How many of the students surveyed do not like either rock or hip-hop music?

24. **Nobel Prize Laureates** A total of 797 Nobel Prizes had been awarded by 2007. Fifteen of the 101 prizes in literature were awarded to Scandinavians. Scandinavians received a total of 55 awards. How many Nobel Prizes outside of literature have been awarded to non-Scandinavians?

25. **Analysis of Sonnet** One of Shakespeare's sonnets has a verb in 11 of its 14 lines, an adjective in 9 lines, and both in 7 lines. How many lines have a verb but no adjective? An adjective but no verb? Neither an adjective nor a verb?

Exam Performance *The results from an exam taken by 130 students were as follows:*

> *90 students correctly answered the first question*
> *62 students correctly answered the second question*
> *50 students correctly answered both questions.*

Exercises 26–30 refer to these students.

26. How many students correctly answered either the first or second question?

27. How many students did not answer either of the two questions correctly?

28. How many students answered either the first or the second question correctly, but not both?

29. How many students answered the second question correctly, but not the first?

30. How many students missed the second question?

31. Class Enrollment Out of 35 students in a finite math class, 22 are male, 19 are business majors, 27 are first-year students, 14 are male business majors, 17 are male first-year students, 15 are first-year students who are business majors, and 11 are male first-year business majors.

(a) Use these data to complete a Venn diagram displaying the characteristics of the students.

(b) How many upper class female non-business majors are in the class?

(c) How many female business majors are in the class?

32. Exercise Preferences A survey of 100 college faculty who exercise regularly found that 45 jog, 30 swim, 20 cycle, 6 jog and swim, 1 jogs and cycles, 5 swim and cycle, and 1 does all three. How many of the faculty members do not do any of these activities? How many just jog?

News Dissemination *A merchant surveyed 400 people to determine from where they found out about an upcoming sale. The results of the survey follow:*

> *180 from the Internet*
> *190 from television*
> *190 from newspapers*
> *80 from Internet and television*
> *90 from Internet and newspapers*
> *50 from television and newspapers*
> *30 from all three sources.*

Exercises 33–38 refer to the people in this survey.

33. How many people learned of the sale from newspapers or the Internet, but not both?

34. How many people learned of the sale only from newspapers?

35. How many people learned of the sale from the Internet or television but not newspapers?

36. How many people learned of the sale from at least two of the three media?

37. How many people learned of the sale from exactly one of the three media?

38. How many people learned of the sale from the Internet and television but not newspapers?

39. Course Enrollments PE Table 1 shows the number of students enrolled in each of three science courses at Gotham College. Although no students are enrolled in all three courses, 15 are enrolled in both Chemistry and Physics, 10 are enrolled in both Physics and Biology, and 5 are enrolled in both Biology and Chemistry. How many students are enrolled in at least one of these science courses?

(a) 75　(b) 80　(c) 90　(d) 100　(e) 130

TABLE 1	
Course	**Enrollment**
Chemistry	60
Physics	40
Biology	30

Foreign Language Courses *A survey in a local high school shows that of the 4000 students in the school,*

> *2000 take French (F)*
> *3000 take Spanish (S)*
> *500 take Latin (L)*
> *1500 take both French and Spanish*
> *300 take both French and Latin*
> *200 take Spanish and Latin*
> *50 take all three languages.*

Use a Venn diagram to find the number of people in the sets given in Exercises 40–44.

40. $L \cap (F \cup S)$　　**41.** $(L \cup F \cup S)'$　　**42.** L'

43. $L \cup S \cup F'$　　**44.** $F \cap S' \cap L'$

45. Voting Preferences One hundred college students were surveyed after voting in an election involving a Democrat and a Republican. Fifty were first-year students, 55 voted Democratic, and 25 were non-first-year students who voted Republican. How many first-year students voted Democratic?

46. Union Membership and Education Status A group of 100 workers were asked if they were college graduates and if they belonged to a union. Sixty were not college graduates, 20 were nonunion college graduates, and 30 were union members. How many of the workers were neither college graduates nor union members?

47. Diagnostic Test Results A class of 30 students was given a diagnostic test on the first day of a mathematics course. At the end of the semester, only 2 of the 21 students who had passed the diagnostic test failed the course. A total of 23 students passed the course. How many students managed to pass the course even though they failed the diagnostic test?

48. Air-Traffic Controllers A group of applicants for training as air-traffic controllers consists of 35 pilots, 20 veterans, 30 pilots who were not veterans, and 50 people who were neither veterans nor pilots. How large was the group?

College Majors *A group of 52 students has the following characteristics:*

> *5 are male biology majors*
> *15 are female biology majors*
> *12 are females majoring in a field other than biology.*

Exercises 49–54 refer to these students. (Hint: The creation of the Venn diagram requires the inclusion–exclusion principle.)

49. How many of the students are either male or are biology majors?

50. How many of the students are male?

51. How many of the students are female?

52. How many of the students are biology majors?

53. How many of the male students are not biology majors?

54. How many of the students are not biology majors?

Music Preferences *A campus radio station surveyed 190 students to determine the genres of music they liked. The survey results follow:*

>   *114 like rock*
>   *50 like country*
>   *15 like rock and jazz*
>   *11 like jazz and country*
>   *20 like jazz only*
>   *10 like rock and jazz, but not country*
>   *9 like rock and country, but not jazz*
>   *20 don't like any of the three types of music*

Exercises 55–62 refer to the students in this survey. (Note: The creation of the Venn diagram requires the inclusion–exclusion principle.)

55. How many students like rock only?

56. How many students like country but not rock?

57. How many students like jazz and country but not rock?

58. How many students like jazz or country but not rock?

59. How many students like exactly one of the genres?

60. How many students like all three genres?

61. How many students like at least two of the three genres?

62. How many students do not like either rock or country?

63. **Magazine Preferences** One hundred and eighty business executives were surveyed to determine if they regularly read *Fortune*, *Time*, or *Money* magazines. Seventy-five read *Fortune*, 70 read *Time*, 55 read *Money*, 45 read exactly two of the three magazines, 25 read *Fortune* and *Time*, 25 read *Time* and *Money*, and 5 read all three magazines. How many read none of the three magazines?

64. **Small Businesses** A survey of the characteristics of 100 small businesses that had failed revealed that 95 of them either were undercapitalized, had inexperienced management, or had a poor location. Four of the businesses had all three of these characteristics. Forty businesses were undercapitalized but had experienced management and good location. Fifteen businesses had inexperienced management but sufficient capitalization and good location. Seven were undercapitalized and had inexperienced management. Nine were undercapitalized and had poor location. Ten had inexperienced management and poor location. How many of the businesses had poor location? Which of the three characteristics was most prevalent in the failed businesses?

65. **Music** Each of the 100 students attending a conservatory of music plays at least one of three instruments: piano, violin, and clarinet. 65 play the piano, 42 play the violin, 28 play the clarinet, 20 play the piano and the violin, 10 play the violin and the clarinet, and 8 play the piano and the clarinet. How many play all three instruments? *Hint:* Let x represent the number of students who play all three instruments.

Solutions to Practice Problems 5.3

1. Draw a Venn diagram with two circles, one for mathematics (M) and one for economics (E) [Fig. 11(a)]. This Venn diagram has four basic regions, and our goal is to label each basic region with the proper number of students. The numbers for two of the basic regions are given directly. Since "300 take mathematics and economics," $n(M \cap E) = 300$. Since "200 do not take any mathematics or economics courses," $n((M \cup E)') = 200$ [Fig. 11(b)]. Now "700 take mathematics courses." Since M is made up of two basic regions and one region has 300 elements, the other basic region of M must contain 400 elements [Fig. 11(c)]. At this point all but one of the basic regions have been labeled and $400 + 300 + 200 = 900$ students have been accounted for. Since there is a total of 1000 students, the remaining basic region has 100 students [Fig. 11(d)].

2. (a) 400. "Economics" refers to the entire circle E, which is made up of two basic regions, one having 300 elements and the other 100. (A common error is to interpret the question as asking for the number of first-year students who take economics exclusively and therefore give the answer 100. To say that a person takes an economics course does not imply anything about the person's enrollment in mathematics courses.)

(b) 100

(Continued)

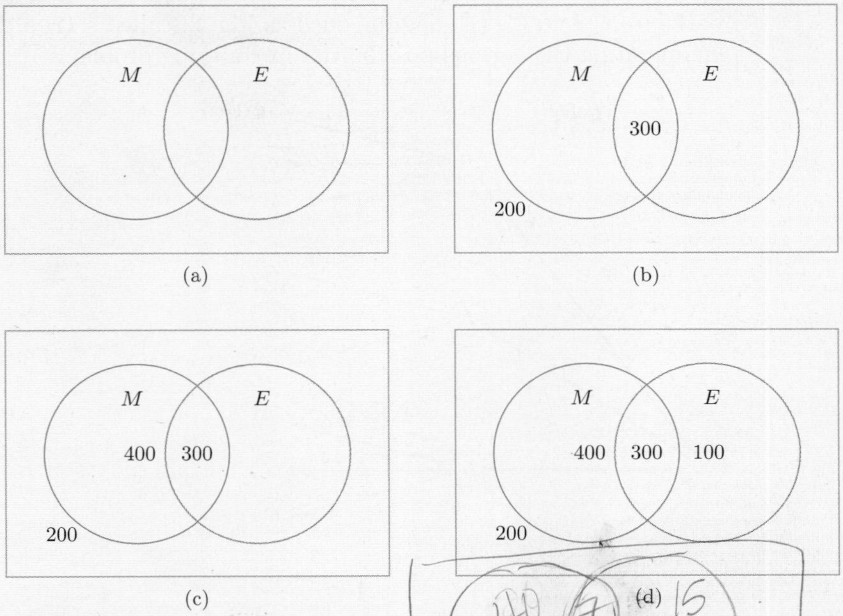

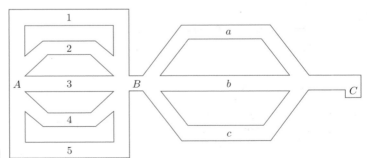

| (a) | (b) |

Figure 11

5.4 The Multiplication Principle

In this section we introduce a second fundamental principle of counting, the *multiplication principle*. By way of motivation, consider the following example.

EXAMPLE 1

Counting paths through a maze A medical researcher wishes to test the effect of a drug on a rat's perception by studying the rat's ability to run a maze while under the influence of the drug. The maze is constructed so that to arrive at the exit point C, the rat must pass through a central point B. There are five paths from the entry point A to B, and three paths from B to C. In how many different ways can the rat run the maze from A to C? (See Fig. 1.)

Figure 1

Solution The paths from A to B have been labeled 1 through 5, and the paths from B to C have been labeled a through c. The various paths through the maze can be schematically represented as in Fig. 2. The diagram shows that there are five ways to go from A to B. For each of these five ways, there are three ways to go from B to C. So there are five groups of three paths each, and therefore $5 \cdot 3 = 15$ possible paths from A to C. (A diagram such as Fig. 2, called a **tree diagram**, is useful in enumerating the various possibilities in counting problems.) ■

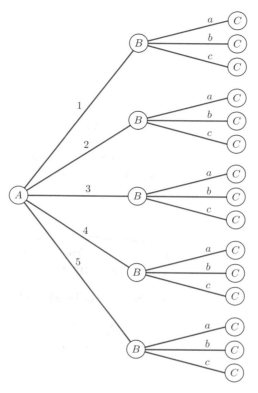

Figure 2

In the preceding problem, selecting a path is a task that can be broken up into two consecutive choices.

The first choice can be performed in five ways and, after the first choice has been carried out, the second can be performed in three ways. And we determined that the entire task can be performed in $5 \cdot 3 = 15$ ways. The same reasoning as just used yields the following useful counting principle:

Multiplication Principle   Suppose that a task is composed of two consecutive choices. If choice 1 can be performed in m ways and, for each of these, choice 2 can be performed in n ways, then the complete task can be performed in $m \cdot n$ ways.

EXAMPLE 2

Counting routes for a trip An airline passenger must fly from New York to Frankfurt via London. There are 8 flights leaving New York for London. All of these provide connections on any one of 19 flights from London to Frankfurt. In how many different ways can the passenger book reservations?

Solution The task "fly from New York to Frankfurt" is composed of two consecutive choices:

Select a flight from New York to London	Select a flight from London to Frankfurt
Choice 1	Choice 2

Now Try Exercise 1

From the data given, the multiplication principle implies that the task can be accomplished in $8 \cdot 19 = 152$ ways. ■

It is possible to generalize the multiplication principle to tasks consisting of more than two choices.

> **Generalized Multiplication Principle** Suppose that a task consists of t choices performed consecutively. Suppose that choice 1 can be performed in m_1 ways; for each of these, choice 2 in m_2 ways; for each of these, choice 3 in m_3 ways; and so forth. Then the task can be performed in
>
> $$m_1 \cdot m_2 \cdot m_3 \cdot \cdots \cdot m_t \quad \text{ways.}$$

EXAMPLE 3

Officers for a board of directors A corporation has a board of directors consisting of 10 members. The board must select from among its members a chairperson, vice chairperson, and secretary. In how many ways can this be done?

Solution The task "select the three officers" can be divided into three consecutive choices:

Select chairperson	Select vice chairperson	Select secretary

Since there are 10 directors, choice 1 can be performed in 10 ways. After the chairperson has been selected, there are 9 directors left as possible candidates for vice chairperson, so that for each way of performing choice 1, choice 2 can be performed in 9 ways. After this has been done, there are 8 directors who are possible candidates for secretary, so choice 3 can be performed in 8 ways. By the generalized multiplication principle, the number of possible ways to perform the sequence of three choices equals $10 \cdot 9 \cdot 8$, or 720. So the officers of the board can be selected in 720 ways. ■

Now Try Exercise 13

In Example 3 we made important use of the phrase "for each of these" in the generalized multiplication principle. The choice "select a vice chairperson" can be performed in 10 ways, since any member of the board is eligible. However, when we view the selection process as a sequence of choices of which "select a vice chairperson" is the second choice, the situation has changed. *For each way* that the first choice is performed, one person will have been used up; hence there will be only 9 possibilities for choosing the vice chairperson.

EXAMPLE 4

Posing for a group picture In how many ways can a baseball team of nine players arrange themselves in a line for a group picture?

Solution Choose the players by their place in the picture, say from left to right. The first can be chosen in nine ways; for each of these outcomes the second can be chosen in eight ways; for each of these outcomes the third can be chosen in seven ways; and so forth. So the number of possible arrangements is

Now Try Exercise 24

$$9 \cdot 8 \cdot 7 \cdot 6 \cdot 5 \cdot 4 \cdot 3 \cdot 2 \cdot 1 = 362{,}880.$$ ■

EXAMPLE 5   **License plates** A certain state uses automobile license plates that consist of three letters followed by three digits. How many such license plates are there?

Solution The task in this case, "form a license plate," consists of a sequence of six choices: three for choosing letters and three for choosing digits. Each letter can be chosen in 26 ways and each digit in 10 ways. So the number of license plates is

Now Try Exercise 33

$$26 \cdot 26 \cdot 26 \cdot 10 \cdot 10 \cdot 10 = 17{,}576{,}000.$$ ∎

Practice Problems 5.4

1. There are six seats available in a sedan. In how many ways can six people be seated if only three can drive?

2. A multiple-choice exam contains 10 questions, each having 3 possible answers. How many different ways are there of completing the exam?

EXERCISES 5.4

1. **Routes** If there are three routes from College Park to Baltimore and five routes from Baltimore to New York, how many routes are there from College Park to New York via Baltimore?

2. **Choosing an Outfit** How many different outfits consisting of a coat and a hat can be chosen from two coats and three hats?

3. **Two-Letter Words** How many different two-letter words (including nonsense words) can be formed when repetition of letters is allowed?

4. **Two-Letter Words** How many different two-letter words (including nonsense words) can be formed such that the two letters are distinct?

5. **Railroad Tickets** A railway has 20 stations. If the names of the point of departure and the destination are printed on each ticket, how many different kinds of single tickets must be printed?

6. **Railroad Tickets** Refer to Exercise 5. How many different kinds of tickets are needed if each ticket may be used in either direction between two stations?

7. **Gloves** A man has five different pairs of gloves. In how many ways can he select a right-hand glove and a left-hand glove that do not match?

8. **License Plates** How many license plates consisting of two letters followed by four digits are possible?

9. **Group Picture** How many ways can five people be arranged in a line for a group picture?

10. **Arranging Books** In how many different ways can four books be arranged on a bookshelf?

11. **Coin Tosses** Toss a coin six times and observe the sequence of heads or tails that results. How many different sequences are possible?

12. **Coin Tosses** Refer to Exercise 11. In how many of the sequences are the first and last tosses identical?

13. **Winners** Twenty athletes enter an Olympic event. How many different possibilities are there for winning the Gold Medal, Silver Medal, and Bronze Medal?

14. **Ranking Teams** A sportswriter is asked to rank eight teams. How many different orderings are possible?

15. **Electing Captains** In how many different ways can a 30-member football team select a captain and an assistant captain?

16. **Selecting an Outfit** How many different outfits can be selected from two coats, three hats, and two scarves?

17. **Rearranging Letters** How many different words (including nonsense words) can be formed using the four letters of the word "MATH"?

18. **Travel Options** If you can travel from Frederick, Maryland, to Baltimore, Maryland, by car, bus, or train and from Baltimore to London by airplane or ship, how many different ways are there to go from Frederick to London?

19. **Exam Questions** An exam contains five "true or false" questions. In how many different ways can the exam be completed?

20. **Pairs of Initials** A company has 700 employees. Explain why there must be two people with the same pair of initials.

21. **Serial Numbers** A computer manufacturer assigns serial numbers to its computers. The first symbol of a serial number is either A, B, or C, indicating the manufacturing plant. The second and third symbols taken together are one of the numbers 01, 02, ..., 12, indicating the month of manufacture. The final four symbols are digits. How many possible serial numbers are there?

22. Forming Words How many four-letter words (including nonsense words) can be made from the letters of "statistics," assuming that each word may not have repeated letters?

23. Forming Words How many four-letter words (including nonsense words) can be made from the letters h, o, t, s, m, x, and e for each of the following conditions?

(a) Letters can be repeated.

(b) Letters cannot be repeated.

(c) Words must begin with an h, and repetitions are allowed.

(d) Words must end with a vowel, and repetitions are not allowed.

24. Group Picture A group of five boys and three girls is to be photographed.

(a) How many ways can they be arranged in one row?

(b) How many ways can they be arranged with the girls in the front row and the boys in the back row?

25. Batting Orders The manager of a Little League baseball team has picked the nine starting players for a game. How many different batting orders are possible under each of the following conditions?

(a) There are no restrictions.

(b) The pitcher must bat last.

(c) The pitcher must bat last, the catcher eighth, and the shortstop first.

26. Shading of Venn Diagrams How many different ways can a Venn diagram with two circles be shaded?

27. Shading of Venn Diagrams How many different ways can a Venn diagram with three circles be shaded?

28. Club Officers A club can elect a member as president and a different member as treasurer in 506 different ways. How many members does the club have?

29. Exam Questions An exam contains six true or false statements. In how many ways can the exam be completed if leaving the answer blank is also an option?

30. Test Volunteers A physiologist wants to test the effects of exercise and meditation on blood pressure. She devises four different exercise programs and three different meditation programs. If she wants 10 subjects for each combination of exercise and meditation program, how many volunteers must she recruit?

31. Menu Selections A college student eats all his meals at a restaurant offering six breakfast specials, seven lunch specials, and four dinner specials. How many days can he go without repeating an entire day's menu selection?

32. Entrances A classroom building has 7 different doors. In how many ways can a student enter by one door and exit by a different door?

33. License Plates A California license plate consists of a digit followed by three letters, and then three digits. How many such license plates are there?

34. Sweaters A clothing store offers three styles of sweaters with each sweater available in six colors. How many different sweaters are there?

35. Area Codes Before 1995, three-digit area codes for the United States had the following restrictions:

(a) Neither 0 nor 1 could be used as the first digit.

(b) 0 or 1 had to be used for the second digit.

(c) There were no restrictions on the third digit. How many different area codes were possible?

36. Area Codes Refer to Exercise 35. Beginning in 1995, restriction (b) was lifted and any digit could be used in the second position. How many different area codes are possible?

37. Handshakes Two ten-member basketball teams play a game. After the game, each of the members of the winning team shakes hands once with each member of both teams. How many handshakes take place?

38. Chair Varieties A furniture manufacturer makes three types of upholstered chairs and offers 20 fabrics. How many different chairs are available?

39. Colored Houses Six houses in a row are each to be painted with one of the colors red, blue, green, and yellow. In how many different ways can the houses be painted so that no two adjacent houses are of the same color?

40. Numbers How many three-digit odd numbers can be formed using the digits 1, 2, 3, 4, 5, 6, and 7?

41. Exam Questions Each of the 10 questions on a multiple-choice exam has four possible answers. How many different ways are there for a student to answer the questions? Assume that every question must be answered.

42. Mismatched Shoes Fred has 10 different pairs of shoes. In how many ways can he put on a pair of shoes that do not match?

43. Transportation Options Suppose that Jack wants to go from Florida to Maine via New York and can travel each leg of the journey by bus, car, train, or airplane. How many different ways can Jack make the trip?

44. Menu Selections A restaurant menu lists 6 appetizers, 10 entrées, and 5 desserts. How many ways can a diner select a three-course meal?

45. Band Selections PE In how many arrangements can a band play three waltzes and three tangos in a row without repeating any song, such that the first, third, and fifth songs are waltzes?

(a) 6   (b) 12   (c) 16   (d) 36   (e) 720

46. Milk Delivery How many ways can a milkman deliver 10 distinguishable bottles of milk on a street containing five houses?

47. Computer Options A computer manufacturer offers a computer with a choice of four types of monitors, two types of keyboards, and three types of hard drives. How many different computers are offered?

48. Ballots Seven candidates for mayor, 4 candidates for city council president, and 12 propositions are being put before the electorate. How many different ballots could be cast, assuming that every voter votes on each of the items? If voters can choose to leave any item blank, how many different ballots are possible?

49. Gift Wrapping The gift-wrap desk at a large department store offers 5 box sizes, 10 wrapping papers, 7 colors of ribbon in two widths, and 9 special items to be added on the bow. How many different ways are there to gift-wrap a package assuming that the customer must choose at least a box but need not choose any of the other offerings?

50. Selecting Fruit José was told to get a dozen oranges, eight apples, and a half-pound of grapes. When he gets to the store he finds five varieties of oranges, five varieties of apples, and two varieties of grapes. Assuming that he buys only one variety of each type of fruit, how many different bags of fruit could he bring home?

51. College Applications Allison is preparing her applications for college. She will apply to three community colleges and has to fill out five parts to each of those applications. She will apply to three four-year schools, each of which has a six-part application. How many application segments must she complete?

52. Car Options An automobile dealer is offering five models of a particular car. On each model the customer may choose cloth or leather seats, each available in three colors, automatic or manual transmission, and a regular or a satellite radio. The car can be ordered in any one of eight exterior colors. How many different cars can be ordered?

53. Game of Clue In the game of *Clue*, there are six suspects in a murder that was committed in any one of nine rooms, using any one of six weapons. How many scenarios are possible?

54. Numbers James chooses a number from 1 to 100 (inclusive), Janet chooses a number between 1 and 100 that is divisible by 7, and Sandy chooses a number between 1 and 100 that is divisible by 21. How many triples of numbers are possible?

55. Numbers How many four-digit numbers can be formed using the digits $\{1, 2, 3, 4, 5, 6, 7\}$ if adjacent digits must be different?

56. Fruit Baskets A grocery store makes up fruit baskets using as many as four apples, three pears, and four oranges. A basket must contain at least one piece of fruit. How many different fruit selections are possible?

57. Social Security Numbers How many Social Security numbers are available if the only restriction is that the number 000-00-0000 cannot be assigned?

58. Displaying Paintings An art gallery has two paintings by each of four artists. In how many ways can the eight paintings be displayed in a row if paintings by the same artist must be adjacent to each other?

59. Paths to Texas Consider the following triangular display of letters. Start with the letter T at the top and move down the triangle to a letter S at the bottom. From any given letter move only to one of the letters directly below it on the left or right. How many different paths spell *TEXAS*?

$$T$$
$$E \quad E$$
$$X \quad X \quad X$$
$$A \quad A \quad A \quad A$$
$$S \quad S \quad S \quad S \quad S$$

60. Choosing an Outfit A girl dresses in the morning in a blouse, a skirt, and shoes. She always wears standard white socks. She wants to wear a different combination on every day of the year. If she has the same number of blouses, skirts, and pairs of shoes, how many of each article would she need to have a different combination every day? (From *The Mathematics Teacher*, February 1996)

61. Seating Arrangements Three couples go on a movie date. In how many ways can they be seated in a row of six seats so that each couple is seated together?

62. Three-Letter Words How many different three-letter words (including nonsense words) are there in which successive letters are different?

63. Seating Arrangements A panel of eight experts is to present opposing arguments in a discussion of legalizing marijuana for medical purposes. The four proponents arrive first and sit in such a way that the panelists will alternate pro and con. In how many ways can the four proponents be seated? In how many ways can all eight panelists be seated?

64. Call Letters TV and radio stations east of the Mississippi River have call letters beginning with the letter W. How many different three- or four-letter call letters are possible?

A number is said to be a palindrome *if it reads the same backwards as forwards (e.g., 58485).*

65. Palindromes How many 5-digit numbers are palindromes?

66. Palindromes How many 6-digit numbers are palindromes?

67. Give an example of a counting problem whose solution is obtained by multiplying 5 by 6.

1. 360. Pretend that you are given the task of seating the six people. This task consists of six choices performed consecutively, as shown in Table 1. After you have performed choice 1, five people will remain, and any one of these five can be seated in the middle front seat. After choice 2, four people remain, and so on. By the generalized multiplication principle, the task can be performed in $3 \cdot 5 \cdot 4 \cdot 3 \cdot 2 \cdot 1 = 360$ ways.

2. 3^{10}. The task of answering the questions consists of 10 consecutive choices, each of which can be performed in three ways. Therefore, by the generalized multiplication principle, the task can be performed in

$$\underbrace{3 \cdot 3 \cdot 3 \cdots \cdots 3}_{10 \text{ terms}} \text{ ways.}$$

(*Note*: The answer can be left as 3^{10} or can be multiplied out to 59,049.)

TABLE 1

Choice	Number of ways choice can be performed
1: Select person to drive	3
2: Select person for middle front seat	5
3: Select person for right front seat	4
4: Select person for left rear seat	3
5: Select person for middle rear seat	2
6: Select person for right rear seat	1

5.5 Permutations and Combinations

In preceding sections we have solved a variety of counting problems using Venn diagrams and the generalized multiplication principle. Let us now turn our attention to two types of counting problems that occur very frequently and that can be solved using formulas derived from the generalized multiplication principle. These problems involve what are called permutations and combinations, which are particular types of arrangements of elements of a set. The sorts of arrangements we have in mind are illustrated in two problems:

Problem A   How many words (by which we mean strings of letters) of two distinct letters can be formed from the letters $\{a, b, c\}$?

Problem B   A construction crew has three members. A team of two must be chosen for a particular job. In how many ways can the team be chosen?

Each of the two problems can be solved by enumerating all possibilities.

Solution of Problem A   There are six possible words, namely

$$ab \quad ac \quad ba \quad bc \quad ca \quad cb.$$

Solution of Problem B   Designate the three crew members by a, b, and c. Then there are three possible two-person teams, namely

$$\{a, b\} \quad \{a, c\} \quad \{b, c\}.$$

(Note that $\{b, a\}$, the team consisting of b and a, is the same as the team $\{a, b\}$.)

We deliberately set up both problems using the same letters in order to facilitate comparison. Both problems are concerned with counting the numbers of arrangements of the elements of the set $\{a, b, c\}$, taken two at a time, without allowing repetition (for example, aa was not allowed). However, in Problem A the order of the arrangement mattered, whereas in Problem B it did not. Arrangements of the sort considered in Problem A are called *permutations*, whereas those in Problem B are called *combinations*.

More precisely, suppose that we are given a set of n objects.[1] Then a **permutation of n objects taken r at a time** is an arrangement of r of the n objects in a specific order. So, for example, Problem A was concerned with permutations of the three objects, a, b, c ($n = 3$), taken two at a time ($r = 2$). A **combination of n objects taken r at a time** is a selection of r objects from among the n, with order disregarded. Thus, for example, in Problem B we considered combinations of the three objects a, b, c ($n = 3$), taken two at a time ($r = 2$).

It is convenient to introduce the following notation for counting permutations and combinations. Let

$P(n, r) =$ the number of permutations of n objects taken r at a time

$C(n, r) =$ the number of combinations of n objects taken r at a time.

Thus, for example, from our solutions to Problems A and B, we have

$$P(3, 2) = 6 \qquad C(3, 2) = 3.$$

Very simple formulas for $P(n, r)$ and $C(n, r)$ allow us to calculate these quantities for any n and r. Let us begin by stating the formula for $P(n, r)$. For $r = 1, 2, 3$, respectively,

$$P(n, 1) = n$$
$$P(n, 2) = n(n - 1) \qquad \text{(two factors)},$$
$$P(n, 3) = n(n - 1)(n - 2) \qquad \text{(three factors)}.$$

Continuing, we obtain the following formula:

Permutation Formula   The number of permutations of n objects taken r at a time is

$$P(n, r) = n(n - 1)(n - 2) \cdot \cdots \cdot (n - r + 1) \qquad \text{(r factors)}. \tag{1}$$

This formula is verified at the end of this section.

EXAMPLE 1

Applying the permutation formula   Compute the following numbers.

(a) $P(100, 2)$ (b) $P(6, 4)$ (c) $P(5, 5)$

Solution (a) Here $n = 100$, $r = 2$. So we take the product of two factors, beginning with 100:

$$P(100, 2) = 100 \cdot 99 = 9900.$$

(b) $P(6, 4) = 6 \cdot 5 \cdot 4 \cdot 3 = 360$

Now Try Exercise 1   (c) $P(5, 5) = 5 \cdot 4 \cdot 3 \cdot 2 \cdot 1 = 120$ ■

In order to state the formula for $C(n, r)$, we must introduce some further notation. Suppose that r is any positive integer. We denote by $r!$ (read "r factorial") the product of all positive integers from r down to 1:

$$r! = r \cdot (r - 1) \cdot \cdots \cdot 2 \cdot 1.$$

---

[1] All are assumed to be different.

For instance,

$$1! = 1$$

$$2! = 2 \cdot 1 = 2$$

$$3! = 3 \cdot 2 \cdot 1 = 6$$

$$4! = 4 \cdot 3 \cdot 2 \cdot 1 = 24$$

$$5! = 5 \cdot 4 \cdot 3 \cdot 2 \cdot 1 = 120.$$

In terms of this notation we can state a very simple formula for $C(n, r)$, the number of combinations of n things taken r at a time.

Combination Formula   The number of combinations of n objects taken r at a time is

$$C(n, r) = \frac{P(n, r)}{r!} = \frac{n(n-1) \cdot \cdots \cdot (n-r+1)}{r(r-1) \cdot \cdots \cdot 1} \tag{2}$$

This formula is verified at the end of this section.

EXAMPLE 2   **Applying the combination formula**   Compute the following numbers.
(a) $C(100, 2)$ **(b)** $C(6, 4)$ **(c)** $C(5, 5)$

Solution   **(a)** $C(100, 2) = \dfrac{P(100, 2)}{2!} = \dfrac{100 \cdot 99}{2 \cdot 1} = 4950$

(b) $C(6, 4) = \dfrac{P(6, 4)}{4!} = \dfrac{6 \cdot 5 \cdot 4 \cdot 3}{4 \cdot 3 \cdot 2 \cdot 1} = 15$

Now Try Exercise 5   **(c)** $C(5, 5) = \dfrac{P(5, 5)}{5!} = \dfrac{5 \cdot 4 \cdot 3 \cdot 2 \cdot 1}{5 \cdot 4 \cdot 3 \cdot 2 \cdot 1} = 1$ ∎

EXAMPLE 3   **Applying the permutation and combination formulas**   Solve Problems A and B using formulas (1) and (2).

Solution   The number of two-letter words that can be formed from the three letters a, b, and c is equal to $P(3, 2) = 3 \cdot 2 = 6$, in agreement with our previous solution.

The number of two-worker teams that can be formed from three individuals is equal to $C(3, 2)$, and

$$C(3, 2) = \frac{P(3, 2)}{2!} = \frac{3 \cdot 2}{2 \cdot 1} = 3,$$

in agreement with our previous result.   ∎

EXAMPLE 4   **Selecting a committee**   The board of directors of a corporation has 10 members. In how many ways can they choose a committee of 3 board members to negotiate a merger?

Solution   Since the committee of three involves no ordering of its members, we are concerned here with combinations. The number of combinations of 10 people taken 3 at a time is $C(10, 3)$, which is

$$C(10, 3) = \frac{10 \cdot 9 \cdot 8}{3 \cdot 2 \cdot 1} = 120.$$

Now Try Exercise 51   Thus there are 120 possibilities for the committee.   ∎

EXAMPLE 5   **Outcomes of a horse race**   Eight horses are entered in a race in which a first, second, and third prize will be awarded. Assuming no ties, how many different outcomes are possible?

Solution   In this example we are considering ordered arrangements of three horses, so we are dealing with permutations. The number of permutations of eight horses taken three at a time is

$$P(8,3) = 8 \cdot 7 \cdot 6 = 336,$$

Now Try Exercise 44 so the number of possible outcomes of the race is 336. ∎

EXAMPLE 6   **Polling sample**   A political pollster wishes to survey 1500 individuals chosen from a sample of 5,000,000 adults. In how many ways can the 1500 individuals be chosen?

Solution   No ordering of the 1500 individuals is involved, so we are dealing with combinations. So the number in question is $C(5,000,000, \ 1500)$, a number too large to be written down in digit form. (It has several thousand digits!) But it could be calculated

Now Try Exercise 45 with the aid of a computer. ∎

EXAMPLE 7   **Selecting club officers**   A club has 10 members. In how many ways can they choose a slate of four officers, consisting of a president, vice president, secretary, and treasurer?

Solution   In this problem we are dealing with an ordering of four members. (The first is the president, the second the vice president, and so on.) So we are dealing with permutations, and the number of ways of choosing the officers is

Now Try Exercise 25

$$P(10,4) = 10 \cdot 9 \cdot 8 \cdot 7 = 5040. \quad ∎$$

Verification of the Formulas for $P(n,r)$ and $C(n,r)$ Let us first derive the formula for $P(n,r)$, the number of permutations of n objects taken r at a time. The task of choosing r objects (in a given order) consists of r consecutive choices (Fig. 1). The first choice can be performed in n ways. For each way that the first choice is performed, one object will have been used up and so we can perform the second choice in $n-1$ ways, and so on. For each way of performing the sequence of choices $1, 2, 3, \ldots, r-1$, the rth choice can be performed in $n - (r-1) = n - r + 1$ ways. By the generalized multiplication principle, the task of choosing the r objects from among the n can be performed in

$$n(n-1) \cdot \ \cdots \ \cdot (n - r + 1) \quad \text{ways.}$$

That is,

$$P(n,r) = n(n-1) \cdot \ \cdots \ \cdot (n - r + 1),$$

which is formula (1).

Let us now verify the formula for $C(n,r)$, the number of combinations of n objects taken r at a time. Each such combination is a set of r objects and therefore can be ordered in

$$P(r,r) = r(r-1) \cdot \ \cdots \ \cdot 2 \cdot 1 = r!$$

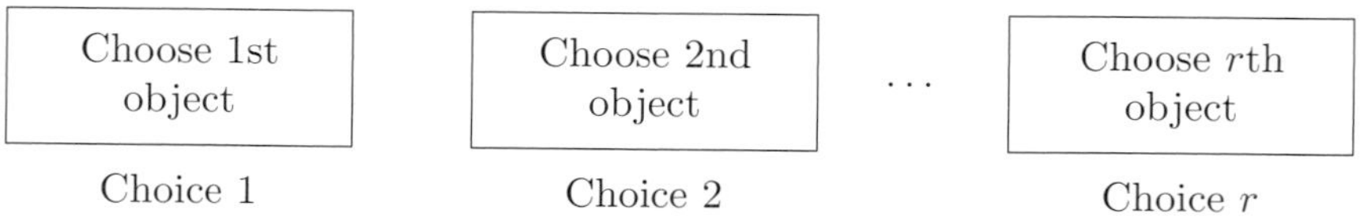

Choose 1st object		Choose 2nd object	···	Choose rth object
Choice 1		Choice 2		Choice r

Figure 1

ways by formula (1). In other words, each different combination of r objects gives rise to $r!$ permutations of the same r objects. On the other hand, each permutation of n objects taken r at a time gives rise to a combination of n objects taken r at a time, by simply ignoring the order of the permutation. Thus, if we start with the $P(n,r)$ permutations, we will have all the combinations of n objects taken r at a time, with each combination repeated $r!$ times. Thus

$$P(n,r) = r!\, C(n,r).$$

On dividing both sides of the equation by $r!$, we obtain formula (2).

INCORPORATING TECHNOLOGY

GC   Most graphing calculators have commands to compute $P(n,r)$, $C(n,r)$, and $n!$. For instance, the MATH key on the TI-83/84 Plus leads to the PRB menu of Fig. 2, which contains the commands **nPr**, **nCr**, and **!**. Figure 3 shows how these commands are used. *Note:* The number **8.799226775E15** represents $8.799226775 \times 10^{15}$. On the TI-89, the first three items on the MATH/Probability menu are **!**, **nPr**, and **nCr**. Figure 4 shows how these commands are used. ∎

Figure 2

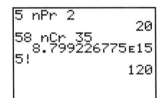

Figure 3

Figure 4

ES   The values of $n!$, $P(n,r)$, and $C(n,r)$ are calculated in an Excel spreadsheet with the functions FACT(n), PERMUT(n,r), and COMBIN(n,r).

Practice Problems 5.5

1. Calculate the following values.
   (a) $5!$ (b) $P(5,5)$ (c) $P(7,3)$ (d) $C(7,3)$

2. A newborn child is to be given a first name and a middle name from a selection of 10 names. How many different possibilities are there?

EXERCISES 5.5

For Exercises 1–20, calculate the values.

1. $P(4,2)$ 2. $P(5,1)$ 3. $P(6,3)$

4. $P(5,4)$ 5. $C(10,3)$ 6. $C(12,2)$

7. $C(5,4)$ 8. $C(6,3)$ 9. $P(7,1)$

10. $P(5,5)$ 11. $P(n,1)$ 12. $P(n,2)$

13. $C(4,4)$ 14. $C(n,2)$ 15. $C(n,n-2)$

16. $C(n,1)$ 17. $6!$ 18. $\dfrac{10!}{4!}$

19. $\dfrac{9!}{7!}$ 20. $7!$

21. **Group Picture** In how many ways can four people line up in a row for a group picture?

22. **Contest Winners** How many different outcomes of "winner" and "runner-up" are possible if there are six contestants in a pie-eating contest?

23. **Book Selection** How many different selections of two books can be made from a set of nine books?

24. **Pizza Varieties** A pizza parlor offers five toppings for the plain cheese base of the pizzas. How many different pizzas are possible that use three of the toppings?

25. Contest Winners How many ways are there to choose first, second, and third prizes in an art contest with 15 entrants?

26. Waiting in Line In how many ways can six people line up at a single counter to order food at McDonald's?

27. Banana Split Options A deluxe chocolate banana split is made with three scoops of chocolate ice cream, one banana, and a choice of 4 out of 10 possible toppings. How many different deluxe chocolate banana splits can be ordered?

28. Selecting Sweaters Suppose that you own 10 sweaters. How many ways can you select four of them to take on a trip?

29. Selecting Sweaters Suppose that you own 10 sweaters and are going on a trip. How many ways can you select six of them to leave at home?

30. Selecting Sweaters Why do Exercises 28 and 29 have the same answer?

31. Player Introductions The five starting players of a basketball team are introduced one at a time. In how many different ways can they be introduced?

32. Supreme Court Decisions In how many different ways can the nine members of the Supreme Court reach a six-to-three decision?

33. Conference Games In an eight-team football conference, each team plays every other team exactly once. How many games must be played?

34. Choosing Exam Questions A student is required to work exactly five problems from an eight-problem exam. In how many ways can the problems be chosen?

35. Arranging Books How many ways can you arrange 5 of 10 books on a shelf?

36. Selecting Books How many ways can you choose 5 of your 10 books to put in your backpack?

37. Guest Lists How many ways can you choose 5 out of 10 friends to invite to a dinner party?

38. Giving Gifts How many ways can you distribute $1, $2, $5, $10, $20 to 5 of your 10 friends? Assume that no one gets more than one bill.

39. CD Changer Suppose that you have 35 CDs and your CD player has five slots numbered 1 through 5. How many ways can you fill your CD player?

40. Job Interviews Of the 20 applicants for a job, 4 will be selected for intensive interviews. In how many ways can the selection be made?

41. Diskettes In a batch of 100 computer diskettes, 7 are defective. A sample of three diskettes is to be selected from the batch. How many samples are possible? How many of the samples consist of all defective diskettes?

42. Course Selection A student must choose five courses out of seven that he would like to take. How many possibilities are there?

43. Three-Letter Words How many different three-letter words are there having no repetition of letters?

44. Ranking Teams A sportswriter makes a preseason guess of the top 5 football teams (in order) from among 40 major teams. How many different possibilities are there?

45. Senate Committees In how many different ways can a committee of 5 senators be selected from the 100 members of the U.S. Senate?

46. Race Winners Theoretically, how many possibilities are there for first, second, and third places in a marathon race with 1000 entries?

Poker Hands *Exercises 47–50 refer to poker hands. A poker hand consists of 5 cards selected from a deck of 52 cards.*

47. How many different poker hands are there?

48. How many different poker hands consist entirely of aces and kings?

49. How many different poker hands consist entirely of clubs?

50. How many different poker hands consist entirely of red cards?

51. Choosing a Board of Directors A fraternity has 20 members. In how many ways can it choose a three-person board of directors?

52. Choosing Appetizers A restaurant offers an "appetizer-plate special" consisting of five selections from its list of appetizers. If there are more than 700 different possible appetizer-plate specials, what is the least possible number of appetizers?

53. Distributing Sandwiches Five students order different sandwiches at a campus eatery. The waiter forgets who ordered what and gives out the sandwiches at random. In how many different ways can the sandwiches be distributed?

54. Nautical Signals A nautical signal consists of three flags arranged vertically on a flagpole. If a sailor has flags of six different colors, how many different signals are possible?

55. Selecting Colleges A high school student decides to apply to four of the eight Ivy League colleges. In how many possible ways can the four colleges be selected?

56. Numbers In how many six digit numbers are the digits strictly decreasing when read from left to right? *Hint:* Start with the number 9876543210 and remove four digits.

57. Choosing Candy Two children, Moe and Joe, are allowed to select candy from a plate of nine pieces of candy. Moe, being younger, is allowed to choose first but can only take two candies. Joe is then allowed to take three of the remaining candies. Joe complains that he has fewer options than Moe. Is Joe correct? How many options will each child have?

58. Franchises In how many ways can three new basketball franchises be distributed to the five cities that have applied for them?

59. Picture Arrangements A nursery school teacher has collected a picture from each of the 12 children in the class. She wants to hang the pictures in four rows of three. How many different arrangements are possible?

60. Racetrack Betting Most racetracks have "compound" bets on two or more horses. An *exacta* is a bet in which the first and second finishers in a race are specified in order. A *quinella* is a bet on the first two finishers in a race, with order not specified. With a field of nine horses, how many different exacta bets can be placed? Quinella bets?

61. Arranging Books In how many ways can five mathematics books and four novels be placed on a bookshelf if the mathematics books must be together?

62. Arranging Books George has three books by each of his four favorite authors. In how many ways can the books be placed on a shelf if books by the same author must be together?

63. Arranging Paintings An art gallery has seven paintings by a new artist. The director wants to place four of them in a row on one wall of the gallery. How many different arrangements are possible?

64. Baseball Lineup On a children's baseball team, there are four players who can play at any of the following infield positions: catcher, first base, third base, and shortstop. There are five possible pitchers, none of whom plays any other position. And there are four players that can play any of the three outfield positions (right, left, center) or second base. In how many ways can the coach assign players to positions?

65. Batting Orders How many batting orders are possible for a team of nine baseball players in which the pitcher always bats last and the first baseman bats in either the third or fourth spot?

66. Selecting Performers A cabaret show is put together by a manager who wishes to present two comedians and three singers. He can choose from 14 comedians and 20 singers. In how many ways can he select the acts for the show?

67. Performance Order The cabaret show manager of Exercise 66 also controls the order of the five acts he selects. In how many ways can he organize the program once he has decided on which acts to present?

68. MRI Processing Seven patients are waiting to have an MRI scan, but there is time to process only three of them before the office closes for the day. In how many ways can the three patients be chosen?

69. Poker Hands How many five-card combinations from a standard playing-card deck have cards from exactly two suits?

70. Ten-Letter Words A 10-letter word consists of 4 A's and 6 B's. How many different words are possible if no two A's can be next to each other? *Hint*: Start with $BBBBBB$ and decide where to insert the A's.

71. ZIP Codes How many five-digit ZIP codes are possible in which the product of the digits is even? (From *The Mathematics Teacher*, February 1997)

72. League Games In a six-team softball league, each team plays every other team three times during the season. How many games must be scheduled?

73. Handshakes At a party, everyone shakes hands with everyone else. If 45 handshakes take place, how many people are at the party?

74. Distributing Jerseys PE Each of the 25 contestants in a race wears a jersey in either a single color or a pair of colors. What is the minimum number of colors so that no two contestants have the same color jersey?

(a) 5   (b) 6   (c) 7   (d) 25   (e) 50

75. Side Dishes A restaurant offers its customers a choice of 3 side dishes with each meal. The side dishes can be chosen from a list of fifteen possibilities with duplications allowed. For instance, a customer can order two sides of mashed potatoes and one side of string beans. Show that there are 680 possible options for the three side dishes.

76. Ice Cream Specials An ice cream parlor offers a special consisting of three scoops of ice cream chosen from 16 different flavors. Duplication of flavors is allowed. For instance, one possibility is two scoops of chocolate and one scoop of vanilla. Show that there are 816 different possible options for the special.

When the New York State lottery (Lotto) was first established, a contestant had to select six numbers from 1 to 49. A few years later the numbers 50 through 54 were added. In March 2007, the numbers 55 through 59 were added.

77. Lotto The number of possible combinations of six numbers selected from 1 to 59 is approximately _____ times the number of combinations selected from 1 through 49.

(a) 2   (b) 3   (c) 10   (d) 100

78. Lotto Drawings for Lotto are held twice per week. Suppose you decide to purchase 110 tickets for each drawing and never use the same combination twice. Approximately how many years would be required before you would have bet on every possible combination?

(a) 100   (b) 1000   (c) 2000   (d) 4000

79. Triangles How many distinct triangles can be constructed by connecting three different vertices of a cube?

80. Explain why $P(n, r)$ also can be calculated as $\frac{n!}{(n-r)!}$.

In Exercises 81–83, use a graphing calculator or spreadsheet to calculate the answers.

81. **Course Options** Students attending a college that operates on the semester system choose five courses each semester from a catalog containing 752 courses. The students who attend a college on the trimester system choose three courses each term from 937 courses in the catalog. Assume all courses are taught every term. In the standard four-year undergraduate program, which students have a greater number of different programs?

82. **Arranging Microchips** A computer manufacturer has 50 distinct microchips to place into a rectangular array that is 5 units wide by 10 units long.

    (a) In how many ways can the chips be arranged?

    (b) Ten of the chips control special functions. How many arrangements are possible if these must occupy the first column?

(c) Find the number of arrangements having no special-function chips in the first column.

83. **Lottery**

    (a) Calculate the number of possible lottery tickets if the player must choose five distinct numbers from 0 to 44, inclusive, where the order does not matter. The winner must match all five.

    (b) Calculate the number of lottery tickets if the player must choose four distinct numbers from 0 to 99, inclusive, where the order does not matter. The winner must match all four.

    (c) In which lottery does the player have a better chance of choosing the randomly selected winning numbers?

    (d) Find the answer to (c) if the order in which the numbers appear on the ticket must match the order on the winning ticket.

Solutions to Practice Problems 5.5

1. (a) $5! = 5 \cdot 4 \cdot 3 \cdot 2 \cdot 1 = 120$

   (b) $P(5,5) = 5 \cdot 4 \cdot 3 \cdot 2 \cdot 1 = 120$
   $[P(n,n)$ is the same as $n!]$

   (c) $P(7,3) = \underbrace{7 \cdot 6 \cdot 5}_{3 \text{ factors}} = 210$

   $[P(n,r)$ is the product of the first r factors in the descending expansion of $n!.]$

   (d) $C(7,3) = \dfrac{7 \cdot 6 \cdot 5}{3 \cdot 2 \cdot 1} = \dfrac{7 \cdot \cancel{6} \cdot 5}{\cancel{3} \cdot \cancel{2} \cdot 1} = 35$

   [A convenient procedure to follow when calculating $C(n,r)$ is first to write the product expansion of

$r!$ in the denominator and then to write in the numerator an integer from the descending expansion of $n!$ above each integer in the denominator.]

2. 90. The first question to be asked here is whether permutations or combinations are involved. Two names are to be selected, and the order of the names is important. (The name Amanda Beth is different from the name Beth Amanda.) Since the problem asks for arrangements of 10 names taken 2 at a time in a *specific order*, the number of arrangements is $P(10,2) = 10 \cdot 9 = 90$. In general, order is important if a different outcome results when two items in the selection are interchanged.

5.6 Further Counting Problems

In Section 5.5 we introduced permutations and combinations and developed formulas for counting all permutations (or combinations) of a given type. Many counting problems can be formulated in terms of permutations or combinations. But to use the formulas of Section 5.5 successfully, we must be able to recognize these problems when they occur and to translate them into a form in which the formulas may be applied. In this section we practice doing that. We consider five typical applications giving rise to permutations or combinations. At first glance, the first two applications may seem to have little practical significance. However, they suggest a common way to "model" outcomes of real-life situations having two equally likely results.

As our first application, consider a coin-tossing experiment in which we toss a coin a fixed number of times. We can describe the outcome of the experiment as a sequence of "heads" and "tails." For instance, if a coin is tossed three times, then one possible outcome is "heads on the first toss, tails on the second toss, and tails on third toss." This outcome can be abbreviated as HTT. We can use the methods of the preceding section to count the number of possible outcomes having various prescribed properties.

EXAMPLE 1

Tossing a coin ten times Suppose that an experiment consists of tossing a coin 10 times and observing the sequence of heads and tails.

(a) How many different outcomes are possible?

(b) How many different outcomes have exactly four heads?

Solution (a) Visualize each outcome of the experiment as a sequence of 10 boxes, where each box contains one letter, H or T, with the first box recording the result of the first toss, the second box recording the result of the second toss, and so forth.

$$\boxed{H}\boxed{T}\boxed{H}\boxed{T}\boxed{T}\boxed{T}\boxed{H}\boxed{T}\boxed{H}\boxed{T}$$
$$\quad 1 \quad 2 \quad 3 \quad 4 \quad 5 \quad 6 \quad 7 \quad 8 \quad 9 \quad 10$$

Each box can be filled in two ways. So by the generalized multiplication principle, the sequence of 10 boxes can be filled in

$$\underbrace{2 \cdot 2 \cdot \ \cdots \ \cdot 2}_{10 \text{ factors}} = 2^{10}$$

ways. So there are $2^{10} = 1024$ different possible outcomes.

(b) An outcome with 4 heads corresponds to filling the boxes with 4 H's and 6 T's. A particular outcome is determined as soon as we decide where to place the H's. The 4 boxes to receive H's can be selected from the 10 boxes in $C(10, 4)$ ways. So the number of outcomes with 4 heads is

> **Now Try Exercises 1(a) and (b)**

$$C(10, 4) = \frac{10 \cdot 9 \cdot 8 \cdot 7}{4 \cdot 3 \cdot 2 \cdot 1} = 210. \qquad \blacksquare$$

Ideas similar to those applied in Example 1 are useful in counting even more complicated sets of outcomes of coin-tossing experiments. The second part of our next example highlights a trick that can often save time and effort.

EXAMPLE 2

Tossing a coin ten times Consider the coin-tossing experiment of Example 1.

(a) How many different outcomes have at most two heads?

(b) How many different outcomes have at least three heads?

Solution (a) The outcomes with at most two heads are those having 0, 1, or 2 heads. Let us count the number of these outcomes separately:

0 heads: There is 1 outcome, namely T T T T T T T T T T.

1 head: To determine such an outcome, we just select the box in which to put the single H. And this can be done in $C(10, 1) = 10$ ways.

2 heads: To determine such an outcome, we just select the boxes in which to put the two H's. And this can be done in $C(10, 2) = (10 \cdot 9)/(2 \cdot 1) = 45$ ways.

Adding up all the possible outcomes, we see that the number of outcomes with at most two heads is equal to $1 + 10 + 45 = 56$.

(b) "At least three heads" refers to an outcome with either 3, 4, 5, 6, 7, 8, 9, or 10 heads. The total number of such outcomes is

$$C(10, 3) + C(10, 4) + \cdots + C(10, 10).$$

This sum can, of course, be calculated, but there is a less tedious way to solve the problem. Just start with all outcomes [1024 of them by Example 1(a)] and subtract those with at most two heads [56 of them by part (a)]. So the number of outcomes with at least three heads is $1024 - 56 = 968$. ■

Now Try Exercises 1(c) and (d)

NOTE The solution to part (b) of Example 2 employs a useful counting technique. Sometimes it is easier to count the number of elements in the complement of a set and then subtract it from the total number of possibilities. ■

Let us now turn to a different sort of counting problem, namely one that involves counting the number of paths between two points.

EXAMPLE 3

Routes through a city In Fig. 1 we have drawn a partial map of the streets in a certain city. A tourist wishes to walk from point A to point B. We have drawn two possible routes from A to B. What is the total number of routes (with no backtracking) from A to B?

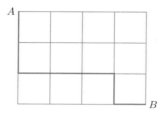 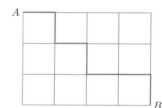

Figure 1

Solution Any particular route can be described by giving the directions of each block walked in the appropriate order. For instance, the route on the left of Fig. 1 is described as "a block south, a block south, a block east, a block east, a block east, a block south, a block east." Using S for south and E for east, this route can be designated by the string of letters SSEEESE. Similarly, the route on the right is ESESEES. Note that each route is then described by a string of seven letters, of which three are S's (we must go three blocks south) and four are E's (we must go four blocks east). Selecting a route is thus the same as placing three S's in a string of seven boxes:

$$\boxed{}\boxed{\text{S}}\boxed{}\boxed{\text{S}}\boxed{}\boxed{}\boxed{\text{S}}$$

The three boxes to receive S's can be selected in $C(7,3) = 35$ ways. So the number of paths from A to B is 35. ■

Now Try Exercise 3

Let us now move on to a third type of counting problem. Suppose that we have an urn in which there are a certain number of red balls and a certain number of white balls. We perform an experiment that consists of selecting a number of balls from the urn and observing the color distribution of the sample selected. (This model may be used, for example, to describe the process of selecting people to be polled in a survey. The different colors correspond to different opinions.) By using familiar counting techniques we can calculate the number of possible samples having a given color distribution. The next example illustrates a typical computation.

EXAMPLE 4

Selecting balls from an urn An urn contains 25 numbered balls, of which 15 are red and 10 are white. A sample of 5 balls is to be selected.

(a) How many different samples are possible?

(b) How many samples contain all red balls?

(c) How many samples contain 3 red balls and 2 white balls?

(d) How many samples contain at least 4 red balls?

Solution (a) A sample is just an unordered selection of 5 balls out of 25. There are $C(25, 5)$ such samples. Numerically, we have

$$C(25, 5) = \frac{25 \cdot 24 \cdot 23 \cdot 22 \cdot 21}{5 \cdot 4 \cdot 3 \cdot 2 \cdot 1} = 53{,}130$$

samples.

(b) To form a sample of all red balls we must select 5 balls from the 15 red ones. This can be done in $C(15, 5)$ ways—that is, in

$$C(15, 5) = \frac{15 \cdot 14 \cdot 13 \cdot 12 \cdot 11}{5 \cdot 4 \cdot 3 \cdot 2 \cdot 1} = 3003$$

ways.

(c) To answer this question we use both the multiplication principle and the formula for $C(n, r)$. We form a sample of 3 red balls and 2 white balls using a sequence of two choices:

Select 3 red balls	Select 2 white balls
Choice 1	Choice 2

The first choice can be performed in $C(15, 3)$ ways and the second in $C(10, 2)$ ways. Thus the total number of samples having 3 red and 2 white balls is $C(15, 3) \cdot C(10, 2)$. That is,

$$C(15, 3) = \frac{15 \cdot 14 \cdot 13}{3 \cdot 2 \cdot 1} = 455$$

$$C(10, 2) = \frac{10 \cdot 9}{2 \cdot 1} = 45$$

$$C(15, 3) \cdot C(10, 2) = 455 \cdot 45 = 20{,}475.$$

So the number of possible samples is 20,475.

(d) A sample with at least 4 red balls has either 4 or 5 red balls. By part (b) the number of samples with 5 red balls is 3003. Using the same reasoning as in part (c), the number of samples with 4 red balls is $C(15, 4) \cdot C(10, 1) = 1365 \cdot 10 = 13{,}650$. Thus the total number of samples having at least 4 red balls is $13{,}650 + 3003 = 16{,}653$. ∎

Now Try Exercise 5

Practice Problems 5.6

1. **School Board** A newspaper reporter wants an indication of how the 15 members of the school board feel about a certain proposal. She decides to question a sample of 6 of the board members.

   (a) How many different samples are possible?

   (b) Suppose that 10 of the board members support the proposal and 5 oppose it. How many of the samples reflect the distribution of the board? That is, in how many of the samples do 4 people support the proposal and 2 oppose it?

2. **Free Throws** A basketball player shoots eight free throws and lists the sequence of results of each trial in order. Let S represent "success" and F represent "failure." Then, for instance, FFSSSSSS represents the outcome of missing the first two shots and hitting the rest.

   (a) How many different outcomes are possible?

   (b) How many of the outcomes have six successes?

EXERCISES 5.6

1. Heads and Tails An experiment consists of tossing a coin six times and observing the sequence of heads and tails.

(a) How many different outcomes are possible?

(b) How many different outcomes have exactly three heads?

(c) How many different outcomes have more heads than tails?

(d) How many different outcomes have at least two heads?

2. Routes through City Streets Refer to the map in Fig. 2. How many routes are there from A to B?

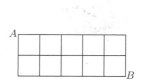

Figure 2

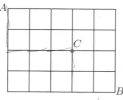

Figure 3

3. Routes through City Streets Refer to the map in Fig. 3. How many routes are there from A to B?

4. Selecting Balls from an Urn An urn contains 12 numbered balls, of which 8 are red and 4 are white. A sample of 4 balls is to be selected.

(a) How many different samples are possible?

(b) How many samples contain all red balls?

(c) How many samples contain 2 red balls and 2 white balls?

(d) How many samples contain at least 3 red balls?

(e) How many samples contain a different number of red balls than white balls?

5. Selecting Apples A bag of 10 apples contains 2 rotten apples and 8 good apples. A shopper selects a sample of 3 apples from the bag.

(a) How many different samples are possible?

(b) How many samples contain all good apples?

(c) How many samples contain at least 1 rotten apple?

6. Heads and Tails An experiment consists of tossing a coin 8 times and observing the sequence of heads and tails.

(a) How many different outcomes are possible?

(b) How many different outcomes have exactly 3 heads?

(c) How many different outcomes have at least 2 heads?

(d) How many different outcomes have 4 heads or 5 heads?

7. Dorm Assignments How many ways can a group of 100 students be assigned to dorms A, B, and C, with 25 assigned to dorm A, 40 to dorm B, and 35 to dorm C?

8. World Series In the World Series the American League team ("A") and the National League team ("N") play until one team wins four games. If the sequence of winners is designated by letters (NAAAA means the National League won the first game and lost the next four), how many different sequences are possible?

9. Routes through City Streets Refer to the map in Fig. 3. How many of the routes from A to B pass through the point C?

10. Selecting Fuses A package contains 100 fuses, of which 10 are defective. A sample of 5 fuses is selected at random.

(a) How many different samples are there?

(b) How many of the samples contain 2 defective fuses?

(c) How many of the samples contain at least 1 defective fuse?

11. Senate Committees In how many ways can a committee of 5 senators be selected from the 100 members of the U.S. Senate so that no two committee members are from the same state?

12. Exam Questions An exam contains five "true or false" questions. How many of the 32 different ways of answering these questions contain 3 or more correct answers?

13. Exam Questions A student is required to work exactly 6 problems from a 10-problem exam and must work exactly 3 of the first 4 problems. In how many ways can the six problems be chosen?

14. Arranging Books The new book shelf at a library contains two novels, six biographies, and four how-to books. In how many ways can the books be arranged on the shelf if the books for each category are placed together?

15. Jury Selection In how many ways can 12 jurors and 2 alternates be chosen from a group of 20 prospective jurors?

16. Subcommittee Selection A committee has four male and five female members. In how many ways can a subcommittee consisting of two males and two females be selected?

17. Investment Portfolio In how many ways can an investor put together a portfolio of five stocks and six bonds selected from her favorite nine stocks and eight bonds?

18. Game Outcomes A football team plays 10 games. In how many ways can these games result in five wins, four losses, and one tie?

19. Marketing Calls A telemarketer makes 15 phone calls in 1 hour. In how many ways can the outcomes of the calls be three sales, eight no-sales, and four no-answers?

20. **Free-Throws** During practice, a basketball player shoots 10 free-throws. In how many ways can the outcomes result in seven hits and three misses?

21. **License Plates** A license plate contains six letters with no repetitions allowed. How many different license plates are possible?

22. **Technology Options** A college mathematics department has 15 calculus classes. Five classes will use graphing calculators and four classes will use computer software. In how many different ways can the classes be selected?

23. **Three-Letter Words** How many different three-letter words (i.e., sequences of letters) can be formed from the letters of the word JUPITER?

24. **Seven-Letter Words** The shortest word containing all five vowels is SEQUOIA. How many seven-letter sequences of letters, with no repeated letters, contain all five vowels?

25. **Arranging Letters** In how many arrangements of the letters in the word ABSTEMIOUS are the vowels in alphabetical order?

26. **Teaching Assignments** Out of a group of 20 senior education majors at the University of Maryland, five will be selected to student-teach in Montgomery County, four will be selected to student-teach in Prince Georges County, and three will be selected to student-teach in Howard County. In how many ways can this be done?

27. **Group Picture** The student council at Gotham College is made up of four freshmen, five sophomores, six juniors, and seven seniors. A yearbook photographer would like to line up three council members from each class for a picture. How many different pictures are possible if each group of classmates stands together?

28. **Delivery Schedule** A truck driver has to deliver bread to five grocery stores. In how many different ways can he schedule the order of his stops?

29. **Delivery Schedule** Suppose that the stores in Exercise 28 are located in two towns far enough apart that the driver wants to make all stops in one town before going on to the next. In how many different ways can he schedule the order of his stops if the larger town has three stores?

30. **Job Allocation** Of the 14 new programmers hired by a major software company, 3 will be selected to work on programming languages, 4 will be selected to work on word processing software, and 5 will be selected to work on spreadsheet software. In how many ways can this be done?

31. **Poker** How many poker hands consist of 3 aces and 2 kings?

32. **Poker** How many poker hands consist of 2 aces, 2 cards of another denomination, and 1 card of a third denomination?

33. **Poker** How many poker hands consist of 3 cards of one denomination and 2 cards of another denomination? (Such a poker hand is called a "full house.")

34. **Poker** How many poker hands consist of 2 cards of one denomination, 2 cards of another (different) denomination, and 1 card of a third denomination? (Such a poker hand is called "two pairs.")

35. **Detour-Prone ZIP Codes** A five-digit ZIP code is said to be detour-prone if it looks like a valid and different ZIP code when read upside down (Fig. 4). For instance, 68901 and 88111 are detour-prone, whereas 32145 and 10801 are not. How many of the 10^5 possible ZIP code numbers are detour-prone?

Figure 4

36. **Dorm Assignments** In how many ways can a residence director assign six students to four dormitory rooms if two rooms are doubles, two rooms are singles, and two of the students cannot be placed together?

37. **Committee Selection** A class has 12 students, of which 3 are seniors. How many committees of size 4 can be selected if at least one member of each committee must be a senior?

38. **Dance Routines** A dance team knows 15 routines of which 8 are tap, 5 are ballet, and 2 are modern. The program can consist of any five routines. In how many ways can the manager choose which routines to present if there are no restrictions?

39. **Dance Routines** Refer to Exercise 38. In how many ways can the manager choose the routines if at least one routine of each type must be included?

40. **Seating Arrangements** In how many ways can 6 married couples sit in a row if men and women alternate?

41. **Seating Arrangements** In how many ways can 6 married couples sit in a row if no 2 women sit next to each other?

42. **Family Dinner** A family has 6 members. In how many different ways can exactly three of them come to dinner? In how many different ways can three or more of them come to dinner?

43. **Family Dinner** A family has 6 members. How many different family groups can come to dinner?

44. **Placemat Arrangement** A family has 6 members. Each member has a placemat with his or her name on it. In how many ways can the placemats be placed around a round table?

45. Selecting Marbles There are 8 marbles in a bag, numbered 1 through 8. Three (1, 2, 3) are blue and five (4, 5, 6, 7, 8) are white. Choose three marbles from the bag. In how many samples will the number of blue marbles chosen exceed the number of white marbles chosen?

46. Handshakes In a room of 10 people, each person shakes hands with 5 people. How many handshakes take place?

47. English Words How many four-digit sequences of letters could possibly be an English word? *Note:* A word in the English language must contain at least one of the five vowels.

In Exercises 48–51, use a graphing calculator or spreadsheet to calculate the answers.

48. Class Formation The dean at a small college wishes to form an experimental section of General Psychology with 22 students chosen from 20 women and 18 men interested in social science.

  (a) How many different such classes are possible?

  (b) The dean decides the class should have 12 women and 10 men. Compare the number of possible classes to the solution to (a).

49. Bridge A bridge hand contains 13 cards. What percentage of bridge hands contains all four aces?

50. Bridge Which is more likely—a bridge hand with four aces or one with exactly two kings and two queens?

51. Bridge Which is more likely—a bridge hand with four aces or one with the two red kings, the two red queens, and no other kings or queens?

Solutions to Practice Problems 5.6

1. (a) $C(15, 6)$. Each sample is an unordered selection of 15 objects taken 6 at a time.

  (b) $C(10, 4) \cdot C(5, 2)$. Asking for the number of samples of a certain type is the same as asking for the number of ways that the task of forming such a sample can be performed. This task is composed of two consecutive choices. Choice 1, selecting 4 people from among the 10 that support the proposal, can be performed in $C(10, 4)$ ways. Choice 2, selecting 2 people from among the 5 people that oppose the proposal, can be performed in $C(5, 2)$ ways. Therefore, by the multiplication principle, the complete task can be performed in $C(10, 4) \cdot C(5, 2)$ ways. [*Note:* $C(15, 6) = 5005$ and $C(10, 4) \cdot C(5, 2) = 2100$. Therefore, less than half of the possible samples reflect the true distribution of the school board.]

2. (a) 2^8 or 256. Apply the generalized multiplication principle.

  (b) $C(8, 6)$ or 28. Each outcome having 6 successes corresponds to a sequence of 8 letters of which 6 are S's and 2 are F's. Such an outcome is specified by selecting the 6 locations for the S's from among the 8 locations, and this has $C(8, 6)$ possibilities.

5.7 The Binomial Theorem

In Sections 5.5 and 5.6 we dealt with permutations and combinations and, in particular, derived a formula for $C(n, r)$, the number of combinations of n objects taken r at a time. Namely, we have

$$C(n, r) = \frac{P(n, r)}{r!} = \frac{n(n-1) \cdot \cdots \cdot (n - r + 1)}{r!}. \tag{1}$$

Actually, formula (1) was verified in case both n and r are positive integers. But it is useful to consider $C(n, r)$ also in case $r = 0$. In this case we are considering the number of combinations of n things taken 0 at a time. There is clearly only one such combination: the one containing no elements. Therefore,

$$C(n, 0) = 1. \tag{2}$$

Here is another convenient formula for $C(n, r)$:

$$C(n, r) = \frac{n!}{r! \, (n - r)!}. \tag{3}$$

For instance, according to formula (3),

$$C(8,3) = \frac{8!}{3!\,(8-3)!} = \frac{8!}{3!\,5!} = \frac{8 \cdot 7 \cdot 6 \cdot \cancel{5} \cdot \cancel{4} \cdot \cancel{3} \cdot \cancel{2} \cdot \cancel{1}}{3 \cdot 2 \cdot 1 \cdot \cancel{5} \cdot \cancel{4} \cdot \cancel{3} \cdot \cancel{2} \cdot \cancel{1}} = \frac{8 \cdot 7 \cdot 6}{3 \cdot 2 \cdot 1},$$

which agrees with the result given by formula (1).

Verification of Formula (3)   Note that

$$n(n-1) \cdot \,\cdots\, \cdot (n-r+1) =$$

$$\frac{n(n-1) \cdot \,\cdots\, \cdot (n-r+1)\cancel{(n-r)}\cancel{(n-r-1)} \cdot \,\cdots\, \cdot \cancel{2} \cdot \cancel{1}}{\cancel{(n-r)}\cancel{(n-r-1)} \cdot \,\cdots\, \cdot \cancel{2} \cdot \cancel{1}} = \frac{n!}{(n-r)!}.$$

Then, by formula (1), we have

$$C(n,r) = \frac{n(n-1) \cdot \,\cdots\, \cdot (n-r+1)}{r!} = \frac{\dfrac{n!}{(n-r)!}}{r!} = \frac{n!}{r!\,(n-r)!},$$

which is formula (3).

Note that for $r = 0$, formula (3) reads

$$C(n,0) = \frac{n!}{0!\,(n-0)!} = \frac{n!}{0!\,n!} = \frac{1}{0!}.$$

Let us agree that the value of $0!$ is 1. Then the right-hand side of the equation above is 1, so that formula (3) also holds for $r = 0$.

Formula (3) can be used to prove many facts about $C(n,r)$. For example, the following formula is useful in calculating $C(n,r)$ for large values of r:

$$C(n,r) = C(n, n-r). \tag{4}$$

Suppose that we wish to calculate $C(100, 98)$. If we apply formula (4), we have

$$C(100, 98) = C(100, 100 - 98) = C(100, 2) = \frac{100 \cdot 99}{2 \cdot 1} = 4950.$$

Verification of Formula (4)   Apply formula (3) to evaluate $C(n, n-r)$:

$$C(n, n-r) = \frac{n!}{(n-r)!\,(n-(n-r))!} = \frac{n!}{(n-r)!\,r!}$$

$$= C(n,r) \quad \text{[by formula (3) again].}$$

The formula is intuitively reasonable since each time we select a subset of r elements we are selecting a subset of $n - r$ elements to be excluded. Thus there are as many subsets of $n - r$ elements as there are subsets of r elements.

An alternative notation for $C(n,r)$ is $\binom{n}{r}$. Thus, for example,

$$\binom{5}{2} = C(5,2) = \frac{5 \cdot 4}{2 \cdot 1} = 10.$$

The symbol $\binom{n}{r}$ is called a **binomial coefficient**. To discover why, let us tabulate the values of $\binom{n}{r}$ for some small values of n and r.

$$n = 2: \quad \binom{2}{0} = 1 \quad \binom{2}{1} = 2 \quad \binom{2}{2} = 1$$

$$n = 3: \quad \binom{3}{0} = 1 \quad \binom{3}{1} = 3 \quad \binom{3}{2} = 3 \quad \binom{3}{3} = 1$$

$$n = 4: \quad \binom{4}{0} = 1 \quad \binom{4}{1} = 4 \quad \binom{4}{2} = 6 \quad \binom{4}{3} = 4 \quad \binom{4}{4} = 1$$

$$n = 5: \quad \binom{5}{0} = 1 \quad \binom{5}{1} = 5 \quad \binom{5}{2} = 10 \quad \binom{5}{3} = 10 \quad \binom{5}{4} = 5 \quad \binom{5}{5} = 1$$

Each row consists of the coefficients that arise in expanding $(x + y)^n$. To see this, inspect the results of expanding $(x + y)^n$ for $n = 2$, 3, 4, and 5:

$$(x + y)^2 = x^2 + 2xy + y^2$$
$$(x + y)^3 = x^3 + 3x^2y + 3xy^2 + y^3$$
$$(x + y)^4 = x^4 + 4x^3y + 6x^2y^2 + 4xy^3 + y^4$$
$$(x + y)^5 = x^5 + 5x^4y + 10x^3y^2 + 10x^2y^3 + 5xy^4 + y^5.$$

Compare the coefficients in any row with the values in the corresponding row of binomial coefficients. Note that they are the same. Thus we see that the binomial coefficients arise as coefficients in multiplying out powers of the binomial $x + y$; hence the name *binomial coefficient*.

What we observed for the exponents $n = 2$, 3, 4, and 5 holds true for any positive integer n. We have the following result, a proof of which is given at the end of this section.

Binomial Theorem

$$(x + y)^n = \binom{n}{0}x^n + \binom{n}{1}x^{n-1}y + \binom{n}{2}x^{n-2}y^2 + \cdots + \binom{n}{n-1}xy^{n-1} + \binom{n}{n}y^n$$

EXAMPLE 1

Applying the binomial theorem Expand $(x + y)^6$.

Solution By the binomial theorem,

$$(x + y)^6 = \binom{6}{0}x^6 + \binom{6}{1}x^5y + \binom{6}{2}x^4y^2 + \binom{6}{3}x^3y^3$$

$$+ \binom{6}{4}x^2y^4 + \binom{6}{5}xy^5 + \binom{6}{6}y^6.$$

Furthermore,

$$\binom{6}{0} = 1 \qquad \binom{6}{1} = \frac{6}{1} = 6 \qquad \binom{6}{2} = \frac{6 \cdot 5}{2 \cdot 1} = 15$$

$$\binom{6}{3} = \frac{6 \cdot 5 \cdot 4}{3 \cdot 2 \cdot 1} = 20 \qquad \binom{6}{4} = \frac{6 \cdot 5 \cdot 4 \cdot 3}{4 \cdot 3 \cdot 2 \cdot 1} = 15$$

$$\binom{6}{5} = \frac{6 \cdot 5 \cdot 4 \cdot 3 \cdot 2}{5 \cdot 4 \cdot 3 \cdot 2 \cdot 1} = 6 \qquad \binom{6}{6} = \frac{6 \cdot 5 \cdot 4 \cdot 3 \cdot 2 \cdot 1}{6 \cdot 5 \cdot 4 \cdot 3 \cdot 2 \cdot 1} = 1.$$

Thus

Now Try Exercise 19

$$(x + y)^6 = x^6 + 6x^5y + 15x^4y^2 + 20x^3y^3 + 15x^2y^4 + 6xy^5 + y^6.$$ ∎

The binomial theorem can be used to count the number of subsets of a set, as shown in the next example.

EXAMPLE 2

Counting the number of subsets of a set   Determine the number of subsets of a set with five elements.

Solution   Let us count the number of subsets of each possible size. A subset of r elements can be chosen in $\binom{5}{r}$ ways, since $C(5, r) = \binom{5}{r}$. So the set has $\binom{5}{0}$ subsets with 0 elements, $\binom{5}{1}$ subsets with 1 element, $\binom{5}{2}$ subsets with 2 elements, and so on. Therefore, the total number of subsets is

$$\binom{5}{0} + \binom{5}{1} + \binom{5}{2} + \binom{5}{3} + \binom{5}{4} + \binom{5}{5}.$$

On the other hand, the binomial theorem for $n = 5$ gives

$$(x + y)^5 = \binom{5}{0}x^5 + \binom{5}{1}x^4y + \binom{5}{2}x^3y^2 + \binom{5}{3}x^2y^3 + \binom{5}{4}xy^4 + \binom{5}{5}y^5.$$

Set $x = 1$ and $y = 1$ in this formula.

$$(1 + 1)^5 = \binom{5}{0}1^5 + \binom{5}{1}1^4 \cdot 1 + \binom{5}{2}1^3 \cdot 1^2 + \binom{5}{3}1^2 \cdot 1^3 + \binom{5}{4}1 \cdot 1^4 + \binom{5}{5}1^5$$

$$2^5 = \binom{5}{0} + \binom{5}{1} + \binom{5}{2} + \binom{5}{3} + \binom{5}{4} + \binom{5}{5}$$

Now Try Exercise 27

Thus the total number of subsets of a set with five elements (the right side) equals $2^5 = 32$.   ∎

There is nothing special about the number 5 in the preceding example. An analogous argument gives the following result:

A set of n elements has 2^n subsets.

EXAMPLE 3

Counting pizza options   A pizza parlor offers a plain cheese pizza to which any number of six possible toppings can be added. How many different pizzas can be ordered?

Solution   Ordering a pizza requires selecting a subset of the six possible toppings. Since the set of six toppings has 2^6 different subsets, there are 2^6 or 64 different pizzas. (Note that the plain cheese pizza corresponds to selecting the empty subset of toppings.)

Now Try Exercise 31

∎

Proof of the Binomial Theorem   Note that

$$(x + y)^n = \underbrace{(x + y)(x + y) \cdot \cdots \cdot (x + y)}_{n \text{ factors}}.$$

Multiplying out these factors involves forming all products, where one term is selected from each factor, and then combining like products. For instance,

$$(x + y)(x + y)(x + y) = x \cdot x \cdot x + x \cdot x \cdot y + x \cdot y \cdot x + y \cdot x \cdot x$$
$$+ x \cdot y \cdot y + y \cdot x \cdot y + y \cdot y \cdot x + y \cdot y \cdot y.$$

The first product on the right, $x \cdot x \cdot x$, is obtained by selecting the x-term from each of the three factors. The next term, $x \cdot x \cdot y$, is obtained by selecting the x-terms from the first two factors and the y-term from the third. The next product, $x \cdot y \cdot x$, is obtained by selecting the x-terms from the first and third factors and the y-term from the second. And so on. There are as many products containing two x's and one y as there are ways of selecting the factor from which to pick the y-term—namely $\binom{3}{1}$.

In general, when multiplying the n factors $(x+y)(x+y)\cdots(x+y)$, the number of products having k y's (and therefore $(n-k)$ x's) is equal to the number of different ways of selecting the k factors from which to take the y-term—that is, $\binom{n}{k}$. Therefore, the coefficient of $x^{n-k}y^k$ is $\binom{n}{k}$. This proves the binomial theorem. ■

Practice Problems 5.7

1. Calculate $\binom{12}{8}$.

2. An ice cream parlor offers 10 flavors of ice cream and 5 toppings. How many different servings are possible

if each serving consists of one flavor of ice cream and as many toppings as desired?

EXERCISES 5.7

Calculate the value for each of Exercises 1–18.

1. $\binom{6}{2}$ 2. $\binom{7}{3}$ 3. $\binom{8}{1}$ 4. $\binom{9}{9}$

5. $\binom{18}{16}$ 6. $\binom{25}{24}$ 7. $\binom{7}{0}$ 8. $\binom{6}{1}$

9. $\binom{8}{8}$ 10. $\binom{9}{0}$ 11. $\binom{n}{n-1}$

12. $\binom{n}{n}$ 13. $0!$ 14. $1!$

15. $n \cdot (n-1)!$ 16. $\dfrac{n!}{n}$

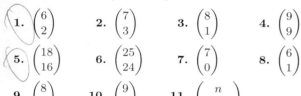

17. $\binom{6}{0} + \binom{6}{1} + \binom{6}{2} + \binom{6}{3} + \binom{6}{4} + \binom{6}{5} + \binom{6}{6}$

18. $\binom{7}{0} + \binom{7}{1} + \binom{7}{2} + \binom{7}{3} + \binom{7}{4} + \binom{7}{5} + \binom{7}{6} + \binom{7}{7}$

19. Determine the first three terms in the binomial expansion of $(x+y)^{10}$.

20. Determine the first three terms in the binomial expansion of $(x+y)^{20}$.

21. Determine the last three terms in the binomial expansion of $(x+y)^{15}$.

22. Determine the last three terms in the binomial expansion of $(x+y)^{12}$.

23. Determine the middle term in the binomial expansion of $(x+y)^{20}$.

24. Determine the middle term in the binomial expansion of $(x+y)^{10}$.

25. Determine the coefficient of x^4y^7 in the binomial expansion of $(x+y)^{11}$.

26. Determine the coefficient of x^8y^5 in the binomial expansion of $(x+y)^{13}$.

27. How many different subsets can be chosen from a set of six elements?

28. How many different subsets can be chosen from a set of 100 elements?

29. **Restaurant Tip** How many different tips could you leave in a restaurant if you had a nickel, a dime, a quarter, and a half-dollar?

30. **Pizza Options** A pizza parlor offers mushrooms, green peppers, onions, and sausage as toppings for the plain cheese base. How many different types of pizzas can be made?

31. **Cable TV Options** A cable TV franchise offers 20 basic channels plus a selection (at an extra cost per channel) from a collection of 5 premium channels. How many different options are available to the subscriber?

32. **Salad Options** A salad bar offers a base of lettuce to which tomatoes, chickpeas, beets, pinto beans, olives, and green peppers can be added. Five salad dressings are available. How many different salads are possible? (Assume that each salad contains at least lettuce and at most one salad dressing.)

33. **Book Selection** In how many ways can a selection of at least one book be made from a set of eight books?

34. **Dessert Choices** In how many ways can a selection of at most five desserts be made from a dessert trolley containing six desserts?

35. Pizza Options Armand's Chicago Pizzeria offers thin-crust and deep-dish pizzas in 9-, 12-, and 14-inch sizes, with 15 possible toppings. How many different types of pizzas can be ordered?

36. CD Selection In how many ways can a selection of at least two CDs be made from a set of seven CDs?

37. Appetizers Selection In how many ways can a selection of at most five appetizers be made from a menu containing seven appetizers?

38. Ice Cream Sundaes An ice cream parlor offers four flavors of ice cream, three sauces, and two types of nuts. How many different sundaes consisting of a single flavor of ice cream plus one or more toppings are possible?

39. How many subsets of the set $\{a, b, c, d, e\}$ do not contain the letter c?

40. How many subsets of the set $\{1, 2, 3, 4, 5\}$ do not contain an even digit?

41. Lab Projects Students in a physics class are required to complete at least two out of a collection of eight lab projects. In how many ways can a student satisfy the requirement?

42. Suppose that a set has an odd number of elements. Explain why half of the subsets will have an odd number of elements.

43. Seminar Attendance How many different groups of students can show up for a seminar with an enrollment of 12?

44. Menu Planning In planning a menu, a dietitian must choose 2 carbohydrates from the 7 available ones, 3 vegetables from the 10 available ones, and 1 protein from the 5 available ones. How many menus are possible?

45. Show that in a Venn diagram containing three sets, there are eight basic regions. Use binomial coefficients to explain why.

46. Car Showroom A car dealership has 20 different models that could be placed on display in the showroom, but it has room for at most 5 of these. In how many ways can the manager choose the "show cars"? (Assume that at least 1 car will be shown.)

47. Car Showroom A car dealership has 20 different models, of which 8 are two-door and 12 are four-door vehicles. In how many ways can the manager choose three of the two-door and two of the four-door models for a showroom display?

48. Car Sales In how many ways can a car dealership with 20 cars available on a particular day make at least one sale?

49. What is the coefficient of y^4 in the expansion of $(x - 3y)^7$?

50. (a) Use equation (4) to show that

$$\binom{5}{0} - \binom{5}{1} + \binom{5}{2} - \binom{5}{3} + \binom{5}{4} - \binom{5}{5} = 0.$$

(b) For what values of n can equation (4) be used to show that

$$\binom{n}{0} - \binom{n}{1} + \binom{n}{2} - \binom{n}{3} + \cdots \pm \binom{n}{n} = 0?$$

(c) Use the binomial theorem to prove the result in part (a). *Hint:* Apply the binomial theorem to $(x + y)^5$ with $x = 1$ and $y = -1$.

(d) For what values of n can the binomial theorem be used to prove the result in part (b)?

51. Club Contingent The Scrabble club at Gotham College agrees to be represented at a national intercollegiate Scrabble tournament. The contingent can consist of as many members of the club as desired, but must consist of at least one person. If the club has 15 members, how many different contingents are possible?

Solutions to Practice Problems 5.7

1. 495. $\binom{12}{8}$ is the same as $C(12, 8)$, which equals $C(12, 12 - 8)$ or $C(12, 4)$.

$$C(12, 4) = \frac{12 \cdot 11 \cdot 10 \cdot 9}{4 \cdot 3 \cdot 2 \cdot 1} = \frac{\cancel{12} \cdot 11 \cdot \overset{5}{\cancel{10}} \cdot 9}{\cancel{4} \cdot \cancel{3} \cdot \cancel{2} \cdot 1} = 495$$

2. 320. The task of deciding what sort of serving to have consists of two choices. The first choice, selecting the flavor of ice cream, can be performed in 10 ways. The second choice, selecting the toppings, can be performed in 2^5 or 32 ways, since selecting the toppings amounts to selecting a subset from the set of 5 toppings, and a set of 5 elements has 2^5 subsets. (Notice that selecting the empty subset corresponds to ordering a plain dish of ice cream.) By the multiplication principle, the task can be performed in $10 \cdot 32 = 320$ ways.

5.8 Multinomial Coefficients and Partitions

Permutation and combination problems are only two of the many types of counting problems. By appropriately generalizing the binomial coefficients to the *multinomial coefficients*, we can consider certain generalizations of combinations, namely *partitions*. To introduce the notion of a partition, let us return to combinations and look at them from another viewpoint. Suppose that we consider combinations of n objects taken r at a time. View the n objects as the elements of a set S. Then each combination determines an ordered division of S into two subsets, S_1 and S_2, the first containing the r elements selected and the second containing the $n-r$ elements remaining (Fig. 1). We see that

$$S = S_1 \cup S_2 \quad \text{and} \quad n(S_1) + n(S_2) = n.$$

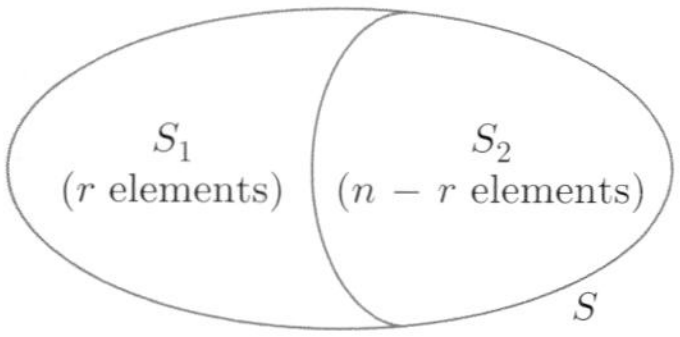

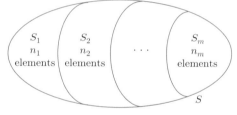

S_1
(r elements) S_2
($n - r$ elements)

S

Figure 1

This ordered division is called an **ordered partition of type $(r, n-r)$**. We know that the number of such partitions is just the number of ways of selecting the first subset, that is, $n!/[r!(n-r)!]$. If we let $n_1 = n(S_1) = r$ and $n_2 = n(S_2) = n-r$, then we find that the number of ordered partitions of type (n_1, n_2) is $n!/n_1! n_2!$.

We may generalize the aforementioned situation as follows: Let S be a set of n elements. An **ordered partition of S of type $(n_1, n_2, \ldots, n_m)$** is a decomposition of S into m subsets (given in a specific order) $S_1, S_2, \ldots, S_m$, where no two of these intersect and where

$$n(S_1) = n_1, \qquad n(S_2) = n_2, \quad \ldots \quad, n(S_m) = n_m$$

(Fig. 2). Since S has n elements, we clearly must have $n = n_1 + n_2 + \cdots + n_m$.

S_1
n_1
elements

S_2
n_2
elements

$\cdots$

S_m
n_m
elements

S

Figure 2

EXAMPLE 1

Ordered partitions of a set   List all ordered partitions of $S = \{a, b, c, d\}$ of type $(1, 1, 2)$.

Solution

$$(\{a\}, \{b\}, \{c, d\}) \qquad (\{c\}, \{a\}, \{b, d\})$$
$$(\{a\}, \{c\}, \{b, d\}) \qquad (\{c\}, \{b\}, \{a, d\})$$
$$(\{a\}, \{d\}, \{b, c\}) \qquad (\{c\}, \{d\}, \{a, b\})$$
$$(\{b\}, \{a\}, \{c, d\}) \qquad (\{d\}, \{a\}, \{b, c\})$$
$$(\{b\}, \{c\}, \{a, d\}) \qquad (\{d\}, \{b\}, \{a, c\})$$
$$(\{b\}, \{d\}, \{a, c\}) \qquad (\{d\}, \{c\}, \{a, b\})$$

Note that the ordered partition $(\{a\}, \{b\}, \{c, d\})$ is different from the ordered partition $(\{b\}, \{a\}, \{c, d\})$, since in the first S_1 is $\{a\}$, whereas in the second S_1 is $\{b\}$. The order in which the subsets are given is significant. ■

We saw earlier that the number of ordered partitions of type (n_1, n_2) for a set of n elements is $n!/n_1! n_2!$. This result generalizes.

Number of Ordered Partitions of Type ($n_1, n_2, \ldots, n_m$)   Let S be a set of n elements. Then the number of ordered partitions of S of type $(n_1, n_2, \ldots, n_m)$ where $n_1 + n_2 + \cdots + n_m = n$ is

$$\frac{n!}{n_1! \, n_2! \cdots n_m!}. \tag{1}$$

The number of ordered partitions of type $(n_1, n_2, \ldots, n_m)$ for a set of n elements is often denoted

$$\binom{n}{n_1, n_2, \ldots, n_m}.$$

Using the preceding notation, result (1) says that

$$\binom{n}{n_1, n_2, \ldots, n_m} = \frac{n!}{n_1! \, n_2! \cdots n_m!}.$$

The binomial coefficient $\binom{n}{n_1}$ can also be written $\binom{n}{n_1, n_2}$. The number

$$\binom{n}{n_1, n_2, \ldots, n_m}$$

is known as a **multinomial coefficient** since it appears as the coefficient of $x_1^{n_1} x_2^{n_2} \cdots x_m^{n_m}$ in the expansion of $(x_1 + x_2 + \cdots + x_m)^n$.

EXAMPLE 2

Ordered partitions of a set   Let S be a set of four elements. Use the formula in (1) to determine the number of ordered partitions of S of type $(1, 1, 2)$.

Solution   Here $n = 4$, $n_1 = 1$, $n_2 = 1$, and $n_3 = 2$. Therefore, the number of ordered partitions of type $(1, 1, 2)$ is

$$\binom{4}{1, 1, 2} = \frac{4!}{1! \, 1! \, 2!} = \frac{4 \cdot 3 \cdot 2 \cdot 1}{1 \cdot 1 \cdot 2 \cdot 1} = 12.$$

Now Try Exercise 1   This result is the same as obtained in Example 1 by enumeration.   ■

EXAMPLE 3

Assigning tasks to construction workers   A work crew consists of 12 construction workers, all having the same skills. A construction job requires four welders, three concrete workers, three heavy equipment operators, and two bricklayers. In how many ways can the 12 workers be assigned to the required tasks?

Solution   Each assignment of jobs corresponds to an ordered partition of the type $(4, 3, 3, 2)$. The number of such ordered partitions is

Now Try Exercise 15

$$\binom{12}{4, 3, 3, 2} = \frac{12!}{4! \, 3! \, 3! \, 2!} = 277{,}200. \qquad ■$$

Sometimes all of the m subsets of an ordered partition are required to have the same number of elements. If the set has n elements and each of the m subsets has r elements, then the number of ordered partitions of type

$$\underbrace{(r, r, \ldots, r)}_{m}$$

is

$$\binom{n}{r, r, \ldots, r} = \frac{n!}{r! \, r! \cdots r!} = \frac{n!}{(r!)^m}. \tag{2}$$

EXAMPLE 4

Counting the number of bridge hands In the game of bridge, four players seated in a specific order are each dealt 13 cards. How many different possibilities are there for the hands dealt to the players?

Solution Each deal results in an ordered partition of the 52 cards of type $(13, 13, 13, 13)$. The number of such partitions is

$$\binom{52}{13, 13, 13, 13} = \frac{52!}{(13!)^4}.$$

This number is approximately 5.36×10^{28}. ∎

Unordered Partitions Determining the number of unordered partitions of a certain type is a complex matter. We will restrict our attention to the special case in which each subset is of the same size.

EXAMPLE 5

Unordered partitions of a set List all unordered partitions of $S = \{a, b, c, d\}$ of type $(2, 2)$.

Solution

$$(\{a, b\}, \{c, d\})$$
$$(\{a, c\}, \{b, d\})$$
$$(\{a, d\}, \{b, c\})$$ ∎

Note that the partition $(\{c, d\}, \{a, b\})$ is the same as the partition $(\{a, b\}, \{c, d\})$ when order is not taken into account.

> **Number of Unordered Partitions of Type ($r, r, \ldots, r$)** Let S be a set of n elements where $n = m \cdot r$. Then the number of unordered partitions of S of type $(r, r, \ldots, r)$ is
>
> $$\frac{1}{m!} \cdot \frac{n!}{(r!)^m}. \qquad (3)$$

Formula (3) follows from the fact that each unordered partition of the m subsets gives rise to $m!$ ordered partitions. Therefore,

$$(m!)\,[\text{number of unordered partitions}] = [\text{number of ordered partitions}]$$

or

$$[\text{number of unordered partitions}] = \frac{1}{m!} \cdot [\text{number of ordered partitions}]$$

$$= \frac{1}{m!} \cdot \frac{n!}{(r!)^m} \quad [\text{by formula (2)}].$$

EXAMPLE 6

Unordered partitions of a set Let S be a set of four elements. Use formula (3) to determine the number of unordered partitions of S of type $(2, 2)$.

Solution Here $n = 4$, $r = 2$, and $m = 2$. Therefore, the number of unordered partitions of type $(2, 2)$ is

$$\frac{1}{2!} \cdot \frac{4!}{(2!)^2} = \frac{1}{2} \cdot \frac{4 \cdot 3 \cdot 2 \cdot 1}{(2 \cdot 1)^2} = 3.$$

Now Try Exercise 11   This result is the same as that obtained in Example 5 by enumeration. ∎

EXAMPLE 7   **Grouping construction workers** A construction crew contains 12 workers, all having similar skills. In how many ways can the workers be divided into four groups of three?

Solution   The order of the four groups is not relevant. (It does not matter which is labeled S_1 and which S_2, and so on. Only the composition of the groups is important.) Applying formula (3) with $n = 12$, $r = 3$, and $m = 4$, we see that the number of ways is

$$\frac{1}{m!} \cdot \frac{n!}{(r!)^m} = \frac{1}{4!} \cdot \frac{12!}{(3!)^4}$$

$$= \frac{1}{4 \cdot 3 \cdot 2 \cdot 1} \frac{12 \cdot 11 \cdot 10 \cdot 9 \cdot 8 \cdot 7 \cdot 6 \cdot 5 \cdot 4 \cdot 3 \cdot 2 \cdot 1}{6^4}$$

Now Try Exercise 19

$$= \frac{12 \cdot 11 \cdot 10 \cdot 9 \cdot 8 \cdot 7 \cdot 6 \cdot 5}{6 \cdot 6 \cdot 6 \cdot 6} = 15{,}400.$$ ∎

Practice Problems 5.8

1. A foundation wishes to award one grant of \$100,000, two grants of \$10,000, five grants of \$5000, and five grants of \$2000. Its list of potential grant recipients has been narrowed to 13 possibilities. In how many ways can the awards be made?

2. In how many different ways can six medical interns be put into three groups of two and assigned to

   (a) The radiology, neurology, and surgery departments?

   (b) Share living quarters?

EXERCISES 5.8

Let S be a set of n elements. Determine the number of ordered partitions of the types in Exercises 1–10.

1. $n = 5$; $(3, 1, 1)$
2. $n = 5$; $(2, 1, 2)$
3. $n = 6$; $(2, 1, 2, 1)$
4. $n = 6$; $(3, 3)$
5. $n = 7$; $(3, 2, 2)$
6. $n = 7$; $(4, 1, 2)$
7. $n = 12$; $(4, 4, 4)$
8. $n = 8$; $(3, 3, 2)$
9. $n = 12$; $(5, 3, 2, 2)$
10. $n = 8$; $(2, 2, 2, 2)$

Let S be a set of n elements. Determine the number of unordered partitions of the types in Exercises 11–14.

11. $n = 15$; $(3, 3, 3, 3, 3)$
12. $n = 10$; $(5, 5)$
13. $n = 18$; $(6, 6, 6)$
14. $n = 12$; $(4, 4, 4)$

15. **Stock Reports** A brokerage house regularly reports the behavior of a group of 20 stocks, each stock being reported as "up," "down," or "unchanged." How many different reports can show seven stocks up, five stocks down, and eight stocks unchanged?

16. **Investment Ratings** An investment advisory service rates investments as A, AA, and AAA. On a certain week, it rates 15 investments. In how many ways can it rate five investments in each of the categories?

17. **Observation Groups** A psychology experiment observes groups of four individuals. In how many ways can an experimenter choose 5 groups of 4 from among 20 subjects?

18. **Weather** In a certain month (of 30 days) it rains 10 days, snows 2 days, and is clear 18 days. In how many ways can such weather be distributed over the month?

19. **Orientation Groups** During orientation, new students are divided into groups of five people. In how many ways can 4 groups be chosen from among 20 people?

20. **Awarding Prizes** Of the nine contestants in a contest, three will receive cars, three will receive TV sets, and three will receive radios. In how many different ways can the prizes be awarded?

21. **Job Promotions** A corporation has four employees that it wants to place in high executive positions. One will become president, one will become vice president, and two will be appointed to the board of directors. In how many different ways can this be accomplished?

22. **Forming Committees** The 10 members of a city council decide to form two committees of six to study zoning ordinances and street-repair schedules, with an overlap of two committee members. In how many ways can the committees be formed? (*Hint:* Specify three groups, not two.)

23. **Field Trip** In how many ways can the 14 children in a third-grade class be paired up for a trip to a museum?

24. **Work Schedule** A sales representative must travel to three cities twice each in the next 10 days. Her non-travel days are spent in the office. In how many different ways can she schedule her travel, assuming that she does not want to spend four consecutive days in the office?

25. **Basketball Teams** Ten students in a physical education class are to be divided into five-member teams for a basketball game. In how many ways can the two teams be selected?

26. Derive formula (1) using the generalized multiplication principle and the formula for $\binom{n}{r}$. (*Hint:* First select the elements of S_1, then the elements of S_2, and so on.)

In Exercises 27 and 28, use a graphing calculator or spreadsheet to calculate the answers.

27. **Assignments to Seminars** Calculate the number of ways that 38 students can be assigned to four seminars of size 10, 12, 10, and 6, respectively.

28. **Campaign Tasks** Calculate the number of ways that 65 phone numbers can be distributed to 5 campaign workers if each worker gets the same number of names.

Solutions to Practice Problems 5.8

1. Each choice of recipients is an ordered partition of the 13 finalists into a first subset of one ($100,000 award), a second subset of two ($10,000 award), a third subset of five ($5000 award), and a fourth subset of five ($2000 award). The number of ways to choose the recipients is thus

$$\binom{13}{1,2,5,5} = \frac{13!}{1!\,2!\,5!\,5!}$$

$$= \frac{13 \cdot 12 \cdot 11 \cdot \overset{3}{\cancel{10}} \cdot \cancel{9} \cdot \cancel{8} \cdot 7 \cdot 6 \cdot \cancel{5} \cdot \cancel{4} \cdot \cancel{3} \cdot \cancel{2} \cdot \cancel{1}}{1 \cdot \cancel{2} \cdot 1 \cdot \cancel{5} \cdot \cancel{4} \cdot \cancel{3} \cdot \cancel{2} \cdot 1 \cdot \cancel{5} \cdot \cancel{4} \cdot \cancel{3} \cdot \cancel{2} \cdot \cancel{1}}$$

$$= 13 \cdot 12 \cdot 11 \cdot 3 \cdot 7 \cdot 6 = 216{,}216.$$

2. Each partition is of the type (2, 2, 2). In part (a) the order of the subsets is important, whereas in part (b) the order is irrelevant. Consider the partitions

$$(\{\text{Dr. A, Dr. B}\},\ \{\text{Dr. C, Dr. D}\},\ \{\text{Dr. E, Dr. F}\})$$

and

$$(\{\text{Dr. C, Dr. D}\},\ \{\text{Dr. A, Dr. B}\},\ \{\text{Dr. E, Dr. F}\}).$$

With respect to part (a) these two partitions are different since in one Drs. A and B are assigned to the radiology department and in the other they are assigned to the neurology department. With respect to part (b), these two partitions are the same since, for instance, Drs. A and B are roommates in both partitions. Therefore, the answers are

(a) $\binom{6}{2,2,2} = \frac{6!}{(2!)^3} = \frac{6 \cdot 5 \cdot \cancel{4} \cdot 3 \cdot \cancel{2} \cdot 1}{\cancel{2} \cdot \cancel{2} \cdot \cancel{2}} = 90.$

(b) $\frac{1}{3!} \cdot \frac{6!}{(2!)^3} = \frac{1}{\cancel{6}} \cdot \frac{\cancel{6} \cdot 5 \cdot \cancel{4} \cdot 3 \cdot \cancel{2} \cdot 1}{\cancel{2} \cdot \cancel{2} \cdot \cancel{2}} = 15.$

CHAPTER SUMMARY

1. A *set* is a collection of objects. Each object is called an *element* of the set. The *empty set* is the set containing no objects.

2. The *union* of two sets is the set consisting of all elements that belong to **at least one** of the sets. The *intersection* of two sets is the set consisting of all elements that belong to **both** of the sets.

3. Set A is a *subset* of set B (written $A \subseteq B$) if every element of set A is also an element of set B. In each situation or problem, all sets are considered to be subsets of a *universal set*. The set of all elements in the universal set that do not belong to the set A is called the *complement of* A, denoted A'.

4. The inclusion-exclusion principle says that the number of elements in the union of two sets is the sum of the number of elements in each set minus the number of elements in their intersection.

5. A Venn diagram consists of a rectangle containing overlapping circles and is used to illustrate set operations. The rectangle represents the universal set and the circles represent subsets of the universal set.

6. De Morgan's laws state that the complement of the union (intersection) of two sets is the intersection (union) of their complements.

7. The multiplication principle states that the number of ways a sequence of several choices can be performed is the product of the number of ways each individual choice can be performed.

8. The number of ordered arrangements, each called a *permutation*, of n objects taken r at a time is

$$P(n, r) = n(n - 1)(n - 2) \cdots (n - r + 1).$$

9. The number of unordered arrangements, each called a *combination*, of n objects taken r at a time is

$$C(n, r) = \frac{P(n, r)}{r!} = \frac{n(n - 1)(n - 2) \cdots (n - r + 1)}{r(r - 1) \cdots 1}.$$

$C(n, r)$ is also denoted $\binom{n}{r}$.

10. The formula $C(n, r) = C(n, n - r)$ simplifies the computation of $C(n, r)$ when r is greater than $\frac{n}{2}$.

11. The binomial theorem states that

$$(x + y)^n = \binom{n}{0} x^n + \binom{n}{1} x^{n-1} y + \binom{n}{2} x^{n-2} y^2$$
$$+ \cdots + \binom{n}{n-1} xy^{n-1} + \binom{n}{n} y^n.$$

12. A set of n elements has 2^n subsets.

13. Let S be a set of n elements, and suppose that $n = n_1 + n_2 + \cdots + n_m$ where each number in the sum is a positive integer. Then the number of ordered partitions of S into subsets of sizes $n_1, n_2, \ldots, n_m$ is

$$\frac{n!}{n_1! \, n_2! \cdots n_m!}.$$

This number is also denoted

$$\binom{n}{n_1, n_2, \ldots, n_m}.$$

14. Let S be a set of n elements, where $n = m \cdot r$. Then the number of unordered partitions of S into m subsets of size r is $\dfrac{1}{m!} \cdot \dfrac{n!}{(r!)^m}$.

REVIEW OF FUNDAMENTAL CONCEPTS

1. What is a set?

2. What is a subset of a set?

3. What is an element of a set?

4. Define a universal set.

5. Define the empty set.

6. Use a Venn diagram to draw the complement of a set A.

7. Use a Venn diagram to draw the sets $A \cap B$ and $A \cup B$.

8. Use a Venn diagram to draw the sets $A \cap (B \cup C)$ and $A \cup (B \cap C)$.

9. State the generalized multiplication principle for counting.

10. What is meant by a permutation of n items taken r at a time?

11. How would you calculate the number of permutations of n items taken r at a time?

12. What is the difference between a permutation and a combination?

13. How would you calculate the number of combinations of n items taken r at a time?

14. Give a formula that can be used to calculate each of the following:

$$n! \qquad \binom{n}{r} \qquad C(n, r) \qquad P(n, r).$$

15. State the binomial theorem.

16. If a set contains n elements, how many subsets does it have?

17. Explain what is meant by an ordered partition of a set.

18. Explain how to calculate the number of ordered partitions of a set.

19. Give a formula that can be used to calculate

$$\binom{n}{n_1, n_2, \ldots, n_m}.$$

KEY FORMULAS

Inclusion–Exclusion Principle:

$$n(S \cup T) = n(S) + n(T) - n(S \cap T)$$

De Morgan's Law:

$$(S \cup T)' = S' \cap T' \quad \text{and} \quad (S \cap T)' = S' \cup T'$$

Permutations:

$$P(n, r) = n(n-1)(n-2) \cdot \cdots \cdot (n-r+1) \quad (r \text{ factors})$$

Combinations:

$$C(n, r) = \frac{P(n, r)}{r!} = \frac{n(n-1) \cdot \cdots \cdot (n-r+1)}{r(r-1) \cdot \cdots \cdot 1}$$

$$= \frac{n!}{r!(n-r)!}$$

A Property of Binomial Coefficients: $C(n, r) = C(n, n-r)$

Binomial Theorem:

$$(x+y)^n = \binom{n}{0} x^n + \binom{n}{1} x^{n-1} y + \binom{n}{2} x^{n-2} y^2$$

$$+ \cdots + \binom{n}{n-1} xy^{n-1} + \binom{n}{n} y^n$$

Number of subsets in a set of n elements: 2^n

Number of Ordered Partitions of Type $(n_1, n_2, \ldots, n_m)$, where $n = n_1 + \cdots + n_m$:

$$\frac{n!}{n_1! \, n_2! \cdots n_m!}$$

Number of Unordered Partitions of Type $(r, r, \ldots, r)$, where there are m r's and $n = m \cdot r$:

$$\frac{1}{m!} \cdot \frac{n!}{(r!)^m}$$

SUPPLEMENTARY EXERCISES

1. List all subsets of the set $\{a, b\}$.

2. Draw a two-circle Venn diagram and shade the portion corresponding to the set $(S \cup T')'$.

3. **Tennis Finalists** There are 16 contestants in a tennis tournament. How many different possibilities are there for the two people who will play in the final round?

4. **Team Picture** In how many ways can a coach and five basketball players line up in a row for a picture if the coach insists on standing at one of the ends of the row?

5. Draw a three-circle Venn diagram and shade the portion corresponding to the set $R' \cap (S \cup T)$.

6. Calculate the first three terms in the binomial expansion of $(x+y)^{12}$.

7. **Balls in an Urn** An urn contains 14 numbered balls, of which 8 are red and 6 are green. How many different possibilities are there for selecting a sample of 5 balls in which 3 are red and 2 are green?

8. **Testing a Drug** Sixty people with a certain medical condition were given pills. Fifteen of these people received placebos. Forty people showed improvement, and 30 of these people received an actual drug. How many of the people who received the drug showed no improvement?

9. **Appliance Purchase** An appliance store carries seven different types of washing machines and five different types of dryers. How many different combinations are possible for a customer who wants to purchase a washing machine and a dryer?

10. **Contest Prizes** There are 12 contestants in a contest. Two will receive trips around the world, four will receive cars, and six will receive TV sets. In how many different ways can the prizes be awarded?

11. **Languages** Out of a group of 115 applicants for jobs at the World Bank, 70 speak French, 65 speak Spanish, 65 speak German, 45 speak French and Spanish, 35 speak

Spanish and German, 40 speak French and German, and 35 speak all three languages. How many of the people speak none of the three languages?

12. Calculate $\binom{17}{15}$.

Environmental Poll *The 100 members of the Earth Club were asked what they felt the club's priorities should be in the coming year: clean water, clean air, or recycling. The responses were 45 for clean water, 30 for clean air, 42 for recycling, 13 for both clean air and clean water, 20 for clean air and recycling, 16 for clean water and recycling, and 9 for all three. Exercises 13–20 refer to this poll.*

13. How many members thought the priority should be clean air only?

14. How many members thought the priority should be clean water or clean air, but not both?

15. How many members thought the priority should be clean water or recycling but not clean air?

16. How many members thought the priority should be clean air and recycling but not clean water?

17. How many members thought the priority should be exactly one of the three issues?

18. How many members thought recycling should not be a priority?

19. How many members thought the priority should be recycling but not clean air?

20. How many members thought the priority should be something other than one of these three issues?

21. **Nine-Letter Words** How many different nine-letter words (i.e., sequences of letters) can be made using four S's and five T's?

22. Passing an Exam Forty people take an exam. How many different possibilities are there for the set of people who pass the exam?

23. Winter Sports A survey at a small New England college showed that 400 students skied, 300 played ice hockey, and 150 did both. How many students participated in at least one of these sports?

24. Meal Choices How many different meals can be chosen if there are 6 appetizers, 10 main dishes, and 8 desserts, assuming a meal consists of one item from each category?

25. Test Scoring On an essay test there are 5 questions worth 20 points each. In how many ways can a student get 10 points on one question, 15 points on each of three questions, and 20 points on another question?

26. Seven-Digit Numbers How many seven-digit numbers are even and have a 3 in the hundreds place?

27. Telephone Numbers How many telephone numbers are theoretically possible if all numbers are of the form *abc-def-ghij* and neither of the first two leading digits (*a* and *d*) is zero?

28. Calculate the number of different strings of letters of length at least 1 but less than 11.

29. How many strings of length 8 can be formed from the symbols *a*, *b*, *c*, *d*, and *e*? How many of the strings have at least one *e*?

30. Basketball Teams How many different 5-person basketball teams can be formed from a pool of 12 players?

31. Selecting Students Fourteen students in the 100-student eighth grade are to be chosen to tour the United Nations. How many different groups of 14 are possible?

32. Journal Subscriptions In one ZIP code, there are 40,000 households. Of them, 4000 households get *Fancy Diet Magazine*, 10,000 households get *Clean Living Journal*, and 1500 households get both publications. How many households get neither?

33. Computer Program At each stage in a decision process, a computer program has three branches. There are 10 stages at which these branches appear. How many different paths could the process follow?

34. Filling Jobs Sixty people apply for 10 job openings. In how many ways can all the jobs be filled?

35. Generating Tests A computerized test generator can generate any one of 5 problems for each of the 10 areas being tested. How many different tests can be generated?

36. If a string of six letters cannot contain any vowels (a, e, i, o, u), how many strings are possible?

37. Choosing Delegations How many different 4-person delegations can be chosen from 10 ambassadors?

38. Subdividing a Class In how many ways can a teacher divide a class of 21 students into groups of 7 students each?

39. Distributing Candy In how many ways can 14 different candies be distributed to 14 scouts?

40. Senate Subdivision In how many ways can 100 senators be divided into groups of 20 each?

41. Senate Subdivision In how many ways can 100 senators be assigned to groups of 20 each if the 2 senators from the state of New York cannot be in the same group?

42. If every team in a ten-team softball league plays every other team three times, how many games are played?

43. How many diagonals does an *n*-sided polygon have?

44. Racetrack Betting Racetracks have a compound bet called the *daily double*, in which the bettor tries to select the winners of the first two races. If 8 horses compete in the first race and 6 horses compete in the second race, determine the possible number of daily double bets.

45. Hat Displays A designer of a window display wants to form a pyramid with 15 hats. She wants to place the five men's hats in the bottom row, the four women's hats in the next row, next the three baseball caps, then the two berets, and a clown's hat at the top. All the hats are different. How many displays are possible?

46. Seat Assignments In how many ways can 5 people be assigned to seats in a 12-seat room?

47. Poker A poker hand consists of five cards. How many different poker hands contain all cards of the same suit? (Such a hand is called a "flush.")

48. How many three-digit numbers are there in which no two digits are alike?

49. How many three-digit numbers are there in which exactly two digits are alike?

50. Poker How many hands of five cards contain exactly three aces?

51. Greek-Letter Societies Fraternity and sorority names consist of two or three letters from the Greek alphabet. How many different names are there in which no letter appears more than once? (The Greek alphabet contains 24 letters.)

Party Guests *In Exercises 52–54 suppose there are three boys and three girls at a party.*

52. How many different pairings of the six into three boy-girl pairs can be formed?

53. In how many ways can they be seated in a row such that no person is seated next to someone of the same sex?

54. In how many ways can they be seated at a round table such that no person is seated next to someone of the same sex?

55. Feasible Set If 10 lines are drawn in the plane so that none of them are parallel and no three lines intersect at the same point, how many points of intersection are there? If each of these 10 lines forms the boundary of the bounded feasible set of a system of linear inequalities, how many of the intersections occur outside the feasible set?

56. Splitting Classes Two elementary school teachers have 24 students each. The first teacher splits his students into four groups of six. The second teacher splits her students into six groups of four. Which teacher has more options?

57. Consultation Schedule A consulting engineer agrees to spend three days at Widgets International, four days at Gadgets Unlimited, and three days at Doodads Incorporated in the next two workweeks. In how many different ways can she schedule her consultations?

58. Arranging Books A set of books can be arranged on a bookshelf in 120 different ways. How many books are in the set?

59. Batting Order How many batting orders are possible in a nine-member baseball team if the catcher must bat fourth and the pitcher last?

60. Choosing Committees In how many ways can a committee of 5 people be chosen from 12 married couples if

(a) The committee must consist of two men and three women?

(b) A husband and wife cannot both serve on the committee?

61. Voting Suppose that you are voting in an election for state delegate. Two state delegates are to be elected from among seven candidates. In how many different ways can you cast your ballot? (*Note*: You may vote for two candidates. However, some people "single-shoot," and others don't pull any levers.)

62. Spelling Algebraic The object is to start with the letter *A* on top and to move down the diagram to the *C* at the bottom. From any given letter, move only to one of the letters directly below it on the left or right. If these rules are followed, how many different paths spell *ALGEBRAIC*?

$$A$$
$$L \quad L$$
$$G \quad G \quad G$$
$$E \quad E \quad E \quad E$$
$$B \quad B \quad B \quad B \quad B$$
$$R \quad R \quad R \quad R$$
$$A \quad A \quad A$$
$$I \quad I$$
$$C$$

63. Call Letters The call letters of radio stations in the U.S. consist of either three or four letters, where the first letter is K or W. How many different call letters are possible?

In Exercises 64–66, use a graphing calculator or spreadsheet to calculate the answer.

64. Arranging Students A group of students can be arranged in a row of seats in 479,001,600 ways. How many students are there?

65. Assigning Jobs There are 25 people in a department who must be deployed to work on three projects requiring 10, 9, and 6 people. All the people are eligible for all jobs. Calculate the number of ways this can be done.

66. License Plates

(a) Calculate the number of license plates that can be formed using three distinct letters and three distinct numbers in any order.

(b) Compare the solution to (a) with the number of license plates consisting of three distinct letters followed by three distinct numbers. (See Section 4, Example 5.)

Conceptual Exercises

67. What is the relationship between the two sets A and B if $A \cap B = \emptyset$?

68. What is the relationship between the two sets A and B if $n(A \cup B) = n(A) + n(B)$?

69. Explain why $n \cdot (n-1)! = n!$.

70. Use the result in Exercise 69 to explain why 0! is defined to be 1.

71. Express in your own words the difference between a permutation and a combination.

72. Consider a group of 10 people. Without doing any computation, explain why the number of committees of size 6 is equal to the number of committees of 4 people.

73. Without doing any computation, explain why $C(10,3) = C(10,7)$.

74. Without doing any computation, explain why $C(10,4) + C(10,5) = C(11,5)$. *Hint:* Suppose a committee of size 5 is to be chosen from a pool of 11 people, and John Doe is one of the people. How many committees are there which include John? How many committees are there that don't include John?

CHAPTER TEST

1. Calculate each of the following:
   (a) $4!$ (b) $P(7,3)$ (c) $C(18,16)$
   (d) $\begin{pmatrix} 6 \\ 0 \end{pmatrix}$ (e) $\begin{pmatrix} 5 \\ 2,1,2 \end{pmatrix}$

2. True or false?
   (a) $\{a,b\} = \{b,a,b\}$.
   (b) If $A \cup B = A$, then $A \cap B = B$.
   (c) $(A \cap B)' = A' \cap B'$.

3. Let $U = \{a,b,c,d,e\}$, $S = \{b,c,d\}$, and $T = \{a,c,e\}$. List the elements of the following sets.
   (a) $S' \cap T$ (b) $(S \cup T)'$

4. Let
$$U = \{\text{all people}\}$$
$$C = \{\text{certified public accountants}\}$$
$$E = \{\text{self-employed people}\}.$$
   Describe verbally the sets $C \cap E$ and $C \cup E'$.

5. Draw a three-circle Venn diagram and shade the portion corresponding to the set $A \cap (B' \cup C)$.

6. **Group Membership** The Choral Society and the Drama Club at State University hold a joint party. Of the 60 people attending, 40 are members of the Choral Society and 30 are members of the Drama Club. How many are members of both groups?

7. **Freshmen Survey** Out of a group of 100 college freshmen, 9 are education majors, 43 describe themselves as middle-of-the-road politically, and 82 did volunteer work during the past year. Of the education majors, 4 describe themselves as middle-of-the-road politically and 6 did volunteer work during the past year. Thirty-two students did volunteer work during the past year and describe themselves as middle-of-the-road politically. Three freshmen are education majors who describe themselves as middle-of-the-road politically and who did volunteer work during the past year. How many of the freshmen did not meet any of the three criteria? (*Note*: The data for this problem are based on a survey conducted in the fall semester of 2007 by the American Council of Education.)

8. **Executive Positions** An Internet company is considering three candidates for CEO, five candidates for CFO, and four candidates for marketing director. In how many different ways can these positions be filled?

9. **Exam Questions**
   (a) In choosing problems for an exam consisting of 10 true/false questions, a teacher uses a data bank of 20 easy and 30 hard questions. How many ways can he select the questions for an exam consisting of 5 questions of each type?
   (b) A student who is totally unprepared for the exam decides to answer six of the questions true and the remainder false without even reading the questions. How many different ways can he answer the questions?

10. How many three-digit numbers can be formed from the numbers $\{1,2,3,4,5,6,7\}$ if no digit is repeated?

11. **Family Picture** A family consisting of two parents and four children is to be seated in a row for a picture. How many different arrangements are possible in which the children are seated together?

12. **Selecting Students** The 30 students in a math class consist of 10 science majors and 20 humanities majors. In how many ways can a group of 6 students be selected so that 3 students from each type of major are in the group?

13. Determine the coefficient of $x^7 y^5$ in the binomial expansion of $(x+y)^{12}$.

14. **Hot Dogs** The most popular condiments for hot dogs are mustard, ketchup, onions, relish, chili, sauerkraut, and mayonnaise. How many types of hot dogs can be ordered?

15. **Assigning Volunteers** In how many ways can eight volunteers be assigned to four pairs for visiting the sick?

CHAPTER 5 | PROJECT

Pascal's Triangle

In the following triangular table, known as **Pascal's triangle**, the entries in the nth row are the binomial coefficients $\binom{n}{0}, \binom{n}{1}, \binom{n}{2}, \ldots, \binom{n}{n}$.

					1					0th row
				1		1				1st row
			1		2		1			2nd row
		1		3		3		1		3rd row
	1		4		6		4		1	4th row
1		5		10		10		5		1
1	6	15	20	15	6	1				6th row
1	7	21	35	35	21	7	1			7th row

Observe that each number (other than the ones) is the sum of the two numbers directly above it. For example, in the 5th row the number 5 is the sum of the numbers 1 and 4 from the 4th row, and the number 10 is the sum of the numbers 4 and 6 from the 4th row. This fact is known as **Pascal's formula**. Namely, the formula says that

$$\binom{n}{r} = \binom{n-1}{r-1} + \binom{n-1}{r}.$$

1. For what values of n and r does Pascal's formula say that the number 10 in the triangle above is the sum of the numbers 4 and 6?

2. Derive Pascal's formula from the fact that $C(n,r) = \dfrac{n!}{r!\,(n-r)!}$.

3. Derive Pascal's formula from the fact that $C(n,r)$ is the number of ways of selecting r objects from a set of n objects. (*Hint*: Let x denote the nth object of the set. Count the number of ways a subset of r objects containing x can be selected and then count the number of ways a subset of r objects not containing x can be selected.)

4. Use Pascal's formula to extend Pascal's triangle to the 12th row. Determine the values of $\binom{12}{5}$ and $\binom{12}{6}$ from the extended triangle.

5. (a) Show that for any positive integer n,

$$\binom{n}{0} + \binom{n}{1} + \binom{n}{2} + \binom{n}{3} + \cdots + \binom{n}{n} = 2^n.$$

   Hint: Apply the binomial theorem to $(x+y)^n$ with $x = 1$, $y = 1$.

   (b) Show that for any positive integer n,

$$\binom{n}{0} - \binom{n}{1} + \binom{n}{2} - \binom{n}{3} + \cdots \pm \binom{n}{n} = 0.$$

   Hint: Apply the binomial theorem to $(x+y)^n$ with $x = 1$, $y = -1$.

   (c) Show that for the 7th row of Pascal's triangle, the sum of the even-numbered elements equals the sum of the odd-numbered elements; that is,

$$\binom{7}{0} + \binom{7}{2} + \binom{7}{4} + \binom{7}{6} = \binom{7}{1} + \binom{7}{3} + \binom{7}{5} + \binom{7}{7}.$$

(d) Use the result of parts (a) and (b) to show that for any row of Pascal's triangle, the sum of the even-numbered elements equals the sum of the odd-numbered elements, and give that common sum for the nth row in terms of n. [*Hint*: Add the two equations in parts (a) and (b).]

(e) Suppose S is a set of n elements. Use the result of part (d) to determine the number of subsets of S that have an even number of elements.

6. (a) Show that for any positive integer n,

$$1 + 2 + 4 + 8 + \cdots + 2^n = 2^{n+1} - 1.$$

(*Hint*: Let $S = 1 + 2 + 4 + 8 + \cdots + 2^n$, multiply both sides of the equation by 2, and subtract the first equation from the second.)

(b) Show that the sum of the elements of any row of Pascal's triangle equals one more than the sum of the elements of all previous rows.

7. (a) Consider the 7th row of Pascal's triangle. Observe that each interior number (that is, a number other than 1) is divisible by 7. For what values of n, for $1 \leq n \leq 12$, are the interior numbers of the nth row divisible by n?

(b) Confirm that each of the values of n from part (a) is a prime number. (*Note*: A number p is a *prime* number if the only positive integers that divide it are p and 1.) Prove that if p is a prime number, then each interior number of the pth row of Pascal's triangle is divisible by p. [*Hint*: Use the fact that $\binom{p}{r} = \frac{p(p-1)(p-2)\cdots(p-r+1)}{1 \cdot 2 \cdot 3 \cdots r}$.]

(c) Show that for any prime number p, the sum of the interior numbers of the pth row is $2^p - 2$.

(d) Calculate $2^p - 2$ for $p = 7$ and show that it is a multiple of 7.

(e) Use the results of parts (b) and (c) to show that for any prime number p, $2^p - 2$ is a multiple of p. (*Note*: This is a special case of Fermat's theorem, which states that for any prime number p and any integer a, $a^p - a$ is a multiple of p.)

8. There are 4 odd numbers in the 6th row of Pascal's triangle $(1, 15, 15, 1)$ and $4 = 2^2$ is a power of 2. For the 0th through 12th rows of Pascal's triangle, show that the number of odd numbers in each row is a power of 2.

In Fig. 1(a) each odd number in the first eight rows of Pascal's triangle has been replaced by a dot and each even number has been replaced by a space. In Fig. 1(b) the pattern for the first four rows is shown in blue. Notice that this pattern appears twice in the next four rows, with the two appearances separated by an inverted triangle. Figure 1(c) shows the locations of the odd numbers in the first 16 rows of Pascal's triangle, and Fig. 1(d) shows that the pattern for the first eight rows appears twice in the next eight rows separated by an inverted triangle. Figure 2 on the next page demonstrates that the first 32 rows of Pascal's triangle have the same property.

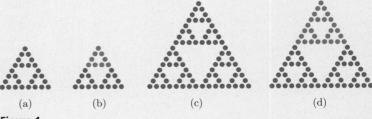

(a) (b) (c) (d)

Figure 1

9. Assume that the property shown in Figs. 1 and 2 continues to hold for subsequent rows of Pascal's triangle. Use this result to explain why the number of odd numbers in each row of Pascal's triangle is a power of 2.

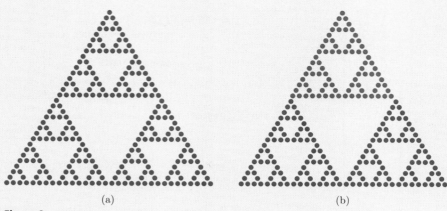

(a)   (b)

Figure 2

PROBABILITY

In this chapter we discuss probability, the mathematics of chance. We consider the basic concepts that allow us to associate realistic probabilities to random events that we see in both our personal and professional lives.

6.1 Introduction

Uncertainty faces us every day. We wake up in the morning and check the weather report (60% chance of rain). We decide on our breakfast cereal (oatmeal might reduce cholesterol). We choose the route to school or work (average delay on Route 450 is 20 minutes, average delay on the alternate is 15 minutes). We call our stockbroker and check the bank rates to decide how to handle our paycheck. We get a flat tire on the way to an important date (what's the chance of that?). And so on.

Many events in the world around us exhibit a random character. Yet, by repeated observations of such events we can often discern long-term patterns that persist despite random, short-term fluctuations. Probability is the branch of mathematics devoted to the study of such events.

Human beings have always been interested in games of chance and gambling. We have evidence that games such as dice have been in existence since 3000 B.C. But the mathematical treatment of such games did not begin until the fifteenth century in Italy. The French contributed to the literature in the seventeenth century in an attempt to calculate probabilities and develop the theory. The foundations of modern probability theory are generally credited to Kolmogorov, the Russian mathematician, who in 1933 proposed the axioms on which the present subject of probability rests. Even now in the twenty-first century, contemporary mathematicians continue to develop new ideas that are applied to such varied areas as investment and risk analysis, card shuffling, diagnostic medical procedures, cryptography, and the efficacy of treatment modalities in medical and social programs. To obtain an idea of the sorts of events that are considered, let us consider a concrete example from the field of medicine.

Suppose that we wish to analyze the reliability of a skin test for active pulmonary tuberculosis. Unfortunately, such a test is not completely reliable. On one hand, the test may be negative even for a person with tuberculosis. On the other hand, the test may be positive for a person who does not have tuberculosis. For the moment, let us concentrate on errors of the first sort and consider only individuals actually having tuberculosis. Suppose that by observing the results of the test on increasingly large populations of tuberculosis patients we accumulate the data shown in Table 1. Note that out of each group of tuberculosis patients the test fails to identify a certain number. However, the data do exhibit a pattern. It appears that out of a very large population of tuberculosis patients the skin test will successfully identify about 98% of them. In fact, it appears that as the size of the population is increased, the relative frequency m/N more and more closely approximates the number .98. In a situation like this, we say that the skin test detects tuberculosis with a 98% likelihood or that the *probability* that the test detects tuberculosis (when present) is .98.

TABLE 1

Number of tuberculosis patients N	Number of positive test results m	Relative frequency of positive test results m/N
100	97	.97
500	494	.988
1000	981	.981
10,000	9806	.9806
50,000	49,008	.98016
100,000	98,005	.98005

More generally, the **probability of an event** is a number that expresses the long-run likelihood that the event will occur. Such numbers are always chosen to lie between 0 and 1. The smaller the probability, the less likely the event is to occur. So, for example, an event having probability .1 is rather unlikely to occur; an event with probability .9 is very likely to occur; and an event with probability .5 is just as likely to occur as not.

We assign probabilities to events on the following intuitive basis: The probability of an event should represent the long-run proportion of the time that the event can be expected to occur. For example, an event with probability .9 can be expected to occur 90% of the time, and an event with probability .1 can be expected to occur 10% of the time.

As we shall see, many real-life problems require us to calculate probabilities from known data. Here is one example that arises in connection with the skin test for tuberculosis.

Medical Diagnosis A clinic tests for active pulmonary tuberculosis. If a person has tuberculosis, the probability of a positive test result is .98. If a person does not have tuberculosis, the probability of a negative test result is .99. The incidence of tuberculosis in a certain city is 2 cases per 10,000 population. Suppose that an individual is tested and a positive result is noted. What is the probability that the individual actually has active pulmonary tuberculosis?

Before we can solve this problem, it will be necessary to do considerable preliminary work. We begin this work in Section 6.2, where we introduce a convenient language for discussing events and the process of observing them. In Section 6.3 we introduce probabilities of events, and in Sections 6.4, 6.5, 6.6, and 6.7 we develop methods for calculating probabilities of various sorts of events. The solution of the medical diagnosis problem is presented in Section 6.6. Section 6.8 is devoted to the simulation of simple experiments.

6.2 Experiments, Outcomes, Sample Spaces, and Events

The events whose probabilities we wish to compute all arise as outcomes of various experiments. So as our first step in developing probability theory, let us define *experiments*, *outcomes*, *events*, and the associated concept *sample spaces*.

> **DEFINITIONS** An **experiment** is an activity with an observable result.
> Each possible result is called an **outcome** of the experiment.
> The set of all possible outcomes is called the **sample space** of the experiment.
> An **event** is a subset of the sample space. (We say that the event E has occurred when the outcome of the experiment is an element of E.)

EXAMPLE 1 **Rolling a die** Illustrate the definitions above for the experiment of rolling a die and observing the number on the uppermost face.

Solution (a) The possible outcomes are the numbers 1, 2, 3, 4, 5, and 6.

(b) The sample space is $\{1, 2, 3, 4, 5, 6\}$

(c) One possible event is $\{2, 4, 6\}$. This event also can be described as "the event that the outcome is an even number." ■

EXAMPLE 2 **Rolling a pair of dice** Illustrate the definitions above for the experiment of rolling two dice, one red and one green, and observing the number on the uppermost face of each.

Solution (a) Each outcome of the experiment can be regarded as an ordered pair of numbers, the first representing the number on the red die and the second the number on the green die. Thus, for example, the pair of numbers $(3, 5)$ represents the outcome "3 on the red die, 5 on the green die." That is, each outcome is an ordered pair of numbers (r, g), where r and g are each one of the numbers 1, 2, 3, 4, 5, 6.

(b) The sample space, which has 36 elements, is as follows:

$$\{(1,1), (1,2), (1,3), (1,4), (1,5), (1,6),$$
$$(2,1), (2,2), (2,3), (2,4), (2,5), (2,6),$$
$$(3,1), (3,2), (3,3), (3,4), (3,5), (3,6),$$
$$(4,1), (4,2), (4,3), (4,4), (4,5), (4,6),$$
$$(5,1), (5,2), (5,3), (5,4), (5,5), (5,6),$$
$$(6,1), (6,2), (6,3), (6,4), (6,5), (6,6)\}.$$

(c) One possible event is $\{(1,4), (2,3), (3,2), (4,1)\}$. This event also can be described as "the event that the sum of the two numbers is 5."

Now Try Exercise 3(a)   ■

EXAMPLE 3   **Number of people in a queue** Once an hour a supermarket manager observes the number of people standing in checkout lines. The store has space for at most 30 customers to wait in line. Illustrate the above definitions for this situation.

Solution **(a)** The possible outcomes are the numbers 0, 1, 2, 3, ..., 30.

(b) The sample space is $\{0, 1, 2, 3, \dots, 30\}$.

(c) One possible event is $\{0, 1, 2, 3, 4, 5\}$. This event also can be described as "the event that there are at most five people standing in the line."   ■

EXAMPLE 4   **Sample space for pollutant levels** The Environmental Protection Agency orders Middle States Edison Corporation to install "scrubbers" to remove the pollutants from its smokestacks. To monitor the effectiveness of the scrubbers, the corporation installs monitoring devices to record the levels of sulfur dioxide, particulate matter, and oxides of nitrogen in the smokestack emissions. Consider the monitoring operation as an experiment. Describe the associated sample space.

Solution Each reading of the instruments consists of an ordered triple of numbers (x, y, z), where $x =$ level of sulfur dioxide, $y =$ level of particulate matter, and $z =$ level of oxides of nitrogen. The sample space thus consists of all possible triples (x, y, z), where $x \geq 0$, $y \geq 0$, and $z \geq 0$.

Now Try Exercise 7(a)   ■

The sample spaces in Examples 1, 2, and 3 are *finite*. That is, the associated experiments have only a finite number of possible outcomes. However, the sample space of Example 4 is *infinite*, since there are infinitely many triples (x, y, z), where $x \geq 0$, $y \geq 0$, and $z \geq 0$.

EXAMPLE 5   **Tossing a coin three times** Suppose that an experiment consists of tossing a coin three times and observing the sequence of heads and tails. (Order counts.)

(a) Determine the sample space S.

(b) Determine the event $E = $ "exactly two heads."

Solution **(a)** Denote "heads" by H and "tails" by T. Then a typical outcome of the experiment is a sequence of H's and T's. So, for instance, the sequence HTT would stand for a head followed by two tails. We exhibit all such sequences and arrive at the sample space S:

$$S = \{\text{HHH, HHT, HTH, THH, HTT, THT, TTH, TTT}\}.$$

(b) Here are the outcomes in which exactly two heads occur: HHT, HTH, THH. Therefore, event E is

Now Try Exercise 3(b)

$$E = \{\text{HHT, HTH, THH}\}. \qquad \blacksquare$$

EXAMPLE 6

Political poll A political poll surveys a group of people to determine their income levels and political affiliations. People are classified as either low-, middle-, or upper-level income and as either Democrat, Republican, or Independent.

(a) Find the sample space corresponding to the poll.

(b) Determine the event $E_1 = $ "Independent."

(c) Determine the event $E_2 = $ "low income and not Independent."

(d) Determine the event $E_3 = $ "neither upper income nor Independent."

Solution **(a)** Let us abbreviate low, middle, and upper income, respectively, by the letters L, M, and U, respectively. And let us abbreviate Democrat, Republican, and Independent by the letters D, R, and I, respectively. Then a response to the poll can be represented as a pair of letters. For example, the pair (L, D) refers to a low-income-level Democrat. The sample space S is then given by

$$S = \{(\text{L, D}), (\text{L, R}), (\text{L, I}), (\text{M, D}), (\text{M, R}), (\text{M, I}), (\text{U, D}), (\text{U, R}), (\text{U, I})\}.$$

(b) For event E_1 the income level may be anything, but the political affiliation is Independent. Thus

$$E_1 = \{(\text{L, I}), (\text{M, I}), (\text{U, I})\}.$$

(c) For event E_2 the income level is low and the political affiliation may be either Democrat or Republican, so that

$$E_2 = \{(\text{L, D}), (\text{L, R})\}.$$

(d) For event E_3 the income level may be either low or middle and the political affiliation may be Democrat or Republican. Thus

Now Try Exercise 9

$$E_3 = \{(\text{L, D}), (\text{L, R}), (\text{M, D}), (\text{M, R})\}. \qquad \blacksquare$$

The *New York Times* of November 21, 1996 reported that in the New York City public schools with total enrollment of 1.06 million students, 88.1% of the students are in regular classrooms, 4.5% get part-time special education, and 7.4% get full-time special education. Students in New York City attend schools in one of the five boroughs (Manhattan, Bronx, Brooklyn, Queens, Staten Island). If we choose a student at random, we can determine whether the student is in a regular classroom (C), gets part-time special education (P), or gets full-time special education (F). Likewise, for each student we can determine in what borough (M, Bx, Bk, Q, SI) the student goes to school. The sample space is

$$S = \{(\text{C, M}), (\text{C, Bx}), (\text{C, Bk}), (\text{C, Q}), (\text{C, SI}),$$
$$(\text{P, M}), (\text{P, Bx}), (\text{P, Bk}), (\text{P, Q}), (\text{P, SI}),$$
$$(\text{F, M}), (\text{F, Bx}), (\text{F, Bk}), (\text{F, Q}), (\text{F, SI})\}.$$

A student corresponding to the sample point (F, Bk) is getting full-time special education in Brooklyn.

As we have seen, an event is a subset of the sample space. Two events are worthy of special mention. The first is the event corresponding to the empty set, Ø. This is called the **impossible event**, since it can never occur. The second special event is the set S, the sample space itself. Every outcome is an element of S, so S always occurs. For this reason S is called the **certain event**.

One particular advantage of defining experiments and events in terms of sets is that it allows us to define new events from given ones by applying the operations of set theory. When so doing we always let the sample space S play the role of universal set. (All outcomes belong to the universal set.)

If E and F are events, then so are $E \cup F$, $E \cap F$, and E'. For example, consider the die-rolling experiment of Example 1. Then

$$S = \{1, 2, 3, 4, 5, 6\}.$$

Let E and F be the events given by

$$E = \{3, 4, 5, 6\} \qquad F = \{1, 4, 6\}.$$

Then we have

$$E \cup F = \{1, 3, 4, 5, 6\}$$
$$E \cap F = \{4, 6\}$$
$$E' = \{1, 2\}.$$

Let us interpret the events $E \cup F$, $E \cap F$, and E' using Venn diagrams. In Fig. 1 we have drawn a Venn diagram for $E \cup F$. Note that $E \cup F$ occurs precisely when the experimental outcome belongs to the shaded region—that is, to either E or F. Thus we have the following result.

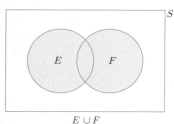

$E \cup F$

Figure 1

DEFINITION Union of Two Events The event $E \cup F$ occurs precisely when either E or F (or both) occurs.

Similarly, we can interpret the event $E \cap F$. This event occurs when the experimental outcome belongs to the shaded region of Fig. 2—that is, to both E and F. Thus we have an interpretation for $E \cap F$:

DEFINITION Intersection of Two Events The event $E \cap F$ occurs precisely when both E and F occur.

Finally, the event E' consists of all those outcomes not in E (Fig. 3). Therefore, we have

DEFINITION Complement of an Event The event E' occurs precisely when E does not occur.

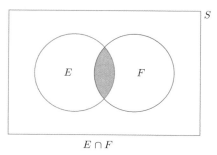

$E \cap F$

Figure 2

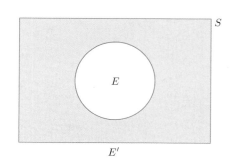

E'

Figure 3

EXAMPLE 7

Events related to pollution control   Consider the pollution monitoring described in Example 4. Let E, F, and G be the events

$$E = \text{“level of sulfur dioxide} \geq 100\text{”}$$

$$F = \text{“level of particulate matter} \leq 50\text{”}$$

$$G = \text{“level of oxides of nitrogen} \leq 30.\text{”}$$

Describe the following events.

(a) $E \cap F$ (b) E' (c) $E \cup G$ (d) $E' \cap F \cap G$

Solution (a) $E \cap F$ = “level of sulfur dioxide ≥ 100 *and* level of particulate matter ≤ 50.”

(b) E' = “level of sulfur dioxide < 100.”

(c) $E \cup G$ = “level of sulfur dioxide ≥ 100 *or* level of oxides of nitrogen ≤ 30.”

(d) $E' \cap F \cap G$ = “level of sulfur dioxide < 100 *and* level of particulate matter ≤ 50 *and* level of oxides of nitrogen ≤ 30.”

Now Try Exercise 7(b)

Suppose that E and F are events in a sample space S. We say that E and F are **mutually exclusive** (or *disjoint*) provided that $E \cap F = \varnothing$. In terms of Venn diagrams, we may represent a pair of mutually exclusive events as a pair of circles with no points in common (Fig. 4). If the events E and F are mutually exclusive, then E and F cannot simultaneously occur; if E occurs, then F does not; and if F occurs, then E does not.

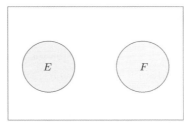

Figure 4 E and F are mutually exclusive.

EXAMPLE 8

Determining whether events are mutually exclusive   Let $S = \{a, b, c, d, e, f, g\}$ be a sample space, and let $E = \{a, b, c\}$, $F = \{e, f, g\}$, and $G = \{c, d, f\}$.

(a) Are E and F mutually exclusive?

(b) Are F and G mutually exclusive?

Solution (a) $E \cap F = \varnothing$, and so E and F are mutually exclusive.

Now Try Exercise 11 (b) $F \cap G = \{f\}$, and so F and G are *not* mutually exclusive.

Practice Problems 6.2

1. **Light Bulbs** A machine produces light bulbs. As part of a quality control procedure, a sample of five light bulbs is collected each hour and the number of defective light bulbs among these is observed.

(a) What is the sample space for this experiment?

(b) Describe the event “there are at most two defective light bulbs” as a subset of the sample space.

(Continued)

2. **Citrus Fruit** Suppose that there are two crates of citrus fruit and each crate contains oranges, grapefruit, and tangelos. An experiment consists of selecting a crate and then selecting a piece of fruit from that crate. Both the crate and the type of fruit are noted.

Refer to the crates as crate I and crate II.

(a) What is the sample space for this experiment?

(b) Describe the event "a tangelo is selected" as a subset of the sample space.

EXERCISES 6.2

1. **Committee Selection** A committee of two people is to be selected from five people, R, S, T, U, and V.

   (a) What is the sample space for this experiment?

   (b) Describe the event "R is on the committee" as a subset of the sample space.

   (c) Describe the event "neither R nor S is on the committee" as a subset of the sample space.

2. A letter is selected at random from the word "MISSISSIPPI."

   (a) What is the sample space for this experiment?

   (b) Describe the event "the letter chosen is a vowel" as a subset of the sample space.

3. **Heads and Tails** An experiment consists of tossing a coin two times and observing the sequence of heads and tails.

   (a) What is the sample space of this experiment?

   (b) Describe the event "the first toss is a head" as a subset of the sample space.

4. **Four-Sided Dice** A pair of four-sided dice, each with the numbers from 1 to 4 on their sides, are rolled and the numbers facing down are observed.

   (a) List the sample space.

   (b) Describe each of the following events as a subset of the sample space.
   - (i) Both numbers are even.
   - (ii) At least one number is even.
   - (iii) Neither number is less than or equal to 2.
   - (iv) The sum of the numbers is 6.
   - (v) The sum of the numbers is greater than or equal to 5.
   - (vi) The numbers are the same.
   - (vii) A 2 or 3 occurs, but not both 2 and 3.
   - (viii) No 4 appears.

5. **Selecting from Urns** Suppose that we have two urns— call them urn I and urn II—each containing red balls and white balls. An experiment consists of selecting an urn and then selecting a ball from that urn and noting its color.

   (a) What is a suitable sample space for this experiment?

   (b) Describe the event "urn I is selected" as a subset of the sample space.

6. **Coin Tosses** An experiment consists of tossing a coin four times and observing the sequence of heads and tails.

   (a) What is the sample space of this experiment?

   (b) Determine the event $E_1 =$ "more heads than tails occur."

   (c) Determine the event $E_2 =$ "the first toss is a head."

   (d) Determine the event $E_1 \cap E_2$.

7. **Efficiency Studies** A corporation efficiency expert records the time it takes an assembly line worker to perform a particular task. Let E be the event "more than 5 minutes," F the event "less than 8 minutes," and G the event "less than 4 minutes."

   (a) Describe the sample space for this experiment.

   (b) Describe the events $E \cap F$, $E \cap G$, E', F', $E' \cap F$, $E' \cap F \cap G$, and $E \cup F$.

8. **Product Reliability** A manufacturer of kitchen appliances tests the reliability of its refrigerators by recording in a laboratory test the elapsed time between consecutive failures. Let E be the event "more than nine months" and F the event "less than two years." Describe the events $E \cap F$, E', and F'.

9. **Student Poll** A campus survey is taken to correlate the number of years that students have been on campus with their political leanings. Students are classified as first-year, sophomore, junior, or senior and as conservative or liberal.

   (a) Find the sample space corresponding to the poll.

   (b) Determine the event $E_1 =$ "conservative."

   (c) Determine the event $E_2 =$ "junior and liberal."

   (d) Determine the event $E_3 =$ "neither first-year nor conservative."

10. **Automobiles** An experiment consists of selecting a car at random from a college parking lot and observing the color and make. Let E be the event "the car is red," F be the event "the car is a Chevrolet," G be the event "the car is a green Ford," and H be the event "the car is black or a Chrysler."

(a) Which of the following pairs of events are mutually exclusive?

(i) E and F (ii) E and G
(iii) F and G (iv) E and H
(v) F and H (vi) G and H
(vii) E' and G (viii) F' and H'

(b) Describe each of the following events:

(i) $E \cap F$ (ii) $E \cup F$
(iii) E' (iv) F'
(v) G' (vi) H'
(vii) $E \cup G$ (viii) $E \cap G$
(ix) $E \cap H$ (x) $E \cup H$
(xi) $G \cap H$ (xii) $E' \cap F'$
(xiii) $E' \cup G'$

11. Let $S = \{1, 2, 3, 4, 5, 6\}$ be a sample space,

$$E = \{1, 2\} \qquad F = \{2, 3\} \qquad G = \{1, 5, 6\}.$$

(a) Are E and F mutually exclusive?

(b) Are F and G mutually exclusive?

12. Show that if E is any event, and E' its complement, then E and E' are mutually exclusive.

13. Let $S = \{a, b, c\}$ be a sample space. Determine all possible events associated with S.

14. Let S be a sample space with n outcomes. How many events are associated with S?

15. Let $S = \{1, 2, 3, 4\}$ be a sample space, $E = \{1\}$, and $F = \{2, 3\}$. Are the events $E \cup F$ and $E' \cap F'$ mutually exclusive?

16. Let S be any sample space, and E, F any events associated with S. Are the events $E \cup F$ and $E' \cap F'$ mutually exclusive? (*Hint*: Apply De Morgan's laws.)

17. Coin Tosses Suppose that 10 coins are tossed and the number of heads observed.

(a) Describe the sample space for this experiment.

(b) Describe the event "more heads than tails" in terms of the sample space.

18. Coin Tosses Suppose that three nickels and three dimes are tossed and the numbers of heads from each group recorded.

(a) Describe the sample space for this experiment.

(b) Describe the event "more heads on the nickels than on the dimes" in terms of the sample space.

19. Genetic Traits An experiment consists of observing the eye color and gender of the students at a certain school. Let E be the event "blue eyes," F the event "male," and G the event "brown eyes and female."

(a) Are E and F mutually exclusive?

(b) Are E and G mutually exclusive?

(c) Are F and G mutually exclusive?

20. Genetic Traits Consider the experiment and events of Exercise 19. Describe the following events.

(a) $E \cup F$ **(b)** $E \cap G$ **(c)** E'

(d) F' **(e)** $(G \cup F) \cap E$ **(f)** $G' \cap E$

21. Shuttle Bus Suppose you observe the number of passengers arriving at a Metro station on a shuttle bus that holds up to 8 passengers. Describe the sample space.

22. Dice A pair of dice is rolled and the sum of the numbers on the two uppermost faces is observed. What is the sample space of this experiment?

23. Selecting Balls from an Urn An urn contains balls numbered 1 through 9. Suppose you draw a ball from the urn, observe its number, replace the ball, draw a ball again, and observe its number. Give an example of an output of the experiment. How large is the sample space?

24. Selecting Balls from an Urn Repeat Exercise 23 in the case that the first ball is not replaced.

25. NBA Draft Lottery In the NBA, the fourteen basketball teams that did not make the playoffs participate in the draft lottery. Ping pong balls numbered 1 through 14 are placed in a lottery machine and a sample of four balls is drawn randomly to determine which team will have the first overall draft pick. The combination $\{11, 12, 13, 14\}$ is ignored if it is drawn. (*Note*: Each team is assigned between 5 and 250 combinations prior to the drawing in order of their regular season record.) Give an example of an outcome of the draw. In 2008, the Chicago Bulls, who had the ninth worst record in the NBA and were assigned 17 combinations, won the first overall pick. What percentage of the combinations was assigned to the Chicago Bulls?

26. Suppose a coin is tossed and a die is rolled and the face and number appearing are observed. How many outcomes are in the sample space?

27. The Game of Clue *Clue* is a board game in which players are given the opportunity to solve a murder that has six suspects, six possible weapons, and nine possible rooms where the murder may have occurred. The six suspects are Colonel Mustard, Miss Scarlet, Professor Plum, Mrs. White, Mr. Green, and Mrs. Peacock. Determine a sample space for the choice of murderer. Discuss how to form a sample space with the entire solution to the murder, giving murderer, weapon, and site.

(a) How many outcomes would the sample space for the entire solution have?

Let E be the event that the murder occurred in the library. Let F be the event that the weapon was a gun.

(b) Describe $E \cap F$.   **(c)** Describe $E \cup F$.

1. **(a)** $\{0, 1, 2, 3, 4, 5\}$. The sample space is the set of all outcomes of the experiment. At first glance it might seem that each outcome is a set of five light bulbs. What is observed, however, is not the specific sample but rather the number of defective bulbs in the sample. Therefore, the outcome must be a number.

(b) $\{0, 1, 2\}$. "At most 2" means "2 or less."

2. **(a)** {(crate I, orange), (crate I, grapefruit), (crate I, tangelo), (crate II, orange), (crate II, grapefruit), (crate II, tangelo)}. Two selections are being made and both should be recorded.

(b) {(crate I, tangelo), (crate II, tangelo)}. This set consists of those outcomes in which a tangelo is selected.

6.3 Assignment of Probabilities

In Section 6.2 we introduced the sample space of an experiment and used it to describe events. We complete our description of experiments by introducing probabilities associated to events. For the remainder of this chapter, let us limit our discussion to experiments with only a finite number of outcomes.[1]

What do we mean when we say that the probability of getting a "head" on a toss of a fair coin is 50%? What is meant by the statement that the chance was 1 in 100 of choosing a particular number from the numbers $0, 1, 2, 3, \ldots, 97, 98, 99$? Similar notions are used every day. Probability occurs in the news, in strategies used in games and in war, and in decisions that involve medical treatments, insurance policies, and all kinds of risk.

Suppose that you took a coin and tossed it 152 times and kept track of the results on a chart recording the number of heads and tails as you tossed. You might try this with a real coin, or as we will see later, with a simulation device of some kind. Assume that the tally looked like this:

	Number	Relative frequency
Heads	67	$67/152 = 44\%$
Tails	85	$85/152 = 56\%$
Total	152	1 or 100%

How "fair" does the coin seem to be? We have computed the actual relative frequency of the two outcomes and noted that heads occurs on about 44% of the tosses, and tails on about 56% of the tosses. For this experiment, the **experimental probability**, or **relative frequency**, of heads is 44%.

This experiment is just that—an experiment—and repeating it would generally yield different tallies and different experimental probabilities. But if the coin is fair, the probability assigned to these two outcomes is the fixed theoretical value of 50% for heads and 50% for tails. What this tells us is that in theory, if a fair coin is tossed many, many times, heads will occur about 50% of the time. The experimental probability (relative frequency) of an event may be quite different from the probability.

Suppose that an experiment has a sample space S consisting of a finite number of outcomes $s_1, s_2, \ldots, s_N$. To each outcome we associate a number, called the *probability* of the outcome, which represents the likelihood that the outcome will occur. Suppose that to the outcome s_1 we associate the probability p_1, to the outcome s_2 the probability p_2, and so forth. We can summarize these data in a

---

[1] This restriction will remain in effect until our discussion of the normal distribution in Section 7.6.

chart of the following sort:

Outcome	Probability
s_1	p_1
s_2	p_2
$\vdots$	$\vdots$
s_N	p_N

Such a chart is called the **probability distribution** for the experiment. The numbers $p_1, p_2, \ldots, p_N$ are chosen so that each probability represents the long-run proportion of trials in which the associated outcome can be expected to occur. Central to our assignment of probabilities is the requirement that the total probability is 1. That is,

$$p_1 + p_2 + \cdots + p_N = 1.$$

The next three examples illustrate some methods for determining probability distributions.

EXAMPLE 1   **Probability distribution for coin toss**   Toss an unbiased coin and observe the side that faces upward. Determine the probability distribution for this experiment.

Solution   Since the coin is unbiased, we expect each of the outcomes "heads" and "tails" to be equally likely. We assign the two outcomes equal probabilities, namely $\frac{1}{2}$. The probability distribution is

Outcome	Probability
Heads	$\frac{1}{2}$
Tails	$\frac{1}{2}$

∎

EXAMPLE 2   **Probability distribution for roll of a die**   Roll a die and observe the side that faces upward. Determine the probability distribution for this experiment.

Solution   There are six possible outcomes, namely 1, 2, 3, 4, 5, 6. Assuming that the die is unbiased, these outcomes are equally likely. So we assign to each outcome the probability $\frac{1}{6}$. Here is the probability distribution for the experiment:

Outcome	Probability	Outcome	Probability
1	$\frac{1}{6}$	4	$\frac{1}{6}$
2	$\frac{1}{6}$	5	$\frac{1}{6}$
3	$\frac{1}{6}$	6	$\frac{1}{6}$

∎

Probabilities may be assigned to the elements of a sample space using common sense about the physical nature of the experiment. The fair coin has two sides, both equally likely to be face up. The balanced die has six equally probable faces. However, it may not be possible to use intuition alone to decide on a realistic probability to assign to individual sample elements. Sometimes it is necessary to conduct an experiment and use the data to shed light on the long-run relative frequency with which events occur. The following example demonstrates this technique.

EXAMPLE 3   **Probability distribution for traffic volume**   Traffic engineers measure the volume of traffic on a major highway during the rush hour from 5 to 6 P.M. By observing the number of cars that pass a fixed point for 300 consecutive weekdays, they collect the following data:

Number of cars observed	Frequency observed
at most 1000	30
1001–3000	45
3001–5000	135
5001–7000	75
more than 7000	15

(a) Describe the sample space associated to this experiment.

(b) Assign a probability distribution to this experiment.

Solution (a) The experiment consists of counting the number of cars during rush hour on 300 weekdays and assigning each day to a category depending on the number of cars observed on that day. So, for instance, if we observe 6241 cars on a particular day, we add one to the tally for the category 5001–7000. We let

$$s_1 = \text{"at most 1000 cars"}$$

$$s_2 = \text{"1001–3000 cars"}$$

$$s_3 = \text{"3001–5000 cars"}$$

$$s_4 = \text{"5001–7000 cars"}$$

$$s_5 = \text{"more than 7000 cars."}$$

The sample space is

$$S = \{s_1, s_2, s_3, s_4, s_5\}.$$

(b) For each outcome we use the available data to compute its relative frequency. For example, on 30 days of the 300 observed, the number of cars passing the fixed point is at most 1000. So the outcome s_1 occurred in $30/300 = 10\%$ of the observations. If we assume that the 300 consecutive observations are representative of rush hours in general, it seems reasonable to assign to the outcome s_1 the probability .10. Similarly, we can assign probabilities to the other outcomes based on the percentages of observations in which they occur.

Outcome	Probability
s_1	$\frac{30}{300} = .10$
s_2	$\frac{45}{300} = .15$
s_3	$\frac{135}{300} = .45$
s_4	$\frac{75}{300} = .25$
s_5	$\frac{15}{300} = .05$

■

This method of assigning probabilities to outcomes is valid only insofar as the observed trials are "representative." If such probability models are to be used for planning roadways or traffic patterns, they would have to be tested extensively to be sure that the probabilities are realistic representations of the long-run frequency of events.

In fact, in many instances we cannot rely on intuition or perform such experiments to help us in assigning probabilities; instead, we must use our knowledge of sets and counting to construct a theoretical model of the experiment along with associated probabilities. We need to keep in mind that certain fundamental properties must hold when the set of outcomes (the sample space) is a finite set. These can be observed in the following probability distribution for the number of heads in four tosses of a fair coin:

Events	Probability
0 heads	$\frac{1}{16}$
1 head	$\frac{4}{16} = \frac{1}{4}$
2 heads	$\frac{6}{16} = \frac{3}{8}$
3 heads	$\frac{4}{16} = \frac{1}{4}$
4 heads	$\frac{1}{16}$
Total	1

Note that the column labeled "Events" contains all possible outcomes in the sample space. Also, all of the entries in the probability column are nonnegative numbers between 0 and 1. Furthermore, the sum of the probabilities is 1. These properties hold for every probability distribution.

Let an experiment have outcomes $s_1, s_2, \ldots, s_N$ with respective probabilities $p_1, p_2, p_3, \ldots, p_N$. Then the numbers $p_1, p_2, p_3, \ldots, p_N$ must satisfy two basic properties

Fundamental Property 1   Each of the numbers $p_1, p_2, \ldots, p_N$ is between 0 and 1.

Fundamental Property 2 $p_1 + p_2 + \cdots + p_N = 1$.

Roughly speaking, Fundamental Property 1 says that the likelihood of each outcome lies between 0% and 100%, whereas Fundamental Property 2 says that there is a 100% likelihood that one of the outcomes $s_1, s_2, \ldots, s_N$ will occur. The two fundamental properties may be easily verified for the probability distributions of Examples 1, 2, and 3.

**EXAMPLE 3
(Continued)**

Verify that the probabilities assigned to the outcomes of Example 3 satisfy Fundamental Properties 1 and 2.

Solution   The probabilities are .10, .15, .45, .25, and .05. Clearly, each is between 0 and 1, so Property 1 is satisfied. Adding the probabilities shows that their sum is 1, satisfying Property 2.   ■

Suppose that we are given an experiment with a finite number of outcomes. Let us now assign to each event E a probability, which we denote by $\Pr(E)$. If E consists of a single outcome, say $E = \{s\}$, then E is called an **elementary event**. In this case we associate to E the probability of the outcome s. If E consists of more than one outcome, we may compute $\Pr(E)$ via the **addition principle**.

> **Addition Principle**   Suppose that an event E consists of the finite number of outcomes $s, t, u, \ldots, z$. That is,
>
> $$E = \{s, t, u, \ldots, z\}.$$
>
> Then
>
> $$\Pr(E) = \Pr(s) + \Pr(t) + \Pr(u) + \cdots + \Pr(z).$$

We supplement the addition principle with the convention that the probability of the impossible event $\varnothing$ is 0. This is certainly reasonable, since the impossible event never occurs.

EXAMPLE 4   **Probability distribution for the number of boys in two-child families**   Observe two-child families. Describe the sample space for counting the number of boys, and assign probabilities to each outcome.

Solution   The sample space $S = \{GG, GB, BG, BB\}$ describes the sex and birth order in two-child families. (Here, for instance, GB denotes the birth sequence "first child is a girl, second child is a boy.") If we assume that each of the four outcomes in S is equally likely to occur, we should assign probability $\frac{1}{4}$ to each outcome. Then

$$\Pr(\text{no boys}) = \Pr(GG) = \tfrac{1}{4}$$

$$\Pr(\text{one boy}) = \Pr(GB) + \Pr(BG) = \tfrac{1}{4} + \tfrac{1}{4} = \tfrac{1}{2}$$

$$\Pr(\text{two boys}) = \Pr(BB) = \tfrac{1}{4}.$$

We are making a reasonable assignment of probabilities here, although U.S. statistics show that 51% of all live births are boys and 49% are girls. If we wish to take many years of census data into account for a more accurate model, we would not assign equal probabilities to each outcome in S.   ■

EXAMPLE 5   **Probability associated with a die**   Suppose that we roll a die and observe the side that faces upward. What is the probability that an odd number will occur?

Solution   The event "odd number occurs" corresponds to the subset of the sample space given by

$$E = \{1, 3, 5\}.$$

That is, the event occurs if a 1, 3, or 5 appears on the side that faces upward. By the addition principle,

$$\Pr(E) = \Pr(1) + \Pr(3) + \Pr(5).$$

As we observed in Example 2, each of the outcomes in the die-rolling experiment has probability $\frac{1}{6}$. Therefore,

$$\Pr(E) = \tfrac{1}{6} + \tfrac{1}{6} + \tfrac{1}{6} = \tfrac{1}{2}.$$

Now Try Exercise 5   So we expect an odd number to occur approximately half of the time.   ■

EXAMPLE 6   **A paradox**   In the December 1, 1996 issue of *Parade* magazine, Marilyn vos Savant presented the following question in her column *Ask Marilyn*. "A woman and a man (who are unrelated) each has two children. At least one of the woman's children is a boy, and the man's older child is a boy. Does the chance that the woman has two boys equal the chance that the man has two boys?"

Solution The answer is NO. The sample space for the man is $\{BB, GB\}$ and each outcome has the same probability, $\frac{1}{2}$. Therefore, his likelihood of having two boys is $\Pr(BB) = \frac{1}{2}$. The sample space for the woman is $\{BB, GB, BG\}$ and each outcome has the same probability, $\frac{1}{3}$. Therefore, her likelihood of having two boys is $\Pr(BB) = \frac{1}{3}$.

    A *paradox* is a statement that is counter to many people's intuition and yet is actually true. After the column was published, Marilyn vos Savant received many letters from irate readers criticizing her answer. They reasoned that among families with at least one boy, the other child is just as likely to be a boy as a girl. Therefore, they concluded incorrectly that the probability is $\frac{1}{2}$ in each case. ■

Now Try Exercise 33

EXAMPLE 7

Probability associated with traffic volume Consider the traffic study of Example 3. What is the probability that at most 5000 cars will use the highway during rush hour?

Solution The event

$$\text{"at most 5000 cars"}$$

is the same as

$$\{s_1, s_2, s_3\},$$

where we use the same notation for the outcomes as we used in Example 3. Thus the probability of the event is

$$\Pr(s_1) + \Pr(s_2) + \Pr(s_3) = .10 + .15 + .45 = .70.$$

Therefore, we expect that traffic will involve at most 5000 cars in approximately 70% of the rush hours. ■

Now Try Exercise 23(a)

EXAMPLE 8

Probability associated with the roll of a pair of dice Suppose that we roll a red die and a green die and observe the numbers on the sides that face upward.

(a) Calculate the probabilities of the elementary events.

(b) Calculate the probability that the two dice show the same number.

Solution **(a)** As shown in Example 2 of Section 6.2, the sample space consists of 36 pairs of numbers:

$$S = \{(1,1), (1,2), \ldots, (6,5), (6,6)\}.$$

Each of these pairs is equally likely to occur. (How could the dice show favoritism to a particular pair?) Therefore, each outcome is expected to occur about $\frac{1}{36}$ of the time, and the probability of each elementary event is $\frac{1}{36}$.

(b) The event

$$E = \text{"both dice show the same number"}$$

consists of six outcomes:

$$E = \{(1,1), (2,2), (3,3), (4,4), (5,5), (6,6)\}.$$

Thus, by the addition principle,

$$\Pr(E) = \tfrac{1}{36} + \tfrac{1}{36} + \tfrac{1}{36} + \tfrac{1}{36} + \tfrac{1}{36} + \tfrac{1}{36} = \tfrac{6}{36} = \tfrac{1}{6}. \quad ■$$

Now Try Exercise 3

EXAMPLE 9

Probability associated with a small lottery A person playing a certain lottery can win $100, $10, or $1, can break even, or can lose $10. These five outcomes with their corresponding probabilities are given by the probability distribution in Table 1 on the next page.

(a) Which outcome has the greatest probability?

(b) Which outcome has the least probability?

(c) What is the probability that the person will win some money?

Solution (a) Table 1 reveals that the outcome -10 has the greatest probability, .50. (A person playing the lottery repeatedly can expect to lose \$10 about 50% of the time.) This outcome is just as likely to occur as not.

TABLE 1

Winnings	Probability
100	.02
10	.05
1	.40
0	.03
-10	.50

(b) The outcome 100 has the least probability, .02. A person playing the lottery can expect to win \$100 about 2% of the time. (This outcome is quite unlikely to occur.)

(c) We are asked to determine the probability that the event E occurs, where $E = \{100, 10, 1\}$. By the addition principle,

$$\begin{aligned} \Pr(E) &= \Pr(100) + \Pr(10) + \Pr(1) \\ &= \quad .02 \quad + \quad .05 \quad + \quad .40 \\ &= \quad .47. \end{aligned}$$

  ∎

Here is a useful formula that relates $\Pr(E \cup F)$ to $\Pr(E \cap F)$:

Inclusion–Exclusion Principle   Let E and F be any events. Then

$$\Pr(E \cup F) = \Pr(E) + \Pr(F) - \Pr(E \cap F).$$

In particular, if E and F are mutually exclusive, then

$$\Pr(E \cup F) = \Pr(E) + \Pr(F).$$

Note the similarity of this principle to the principle of the same name that was used in Section 5.2 to count the elements in a set.

EXAMPLE 10

Resource availability   A factory needs two raw materials. The probability of not having an adequate supply of material A is .05, whereas the probability of not having an adequate supply of material B is .03. A study determines that the probability of a shortage of both A and B is .01. What proportion of the time can the factory operate?

Solution Let E be the event "shortage of A" and F the event "shortage of B." We are given that

$$\Pr(E) = .05 \qquad \Pr(F) = .03 \qquad \Pr(E \cap F) = .01.$$

The factory can operate only if it has both raw materials. Therefore, we must calculate the proportion of the time in which there is no shortage of material A or material B. A shortage of A or B is the event $E \cup F$. By the inclusion–exclusion principle,

$$\begin{aligned} \Pr(E \cup F) &= \Pr(E) + \Pr(F) - \Pr(E \cap F) \\ &= \quad .05 \quad + \quad .03 \quad - \quad .01 \\ &= \quad .07. \end{aligned}$$

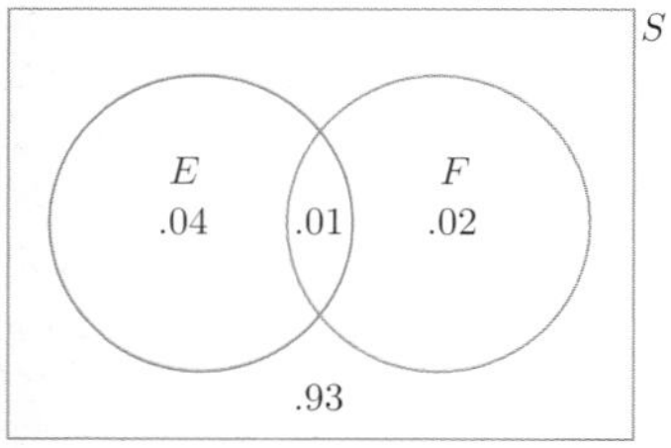

Figure 1

Now Try Exercise 21

Thus the factory is likely to be short of one raw material or the other 7% of the time. Therefore, the factory can expect to operate 93% of the time.   ∎

Probabilities involving unions and intersections of events are often conveniently displayed in a Venn diagram. Figure 1 displays the probabilities from Example 10.

Odds   Probability expresses the likelihood of an event occurring as a number from 0 to 1. Odds provide another way to express the likelihood. Odds gives the likelihood as a pair of integers contrasting the chances in favor of the event to the chances against the event. As an example, we say that the odds in favor of obtaining a *three* when rolling a die are 1 to 5. (There is 1 way for the event to be achieved and 5 ways for the event to fail.)

As another example, if a meteorologist says that the odds for rain tomorrow are 3 to 4, he means that on days when weather conditions are similar to today's, we can expect 3 tomorrows with rain for every 4 without rain. In general, when we say that the odds in favor of event E occurring are a to b, we expect that in $a + b$ trials the event would occur a times and fail to occur b times.

> **Converting between Odds and Probabilities**   If the odds in favor of the event E occurring are a to b, then
> $$\Pr(E) = \frac{a}{a+b}.$$
> If $\Pr(E) = p$, then the odds in favor of E are found by reducing the fraction $\frac{p}{1-p}$ to the form $\frac{a}{b}$, where a and b are integers having no common divisor. Then the odds in favor of E are
> $$a \text{ to } b.$$

EXAMPLE 11   **Chance of rain**   Suppose that the odds of rain tomorrow are 5 to 3. What is the probability that rain will occur?

Solution   The probability that rain will occur is

Now Try Exercise 11

$$\frac{5}{5+3} = \frac{5}{8}.$$ ∎

EXAMPLE 12   **Rolling a pair of dice**   The probability of obtaining a sum of eight or more when rolling a pair of dice is $\frac{15}{36}$. What are the odds of obtaining a sum of eight or more?

Solution   With $p = \frac{15}{36}$,

$$\frac{p}{1-p} = \frac{\frac{15}{36}}{1-\frac{15}{36}} = \frac{\frac{15}{36}}{\frac{21}{36}} = \frac{15}{21} = \frac{5}{7}.$$

Now Try Exercise 13   Therefore, the odds in favor of obtaining a sum of eight or more are 5 to 7.   ∎

Odds are often stated as *odds against*. This is always the case with gambling odds. If the odds in favor of an event are a to b, then the odds against the event are b to a. For instance, in Las Vegas roulette, the odds against winning when *red* is bet are 10 to 9. Casinos also have the concept of *house odds*, that are different from true odds. House odds are always in the form m to 1 where m is the amount of money a player wins on a one dollar bet. For instance, the house odds on a *red* bet are 1 to 1. If the ball lands on red, the player wins $1 (in addition to getting his $1 bet back).

Big numbers are easier to get a handle on than small numbers. For instance, the odds of winning the Powerball Lottery with a single ticket are 1 to 146,107,961 and the probability of winning the lottery is .000000006844254. We can easily pronounce the large number in the odds, and we have a reasonable idea of how large 146 million dollars is. But, how does one even pronounce the small probability? One way to pronounce it is 6,844,254 quadrillionths. But very few people have a good feel for how small that number is. Therefore, odds are usually preferable to probabilities in the discussion of highly unlikely events.

Paradoxes Counterintuitive results abound in probability. Example 6 (two-boy families) provides one illustration. Some other examples of counterintuitive results discussed in this book are as follows.

- *The Famous Birthday Problem* In a group as small as 23 people, the probability that at least two people have the same birthday is greater that $\frac{1}{2}$. See Example 6, Exercise 61, and Exercise 62 of Section 6.4.
- *Suit Distribution in Bridge* The most likely distribution of suits in a bridge hand is not 4-3-3-3; that is, four cards of one suit and three cards of each of the other suits. See Exercise 55 in Section 6.4.
- *Medical Diagnosis* Even with highly reliable tests, a person who tests positive for a certain disease might have a very low probability of actually having the disease. See Example 2 of Section 6.6.
- *Matches Consisting of Multiple Games* You can have a higher probability than your opponent of winning each game, yet your opponent can have a higher probability of winning the match. See Exercises 38 and 39 of Section 6.6.
- *Tennis Tournament* Under certain circumstances you have your best chance of winning a tennis tournament if you play most of your games against the best possible opponent. See the first project at the end of Chapter 6.
- *Gender Bias in College Admissions* In 1973, the University of California at Berkeley was sued for discrimination against women in graduate school admissions. That year 44% of male applicants were admitted and only 30% of female applicants. However, admission is decided by departments and nearly every department favored the female applicants. The second project at the end of Chapter 6 shows how the probability of admission for women can be higher than for men in *every* department and yet the probability of admission for men will be higher in the university as a whole.
- *Family Composition* A family of four children is more likely to consist of three children of one sex and one of the other, than to consist of two boys and two girls. See Exercise 29 in Section 7.3.

Practice Problems 6.3

1. **T-Maze** A mouse is put into a T-maze (a maze shaped like a "T") (Fig. 2). If he turns to the left he receives cheese, and if he turns to the right he receives a mild shock. This trial is done twice with the same mouse and the directions of the turns recorded.

    (a) What is the sample space for this experiment?

    (b) Why would it not be reasonable to assign each outcome the same probability?

2. What are the odds in favor of an event that is just as likely to occur as not?

3. Suppose that E and F are any events. Show that

$$\Pr(E) = \Pr(E \cap F) + \Pr(E \cap F').$$

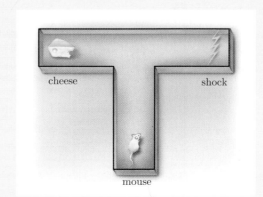

cheese   shock

mouse

Figure 2

(Continued)

4. The New York State lottery (Lotto) requires a contestant to select six numbers from 1 to 59. The probability of the same combination of six numbers occurring twice in one year is exceptionally low. Lotto system books advise people to avoid number combinations that have been drawn before. What is your assessment of this advice?

EXERCISES 6.3

1. **Word Frequencies** There are 774,746 words in the Bible. The word "and" occurs 46,277 times and the word "Lord" occurs 1855 times.[2] Suppose that a word is selected at random from the Bible.

   (a) What is the probability that the word is "and"?

   (b) What is the probability that the word is "and" or "Lord"?

   (c) What is the probability that the word is neither "and" nor "Lord"?

2. **Heads and Tails** An experiment consists of tossing a coin two times and observing the sequence of heads and tails. Each of the four outcomes has the same probability of occurring.

   (a) What is the probability that "HH" is the outcome?

   (b) What is the probability of the event "at least one head"?

3. **Dice** Suppose that a red die and a green die are rolled and the numbers on the sides that face upward are observed. (See Example 8.)

   (a) What is the probability that the numbers add up to 8?

   (b) What is the probability that the sum of the numbers is less than 5?

4. **U.S. States** A state is selected at random from the 50 states of the United States. What is the probability that it is one of the six New England states?

5. **Roulette** The modern American roulette wheel has 38 slots, which are labeled with 36 numbers evenly divided between red and black, plus two green numbers 0 and 00. What is the probability that the ball lands on a green number?

6. **Selecting a Number** An experiment consists of selecting a number at random from the set of numbers $\{1, 2, 3, 4, 5, 6, 7, 8, 9\}$. Find the probability that the number selected is

   (a) Less than 4.   (b) Odd.

   (c) Less than 4 or odd.

7. **Horse Race** Three horses, call them A, B, and C, are going to race against each other. The probability that A will win is $\frac{1}{3}$ and the probability that B will win is $\frac{1}{2}$.

   (a) What is the probability that C will win? (Assume that there are no ties.)

   (b) What are the odds that C will win?

8. Which of the following probabilities are feasible for an experiment having sample space $\{s_1, s_2, s_3\}$?

   (a) $\Pr(s_1) = .4$, $\Pr(s_2) = .4$, $\Pr(s_3) = .4$

   (b) $\Pr(s_1) = .5$, $\Pr(s_2) = .7$, $\Pr(s_3) = -.2$

   (c) $\Pr(s_1) = 2$, $\Pr(s_2) = 1$, $\Pr(s_3) = \frac{1}{2}$

   (d) $\Pr(s_1) = \frac{1}{4}$, $\Pr(s_2) = \frac{1}{2}$, $\Pr(s_3) = \frac{1}{4}$

9. An experiment with outcomes s_1, s_2, s_3, s_4 is described by the following probability table:

Outcome	Probability
s_1	.1
s_2	.6
s_3	.2
s_4	.1

   (a) What is $\Pr(\{s_1, s_2\})$?

   (b) What is $\Pr(\{s_2, s_4\})$?

10. An experiment with outcomes $s_1, s_2, s_3, s_4, s_5, s_6$ is described by the following probability table:

Outcome	Probability
s_1	.05
s_2	.25
s_3	.05
s_4	.01
s_5	.63
s_6	.01

   Let $E = \{s_1, s_2\}$ and $F = \{s_3, s_5, s_6\}$.
   (a) Determine $\Pr(E)$ and $\Pr(F)$.

   (b) Determine $\Pr(E')$.

   (c) Determine $\Pr(E \cap F)$.

   (d) Determine $\Pr(E \cup F)$.

11. Convert the following odds to probabilities.

   (a) 10 to 1   (b) 1 to 2   (c) 4 to 5

---

[2] According to *The People's Almanac* by Wallechinsky and Wallace (New York: Doubleday, 1975).

12. Poker In poker, the probability of being dealt a hand containing a pair of jacks or better is about $\frac{1}{6}$. What are the corresponding odds?

13. Candy Bars Nine percent of all candy bars sold in the United States are Snickers™ bars. What are the odds that a randomly selected candy bar purchased is a Snickers™ bar?

14. Birth States The odds of Americans living in the state where they were born is 17 to 8. What is the probability that an American selected at random lives in his or her birth state?

15. Horse Race If the odds for Secretariat to win a horse race are 11 to 7, what is the probability that Secretariat wins? Loses?

16. Class Election Four people are running for class president: Liz, Sam, Sue, and Tom. The probabilities of Sam, Sue, and Tom winning are .18, .23, and .31, respectively.

(a) What is the probability of Liz winning?

(b) What is the probability that a boy wins?

(c) What is the probability that Tom loses?

(d) What are the odds that Sue loses?

(e) What are the odds that a girl wins?

(f) What are the odds that Sam wins?

17. Let E and F be events for which $\Pr(E) = .6$, $\Pr(F) = .5$, and $\Pr(E \cap F) = .4$. Find

(a) $\Pr(E \cup F)$

(b) $\Pr(E \cap F')$ (*Hint*: Make a Venn diagram similar to Fig. 1.)

18. Let E and F be events for which $\Pr(E) = .4$, $\Pr(F) = .5$, and $\Pr(E \cap F') = .3$. Find

(a) $\Pr(E \cap F)$ (b) $\Pr(E \cup F)$

19. Suppose $\Pr(E) = .4$ and $\Pr(F) = .5$, where E and F are mutually exclusive. Find $\Pr(E \cup F)$.

20. Pair of Dice Suppose a pair of dice is rolled. The probability is $\frac{1}{6}$ that the sum of the numbers on the uppermost faces is 7, and the probability is $\frac{1}{18}$ that the sum is 11. Find the probability that the sum is 7 or 11.

21. Grades Joe feels that the probability of getting an A in history is .7, the probability of getting an A in psychology is .8, and the probability of getting an A in history or psychology is .9. What is the probability that he will get an A in both subjects?

22. Suppose $\Pr(E) = .5$, $\Pr(F) = .6$, and $\Pr(E \cup F) = .9$. Find $\Pr(E \cap F)$.

23. Supermarket Queue A statistical analysis of the wait (in minutes) at the checkout line of a certain supermarket

yields the following probability distribution:

Wait (in minutes)	Probability
At most 3	.10
More than 3 and at most 5	.20
More than 5 and at most 10	.25
More than 10 and at most 15	.25
More than 15	.20

(a) What is the probability of waiting more than 3 minutes but at most 15?

(b) If you observed the waiting times of a representative sample of 10,000 supermarket customers, approximately how many would you expect to wait for more than 3 minutes but at most 15?

24. What is the probability of the certain event?

25. College Applications The following table was derived from a survey of college freshmen attending baccalaureate colleges and universities. Each probability is the likelihood that a randomly selected freshman applied to the specified number of colleges. For instance, 17% of the freshmen applied to just one college and therefore the probability that a student selected at random applied to just one college is .17. Convert these data into a probability distribution.

Number of Colleges Applied to	Probability
1	.17
2 or less	.29
3 or less	.43
4 or less	.59
20 or less	1

Source: The American Freshman: National Norms for Fall 2007, Los Angeles, Calif.: American Council on Education, 2008.

26. College Applications Refer to the data of Exercise 25. What is the probability that a student applied to three or more colleges?

27. Employees' Ages In a study of the ages of its employees, over a period of several years a university finds the following:

Age (years)	Probability
20–34	.15
20–49	.70
20–64	.90
20–79	1.00

(a) Find the probability associated with each of the events: 20–34 years, 35–49 years, 50–64 years, and 65–79 years.

(b) Find the probability that an employee selected at random is at least 50 years old.

28. House Sales A realtor analyzes the office's sales over the past two years. She sorts the sales by the age of the house at the time of sale.

Age	Number of Houses Sold
1–2	1200
3–4	1570
5–6	1600
7–8	1520
9–10	1480

(a) Determine the probability that a sale chosen at random is a house between five and six years old.

(b) What are the odds that the house is less than seven years old?

29. Computer Usage Computer usage in a community is segmented by the kind of use:

Kind of use	Frequency
School only	20%
Work only	22%
Home computer only	20%
No computer anywhere	17%

(a) Explain why the percentages listed above do not add up to 100%.

(b) What is the probability that someone in the community uses a computer?

30. According to Food Processing Magazine (December 2007), the colors in a bag of milk chocolate M&M's have the following distribution:

Color	Probability
Brown	.3
Yellow	.2
Red	.2
Orange	.1
Blue	.1
Green	.1

(a) What is the probability of randomly selecting a blue or yellow M&M?

(b) What is the probability of randomly selecting a brown, orange, or red M&M?

31. College Freshmen Eighty-two percent of the s... who entered college in the fall of 2007 had atte... public schools. What are the odds that a rando... selected college freshman in the fall of 2007 attended public school?

32. Odds of an Earthquake The probability that there will be a major earthquake in the San Francisco area during the next 30 years is .7. What are the corresponding odds?

33. Bookies Gamblers usually give odds *against* an event happening. For instance, if a bookie gives the odds 4 to 1 that the Yankees win the next World Series, he is stating that the probability that the Yankees will win are $\frac{1}{5}$ or .2. Also, if a bettor bets $1 that the Yankees will win and the Yankees do win, then the bettor will receive $5 (his original bet + a profit of $4). The following are typical odds set by a bookie for the eventual winner in a fictitious four-team league: Sparks (5 to 3), Meteors (3 to 1), Asteroids (3 to 2), Suns (4 to 1).

(a) Convert the odds to probabilities of winning for each team.

(b) Add the four probabilities.

(c) Explain why the answer to (b) makes sense.

34. Coin Toss A fair coin is tossed twice and we are told that at least one of the tosses is a head. What is the probability that both tosses are heads?

35. Zodiac Signs A high school astrology club has 13 members. What is the probability that two or more members have the same zodiac sign? *Note*: There are twelve zodiac signs.

36. Birth Day A basketball team has eight players. What is the probability that at least two of them were born on the same day of the week?

37. Absent-Minded Attendant Twenty people check their coats at a restaurant's coat-check counter. If the attendant returns the coats to the people at random, what is the probability that exactly 19 of the people receive the correct coat?

38. Tennis The probability that Alice beats Ben in a game of tennis is twice the probability that Ben beats Alice. Determine the two probabilities.

Solutions to Practice Problems 6.3

1. (a) {LL, LR, RR, RL}. Here LL means that the mouse turned left both times, LR means that the mouse turned left the first time and right the second, and so on.

(b) The mouse will learn something from the first trial. If he turned left the first time and got rewarded, then he is more likely to turn left again on the second trial. Hence LL should have a greater probability than LR. Similarly, RL should be more likely than RR.

(Continued)

2. 1 to 1. An event that is just as likely to occur as not has probability $\frac{1}{2}$ and $\frac{.5}{1-.5} = \frac{.5}{.5} = \frac{1}{1}$.

3. The sets $(E \cap F)$ and $(E \cap F')$ have no elements in common and so are mutually exclusive. Since $E = (E \cap F) \cup (E \cap F')$, the result follows from the inclusion–exclusion principle.

4. The ping pong balls don't remember what combinations they produced in the past. Any combination of six numbers is just as likely to occur as any other combination.

6.4 Calculating Probabilities of Events

As mentioned in Section 6.3, there are several ways to assign probabilities to the events of a sample space. One way is to perform the experiment many times and assign probabilities based on empirical data. Sometimes our intuition about situations suffices, as in simple coin-tossing experiments. But we frequently are faced with forming a model of an experiment to assign probabilities consistent with Fundamental Properties 1 and 2. This section shows how the counting techniques of Chapter 5 may be used to extend these ideas to more complex situations. In addition, the exceptionally wide range of applications that make use of probability theory is illustrated.

Experiments with Equally Likely Outcomes   In the experiments associated to many common applications, all outcomes are **equally likely**—that is, they all have the same probability. This is the case, for example, if we toss an unbiased coin or select a person at random from a population. If a sample space has N equally likely outcomes, then the probability of each outcome is $1/N$ (since the probabilities must add up to 1). If we use this fact, the probability of any event is easy to compute. Namely, suppose that E is an event consisting of M outcomes. Then, by the addition principle,

$$\Pr(E) = \underbrace{\frac{1}{N} + \frac{1}{N} + \cdots + \frac{1}{N}}_{M \text{ times}} = \frac{M}{N}.$$

We can restate this fundamental result as follows:

Let S be a sample space consisting of N equally likely outcomes. Let E be any event. Then

$$\Pr(E) = \frac{[\text{number of outcomes in } E]}{N}. \tag{1}$$

In order to apply formula (1) in particular examples, it is necessary to compute N, the number of equally likely outcomes in the sample space, and [number of outcomes in E]. Often these quantities can be determined using the counting techniques of Chapter 5. Some illustrative computations are provided in Examples 1 through 7 here.

We should mention that, although the urn and dice problems considered in this section and the next might seem artificial and removed from applications, many applied problems can be described in mathematical terms as urn or dice experiments. We begin our discussion with two examples involving abstract urn problems. Then in two more examples we show the utility of urn models by applying them to quality control and medical screening problems (Examples 3 and 5, respectively).

EXAMPLE 1   **Selecting balls from an urn**   An urn contains eight white balls and two green balls. A sample of three balls is selected at random. What is the probability of selecting only white balls?

Solution   The experiment consists of selecting 3 balls from the 10. Since the order in which the 3 balls are selected is immaterial, the samples are combinations of 10 balls taken 3 at a time. The total number of samples is therefore $C(10, 3)$, and this is N, the number of elements in the sample space. Since the selection of the sample is random, all samples are equally likely, and thus we can use formula (1) to compute the probability of any event. The problem asks us to compute the probability of the event $E =$ "all three balls selected are white." Since there are 8 white balls, the number of different samples in which all are white is $C(8, 3)$. Thus

$$\Pr(E) = \frac{[\text{number of outcomes in } E]}{N} = \frac{C(8, 3)}{C(10, 3)} = \frac{56}{120} = \frac{7}{15}. \qquad \blacksquare$$

EXAMPLE 2   **Selecting balls from an urn**   An urn contains eight white balls and two green balls. A sample of three balls is selected at random. What is the probability that the sample contains at least one green ball?

Solution   As in Example 1, there are $N = C(10, 3)$ equally likely outcomes. Let F be the event "at least one green ball is selected." Let us determine the number of different outcomes in F. These outcomes contain either one or two green balls. There are $C(2, 1)$ ways to select one green ball from two; and for each of these, there are $C(8, 2)$ ways to select two white balls from eight. By the multiplication principle, the number of samples containing one green ball equals $C(2, 1) \cdot C(8, 2)$. Similarly, the number of samples containing two green balls equals $C(2, 2) \cdot C(8, 1)$. Note that although the sample size is 3, there are only two green balls in the urn. Since the sampling is done without replacement, no sample can have more than two greens. Therefore, the number of outcomes in F—namely the number of samples having at least one green ball—equals

$$C(2, 1) \cdot C(8, 2) + C(2, 2) \cdot C(8, 1) = 2 \cdot 28 + 1 \cdot 8 = 64,$$

so

Now Try Exercise 9 $$\Pr(F) = \frac{[\text{number of outcomes in } F]}{N} = \frac{64}{C(10, 3)} = \frac{64}{120} = \frac{8}{15}. \qquad \blacksquare$$

EXAMPLE 3   **Quality control**   A toy manufacturer inspects boxes of toys before shipment. Each box contains 10 toys. The inspection procedure consists of randomly selecting three toys from the box. If any are defective, the box is not shipped. Suppose that a given box has two defective toys. What is the probability that it will be shipped?

Solution   This problem is not really new! We solved it in disguise as Example 1. The urn can be regarded as a box of toys, and the balls as individual toys. The white balls are nondefective toys and the green balls defective toys. The random selection of three balls from the urn is just the inspection procedure. And the event "all three balls selected are white" corresponds to the box being shipped. As we calculated previously, the probability of this event is $\frac{7}{15}$. (Since $\frac{7}{15} \approx .47$, there is approximately a 47% chance of shipping a box with two defective toys. This inspection procedure is Now Try Exercise 7   not particularly effective!) $\blacksquare$

EXAMPLE 4

Selecting students A professor is randomly choosing a group of three students to do an oral presentation. In her class of 10 students, 2 are on the debate team. What is the chance that the professor chooses at least one of the debaters for the group?

Solution This is the same as Example 2. Just think of the debate team members as the green balls and the others in the class as white balls. The chance of getting at least one debate team member in the group is $\frac{8}{15} \approx .53$. ∎

Now Try Exercise 29

EXAMPLE 5

Medical screening Suppose that a cruise ship returns to the United States from the Far East. Unknown to anyone, 4 of its 600 passengers have contracted a rare disease. Suppose that the Public Health Service screens 20 passengers, selected at random, to see whether the disease is present aboard ship. What is the probability that the presence of the disease will escape detection?

Solution The sample space consists of samples of 20 drawn from among the 600 passengers. There are $C(600, 20)$ such samples. The number of samples containing none of the sick passengers is $C(596, 20)$. Therefore, the probability of not detecting the disease is

$$\frac{C(596, 20)}{C(600, 20)} = \frac{\dfrac{596!}{20!\,576!}}{\dfrac{600!}{20!\,580!}} = \frac{596!}{600!} \cdot \frac{580!}{576!}$$

$$= \frac{596!}{600 \cdot 599 \cdot 598 \cdot 597 \cdot 596!} \cdot \frac{580 \cdot 579 \cdot 578 \cdot 577 \cdot 576!}{576!}$$

$$= \frac{580 \cdot 579 \cdot 578 \cdot 577}{600 \cdot 599 \cdot 598 \cdot 597} \approx .87.$$

Now Try Exercise 13 So there is approximately an 87% chance that the disease will escape detection. ∎

The Complement Rule The **complement rule** relates the probability of an event E to the probability of its complement E'. When applied together with counting techniques, it often simplifies computation of probabilities.

> **Complement Rule** Let E be any event, E' its complement. Then
> $$\Pr(E) = 1 - \Pr(E').$$

For example, recall Example 1. We determined the probability of the event

$$E = \text{``all three balls selected are white''}$$

associated to the experiment of selecting three balls from an urn containing eight white balls and two green balls. We found that $\Pr(E) = \frac{7}{15}$. On the other hand, in Example 2 we determined the probability of the event

$$F = \text{``at least one green ball is selected.''}$$

The event E is the complement of F:

$$E = F'.$$

So, by the complement rule,

$$\Pr(F) = 1 - \Pr(F') = 1 - \Pr(E) = 1 - \tfrac{7}{15} = \tfrac{8}{15},$$

in agreement with the calculations of Example 2.

The complement rule is especially useful in situations where $\Pr(E')$ is easier to compute than $\Pr(E)$. One of these situations arises in the celebrated *birthday problem*.

EXAMPLE 6   **The famous "birthday problem"**   A group of five people is to be selected at random. What is the probability that two or more of them have the same birthday?

Solution   For simplicity we ignore February 29. Furthermore, we assume that each of the 365 days in a year is an equally likely birthday (not an unreasonable assumption). The experiment we have in mind is this. Pick out five people and observe their birthdays. The outcomes of this experiment are strings of five dates, corresponding to the birthdays. For example, one outcome of the experiment is

(June 2, April 6, Dec. 20, Feb. 12, Aug. 5).

Each birth date has 365 different possibilities. So, by the generalized multiplication principle, the total number N of possible outcomes of the experiment is

$$N = 365 \cdot 365 \cdot 365 \cdot 365 \cdot 365 = 365^5.$$

Let E be the event "at least two people have the same birthday." It is very difficult to calculate directly the number of outcomes in E. However, it is comparatively simple to compute the number of outcomes in E' and hence to compute $\Pr(E')$. This is because E' is the event "all five birthdays are different." An outcome in E' can be selected in a sequence of five steps:

Select a day	Select a different day	Select yet a different day	Select yet a different day	Select yet a different day

These five steps will result in a sequence of five different birthdays. The first step can be performed in 365 ways; for each of these, the next step in 364; for each of these, the next step in 363; for each of these, the next step in 362; and for each of these, the last step in 361 ways. Therefore, E' contains $365 \cdot 364 \cdot 363 \cdot 362 \cdot 361$ [or $P(365,5)$] outcomes, and

$$\Pr(E') = \frac{365 \cdot 364 \cdot 363 \cdot 362 \cdot 361}{365^5} \approx .973.$$

By the complement rule,

$$\Pr(E) = 1 - \Pr(E') \approx 1 - .973 = .027.$$

So the likelihood is about 2.7% that two or more of the five people will have the same birthday. ∎

Now Try Exercise 15

The experiment of Example 6 can be repeated using samples of 8, 10, 20, or any number of people. As before, let E be the event "at least two people have the same birthday," so that $E' =$ "all the birthdays are different." If a sample of r people is used, then the same reasoning as used previously yields

$$\Pr(E') = \frac{365 \cdot 364 \cdot \cdots \cdot (365 - r + 1)}{365^r}.$$

Table 1 on the next page gives the values of $\Pr(E) = 1 - \Pr(E')$ for various values of r. You may be surprised by the numbers in the table. Even with as few as 23 people

TABLE 1	Probability that, in a randomly selected group of r people, at least two will have the same birthday									
r	5	10	15	20	22	23	25	30	40	50
$\Pr(E)$	.027	.117	.253	.411	.476	.507	.569	.706	.891	.970

it is more likely than not that at least two people have the same birthday. With a sample of 50 people we are almost certain to have two with the same birthday. (Try this experiment in your dormitory or class.)

EXAMPLE 7   **Rolling a die five times** A die is rolled five times. What is the probability of obtaining exactly three 4's?

Solution There are $6^5 = 7776$ possible outcomes when a die is rolled five times. These are equally likely to occur. The event we seek is $E =$ "three 4's." How many outcomes are in E? There are $1 \cdot 1 \cdot 1 \cdot 5 \cdot 5 = 25$ ways to get three 4's followed by two rolls yielding anything except 4. But the three 4's need not appear in the first three rolls. What if the 4's appear as 4xx44? The number of possibilities is $1 \cdot 5 \cdot 5 \cdot 1 \cdot 1 = 25$. Thus we need to determine in how many positions these three 4's can appear in the sequence of five rolls. That is just $C(5, 3) = 10$. Therefore, E contains $(10)(25)$ elements, and

$$\Pr(\text{exactly three 4's in five rolls of a die}) = \frac{(10)(25)}{7776} \approx .03.$$

Thus there is about a 3% chance that in five rolls of a fair die we obtain three 4's.

> Now Try Exercise 31

Verification of the Complement Rule If S is the sample space, then $\Pr(S) = 1$, $E \cup E' = S$, and $E \cap E' = \emptyset$. Therefore, by the inclusion–exclusion principle,

$$\Pr(S) = \Pr(E \cup E') = \Pr(E) + \Pr(E').$$

So we have

$$1 = \Pr(E) + \Pr(E') \quad \text{and} \quad \Pr(E) = 1 - \Pr(E').$$

Practice Problems 6.4

1. **Children** A couple decides to have four children. What is the probability that among the children there will be at least one boy and at least one girl?

2. **(a)** Find the probability that all the numbers are different in three spins of a roulette wheel. [*Note:* A roulette wheel has 38 numbers.]

   (b) Guess how many spins are required in order that the probability that all the numbers are different will be less than .5.

EXERCISES 6.4

1. **Course Selection** Each of three people randomly chooses one of three calculus sections to take (A, B, or C).

   (a) What is the probability that they all choose the same one?

   (b) What is the probability that they each choose a different section?

2. **Track Positions** Michael and Christopher are among seven contestants in a race to be run on a seven-lane track. If the runners are assigned to the lanes at random, what is the probability that Michael will be assigned to the inside lane and Christopher will be assigned to the outside lane?

3. Suppose you are asked to choose a whole number between 1 and 13, inclusive.

    (a) What is the probability that it is odd?

    (b) What is the probability that it is even?

    (c) What is the probability that it is a multiple of 3?

    (d) What is the probability that it is odd or a multiple of 3?

4. Five numbers are chosen at random from the whole numbers between 1 and 13, inclusive, with replacement.

    (a) What is the probability that all the numbers are even?

    (b) What is the probability that all the numbers are odd?

    (c) What is the probability that at least one of the numbers is odd?

5. Five numbers are chosen at random from the whole numbers between 1 and 13, inclusive, without replacement.

    (a) What is the probability that all the numbers are even?

    (b) What is the probability that all the numbers are odd?

    (c) What is the probability that at least one of the numbers is odd?

6. **Balls in an Urn** An urn contains 40 balls, some red and some white. If the probability of selecting a red ball is .45, how many red balls are in the urn?

7. **Quality Control** A factory produces fuses, which are packaged in boxes of 10. Three fuses are selected at random from each box for inspection. The box is rejected if at least one of these three fuses is defective. What is the probability that a box containing five defective fuses will be rejected?

8. **Balls in an Urn** An urn contains six white balls and five red balls. A sample of four balls is selected at random from the urn. What is the probability that the sample contains two white balls and two red balls?

9. **Balls in an Urn** An urn contains five red balls and four white balls. A sample of two balls is selected at random from the urn. What is the probability that at least one of the balls is red?

10. **Opinion Polling** Of the nine members of the board of trustees of a college, five agree with the president on a certain issue. The president selects three trustees at random and asks for their opinions. What is the probability that at least two of them will agree with him?

Selecting Students *Exercises 11–14 refer to a classroom of children (12 boys and 10 girls) in which seven students are chosen to go to the blackboard.*

11. What is the probability that at least two girls are chosen?

12. What is the probability that more boys than girls are chosen?

13. What is the probability that no boys are chosen?

14. What is the probability that the first three children chosen are boys?

15. **Date Conflict** Without consultation, each of four organizations announces a one-day convention to be held during June. Find the probability that at least two organizations specify the same day for their convention.

16. Five letters are selected from the alphabet, one at a time with replacement, to form a five-letter "word." What is the probability that the "word" has five different letters?

17. **Track Position** Michael is one of seven contestants entered in two races to be run on a seven-lane track. If in each race the runners are assigned to the lanes at random, what is the probability that Michael will be assigned to the inside lane at least once?

18. **Hotel Choices** An airport limousine has four passengers and stops at six different hotels. What is the probability that two or more people will be staying at the same hotel? (Assume that each person is just as likely to stay in one hotel as another.)

19. **Weather Conditions** In a certain agricultural region the probability of a drought during the growing season is .2, the probability of a severe cold spell is .15, and the probability of both is .1. Find the probability of

    (a) either a drought or a severe cold spell.

    (b) neither a drought nor a severe cold spell.

    (c) not having a drought.

20. **Coin Tosses** A coin is to be tossed seven times. What is the probability of obtaining four heads and three tails?

21. Let E and F be events such that

$$\Pr(E) = .3 \quad \Pr(F') = .6 \quad \text{and} \quad \Pr(E \cup F) = .7.$$

What is $\Pr(E \cap F)$?

22. **Manufacturing Defects** In a certain manufacturing process the probability of a type I defect is .12, the probability of a type II defect is .22, and the probability of having both types of defects is .02. Find the probability of having neither type of defect.

23. **Socks** A man has six different pairs of socks, from which he selects two socks at random. What is the probability that the selected socks will match?

24. **Opinion Polling** Of the 15 members on a Senate committee, 10 plan to vote "yes" and 5 plan to vote "no" on an important issue. A reporter attempts to predict the outcome of the vote by questioning six of the senators. Find the probability that this sample is precisely representative of the final vote. That is, find the probability that four of the six senators questioned plan to vote "yes."

25. Group Picture A man, a woman, and their three children randomly stand in a row for a family picture. What is the probability that the parents will be standing next to each other?

26. Poker Hands In poker the probabilities of being dealt a flush, a straight, and a straight flush are .0019654, .0039246, and .0000154, respectively. What is the probability of being dealt a straight or a flush?

27. Street Routes Figure 1 shows a partial map of the streets in a certain city. A tourist starts at point A and selects at random a path to point B. (We shall assume that he walks only south and east.) Find the probability that

(**a**) he passes through point C.

(**b**) he passes through point D.

(**c**) he passes through point C and point D.

(**d**) he passes through point C or point D.

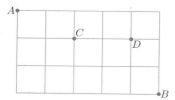

Figure 1

28. Boys and Girls A couple decides to have four children. What is the probability that they will have more girls than boys?

29. Committee Selection A law firm has six senior and four junior partners. A committee of three partners is selected at random to represent the firm at a conference. What is the probability that at least one of the junior partners is on the committee?

30. Rotten Tomato A bag contains nine tomatoes, of which one is rotten. A sample of three tomatoes is selected at random. What is the probability that the sample contains the rotten tomato?

31. Coin Tosses A coin is to be tossed six times. What is the probability of obtaining exactly three heads?

32. Book Selection A vacationer has brought along four novels and four nonfiction books. One day the person selects two at random to take to the beach. What is the probability that both are novels?

Illinois Lotto *Exercises 33 and 34*[1] *refer to the Illinois Lottery Lotto game. In this game, the player chooses six different integers from 1 to 40. If the six match (in any order) the six different integers drawn by the lottery, the player wins the grand prize jackpot, which starts at $1 million and grows weekly until won. Multiple winners split the pot equally. For each $1 bet, the player must pick two (presumably different) sets of six integers.*

33. What is the probability of winning the Illinois Lottery Lotto with a $1 bet?

34. In the game week ending June 18, 1983, 2 million people bought $1 tickets and 78 people matched all six winning integers and split the jackpot. If all numbers were selected randomly, the likelihood of having so many joint winners would be about 10^{-115}. Can you think of any reason that such an unlikely event occurred? (*Note:* The winning numbers were 7, 13, 14, 21, 28, and 35.) What would be the best strategy in selecting the numbers to ensure that in the event you won, you would probably not have to share the jackpot with too many people?

35. Senate Committee The U.S. Senate consists of two senators from each of the 50 states. Five senators are to be selected at random to form a committee. What is the probability that no two members of the committee are from the same state?

36. Subcommittees A politician knows that a committee vote is stacked against her, 6 to 3. However, she has the option of letting a randomly selected subcommittee decide the issue. Show that the smaller the subcommittee is, the better her chances of winning the vote. (Consider only subcommittees with an odd number of members, so that tie votes are precluded.)

37. Birthdays What is the probability that in a group of 25 people at least one person has a birthday on June 13? Why is your answer different from the probability displayed in Table 1 for $r = 25$?

38. Letter Positions What is the probability that a random arrangement of the letters in the word GEESE has all the E's adjacent to one another?

39. Guest List Fred is having a dinner party and is limited to 10 guests. He has 16 men friends and 12 women friends, including Laura and Mary.

(**a**) If Fred chooses his guests at random, what is the probability that Mary and Laura are invited?

(**b**) If Fred decides to invite 5 men and 5 women, what is the probability that Mary and Laura are invited?

40. Baseball Predictions In the American League, the East, Central, and West divisions consist of 5, 5, and 4 baseball teams, respectively. A sportswriter predicts the winner of each of the three divisions by choosing a team completely at random in each division. What is the probability that the sportswriter will predict at least one winner correctly?

41. Baseball Predictions Suppose that the sportswriter in Exercise 40 eliminates from each division one team that clearly has no chance of winning and predicts a winner at random from the remaining teams. Assuming

---

[1] The data for these exercises were taken from Allan J. Gottlieb's "Puzzle Corner" in *Technology Review*, February/March 1985.

the eliminated teams don't end up surprising anyone, what is the writer's chance of predicting at least one winner?

42. Baseball Predictions Suppose that the sportswriter in Exercise 40 simply puts the 14 team names in a hat and draws 3 completely at random. Does this increase or decrease the writer's chance of picking at least one winner?

43. Powerball Lottery The winner of the Powerball[2] lottery must correctly pick a set of 5 numbers from 1 through 55 and then correctly pick one number (called the Powerball) from 1 through 42.

(a) What are the odds of winning the Powerball lottery?

(b) What is the probability of winning the Powerball lottery?

44. License Plate Game Johnny and Doyle are driving along on a lightly traveled road. Johnny proposes the following game. They will look at the license plates of oncoming cars and focus on the last two digits. For instance, the license plates ABC512 or 7412BG would yield 12, and the license plate XY406T would yield the number 6. Johnny bets Doyle that at least two of the next fifteen cars will yield the same number. What is the probability that Johnny wins? Assume that each of the 100 possible numbers is equally likely to occur.

45. Numbers Two distinct numbers are selected at random from the set $\{1, 2, 3, 4, 5, 6, 7\}$. What is the probability that their product is an even number? *Hint:* First find the probability that the product is odd.

46. Matching Socks Ten white socks and six red socks are in a drawer. If two socks are selected at random, what is the probability that both socks are the same color?

47. British Lottery In the British lottery, a player pays 1 euro for a ticket and selects 6 numbers from the numbers 1 through 49. If he matches exactly three of the six numbers drawn, he receives 10 euros. What is the probability of selecting exactly three of the six numbers drawn?

48. Swiss Lottery The winning combination in the Swiss lottery consists of six numbers drawn from the numbers 1 through 45. What is the probability that a single ticket has no matches?

49. Place Settings Fred has five place settings consisting of a dinner plate, a salad plate, and a bowl. Each setting is a different color. If Fred randomly selects a dinner plate, a salad plate, and a bowl, what is the probability that they all have different colors?

50. Balls in an Urn An urn contains red balls and white balls. The probability of removing two red balls, without replacement, from the urn is $\frac{2}{5}$. The probability of removing three red balls, without replacement, from

the urn is $\frac{1}{5}$. Explain why there must be two more red balls than white balls. How many red balls were in the urn? *Hint:* Let r be the number of red balls in the urn, and let w be the number of white balls in the urn. Show that $r = w + 2$.

51. Blink of an Eye Suppose that blinking causes a person's eyes to be closed 10% of the time. If a photographer takes a picture of three people, what is the probability that all three people will have their eyes open?

52. Blink of an Eye Refer to Exercise 51. If the photographer takes two pictures of the three people, what is the probability that at least one of the pictures will be good?

A poker hand consists of five cards drawn from a deck of 52 cards. Each card has one of 13 denominations (2, 3, 4, ..., 10, Jack, Queen, King, Ace) and one of four suits (Spades, Hearts, Diamonds, Clubs).

53. Poker Determine the probability of each of the following types of poker hands.

(a) Full house (three cards of one denomination and two cards of another denomination)

(b) Three of a kind (three cards of one denomination and two cards of distinct denominations, both different than the denomination of the triple)

54. Poker Determine the probability of each of the following types of poker hands.

(a) Two pairs (two cards of one denomination, two cards of a different denomination, and one card of a denomination other than those two denominations)

(b) One pair (two cards of one denomination and three cards of distinct denominations, where each of the three cards has a different denomination than the denomination of the pair)

55. Bridge In a bridge hand, what is the probability of each of the following suit distributions?

(a) 4-3-3-3. That is, four cards of one suit and three cards of each of the other three suits. *Hint:* The number of hands having this distribution is $4 \cdot C(13, 4) \cdot C(13, 3) \cdot C(13, 3) \cdot C(13, 3)$.

(b) 4-4-3-2. That is, four cards of each of two suits, three cards of another suit, and two cards of the remaining suit.

In Exercises 56–63, use a graphing calculator or spreadsheet to calculate the probabilities.

56. Pick a Card Find the probability that at least two people in a group of size $n = 5$ select the same card when drawing from a 52-card deck with replacement. Determine for what size group the probability of such a match first exceeds .5.

---

[2]Powerball drawings are held twice a week. If you buy 50 tickets for each drawing, you can expect to win once every 5000 years.

57. Balls in an Urn Two balls are to be selected at random without replacement from an urn that contains 40 balls, some red and some white. If the probability of selecting two red balls is .1, how many red balls are in the urn?

58. Presidential Choices There were 16 presidents of the Continental Congresses from 1774 to 1788. Each of the five students in a seminar in American history chooses one of these on which to do a report. If all presidents are equally likely to be chosen, calculate the probability that at least two students choose the same president.

59. Rolling a Die A die is rolled 24 times.

(a) How many 3's would you expect?

(b) Calculate the probability of getting exactly four 3's.

60. Term Papers A political science class has 20 students, each of whom chooses a topic from a list for a term paper. How big a pool of topics is necessary for the probability of at least one duplicate to drop below 50%?

61. Birthday Problem Consider the discussion of the general birthday problem following Example 6.

(a) Verify that 23 is the smallest value of r for which the probability that at least two people have the same birthday in a group of r randomly selected people is $\geq .5$.

(b) Find the smallest value of r for which the probability that at least two people have the same birthday in a group of r randomly selected people is $\geq .6$.

62. Birthday Problem Johnny Carson, host of The Tonight Show from 1962–1992, discussed the birthday problem during one of his monologues. To test the hypothesis, he asked the audience if any of them were born on his birthday, October 23. Carson was surprised that no one in the audience of 100 people shared his birthday. What was wrong with Carson's reasoning? What is the probability that one or more people in the audience were born on October 23? How large would the audience have to have been so that the probability that someone in the audience had the same birthday as Carson was at least 50 percent?

63. Blink of an Eye Refer to Exercise 51. How many pictures must the photographer take so that the probability of obtaining at least one good picture is at least 99.9 percent?

Solutions to Practice Problems 6.4

1. Each possible outcome is a string of four letters composed of B's and G's. By the generalized multiplication principle, there are 2^4 or 16 possible outcomes. Let E be the event "children of both sexes." Then $E' = \{BBBB, GGGG\}$, and

$$\Pr(E') = \frac{[\text{number of outcomes in } E']}{[\text{total number of outcomes}]} = \frac{2}{16} = \frac{1}{8}.$$

Therefore,

$$\Pr(E) = 1 - \Pr(E') = 1 - \frac{1}{8} = \frac{7}{8}.$$

So the probability is 87.5% that they will have children of both sexes.

2. (a) Each sequence of three numbers is just as likely to occur as any other. Therefore,

Pr(numbers different)

$$= \frac{[\text{number of outcomes with numbers different}]}{[\text{number of possible outcomes}]}$$

$$= \frac{38 \cdot 37 \cdot 36}{38^3} \approx .92.$$

(b) 8

6.5 Conditional Probability and Independence

The probability of an event depends, often in a critical way, on the sample space in question. In this section we explore this dependence in some detail by introducing what are called *conditional probabilities*.

To illustrate the dependence of probabilities on the sample space, consider the following example.

EXAMPLE 1

College students Suppose that a certain mathematics class contains 26 students. Of these, 14 are economics majors, 15 are first-year students, and 7 are neither. Suppose that a person is selected at random from the class.

(a) What is the probability that the person is both an economics major and a first-year student?

(b) Suppose we are given the additional information that the person selected is a first-year student. What is the probability that he or she is also an economics major?

Solution Let E denote the set of economics majors and F the set of first-year students. A complete Venn diagram of the class can be obtained with the techniques of Section 5.3. See Fig. 1.

(a) In selecting a student from the class, the sample space consists of all 26 students. Since the choice is random, all students are equally likely to be selected. The event "economics major and first-year student" corresponds to the set $E \cap F$ of the Venn diagram. Therefore,

$$\Pr(E \cap F) = \frac{[\text{number of outcomes in } E \cap F]}{[\text{number of possible outcomes}]} = \frac{10}{26} = \frac{5}{13}.$$

So the probability of selecting a first-year economics major is $\frac{5}{13}$.

(b) If we know that the student selected is a first-year student, then the possible outcomes of the experiment are restricted. They must belong to F. In other words, given the additional information, we must alter the sample space from "all students" to "first-year students." Since each of the 15 first-year students is equally likely to be selected, and since 10 of the 15 first-year students are economics majors, the probability of choosing an economics major under these circumstances is equal to $\frac{10}{15} = \frac{2}{3}$. ∎

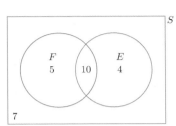

Figure 1

Let us consider Example 1 more carefully. In part (a) the sample space is the set of all students in the mathematics class, E is the event "student is an economics major" and F is the event "student is a first-year student." On the other hand, part (b) poses a condition, "student is a first-year student." The condition is satisfied by every element of F. We are being asked to find the **conditional probability** of E given F, written $\Pr(E|F)$. To do this we shall restrict our attention to the new (restricted) sample space, now just the elements of F. Thus, we consider only first-year students and ask, of these, what is the probability of choosing an economics major? We assign a value to $\Pr(E|F)$ via the following formula:

DEFINITION Conditional Probability

$$\Pr(E|F) = \frac{\Pr(E \cap F)}{\Pr(F)}, \tag{1}$$

provided that $\Pr(F) \neq 0$.

We will provide an intuitive justification of this formula shortly. However, we first give an application.

EXAMPLE 2

Earnings and education Twenty percent of the employees of Acme Steel Company are college graduates. Of all its employees, 25% earn more than $50,000 per year, and 15% are college graduates earning more than $50,000. What is the probability that an employee selected at random earns more than $50,000 per year, given that he or she is a college graduate?

Solution Let H and C be the events

$$H = \text{``earns more than \$50,000 per year''}$$
$$C = \text{``college graduate.''}$$

We are asked to calculate $\Pr(H|C)$. The given data are

$$\Pr(H) = .25 \qquad \Pr(C) = .20 \qquad \Pr(H \cap C) = .15.$$

By formula (1), we have

$$\Pr(H|C) = \frac{\Pr(H \cap C)}{\Pr(C)} = \frac{.15}{.20} = \frac{3}{4}.$$

Now Try Exercise 13(b) Thus $\frac{3}{4}$ of all college graduates at Acme Steel earn more than \$50,000 per year. ∎

Suppose that an experiment has N equally likely outcomes. Then we may apply the following formula to calculate $\Pr(E|F)$.

Conditional Probability in Case of Equally Likely Outcomes

$$\Pr(E|F) = \frac{[\text{number of outcomes in } E \cap F]}{[\text{number of outcomes in } F]}, \tag{2}$$

provided that $[\text{number of outcomes in } F] \neq 0$.

This formula was actually used in Example 1(b) to compute $\Pr(E|F)$. In that example each student had the same likelihood of being selected.

Let us now justify formulas (1) and (2).

Justification of Formula (1) Formula (1) is a definition of conditional probability and as such does not really need any justification. (We can make whatever definitions we choose!) However, let us proceed intuitively and show that the definition is reasonable, in the sense that formula (1) gives the expected long-run proportion of occurrences of E given that F occurs. Assume that our experiment is performed repeatedly, say for 10,000 trials. We would expect F to occur in approximately $10,000 \Pr(F)$ trials. Among these, the trials for which E also occurs are exactly those for which both E and F occur. In other words, the trials for which E also occurs are exactly those for which the event $E \cap F$ occurs; and this event has probability $\Pr(E \cap F)$. Therefore, out of the original 10,000 trials, there should be approximately $10,000 \Pr(E \cap F)$ in which E and F both occur. Thus, considering only those trials in which F occurs, the proportion in which E also occurs is

$$\frac{10,000 \Pr(E \cap F)}{10,000 \Pr(F)} = \frac{\Pr(E \cap F)}{\Pr(F)}.$$

Thus, at least intuitively, it seems reasonable to define $\Pr(E|F)$ by formula (1). ∎

Justification of Formula (2) Suppose that the number of outcomes of the experiment is N. Then

$$\Pr(F) = \frac{[\text{number of outcomes in } F]}{N}$$

$$\Pr(E \cap F) = \frac{[\text{number of outcomes in } E \cap F]}{N}.$$

Therefore, using formula (1), we have

$$\Pr(E|F) = \frac{\Pr(E \cap F)}{\Pr(F)}$$

$$= \frac{\dfrac{[\text{number of outcomes in } E \cap F]}{N}}{\dfrac{[\text{number of outcomes in } F]}{N}}$$

$$= \frac{[\text{number of outcomes in } E \cap F]}{[\text{number of outcomes in } F]}.$$ ∎

From formula (1), multiplying both sides of the equation by $\Pr(F)$, we can deduce the following useful fact.

Product Rule   If $\Pr(F) \neq 0$,
$$\Pr(E \cap F) = \Pr(F) \cdot \Pr(E|F). \qquad (3)$$

The next example illustrates the use of this rule.

EXAMPLE 3   **Color-blind males**   Assume that a certain school contains an equal number of female and male students and that 5% of the male population is color-blind. Find the probability that a randomly selected student is a color-blind male.

Solution   Let $M =$ "male" and $B =$ "color-blind." We wish to calculate $\Pr(B \cap M)$. From the given data,
$$\Pr(M) = .5 \quad \text{and} \quad \Pr(B|M) = .05.$$
Therefore, by the product rule,
$$\Pr(B \cap M) = \Pr(M) \cdot \Pr(B|M) = (.5)(.05) = .025.$$ ∎

Often an event G can be described as a sequence of two other events E and F. That is, G occurs if F occurs and then E occurs. The product rule allows us to compute the probability of G as the probability of F times the conditional probability $\Pr(E|F)$. The next example illustrates this point.

EXAMPLE 4   **Cards**   A sequence of two playing cards is drawn at random (without replacement) from a standard deck of 52 cards. What is the probability that the first card is red and the second is black?

Solution   The event in question is a sequence of two events, namely,
$$F = \text{"the first card is red"}$$
$$E = \text{"the second card is black."}$$

Since half the deck consists of red cards, $\Pr(F) = \frac{1}{2}$. If we are given that F occurs, then there are only 51 cards left in the deck, of which 26 are black, so
$$\Pr(E|F) = \tfrac{26}{51}.$$
By the product rule
$$\Pr(E \cap F) = \Pr(F) \cdot \Pr(E|F) = \tfrac{1}{2} \cdot \tfrac{26}{51} = \tfrac{13}{51}.$$ ∎

The product rule may be generalized to sequences of three events E_1, E_2, and E_3:

$$\Pr(E_1 \cap E_2 \cap E_3) = \Pr(E_1) \cdot \Pr(E_2|E_1) \cdot \Pr(E_3|E_1 \cap E_2).$$

Similar formulas hold for sequences of four or more events.

One of the most important applications of conditional probability is in the discussion of independent events. Intuitively, two events are **independent** of each other if the occurrence of one has no effect on the likelihood that the other will occur. For example, suppose that we roll a die twice. Let the events E and F be

$$F = \text{"first roll is a 6"}$$
$$E = \text{"second roll is a 3."}$$

Then intuitively these events are independent of one another. Rolling a 6 on the first roll has no effect whatsoever on the outcome of the second roll. On the other hand, suppose that we draw a sequence of two cards at random (without replacement) from a deck. Then the events

$$F = \text{"first card is red"}$$
$$E = \text{"second card is black"}$$

are not independent of one another, at least intuitively. Indeed, whether or not we draw a red on the first card affects the likelihood of drawing a black on the second.

The notion of independence of events is easily formulated. If E and F are events in a sample space and $\Pr(F) \neq 0$, then the product rule states that $\Pr(E \cap F) = \Pr(E|F) \cdot \Pr(F)$. However, if the occurrence of event F does not affect the likelihood of the occurrence of event E, we would expect that $\Pr(E|F) = \Pr(E)$. Substitution then shows that $\Pr(E \cap F) = \Pr(E) \cdot \Pr(F)$.

DEFINITION Let E and F be events. We say that E and F are **independent** provided that
$$\Pr(E \cap F) = \Pr(E) \cdot \Pr(F).$$

If $\Pr(E) \neq 0$ and $\Pr(F) \neq 0$, then our definition is equivalent to the intuitive statement of independence stated in terms of conditional probability. The two may be used interchangeably.

Let E and F be events with nonzero probability. E and F are *independent* provided that
$$\Pr(E|F) = \Pr(E) \quad \text{and} \quad \Pr(F|E) = \Pr(F).$$

EXAMPLE 5

Two rolls of a die   An experiment consists of observing the outcome of two consecutive rolls of a die. Let E and F be the events

$$E = \text{"the first roll is a 3"}$$
$$F = \text{"the second roll is a 6."}$$

Show that these events are independent.

Solution Clearly, $\Pr(E) = \Pr(F) = \frac{1}{6}$. To compute $\Pr(E|F)$, assume that F occurs. Then there are six possible outcomes:

$$F = \{(1,6),(2,6),(3,6),(4,6),(5,6),(6,6)\},$$

and all outcomes are equally likely. Moreover,

$$E \cap F = \{(3,6)\},$$

so that

$$\Pr(E|F) = \frac{[\text{number of outcomes in } E \cap F]}{[\text{number of outcomes in } F]} = \frac{1}{6} = \Pr(E).$$

Similarly, $\Pr(F|E) = \Pr(F)$. So E and F are independent events, in agreement with our intuition. ■

EXAMPLE 6   **Cards** Suppose that an experiment consists of observing the results of drawing two consecutive cards from a 52-card deck. Let E and F be the events

$$E = \text{``second card is black''}$$
$$F = \text{``first card is red.''}$$

Are these events independent?

Solution There are the same number of outcomes with the second card red as with the second card black, so $\Pr(E) = \frac{1}{2}$. To compute $\Pr(E|F)$, note that if F occurs, then there are 51 equally likely choices for the second card, of which 26 are black, so that $\Pr(E|F) = \frac{26}{51}$. Note that $\Pr(E|F) \neq \Pr(E)$, so E and F are not independent, in

Now Try Exercise 5 agreement with our intuition. ■

EXAMPLE 7   **Heads and tails** Suppose that we toss a coin three times and record the sequence of heads and tails. Let E be the event "at most one head occurs" and F the event "both heads and tails occur." Are E and F independent?

Solution Using the abbreviations H for "heads" and T for "tails," we have

$$E = \{\text{TTT, HTT, THT, TTH}\}$$
$$F = \{\text{HTT, HTH, HHT, THH, THT, TTH}\}$$
$$E \cap F = \{\text{HTT, THT, TTH}\}.$$

The sample space contains eight equally likely outcomes, so that

$$\Pr(E) = \tfrac{1}{2} \qquad \Pr(F) = \tfrac{3}{4} \qquad \Pr(E \cap F) = \tfrac{3}{8}.$$

Moreover,

$$\Pr(E) \cdot \Pr(F) = \tfrac{1}{2} \cdot \tfrac{3}{4} = \tfrac{3}{8},$$

Now Try Exercise 19 which equals $\Pr(E \cap F)$. So E and F are independent. ■

EXAMPLE 8   **Probabilities associated with four-children families** Suppose that a family has four children. Let E be the event "at most one boy" and F the event "at least one child of each sex." Are E and F independent?

Solution Let B stand for "boy" and G for "girl." Then

$$E = \{\text{GGGG, GGGB, GGBG, GBGG, BGGG}\}$$
$$F = \{\text{GGGB, GGBG, GBGG, BGGG, BBBG, BBGB, BGBB,}$$
$$\text{GBBB, BBGG, BGBG, BGGB, GBBG, GBGB, GGBB}\},$$

and the sample space consists of 16 equally likely outcomes. Furthermore,

$$E \cap F = \{\text{GGGB, GGBG, GBGG, BGGG}\}.$$

Therefore,

$$\Pr(E) = \tfrac{5}{16} \qquad \Pr(F) = \tfrac{7}{8} \qquad \Pr(E \cap F) = \tfrac{1}{4}.$$

In this example

$$\Pr(E) \cdot \Pr(F) = \tfrac{5}{16} \cdot \tfrac{7}{8} \neq \Pr(E \cap F).$$

Now Try Exercise 53   So E and F are *not* independent events.   ∎

Examples 7 and 8 are similar, yet the events they describe are independent in one case and not the other. Although intuition is frequently a big help, in complex problems we shall need to use the definition of independence to verify that our intuition is correct.

EXAMPLE 9   **Reliability of a calculator**   A new calculator is designed to be extra reliable by having two independent calculating units. The probability that a given calculating unit fails within the first 1000 hours of operation is .001. What is the probability that at least one calculating unit will operate without failure for the first 1000 hours of operation?

Solution Let

$$E = \text{“calculating unit 1 fails in first 1000 hours”}$$
$$F = \text{“calculating unit 2 fails in first 1000 hours.”}$$

Then E and F are independent events, since the calculating units are independent of one another. Therefore,

$$\Pr(E \cap F) = \Pr(E) \cdot \Pr(F) = (.001)^2 = .000001$$
$$\Pr((E \cap F)') = 1 - .000001 = .999999.$$

Now Try Exercise 17   Since $(E \cap F)' = $ “not both calculating units fail in first 1000 hours,” the desired probability is .999999.   ∎

The concept of independent events can be extended to more than two events:

> **DEFINITION** A set of events is said to be **independent** if, for each collection of events chosen from them, say $E_1, E_2, \ldots, E_n$, we have
>
> $$\Pr(E_1 \cap E_2 \cap \cdots \cap E_n) = \Pr(E_1) \cdot \Pr(E_2) \cdot \; \cdots \; \cdot \Pr(E_n).$$

EXAMPLE 10   **Probabilities associated with independent events**   Three events A, B, and C are independent; $\Pr(A) = .5$, $\Pr(B) = .3$, and $\Pr(C) = .2$.
(a) Calculate $\Pr(A \cap B \cap C)$.   **(b)** Calculate $\Pr(A \cap C)$.

Solution **(a)** $\Pr(A \cap B \cap C) = \Pr(A) \cdot \Pr(B) \cdot \Pr(C) = (.5)(.3)(.2) = .03.$
(b) $\Pr(A \cap C) = \Pr(A) \cdot \Pr(C) = (.5)(.2) = .1.$ ∎

We shall leave as an exercise the intuitively reasonable result that if E and F are independent events, so are E and F', E' and F, and E' and F'. This result also generalizes to any collection of independent events.

EXAMPLE 11   **Quality control** A company manufactures stereo components. Experience shows that defects in manufacture are independent of one another. Quality control studies reveal that

2% of CD players are defective,

3% of amplifiers are defective,

7% of speakers are defective.

A system consists of a CD player, an amplifier, and two speakers. What is the probability that the system is not defective?

Solution Let C, A, S_1, and S_2 be events corresponding to defective CD player, amplifier, speaker 1, and speaker 2, respectively. Then

$$\Pr(C) = .02 \qquad \Pr(A) = .03 \qquad \Pr(S_1) = \Pr(S_2) = .07.$$

We wish to calculate $\Pr(C' \cap A' \cap S_1' \cap S_2')$. By the complement rule we have

$$\Pr(C') = .98 \qquad \Pr(A') = .97 \qquad \Pr(S_1') = \Pr(S_2') = .93.$$

Since we have assumed that C, A, S_1, and S_2 are independent, so are C', A', S_1', and S_2'. Therefore,

$$\Pr(C' \cap A' \cap S_1' \cap S_2') = \Pr(C') \cdot \Pr(A') \cdot \Pr(S_1') \cdot \Pr(S_2')$$
$$= (.98)(.97)(.93)^2 \approx .822.$$

Now Try Exercise 9   Thus there is an 82.2% chance that the system is not defective. ■

Practice Problems 6.5

1. **Cards** Suppose there are three cards: one red on both sides; one white on both sides; and one having a side of each color. A card is selected at random and placed on a table. If the up side is red, what is the probability that the down side is red? (Try guessing at the answer before working it using the formula for conditional probability.)

2. Show that if events E and F are independent of each other, then so are E and F'. [*Hint*: Since $E \cap F$ and $E \cap F'$ are mutually exclusive, we have

$$\Pr(E) = \Pr(E \cap F) + \Pr(E \cap F').]$$

EXERCISES 6.5

In Exercises 1–4, let S be a sample space and E and F events associated with S. Suppose that $\Pr(E) = .5$, $\Pr(F) = .3$, and $\Pr(E \cap F) = .1$.

1. Calculate $\Pr(E|F)$ and $\Pr(F|E)$.

2. Are E and F independent events? Explain.

3. Calculate $\Pr(E|F')$.

4. Calculate $\Pr(E'|F')$.

5. **Epidemiology** A doctor studies the known cancer patients in a certain town. The probability that a randomly chosen resident has cancer is found to be .001. It is found that 30% of the town works for Ajax Chemical Company. The probability that an employee of Ajax

has cancer is equal to .003. Are the events "has cancer" and "works for Ajax" independent of one another?

6. **Value of College** The proportion of individuals in a certain city earning more than \$35,000 per year is .25. The proportion of individuals earning more than \$35,000 and having a college degree is .10. Suppose that a person is randomly chosen and he turns out to be earning more than \$35,000. What is the probability that he is a college graduate?

7. **Medical Tests** A medical screening program administers three independent medical tests. Of the persons taking the tests, 80% pass test I, 75% pass test II, and 60% pass test III. A participant is chosen at random.

(a) What is the probability that she will pass all three tests?

(b) What is the probability that she will pass at least two of the three tests?

8. **System Reliability** A stereo system contains 50 transistors. The probability that a given transistor will fail in 100,000 hours of use is .0005. Assume that the failures of the various transistors are independent of one another. What is the probability that no transistor will fail during the first 100,000 hours of use?

9. **System Reliability** A TV set contains five circuit boards of type A, five of type B, and three of type C. The probability of failing in its first 5000 hours of use is .01 for a type A circuit board, .02 for a type B circuit board, and .025 for a type C circuit board. Assuming that the failures of the various circuit boards are independent of one another, compute the probability that no circuit board fails in the first 5000 hours of use.

10. **Light Bulbs** A certain brand of a long-life bulb has probability .01 of burning out in less than 1000 hours. Suppose that we wish to light a corridor with a number of independent bulbs in such a way that at least one of the bulbs remains lit for 1000 consecutive hours. What is the minimum number of bulbs needed to ensure that the probability of success is at least .99999?

11. Let E and F be events with $\Pr(E) = \frac{1}{2}$, $\Pr(F) = \frac{1}{3}$, and $\Pr(E \cap F) = \frac{1}{4}$. Compute $\Pr(E|F)$ and $\Pr(F|E)$.

12. Let E and F be events with $\Pr(E) = .3$, $\Pr(F) = .6$, and $\Pr(E \cup F) = .7$. Find
   (a) $\Pr(E \cap F)$ (b) $\Pr(E|F)$ (c) $\Pr(F|E)$
   (d) $\Pr(E' \cap F)$ (e) $\Pr(E'|F)$

13. **Opinion Polling** Of the registered voters in a certain town, 50% are Democrats, 40% favor a school loan, and 30% are Democrats who favor a school loan. Suppose that a registered voter is selected at random from the town.

   (a) What is the probability that the person is not a Democrat and opposes the school loan?

   (b) What is the conditional probability that the person favors the school loan given that he or she is a Democrat?

   (c) What is the conditional probability that the person is a Democrat given that he or she favors the school loan?

14. **Game Attendance** Of the students at a certain college, 50% regularly attend the football games, 30% are first-year students, and 40% are upper-class students who do not regularly attend football games. Suppose that a student is selected at random.

   (a) What is the probability that the person both is a first-year student and regularly attends football games?

(b) What is the conditional probability that the person regularly attends football games given that he is a first-year student?

(c) What is the conditional probability that the person is a first-year student given that he regularly attends football games?

15. **Coin Tosses** A coin is tossed three times. What is the conditional probability that the outcome is HHH given that at least two heads occur?

16. **Balls in an Urn** Two balls are selected at random from an urn containing two white balls and three red balls. What is the conditional probability that both balls are white given that at least one of them is white?

17. **Life Expectancies** The probabilities that a person A and a person B will live an additional 15 years are .8 and .7, respectively. Assuming that their lifespans are independent, what is the probability that A or B will live an additional 15 years?

18. **Spread of a Rumor** Jane has two friends who do not know each other. Each of them has heard the same rumor. The probability that each will tell Jane is 60%. What is the probability that Jane does not hear the rumor from either of these friends?

19. **Balls in an Urn** A sample of two balls is drawn from an urn containing two white balls and three red balls. Are the events "the sample contains at least one white ball" and "the sample contains balls of both colors" independent?

20. **Fishing** The probability that a fisherman catches a tuna in any one excursion is .15. What is the probability that he catches a tuna on each of three excursions? on at least one of three excursions?

21. **Prizes** The probability that a prize appears in a box of breakfast cereal is .005. What is the probability that two boxes of cereal contain at least one prize?

22. **Guessing on an Exam** A "true–false" exam has 10 questions. Assuming that the questions are independent and that a student is guessing, find the probability that she gets 100%.

23. **CD Players** Suppose that in Sleepy Valley only 30% of those over 50 years old own CD players. Find the probability that among four randomly chosen people in that age group none owns a CD player.

24. Assume that A and B are events in a sample space and that $\Pr(A) = .40$ and $\Pr(B|A) = .25$. Find $\Pr(A \cap B)$. With the further assumption that $\Pr(B) = .30$, find $\Pr(A \cup B)$, $\Pr(A' \cap B)$, and $\Pr(A|B)$.

25. Show that if events E and F are independent of each other, then so are E' and F'.

26. Show that if E and F are independent events, then

$$\Pr(E \cup F) = 1 - \Pr(E') \cdot \Pr(F').$$

27. Free-Throws A basketball player makes each free-throw with a probability of .6 and is on the line for a one-and-one free throw. (That is, a second throw is allowed only if the first is successful.) What is the probability that the player will score 0 points? 1 point? 2 points? Assume that the two throws are independent.

28. Let $\Pr(F) > 0$.

(a) Show that $\Pr(E'|F) = 1 - \Pr(E|F)$.

(b) Find an example for which

$$\Pr(E|F') \neq 1 - \Pr(E|F).$$

29. Use the inclusion–exclusion principle for (nonconditional) probabilities to show that if E, F, and G are events in S, then

$$\Pr(E \cup F|G) = \Pr(E|G) + \Pr(F|G) - \Pr(E \cap F|G).$$

30. Marriage Statistics The percentage of the U.S. male population that has ever been married is given in Table 1. Explain how the table relates to the idea of conditional probability by giving a precise definition of "% ever married among 25- to 29-year-olds."

TABLE 1

Ages	Percent ever married
18–19	2.3
20–24	13.3
25–29	42.6
30–34	66.6
35–44	79.2
45–54	87.6

Source: U.S. Census Bureau, *America's Families and Living Arrangements: 2006.*

31. Mortality Rates Two communities are being compared as to their annual death rates. Community A is in the Sunbelt and community B is in Alaska.

Community A: Population: 120,000
Number of deaths: 12,000

Community B: Population: 90,000
Number of deaths: 4500

(a) Find the death rate in community A. Note that this is a conditional probability, namely

$$\Pr(\text{death}|A).$$

(b) Express the probability you found in part (a) as a death rate per 1000 in the population of community A.

(c) Find $\Pr(\text{death}|B)$ and compare to part (b).

32. Blood Tests A hospital uses two tests to classify blood. Every blood sample is subjected to both tests. The first test correctly identifies blood type with probability .7, and the second test correctly identifies blood type with probability .8. The probability that at least one of the tests correctly identifies the blood type is .9.

(a) Find the probability that both tests correctly identify the blood type.

(b) Determine the probability that the second test is correct given that the first test is correct.

(c) Determine the probability that the first test is correct given that the second test is correct.

(d) Are the events "test I correctly identifies the blood type" and "test II correctly identifies the blood type" independent?

33. E.R. Waits Sixty-five percent of the patients in the emergency room of a hospital are seen by a physician immediately. The remainder are kept waiting in the waiting room. Eighty percent of those kept waiting are seen within 2 hours. Seventy-five percent of those seen immediately are admitted to the hospital. Forty percent of those seen within 2 hours (but not immediately) are admitted to the hospital, and 10% of those who wait more than 2 hours are admitted to the hospital. Let A be the event "the patient is seen immediately." Let B be the event "the patient is not seen immediately but is seen within 2 hours." Let C be the event "the patient waits more than 2 hours." Let H be the event "the patient is admitted to the hospital."

(a) Find $\Pr(B)$. (b) Find $\Pr(C)$. (c) Find $\Pr(H)$.

34. Course Choices Out of 250 students interviewed at a community college, 90 were taking mathematics but not computer science, 160 were taking mathematics, and 50 were taking neither mathematics nor computer science. Find the probability that a student chosen at random was

(a) taking just computer science.

(b) taking mathematics or computer science, but not both.

(c) taking computer science.

(d) not taking mathematics.

(e) taking mathematics, given that the student was taking computer science.

(f) taking computer science, given that the student was taking mathematics.

(g) taking mathematics, given that the student was taking computer science or mathematics.

(h) taking computer science, given that the student was not taking mathematics.

(i) not taking mathematics, given that the student was not taking computer science.

35. Sports Choices Out of 250 third-grade boys, 120 played baseball, 140 played soccer, and 50 played both. Find the probability that a boy chosen at random

(a) did not play either sport.

(b) played exactly one sport.

(c) played soccer but not baseball.

(d) played soccer, given that he played baseball.

(e) played baseball, given that he did not play soccer.

(f) did not play soccer, given that he did not play baseball.

36. Voting Table 2 shows the number of voting-age U.S. citizens (in millions) by gender and their participation in the 2006 congressional election. Find the probability that a voting-age citizen selected at random

(a) voted.   (b) is male.

(c) is female, given that they voted.

(d) voted, given that they are male.

TABLE 2

	Voted	Did not vote	Totals
Male	45.2	61.3	106.5
Female	51.0	63.1	114.1
Totals	96.2	124.4	220.6

Source: U.S. Census Bureau.

37. Advanced Degrees Table 3 shows the number of advanced degrees (in thousands) earned in the U.S. during a recent year by gender and type of degree. Find the probability that a person selected at random who received an advanced degree

(a) received a master's degree.

(b) is male.

(c) is female, given that they received a bachelor's degree.

(d) received a doctor's degree, given that they are male.

TABLE 3

	Bachelor's	Master's	Doctor's
Male	573	211	24
Female	775	301	22

Source: National Center for Education Statistics.

38. Student Employment Table 4 provides some information about students at a certain college. Find the probability that a student selected at random is

(a) a senior.

(b) working full time.

(c) working part time, given that the student is a first-year student.

(d) a first-year student, given that the student does not work.

(e) a junior or senior, given that the student does not work.

(f) working part time or full time, given that the student is a sophomore or a junior.

TABLE 4

	Works full time	Works part time	Not working
First-year	130	460	210
Sophomore	100	500	150
Junior	80	420	100
Senior	200	300	50

39. Party Affiliation Table 5 describes the voters in a certain district. Find the probability that a voter chosen at random is a

(a) Democrat.

(b) male.

(c) Independent, given that the voter is female.

(d) male, given that the voter is a Republican.

(e) female, given that the voter is not an Independent.

(f) Democrat, given that the voter is not a Republican.

TABLE 5

	Democrat	Republican	Independent
Male	400	700	300
Female	600	300	200

40. Opinion Poll Table 6 shows the responses when 300 people were asked if they thought executives were paid too much. Find the probability that a person selected at random from those surveyed

(a) answered yes.

(b) is male.

(c) is female, given that they answered yes.

(d) answered no, given that he is male.

TABLE 6

	Yes	No	Neutral
Male	75	39	36
Female	91	16	43

41. Baseball A baseball player's batting average changes every time he goes to bat, and therefore should not be used as the probability of him getting a hit. However, we can still make a subjective assessment of his ability.

(a) If a player with .3 probability of getting a hit bats four times in a game and each at-bat is an independent event, what is the probability of the player getting at least one hit in the game?

(b) What is the probability of the player in part (a) starting off the season with at least one hit in each of the first 10 games?

(c) If there are 20 players with .3 probability of getting a hit, what is the probability that at least one of them will start the season with a 10-game hitting streak?

42. Military Personnel Table 7 shows the numbers of officers and enlisted persons on active military duty on May 31, 2008. Let E be the event that a person selected at random from the active-duty military personnel is enlisted, and let N be the event that a person selected at random from the active-duty military personnel is in the Navy.

TABLE 7

	Army	Navy	Marine Corps	Air Force
Officer	86,028	52,153	20,048	65,276
Enlisted	436,145	275,960	170,603	259,021

(a) Find each of the following probabilities: $\Pr(E)$, $\Pr(N)$, $\Pr(E \cap N)$, $\Pr(E|N)$, $\Pr(N|E)$.

(b) Are the events E and N independent?

43. Balls in an Urn An urn contains 10 red balls and 15 white balls. A ball is selected at random from the urn and not replaced. Then, a second ball is selected. Show that the probability that the second ball is red is the same as the probability that the first ball is red.

44. Choosing Numbers Juan randomly chooses a positive integer that is divisible by 7 and is less than 70. Chita randomly selects a positive integer less than 70 that is divisible by 11. What is the probability that they choose the same number?

45. Bag of Marbles A bag contains four blue marbles, three white marbles, and six red marbles. Three marbles are selected from the bag. What is the probability they are all red? What is the probability that they are all the same color?

46. Spinners A spinner on a wheel with the numbers 2, 5, 6, and 9 in segments of equal area is spun at random. Another spinner on a wheel with equal segments marked with numbers 3, 7, and 8 is also spun. What is the probability that the sum of the two numbers chosen by the spinners is odd?

47. Sandwiches Horatio goes to the deli for sandwiches and orders two roast beef sandwiches and two ham sandwiches. They are wrapped and put into a paper bag. What is the probability that two sandwiches chosen at random will both be roast beef? What is the probability that the two sandwiches chosen at random will be alike?

48. Numbers Ten slips of paper have numbers 1 through 10. Sue chooses two slips at random. What is the probability that the sum of the numbers chosen is even?

49. Bag of Marbles A bag contains five red marbles and eight white marbles. If a sample of four marbles con-

tains at least one white marble, what is the probability that all the marbles in the sample are white?

50. Cards Eight people each have a deck of well-shuffled cards. Each chooses a card at random from his or her own deck. What is the probability that there is at least one match?

51. Prize Drawing One hundred attendees at a conference put their calling cards into a glass bowl for a drawing. Fred cheats and puts in three of his cards to increase his chance of winning. Just before the drawing, it is announced that a second card will be drawn for a second prize after the first card is drawn. What is the probability that Fred will win both prizes and therefore be revealed to have cheated?

52. Conditional Probabilities Suppose a male is selected at random from the adult male population. Let F be the event "he played varsity sports in college." Which of the following two probabilities is greater?

(a) Pr ("he works in a bank and is an avid sports fan"$|F$)

(b) Pr ("he works in a bank"$|F$)

53. Roll a Die Roll a die and consider the following two events: $E = \{2, 4, 6\}$, $F = \{3, 6\}$. Are the events E and F independent?

54. Balls in an Urn An urn contains both red and white balls. A ball is selected at random from the urn and not replaced. Then, a second ball is selected. Show that the sequence of colors "red, white" has the same probability of occurring as the sequence "white, red."

55. Children A newly married couple decides to keep having children until they have a girl. What is the probability that the couple will have at least five children? *Note:* Assume no multiple births.

56. Rolling Dice What is the probability that at least one of the dice shows a 1 or a 2 when four dice are rolled?

57. Lottery Suppose you decide to bet $1000 in a weekly lottery for which the probability of winning the jackpot is p, where p is very small. Are your chances of winning the jackpot better if you bet 1000 different combinations in a single lottery or bet a single combination in 1000 successive weekly lotteries? To answer this question, determine the following:

(a) the probability of winning the jackpot when you bet 1000 different combinations in a single lottery.

(b) the probability of winning the jackpot at least once when you bet a single combination in 1000 successive weekly lotteries.

Note: $(1-p)^{1000} \approx 1 - 1000p + 499{,}500p^2$.

58. Roulette If you bet on the number 7 in roulette, the probability of winning on a single spin of the wheel is $\frac{1}{38}$. Suppose you bet on "7" for 38 consecutive spins.

(a) Which of the following numbers do you think is closest to the probability of winning at least once: 1, .64, or .5?

(b) Calculate the probability of winning at least once.

59. Coin Toss A biased coin shows heads with probability .6. What is the probability of obtaining the sequence HT in two tosses of the coin? TH? Could this coin be used at the start of a football game to fairly determine which team is to kick off?

60. Gold and Silver Coins Consider three boxes where one box contains two gold coins, one box contains two silver coins, and one box contains a gold coin and a silver coin. Suppose you select a box at random and then select a coin at random from that box. If the coin is gold, what is the probability that the other coin in the box is gold?

61. Coin Toss A coin is tossed five times. Is the outcome HTHHT more likely to occur than the outcome HHHHH?

62. Rolling a Die Suppose you roll a die six times and obtain a 1 each time. What is the probability that the next roll will produce a 1?

In Exercises 63–66, use a graphing calculator or spreadsheet to calculate the probabilities.

63. Gender and Unemployment Consider Table 8, with figures in thousands, pertaining to the 2008 American civilian labor force (age 20^+). Determine if gender and unemployment status are independent by finding the probabilities $\Pr(W)$, $\Pr(U)$, and $\Pr(W \cap U)$.

64. Bridge A bridge hand consists of 13 cards selected from a deck of 52 cards.

(a) How many possible bridge hands contain at least one ace?

(b) How many possible bridge hands contain the ace of spades?

(c) Let $E =$ "the hand contains at least two aces." Let $F =$ "the hand contains at least one ace." Let $G =$ "the hand contains the ace of spades." Which is the greater probability: $\Pr(E|F)$ or $\Pr(E|G)$?

65. Cards

(a) Find the probability of drawing four aces from a deck of 52 cards in four repeated draws without replacement.

(b) Calculate the probability of drawing two red queens followed by two red kings in four draws from the deck without replacement.

(c) Which of the two events in (a) or (b) is more likely?

66. Roulette Find that value of N for which the probability of winning in Exercise 58 at least once in N trials is about .5.

TABLE 8			
	Employed (E)	**Unemployed (U)**	**Totals**
Men (M)	74,998	4038	79,036
Women (W)	65,238	3208	68,446
Totals	140,236	7246	147,482

Source: U.S. Bureau of Labor Statistics.

Solutions to Practice Problems 6.5

1. $\frac{2}{3}$. Let F be the event that the up side is red and E the event that the down side is red. $\Pr(F) = \frac{1}{2}$ since half the faces are red. $F \cap E$ is the event that both sides of the card are red—that is, that the card that is red on both sides was selected, an event with probability $\frac{1}{3}$. By (2),

$$\Pr(E|F) = \frac{\Pr(E \cap F)}{\Pr(F)} = \frac{\frac{1}{3}}{\frac{1}{2}} = \frac{2}{3}.$$

(A common error is to conclude that the answer is $\frac{1}{2}$ since the card must be either the red/red card or the red/white card, and each of them is equally likely to have been selected. The correct probability is intuitively evident when you realize that two-thirds of the

time the card will have the same color on the bottom as on the top.)

2. By the hint,

$$\begin{aligned} \Pr(E \cap F') &= \Pr(E) - \Pr(E \cap F) \\ &= \Pr(E) - \Pr(E) \cdot \Pr(F) \\ &\quad \text{(since } E \text{ and } F \text{ are independent)} \\ &= \Pr(E)[1 - \Pr(F)] \\ &= \Pr(E) \cdot \Pr(F') \\ &\quad \text{(by the complement rule).} \end{aligned}$$

Therefore, E and F' are independent events.

6.6 Tree Diagrams

In solving many probability problems, it is helpful to represent the various events and their associated probabilities by a **tree diagram**. To explain this useful notion, suppose that we wish to compute the probability of an event that results from performing a sequence of experiments. The various outcomes of each experiment are represented as branches emanating from a point. For example, Fig. 1 represents an experiment with three outcomes. Notice that each branch has been labeled with the probability of the associated outcome. For example, the probability of outcome 1 is .5.

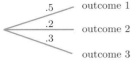

Figure 1

We represent experiments performed one after another by stringing together diagrams of the sort shown in Fig. 1, proceeding from left to right. For example, the diagram in Fig. 2 indicates that first we perform experiment A, having three outcomes, labeled 1–3. If the outcome is 1 or 2, we perform experiment B. If the outcome is 3, we perform experiment C. The probabilities on the right are conditional probabilities. For example, the top probability is the probability of outcome a (of B) given outcome 1 (of A). The probability of a sequence of outcomes may then be computed by multiplying the probabilities along a path. For example, to calculate the probability of outcome 2 followed by outcome b, we must calculate $\Pr(2 \text{ and } b) = \Pr(2) \cdot \Pr(b|2)$. To carry out this calculation, trace out the sequence of outcomes. Multiplying the probabilities along the path gives $(.2)(.6) = .12$—the probability of outcome 2 followed by outcome b.

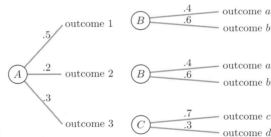

Figure 2

The next example illustrates the use of tree diagrams in calculating probabilities.

EXAMPLE 1

Political polling A pollster is hired by a presidential candidate to determine his support among the voters of Pennsylvania's two big cities: Philadelphia and Pittsburgh. The pollster designs the following sampling technique: Select one of the cities at random and then poll a voter selected at random from that city. Suppose that in Philadelphia two-fifths of the voters favor the Republican candidate and three-fifths favor the Democratic candidate. Suppose that in Pittsburgh two-thirds of the voters favor the Republican candidate and one-third favor the Democratic candidate.

(a) Draw a tree diagram describing the survey.

(b) Find the probability that the voter polled is from Philadelphia and favors the Republican candidate.

(c) Find the probability that the voter favors the Republican candidate.

(d) Find the probability that the voter is from Philadelphia, given that he or she favors the Republican candidate.

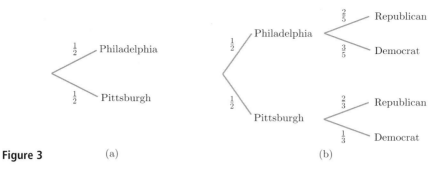

Figure 3 (a) (b)

Solution **(a)** The survey proceeds in two steps: First, select a city, and second, select and poll a voter. Figure 3(a) shows the possible outcomes of the first step and the associated probabilities. For each outcome of the first step there are two possibilities for the second step: The person selected could favor the Republican or the Democrat. In Fig. 3(b) we have represented these possibilities by drawing branches emanating from each of the outcomes of the first step. The probabilities on the new branches are actually conditional probabilities. For instance,

$$\tfrac{2}{5} = \Pr(\text{Rep}|\text{Phila}),$$

the probability that the voter favors the Republican candidate, given that the voter is from Philadelphia.

(b) $\Pr(\text{Phila} \cap \text{Rep}) = \Pr(\text{Phila}) \cdot \Pr(\text{Rep}|\text{Phila}) = \tfrac{1}{2} \cdot \tfrac{2}{5} = \tfrac{1}{5}.$

That is, the probability is $\tfrac{1}{5}$ that the combined outcome corresponds to the blue path in Fig. 4(a). We have written the probability $\tfrac{1}{5}$ at the end of the path to which it corresponds.

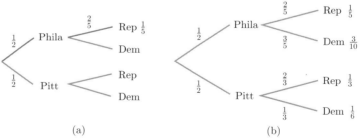

Figure 4 (a) (b)

(c) In Fig. 4(b) we have computed the probabilities for each path of the tree as in part (b). Namely, the probability for a given path is the product of the probabilities for each of its segments. We are asked for $\Pr(\text{Rep})$. There are two paths through the tree leading to Republican, namely

$$\text{Philadelphia} \cap \text{Republican} \quad \text{or} \quad \text{Pittsburgh} \cap \text{Republican}.$$

The probabilities of these two paths are $\tfrac{1}{5}$ and $\tfrac{1}{3}$, respectively. So the probability that the Republican is favored equals $\tfrac{1}{5} + \tfrac{1}{3} = \tfrac{8}{15}$.

(d) Here we are asked for $\Pr(\text{Phila}|\text{Rep})$. By the definition of conditional probability,

Now Try Exercise 13

$$\Pr(\text{Phila}|\text{Rep}) = \frac{\Pr(\text{Phila} \cap \text{Rep})}{\Pr(\text{Rep})} = \frac{\tfrac{1}{5}}{\tfrac{8}{15}} = \frac{3}{8}.$$ ∎

Note that from part (c) we might be led to conclude that the Republican candidate is leading, with $\frac{8}{15}$ of the vote. However, we must always be careful when interpreting surveys. The results depend heavily on the survey design. For example, the survey drew half of its sample from each of the cities. However, Philadelphia is a much larger city and is leaning toward the Democratic candidate—so much so, in fact, that in terms of popular vote the Democratic candidate would win, contrary to our expectations drawn from (c). A pollster must be very careful in designing the procedure for selecting people.

We now finally solve the medical diagnosis problem introduced in Section 6.1.

EXAMPLE 2

Medical screening Suppose that the reliability of a skin test for active pulmonary tuberculosis (TB) is specified as follows: Of people with TB, 98% have a positive reaction and 2% have a negative reaction; of people free of TB, 99% have a negative reaction and 1% have a positive reaction.[1] From a large population of which 2 per 10,000 persons have TB, a person is selected at random and given a skin test, which turns out to be positive. What is the probability that the person has active pulmonary tuberculosis?

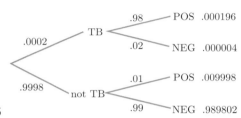

Figure 5

Solution The given data are organized in Fig. 5. The procedure called for is as follows: First select a person at random from the population. There are two possible outcomes: The person has TB,

$$\Pr(\text{TB}) = \frac{2}{10,000} = .0002,$$

or the person does not have TB,

$$\Pr(\text{not TB}) = 1 - .0002 = .9998.$$

For each of these two possibilities, the possible test results and conditional probabilities are given. Multiplying the probabilities along each of the paths through the tree gives the probabilities of the different outcomes. The resulting probabilities are written on the right in Fig. 5. The problem asks for the conditional probability that a person has TB, given that the test is positive. By definition,

$$\Pr(\text{TB}|\text{POS}) = \frac{\Pr(\text{TB} \cap \text{POS})}{\Pr(\text{POS})} = \frac{.000196}{.000196 + .009998} = \frac{.000196}{.010194} \approx .02.$$

Therefore, the probability is .02 that a person with a positive skin test has TB.[2] In other words, although the skin test is quite reliable, only about 2% of those with a positive test turn out to have active TB. This result must be taken into account

---

[1]The probability that a person with the disease has a positive test is called the *sensitivity* of the test. The probability that a disease-free person has a negative test is called the *specificity* of the test. In this case the sensitivity and specificity of the skin test are .98 and .99, respectively.

[2]The probability that a person who tests positive actually has the disease is called the *predictive value of the positive test*.

when large-scale medical diagnostic tests are planned. Because the group of people without TB is so much larger than the group with TB, the small error in the former group is magnified to the point where it dominates the calculation. ■

Now Try Exercise 31

NOTE The numerical data presented in Example 2 are only approximate. Variations in air quality for different localities within the United States cause variations in the incidence of TB and the reliability of skin tests. ■

Tree diagrams come in all shapes and sizes. Three or more branches might emanate from a single point, for example, and some trees may not have the symmetry of those in Examples 1 and 2. Tree diagrams arise whenever an activity can be thought of as a sequence of simpler activities.

EXAMPLE 3

Quality control A box contains five good light bulbs and two defective ones. Bulbs are selected one at a time (without replacement) until a good bulb is found. Find the probability that the number of bulbs selected is (i) one, (ii) two, (iii) three.

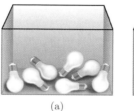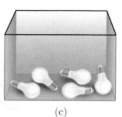

Figure 6   (a)   (b)   (c)

Solution The initial situation in the box is shown in Fig. 6(a). A bulb selected at random will be good (G) with probability $\frac{5}{7}$ and defective (D) with probability $\frac{2}{7}$. If a good bulb is selected, the activity stops. Otherwise, the situation is as shown in Fig. 6(b), and a bulb selected at random has probability $\frac{5}{6}$ of being good and probability $\frac{1}{6}$ of being defective. If the second bulb is good, the activity stops. If the second bulb is defective, then the situation is as shown in Fig. 6(c). At this point a bulb has probability 1 of being good.

The tree diagram corresponding to the sequence of activities is given in Fig. 7. Each of the three paths has a different length. The probability associated with the length of each path has been computed by multiplying the probabilities for its branches. The first path corresponds to the situation where only one bulb is selected, the second path corresponds to two bulbs, and the third path to three bulbs. Therefore,

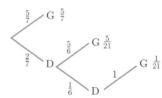

Figure 7

Now Try Exercise 11

$$\text{(i) } \Pr(1) = \tfrac{5}{7} \quad \text{(ii) } \Pr(2) = \tfrac{5}{21} \quad \text{(iii) } \Pr(3) = \tfrac{1}{21}.$$ ■

Practice Problems 6.6

Fifty percent of the students enrolled in a business statistics course had previously taken a finite mathematics course. Thirty percent of these students received an A for the statistics course, whereas 20% of the other students received an A for the statistics course.

1. Draw a tree diagram and label it with the appropriate probabilities.

2. What is the probability that a student selected at random previously took a finite mathematics course and did not receive an A in the statistics course?

3. What is the probability that a student selected at random received an A in the statistics course?

4. What is the conditional probability that a student previously took a finite mathematics course, given that he or she received an A in the statistics course?

EXERCISES 6.6

In Exercises 1–4, draw trees representing the sequence of experiments.

1. Experiment I is performed. Outcome *a* occurs with probability .3, and outcome *b* occurs with probability .7. Then experiment II is performed. Its outcome *c* occurs with probability .6, and its outcome *d* occurs with probability .4.

2. Experiment I is performed twice. The three outcomes of experiment I are equally likely.

3. **Quality Control** A stereo repair shop uses a two-step diagnostic procedure to repair amplifiers. Step I locates the problem in an amplifier with probability .8. Step II (which is executed only if step I fails to locate the problem) locates the problem with probability .6.

4. **Personnel Categories** A training program is used by a corporation to direct hirees to appropriate jobs. The program consists of two steps. Step I identifies 30% as management trainees, 60% as nonmanagerial workers, and 10% to be fired. In step II, 75% of the management trainees are assigned to managerial positions, 20% are assigned to nonmanagerial positions, and 5% are fired. In step II, 60% of the nonmanagerial workers are kept in the same category, 10% are assigned to management positions, and 30% are fired.

5. **Quality Control** Refer to Exercise 3. What is the probability that the procedure will fail to locate the problem?

6. **Personnel Categories** Refer to Exercise 4. What is the probability that a randomly chosen hiree will be assigned to a management position at the end of the training period?

7. **Personnel Categories** Refer to Exercise 4. What is the probability that a randomly chosen hiree will be fired by the end of the training period?

8. **Personnel Categories** Refer to Exercise 4. What is the probability that a randomly chosen hiree will be designated a management trainee but *not* be appointed to a management position?

9. **Selecting from Urns** Suppose that we have a white urn containing two white balls and one red ball and we have a red urn containing one white ball and three red balls. An experiment consists of selecting at random a ball from the white urn and then (without replacing the first ball) selecting at random a ball from the urn having the color of the first ball. Find the probability that the second ball is red.

10. **Cards, Coins, Dice** A card is drawn from a 52-card deck. If the card is a picture card, we toss a coin. If the card is not a picture card, we roll a die. Find the probability that we end the sequence with a "6" on the die. Find the probability that we end the sequence with a "head" on the coin.

11. **Cards** A card is drawn from a 52-card deck. We continue to draw until we have drawn a king or until we have drawn five cards, whichever comes first. Draw a tree diagram that illustrates the experiment. Put the appropriate probabilities on the tree. Find the probability that the drawing ends before the fourth draw.

12. **Final Exams** There are three sections of a mathematics course available at convenient times for a student. There is a 20% chance that Professor Jones gives a final exam, a 10% chance that Professor Cates gives a final exam, and a 5% chance that Professor Smithson gives a final. At other times there are two biology sections, and in those the probabilities of a final are 20% and 13%. Find the probability that a student who randomly chooses one mathematics course and one biology course has to take at least one final examination.

13. **Quality Control** Twenty percent of the library books in the fiction section are worn and need replacement. Ten percent of the nonfiction holdings are worn and need replacement. The library's holdings are 40% fiction and 60% nonfiction. Use a tree diagram to find the probability that a book chosen at random from this library is worn and needs replacement.

14. **School Bussing** Draw a tree diagram that illustrates the following. Three-fifths of kindergarten children are bussed to school, while two-fifths of the first to fifth graders are bussed. The school has grades K through 5, and 17.5% of the students are in kindergarten. De-

termine the probability that a child chosen at random from the school is bussed to school.

15. **Color Blindness** Color blindness is a sex-linked, inherited condition that is much more common among men than women. Suppose that 5% of all men and .4% of all women are color-blind. A person is chosen at random and found to be color-blind. What is the probability that the person is male? (You may assume that 50% of the population are men and 50% are women.)

16. **T-maze** A mouse is put into a T-maze (a maze shaped like a "T"). In this maze he has the choice of turning to the left and being rewarded with cheese or going to the right and receiving a mild shock. Before any conditioning takes place (i.e., on trial 1), the mouse is equally likely to go to the left or to the right. After the first trial his decision is influenced by what happened on the previous trial. If he receives cheese on any trial, the probabilities of his going to the left or right become .9 and .1, respectively, on the following trial. If he receives the electric shock on any trial, the probabilities of his going to the left or right on the next trial become .7 and .3, respectively. What is the probability that the mouse will turn left on the second trial?

17. **T-maze** Refer to Exercise 16. What is the probability that the mouse will turn left on the third trial?

18. **Manufacturing** A factory has two machines that produce bolts. Machine I produces 60% of the daily output of bolts, and 3% of its bolts are defective. Machine II produces 40% of the daily output, and 2% of its bolts are defective.

   (a) What is the probability that a bolt selected at random will be defective?

   (b) If a bolt is selected at random and found to be defective, what is the probability that it was produced by machine I?

19. **Heads or Tails** Three ordinary quarters and a fake quarter with two heads are placed in a hat. One quarter is selected at random and tossed twice. If the outcome is "HH," what is the probability that the fake quarter was selected?

20. **Medical Diagnosis** Suppose that the reliability of a test for hepatitis is specified as follows: Of people with hepatitis, 95% have a positive reaction and 5% have a negative reaction; of people free of hepatitis, 90% have a negative reaction and 10% have a positive reaction. From a large population of which .05% of the people have hepatitis, a person is selected at random and given the test. If the test is positive, what is the probability that the person actually has hepatitis?

21. **Tennis** Kim has a strong first serve; whenever it is good (that is, in) she wins the point 75% of the time. Whenever her second serve is good, she wins the point 50% of the time. Sixty percent of her first serves and 75% of her second serves are good.

   (a) What is the probability that Kim wins the point when she serves?

   (b) If Kim wins a service point, what is the probability that her first serve was good?

22. **Accidental Nuclear War** Suppose that during any year the probability of an accidental nuclear war is .0001 (provided, of course, that there hasn't been one in a previous year). Draw a tree diagram representing the possibilities for the next three years. What is the probability that there will be an accidental nuclear war during the next three years?

23. **Accidental Nuclear War** Refer to Exercise 22. What is the probability that there will be an accidental nuclear war during the next n years?

24. **Coin Tosses** A coin is to be tossed at most five times. The tosser wins as soon as the number of heads exceeds the number of tails and loses as soon as three tails have been tossed. Use a tree diagram for this game to calculate the probability of winning.

25. **Cards** Suppose that instead of tossing a coin, the player in Exercise 24 draws up to five cards from a deck consisting only of three red and three black cards. The player wins as soon as the number of red cards exceeds the number of black cards and loses as soon as three black cards have been drawn. Does the tree diagram for the card game have the same shape as the tree diagram for the coin game? Is there any difference in the probability of winning? If so, which game has the greater probability of winning?

26. **Cards** A man has been guessing the colors of cards drawn from a standard deck. During the first 50 draws he kept track of the number of cards of each color. What is the probability of guessing the color of the fifty-first card?

27. **Genetics** Traits passed from generation to generation are carried by genes. For a certain type of pea plant, the color of the flower produced by the plant (either red or white) is determined by a pair of genes. Each gene is of one of the types C (dominant gene) or c (recessive gene). Plants for which both genes are of type c (said to have genotype cc) produce white flowers. All other plants—that is, plants of genotypes CC and Cc—produce red flowers. When two plants are crossed, the offspring receives one gene from each parent.

   (a) Suppose you cross two pea plants of genotype Cc. What is the probability that the offspring produces white flowers? red flowers?

   (b) Suppose you have a batch of red-flowering pea plants, of which 60% have genotype Cc and 40% have genotype CC. If you select one of these plants at random and cross it with a white-flowering pea plant, what is the probability that the offspring will produce red flowers?

28. Genetics Refer to Exercise 27. Suppose a batch of 99 pea plants contains 33 plants of each of the three genotypes.

(a) If you select one of these plants at random and cross it with a white-flowering pea plant, what is the probability that the offspring will produce white flowers?

(b) If you select one of the 99 pea plants at random, cross it with a white-flowering pea plant, and the offspring produces red flowers, what is the probability that the selected plant had genotype Cc?

29. College Faculty At a local college, four sections of economics are taught during the day and two sections are taught at night. Seventy-five percent of the day sections are taught by full-time faculty. Forty percent of the evening sections are taught by full-time faculty. If Jane has a part-time teacher for her economics course, what is the probability that she is taking a night class?

30. U.S. Car Production Car production in the United States in 2005 was distributed among car manufacturers as follows.

U.S. car production	Type		Percentage of type by brand
60%	Domestic	Chrysler	23%
		Ford	31%
		General Motors	46%
40%	Foreign	Honda	20%
		Toyota	32%
		Other	48%

Source: U.S. Light Vehicle Production by Manufacturer (*Ward's AutoInfo Bank*).

This means that 60% of the cars produced in the United States were manufactured by domestic companies; of them, 23% were Chryslers, 31% were Fords, and 46% were General Motors products.

(a) A 2005 automobile is chosen at random. What is the probability that it is a General Motors car?

(b) What is the probability that a randomly selected 2005 automobile is a Ford or a Toyota?

Exercises 31 and 32 refer to Example 2.

31. Medical Screening Find the predictive value of the negative skin test; that is, the probability of a true negative.

32. Medical Screening The predictive values of a diagnostic test do not depend entirely on the sensitivity and specificity of the test. They also depend on the prevalence of the disease being tested for. Find the predictive values of the positive and negative skin tests if 2 out of 100 people in the population have tuberculosis.

33. Balls in an Urn Urn I contains 5 red balls and 5 white balls. Urn II contains 12 white balls. A ball is selected at random from urn I and placed in urn II. Then a ball is selected at random from urn II. What is the probability that the second ball is white?

34. Balls in an Urn An urn contains five red balls and three green balls. One ball is selected at random and then replaced by a ball of the other color. Then a second ball is selected at random. What is the probability that the second ball is green?

35. Coin Tosses Two people toss two coins each. What is the probability that they get the same number of heads?

36. Quality Control A light bulb manufacturer knows that .05% of all bulbs manufactured are defective. A testing machine is 99% effective; that is, 99% of good bulbs will be declared fine and 99% of flawed bulbs will be declared defective. If a randomly selected light bulb is tested and found to be defective, what is the probability that it actually is defective?

37. Tennis When a tennis player hits his first serve as hard as possible (called a *blast*), he gets the ball in (that is; within bounds) 60% of the time. When the blast first serve is in, he wins the point 80% of the time. When the first serve is out, his gentler second serve wins the point 45% of the time. Draw a tree diagram representing the probabilities of winning the point for the first two serves. Use the tree diagram to determine the probability that the server eventually wins the point when his first serve is a blast.

38. Golf Bud is a very consistent golfer. On par three holes, he always scores a 4. Lou, on the other hand, is quite erratic. On par three holes, Lou scores a 3 seventy percent of the time and scores a 6 thirty percent of the time.

(a) If Bud and Lou play a single par three hole together, who is more likely to win; that is, to have the lowest score?

(b) If Bud and Lou play two consecutive par three holes, who is more likely to have the lowest total score?

39. Pinball Stan and Oliver are playing adjacent pinball machines. Stan is very consistent and scores 400 points each game. Oliver is a bit more aggressive and scores 401 points 99% of the time and 0 points (tilt) the rest of the time.

(a) If they each play one game, what is the probability that Oliver wins; that is, scores the most points?

(b) What is the probability that Oliver has scored the most total points after each person has played 400 games? *Hint*: Stan will have scored 160,000 points. If Oliver loses one or more games, he will have fewer total points than Stan.

40. Selecting from Urns An urn contains 4 red marbles and 3 green marbles. One marble is removed, its color noted, and the marble is not replaced. A second marble is removed and its color noted.

   (a) What is the probability that both marbles are red? green?

   (b) What is the probability that exactly one marble is red?

41. Drug Testing Suppose 500 athletes are tested for a drug, one in ten has used the drug, the test has a 99% specificity, and the test has a 100% sensitivity. That is,

the probability of a false positive is 1% and there is no chance that a user of the drug will go undetected. If an athlete in the group tests positive, what is the probability that he or she has used the drug?

42. Selecting from a Bag A bag is equally likely to contain either one white ball or one red ball. A white ball is added to the bag and then a ball is selected at random from the bag. If the selected ball is white, what is the probability that the bag originally contained a white ball? (*Note:* This problem has been attributed to Lewis Carroll.)

Solutions to Practice Problems 6.6

1.

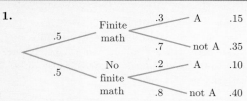

2. The event "finite math and not A" corresponds to

the second path of the tree diagram, which has probability .35.

3. This event is satisfied by the first or third paths and therefore has probability $.15 + .10 = .25$.

4. $\Pr(\text{finite math}|A) = \dfrac{\Pr(\text{finite math and } A)}{\Pr(A)} = \dfrac{.15}{.25} = .6.$

6.7 Bayes' Theorem

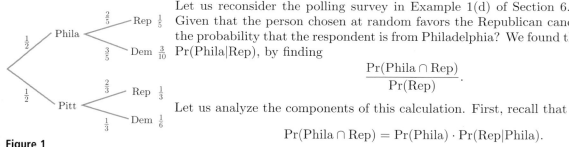

Figure 1

Let us reconsider the polling survey in Example 1(d) of Section 6.6 (see Fig. 1). Given that the person chosen at random favors the Republican candidate, what is the probability that the respondent is from Philadelphia? We found this probability, $\Pr(\text{Phila}|\text{Rep})$, by finding

$$\frac{\Pr(\text{Phila} \cap \text{Rep})}{\Pr(\text{Rep})}.$$

Let us analyze the components of this calculation. First, recall that

$$\Pr(\text{Phila} \cap \text{Rep}) = \Pr(\text{Phila}) \cdot \Pr(\text{Rep}|\text{Phila}).$$

Second,

$$\Pr(\text{Rep}) = \Pr(\text{Phila} \cap \text{Rep}) + \Pr(\text{Pitt} \cap \text{Rep})$$

$$= \Pr(\text{Phila}) \cdot \Pr(\text{Rep}|\text{Phila}) + \Pr(\text{Pitt}) \cdot \Pr(\text{Rep}|\text{Pitt}),$$

by using the tree diagram. Denote the events "Phila," "Pitt," "Rep," and "Dem" by the letters A, B, R, and D, respectively. Then

$$\Pr(\text{Phila}|\text{Rep}) = \Pr(A|R)$$

$$= \frac{\Pr(A \cap R)}{\Pr(R)}$$

$$= \frac{\Pr(A) \cdot \Pr(R|A)}{\Pr(A) \cdot \Pr(R|A) + \Pr(B) \cdot \Pr(R|B)}.$$

This is a special case of Bayes' theorem.

We summarize a simple form of Bayes' theorem. Suppose that A is an event in S, and B_1 and B_2 are mutually exclusive events such that $B_1 \cup B_2 = S$. Then

$$\Pr(B_1|A) = \frac{\Pr(B_1) \cdot \Pr(A|B_1)}{\Pr(B_1) \cdot \Pr(A|B_1) + \Pr(B_2) \cdot \Pr(A|B_2)}.$$

We have the same type of result for the situation in which we have three mutually exclusive sets B_1, B_2, and B_3 whose union is all of S. We state Bayes' theorem for that case and leave the general case for n mutually exclusive sets for the end of the section.

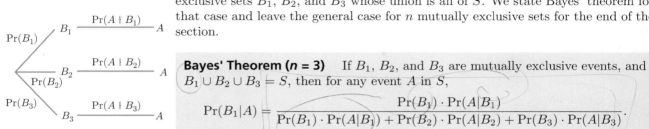

Figure 2

Bayes' Theorem ($n = 3$) If B_1, B_2, and B_3 are mutually exclusive events, and $B_1 \cup B_2 \cup B_3 = S$, then for any event A in S,

$$\Pr(B_1|A) = \frac{\Pr(B_1) \cdot \Pr(A|B_1)}{\Pr(B_1) \cdot \Pr(A|B_1) + \Pr(B_2) \cdot \Pr(A|B_2) + \Pr(B_3) \cdot \Pr(A|B_3)}.$$

See Fig. 2.

EXAMPLE 1

Medical screening Solve the tuberculosis skin test problem of Example 2 of Section 6.6 by using Bayes' theorem.

Solution The observed event A is "positive skin test result." There are two possible events leading to A—namely,

$$B_1 = \text{"person has tuberculosis"}$$

$$B_2 = \text{"person does not have tuberculosis."}$$

We wish to calculate $\Pr(B_1|A)$. From the data given we have

$$\Pr(B_1) = \frac{2}{10,000} = .0002$$

$$\Pr(B_2) = .9998$$

$$\Pr(A|B_1) = \Pr(\text{POS}|\text{TB}) = .98$$

$$\Pr(A|B_2) = \Pr(\text{POS}|\text{not TB}) = .01.$$

Therefore, by Bayes' theorem,

$$\Pr(B_1|A) = \frac{\Pr(B_1)\Pr(A|B_1)}{\Pr(B_1)\Pr(A|B_1) + \Pr(B_2)\Pr(A|B_2)}$$

$$= \frac{(.0002)(.98)}{(.0002)(.98) + (.9998)(.01)} \approx .02,$$

Now Try Exercise 11   in agreement with our calculation of Example 2 of Section 6.6. ∎

The advantages of Bayes' theorem over the use of tree diagrams are that (1) we do not need to draw the tree diagram to calculate the desired probability, and (2) we need not compute extraneous probabilities. These advantages become significant in dealing with experiments having many outcomes.

EXAMPLE 2

Quality control A printer has seven book-binding machines. For each machine, Table 1 on the next page gives the proportion of the total book production that it binds and the probability that the machine produces a defective binding. For instance, machine 1 binds 10% of the books and produces a defective binding with

TABLE 1

Machine	Proportion of books bound	Probability of defective binding
1	.10	.03
2	.05	.03
3	.20	.02
4	.15	.02
5	.25	.01
6	.15	.02
7	.10	.03

probability .03. Suppose that a book is selected at random and found to have a defective binding. What is the probability that it was bound by machine 1?

Solution In this example we have seven mutually exclusive events whose union is the entire sample space (the book was bound by one, and only one, of the seven machines). Bayes' theorem can be extended to any finite number of B_i's.

Let B_i $(i = 1, 2, \ldots, 7)$ be the event that the book was bound by machine i, and let A be the event that the book has a defective binding. Then, for example,

$$\Pr(B_1) = .10 \quad \text{and} \quad \Pr(A|B_1) = .03.$$

The problem asks for the reversed conditional probability, $\Pr(B_1|A)$. By Bayes' theorem,

$$\Pr(B_1|A) = \frac{\Pr(B_1)\Pr(A|B_1)}{\Pr(B_1)\Pr(A|B_1) + \Pr(B_2)\Pr(A|B_2) + \cdots + \Pr(B_7)\Pr(A|B_7)}$$

$$= \frac{(.10)(.03)}{(.10)(.03) + (.05)(.03) + (.20)(.02) + (.15)(.02) + (.25)(.01) + (.15)(.02) + (.10)(.03)}$$

$$= \frac{.003}{.02} = .15.$$

Now Try Exercise 1

Derivation of Bayes' Theorem

To derive Bayes' theorem in general, we consider a two-stage tree. Suppose that at the first stage there are the events $B_1, B_2, \ldots, B_n$, which are mutually exclusive and exhaust all possibilities. Let us examine only the paths of the tree leading to event A at the second stage of the experiment (see Fig. 3). Suppose we are given that the event A occurs. What is $\Pr(B_1|A)$? First, consider $\Pr(B_1 \cap A)$. This can be seen from Fig. 3 to be $\Pr(B_1) \cdot \Pr(A|B_1)$. Next we calculate $\Pr(A)$. Recall that A occurs at stage 2, preceded at stage 1 by either event $B_1, B_2, \ldots,$ or B_n. Since $B_1, B_2, \ldots, B_n$ are mutually exclusive,

$$\Pr(A) = \Pr(B_1 \cap A) + \Pr(B_2 \cap A) + \cdots + \Pr(B_n \cap A).$$

Each of the elements in the sum can be calculated by the product rule, or directly from Fig. 3:

$$\Pr(B_1 \cap A) = \Pr(B_1) \cdot \Pr(A|B_1)$$
$$\Pr(B_2 \cap A) = \Pr(B_2) \cdot \Pr(A|B_2)$$
$$\vdots$$
$$\Pr(B_n \cap A) = \Pr(B_n) \cdot \Pr(A|B_n).$$

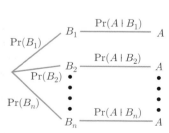

Figure 3

The result is the following:

> **Bayes' Theorem**   If $B_1, B_2, \ldots, B_n$ are mutually exclusive events, and if $B_1 \cup B_2 \cup \cdots \cup B_n = S$, then for any event A in S,
>
> $$\Pr(B_1|A) = \frac{\Pr(B_1)\cdot\Pr(A|B_1)}{\Pr(B_1)\cdot\Pr(A|B_1) + \Pr(B_2)\cdot\Pr(A|B_2) + \cdots + \Pr(B_n)\cdot\Pr(A|B_n)}$$
>
> $$\Pr(B_2|A) = \frac{\Pr(B_2)\cdot\Pr(A|B_2)}{\Pr(B_1)\cdot\Pr(A|B_1) + \Pr(B_2)\cdot\Pr(A|B_2) + \cdots + \Pr(B_n)\cdot\Pr(A|B_n)},$$
>
> and so forth.

Practice Problems 6.7

Quality Control *Refer to Example 2. Suppose that a book is selected at random and found to have a defective binding.*

1. What is the probability that the book was bound by machine 2?

2. By what machine is the book most likely to have been bound?

EXERCISES 6.7

1. **Accident Rates** An automobile insurance company has determined the accident rate (probability of having at least one accident during a year) for various age groups (see Table 2). Suppose that a policyholder calls in to report an accident. What is the probability that he or she is over 60?

TABLE 2

Age group	Proportion of total insured	Accident rate
Under 21	.05	.06
21–30	.10	.04
31–40	.25	.02
41–50	.20	.015
51–60	.30	.025
Over 60	.10	.04

2. **Quality Control** An electronic device has six different types of transistors. For each type of transistor, Table 3 gives the proportion of the total number of transistors of that type and the failure rate (probability of failing within one year). If a transistor fails, what is the probability that it is type 1?

TABLE 3

Type	Proportion of total	Failure rate
1	.30	.0002
2	.25	.0004
3	.20	.0005
4	.10	.001
5	.05	.002
6	.10	.004

3. **Student Performance** The enrollment in a certain course is 10% first-year students, 30% sophomores, 40% juniors, and 20% seniors. Past experience has shown that the likelihood of receiving an A in the course is .2 for first-year students, .4 for sophomores, .3 for juniors, and .1 for seniors. Find the probability that a student who receives an A is a sophomore.

4. **Larceny Rates** A metropolitan police department maintains statistics of larcenies reported in the various precincts of the city. It records the proportion of the city population in each precinct and the precinct larceny rate (= the proportion of the precinct population reporting a larceny within the past year). These statistics are summarized in Table 4. A larceny victim is randomly chosen from the city population. What is

the probability he or she comes from Precinct 3?

TABLE 4

Precinct	Proportion of population	Larceny rate
1	.20	.01
2	.10	.02
3	.40	.05
4	.30	.04

5. **Cars and Income** Table 5 gives the distribution of incomes and shows the proportion of two-car families by income level for a certain suburban county. Suppose that a randomly chosen family has two or more cars. What is the probability that its income is at least $75,000 per year?

TABLE 5

Annual family income	Proportion of people	Proportion having two or more cars
< $30,000	.10	.2
$30,000–$44,999	.20	.5
$45,000–$59,999	.35	.6
$60,000–$74,999	.30	.75
≥ $75,000	.05	.9

6. **Voter Turnout** Table 6 gives the distribution of voter registration and voter turnouts for a certain city. A randomly chosen person is questioned at the polls. What is the probability that the person is an Independent?

TABLE 6

	Proportion registered	Proportion turnout
Democrat	.50	.4
Republican	.20	.5
Independent	.30	.7

7. **Mathematics Exam** In a calculus course, the instructor gave an algebra exam on the first day of class to help students determine whether or not they had enrolled in the appropriate course. Eighty percent of the students in the class passed the exam. Forty percent of those who passed the exam on the first day of class earned an A in the course, whereas only twenty percent of those who failed the exam earned an A in the course. What is the probability that a student selected at random passed the exam on the first day of class, given that he or she earned an A in the course?

8. **Demographics** Table 7 shows the percentages of various portions of the U.S. population in 2008 based on age and gender. Suppose that a person is chosen at random from the entire population.

TABLE 7

	U.S. Population		
Age Group	% of population	% male
Under 5 yrs	7	51
5–19 yrs	21	51
20–44 yrs	35	51
45–64 yrs	25	49
Over 64 yrs	12	42

(a) What is the probability that the person chosen is male?

(b) Given that the person chosen is male, find the probability that he is between 5 and 19 years old.

9. **Bilingual Employees** A multinational company has five divisions: A, B, C, D, and E. The percentage of employees from each division who speak at least two languages fluently is shown in Table 8.

TABLE 8

Division	Number of employees	Percentage of employees who are bilingual
A	20,000	20
B	15,000	15
C	25,000	12
D	30,000	10
E	10,000	10
Total	100,000	

(a) Find the probability that an employee selected at random is bilingual.

(b) Find the probability that a bilingual employee selected at random works for division C.

10. **Customized Dice** A specially made pair of dice has only one- and two-spots on the faces. One of the dice has three faces with a one-spot and three faces with a two-spot. The other die has two faces with a one-spot and four faces with a two-spot. One of the dice is selected at random and then rolled six times. If a two-spot shows up only once, what is the probability that it is the die with four two-spots?

Exercises 11–15 refer to diagnostic tests. A false negative in a diagnostic test is a test result that is negative even though the patient has the condition. A false positive, on the other hand, is a test result that is positive although the patient does not have the condition.

11. **Mammogram Accuracy** The *New York Times* of January 24, 1997, discusses the recommendation of a special panel concerning mammograms for women in their 40s. About 2% of women aged 40 to 49 years old develop

breast cancer in their 40s. But the mammogram used for women in that age group has a high rate of false positives and false negatives; the false positive rate is .30, and the false negative rate is .25. If a woman in her 40s has a positive mammogram, what is the probability that she actually has breast cancer?

12. **Drug Testing** A drug-testing laboratory produces false negative results 2% of the time and false positive results 5% of the time. Suppose that the laboratory has been hired by a company in which 10% of the employees use drugs.

(a) If an employee tests positive for drug use, what is the probability that he or she actually uses drugs?

(b) What is the probability that a nondrug user will test positive for drug use twice in a row?

(c) What is the probability that someone who tests positive twice in a row is not a drug user?

13. **Pregnancy Test** An over-the-counter pregnancy test claims to be 99% accurate. Actually, what the insert says is that if the test is performed properly, it is 99% sure to detect a pregnancy.

(a) What is the probability of a false negative?

(b) Let us assume that the probability is 98% that the test result is negative for a woman who is not pregnant. If the woman estimates that her chances of being pregnant are about 40% and the test result is positive, what is the probability that she is actually pregnant?

14. **Medical Testing** A test for a condition has a high probability of false positives, 20%. Its rate of false negatives is 10%. The condition is estimated to exist in 65% of all patients sent for screening. If the test is positive, what is the chance the patient has the condition? Suppose that the condition is much more rare in the population—say Pr(condition) = .30. Given the same testing situation, what is Pr(condition|pos)?

15. **Steroid Testing** It is estimated that 10% of Olympic athletes use steroids. The test currently being used to detect steroids is said to be 93% effective in correctly detecting steroids in users. It yields false positives in only 2% of the tests. A country's best weightlifter tests positive. What is the probability that he actually takes steroids?

16. **Cookie Jars** There are two cookie jars on the shelf in the kitchen. The red one has 10 chocolate-chip cookies

and 15 gingersnaps. The blue jar has 20 chocolate-chip cookies and 10 gingersnaps. James goes down in the middle of the night and without turning on the light chooses a jar at random and then chooses a cookie at random. If the cookie is chocolate chip, what is the probability that he got the cookie from the blue jar?

17. **Cards** Thirteen cards are dealt from a deck of 52 cards.

(a) What is the probability that the ace of spades is one of the 13 cards?

(b) Suppose one of the 13 cards is chosen at random and found *not* to be the ace of spades. What is the probability that *none* of the 13 cards is the ace of spades?

(c) Suppose the experiment in part (b) is repeated a total of 10 times (replacing the card looked at each time), and the ace of spades is not seen. What is the probability that the ace of spades actually *is* one of the 13 cards?

18. **College Majors** There are three sections of English 101. In Section I there are 25 students, of whom 5 are mathematics majors. In Section II there are 20 students, of whom 6 are mathematics majors. In Section III there are 35 students, of whom 5 are mathematics majors. A student in English 101 is chosen at random. Find the probability that the student is from Section I, given that he or she is a mathematics major.

19. **Scholarship Winners** Twenty percent of the contestants in a scholarship competition come from Pylesville High School, 40% come from Millerville High School, and the remainder come from Lakeside High School. Two percent of the Pylesville students are among the scholarship winners; 3% of the Millerville contestants and 5% of the Lakeside contestants win.

(a) If a winner is chosen at random, what is the probability that he or she is from Lakeside?

(b) What percentage of the winners are from Pylesville?

20. **Manufacturing Reliability** Ten percent of the pens made by Apex are defective. Only 5% of the pens made by its competitor, B-ink, are defective. Since Apex pens are cheaper than B-ink pens, an office orders 70% of its stock from Apex and 30% from B-ink. A pen is chosen at random and found to be defective. What is the probability that it was produced by Apex?

Solutions to Practice Problems 6.7

1. The problem asks for $\Pr(B_2|A)$. Bayes' theorem gives this probability as a quotient with numerator $\Pr(B_2)\Pr(A|B_2)$ and the same denominator as in the solution to Example 2. Therefore,

$$\Pr(B_2|A) = \frac{\Pr(B_2)\Pr(A|B_2)}{.02} = \frac{(.05)(.03)}{.02} = .075.$$

2. To solve this problem we must compute the seven conditional probabilities

$$\Pr(B_1|A), \quad \Pr(B_2|A), \quad \ldots, \quad \Pr(B_7|A)$$

and see which one is the largest. The first two have already been computed. Using the method of the preceding problem we find that

$$\Pr(B_3|A) = .20, \quad \Pr(B_4|A) = .15, \quad \Pr(B_5|A) = .125,$$
$$\Pr(B_6|A) = .15, \quad \text{and} \quad \Pr(B_7|A) = .15.$$

Therefore, the book was most likely bound by machine 3.

6.8 Simulation

Simulation is a method of imitating an experiment by using an artificial device to substitute for the real thing. The technique is used often in industrial and scientific applications. For example, in the 1970s Deaconess Hospital in St. Louis was planning to add an extension to the hospital with 144 medical-surgical beds. The planners knew that an increase in the number of beds would require additional operating rooms and recovery room beds. By studying the pattern of patients already being treated in the existing hospital, Homer H. Schmitz and N. K. Kwak[1] constructed a mathematical model to imitate the rate of flow of patients through the planned hospital (with the additional beds) to see what the typical operating suite schedule would look like. But they did not use patients! They used random numbers and a computer in their simulation model. They built a model in which they could vary the number of operating rooms and adjust the schedule. By repeating the experiment many times, they found the optimal number of new operating rooms and recovery room beds to complement the added beds.

Calculators have a command, usually called **rand** or **randInt**, that can be used to select a number at random from a specified set of numbers. Each number in the set is just as likely to be selected as any other. Although random number tables are generally available and many of the techniques discussed here can be used with such tables, we recommend using a graphing calculator or a computer if at all possible when doing simulations. On the TI-83/84 Plus, the command **randInt(1,n)** generates a random integer from 1 through n, and **randInt(1,n,r)** generates a list of r random numbers. (The command **randInt** is the fifth item on the MATH/PRB menu.) On the TI-89, the command **rand(n)** generates a random integer from 1 through n, and **seq(rand(n),x,1,r)** generates a list of r random numbers. (The command **rand** is the fourth item on the MATH/Probability menu and the command **seq** is the first element on the MATH/List menu.) On either calculator, after the list of random numbers has been assigned to a list variable, the command **SortA($list$)** on the TI-83/84 Plus or **SortA $list$** on the TI-89 sorts the list in ascending order. (**SortA** is found on the LIST/OPS menu of the TI-83/84 Plus, and on the MATH/List menu of the TI-89.) Some examples of the use of these commands follows:

---

[1] Homer H. Schmitz and N. K. Kwak, "Monte Carlo simulation of operating-room and recovery-room usage," *Operations Research* **20**, 1972, pp. 1171–1180.

1. *Simulate the roll of a single die*:

       randInt(1,6)   TI-83/84 Plus
       rand(6)   TI-89

2. *Simulate the sum for a roll of a pair of dice*:

       randInt(1,6) + randInt(1,6)   TI-83/84 Plus
       rand(6) + rand(6)   TI-89

3. *Simulate ten rolls of a pair of dice*:

       randInt(1,6,10) + randInt(1,6,10)   TI-83/84 Plus
       seq(rand(6) + rand(6),x,1,10)   TI-89

4. *Simulate the selection of a ball from an urn containing 7 white balls and 3 red balls*: Think of the white balls as numbered from 1 to 7 and the red balls as numbered from 8 to 10.

       randInt(1,10)   TI-83/84 Plus
       rand(10)   TI-89

5. *Simulate the outcome of a free throw by Michael Jordan, who had an 83% free-throw average*: Consider each shot as a random whole number from 1 to 100, where a number from 1 to 83 represents a successful free throw and a number from 84 to 100 represents a miss.

       randInt(1,100)   TI-83/84 Plus
       rand(100)   TI-89

On an Excel spreadsheet, the formula =**RAND**() produces a randomly selected number from 0 to 1, excluding 1. The formula =**RANDBETWEEN**(m,n) produces a randomly selected whole number from m to n. The Random Number Generation routine that is part of the Data Analysis tool generates a random sample from a probability distribution. (See Appendix C for details.) *Note*: The RAND-BETWEEN function is only available if the Analysis ToolPak has been installed.

EXAMPLE 1

INCORPORATING TECHNOLOGY

Heads and tails Simulate 7 tosses of a fair coin. Then count the number of heads and tails.

Solution (*Graphing Calculator*) We will generate and sort seven numbers that are each either 1 or 2. The number 1 will be interpreted as a Heads and the number 2 will be interpreted as a Tails. See Figures 1 and 2. This simulation of 7 coins tosses yields 4 Heads and 3 Tails on the TI-83/84 Plus, and 5 Heads and 2 Tails on the TI-89.

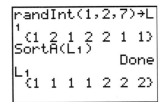

Figure 1

Figure 2

(*Electronic Spreadsheet*) In Fig. 3 on the next page, each cell in the range A1:G1 was generated with the equation =**RANDBETWEEN**(1,2). If we interpret **1** as a Heads and **2** as a Tails, then 3 Heads (and therefore 4 Tails) were produced. The COUNTIF function counts the number of ones appearing in the range of cells. ∎

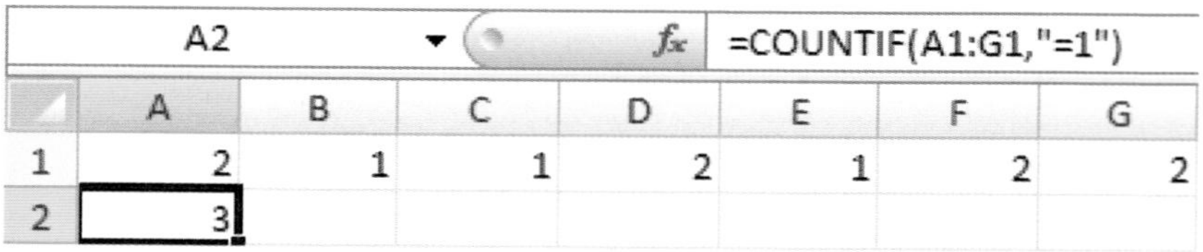

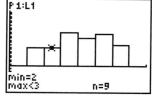

A2		▼	⊙	*fₓ*	=COUNTIF(A1:G1,"=1")	
	A	B	C	D	E	F	G
1	2	1	1	2	1	2	2
2	3						

Figure 3. Example 1 solved with a spreadsheet.

EXAMPLE 2

INCORPORATING TECHNOLOGY

Seventy-two rolls of a die Simulate 72 rolls of a fair die, and tabulate the results. Compare your results with the theoretical probabilities.

Solution (*Graphing Calculator*) Generate the 72 random whole numbers from 1 to 6 and store them in **L₁**. On the TI-83/84 Plus, you may tally the results by setting the STATPLOT as shown in Fig. 4 and setting the WINDOW to $[0, 8]$ *by* $[-10, 30]$ to allow the maximum frequency to show in the bar graph. Such a result is shown in Fig. 5. The GRAPH key will sketch a special type of bar graph indicating the number of tosses resulting in each of the possible outcomes, 1, 2, 3, 4, 5, and 6. Use the TRACE command and the cursor to determine the number of items in each of the bars. In Fig. 5, for example, we can read from the graph that there are $n = 9$ rolls that are greater than or equal to 2 and less than 3 (for a die, this means exactly 2). Figure 6 shows a similar simulation on a TI-89.

Figure 4

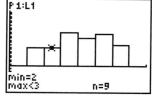

Figure 5

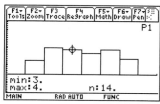

Figure 6

Since the probability of each outcome is $\frac{1}{6}$ and the number of tosses is 72, we would expect that each of the outcomes would occur $(\frac{1}{6})(72) = 12$ times. Observations of the graph or a survey of the generated list will give us the actual number of occurrences in each simulation of 72 tosses.

Now Try Exercise 1

(*Electronic Spreadsheet*) In Fig. 7, each cell in column B has the content **=1/6**. The Random Number Generation routine from the Data Analysis tool used the probability distribution in A1:B6 to generate the random sample in D1:L8. Then the Histogram routine from the Analysis ToolPak used the random sample and the numbers in column A to create the frequency distribution table in N1:O7. (See Appendix C for details.) ∎

EXAMPLE 3

INCORPORATING TECHNOLOGY

Simulation of recovery room Patients having surgery fall into three categories. Sixty percent of them require two hours in the recovery room, 30% require one hour in the recovery room, and the remainder require a half-hour. Simulate the number of hours of recovery room time required by 25 patients.

Solution (*Graphing Calculator*) One technique is to generate 25 random whole numbers from 1 to 10. Numbers 1 to 6 represent a patient who requires two hours in the recovery room, numbers 7 to 9 represent a patient who requires one hour in the recovery room, and the number 10 represents a patient needing a half-hour in the recovery room. After the 25 random numbers are generated, they can be sorted

	A	B	C	D	E	F	G	H	I	J	K	L	M	N	O
1	1	0.166667		5	5	6	4	3	1	3	3	4		Bin	Frequency
2	2	0.166667		3	2	3	1	1	3	5	1	5		1	13
3	3	0.166667		1	4	4	6	3	4	5	4	4		2	9
4	4	0.166667		3	6	6	3	3	6	1	3	4		3	21
5	5	0.166667		3	4	2	2	2	3	5	3	2		4	13
6	6	0.166667		3	5	4	5	3	3	1	3	3		5	9
7	Prob. Dist.			6	4	2	2	5	4	3	4	1		6	7
8				1	1	1	6	3	1	2	1	2			

Figure 7. Example 2 solved with a spreadsheet.

and then displayed. The right-arrow key can be used to scroll along the list so that we can count all those random entries from 1 to 6, those from 7 to 9, and the 10s. Here is one possible outcome:

$$1, 1, 2, 2, 2, 4, 4, 4, 4, 5, 5, 5, 5, 5, 6, \quad 7, 7, 8, 8, 8, 9, \quad 10, 10, 10, 10,$$

giving 15 patients who require two hours, 6 patients who require one hour, and 4 patients who require a half-hour of recovery time. The total amount of time in the recovery room needed by these patients is $15(2) + 6(1) + 4(\frac{1}{2}) = 38$ hours.

(*Electronic Spreadsheet*) In Fig. 8, the Random Number Generation routine from the Data Analysis tool used the probability distribution in A1:B3 to generate the random sample in D1:H5. Then, the Histogram routine from the Analysis ToolPak used the random sample and the numbers in column A to create the frequency distribution table in J1:K4. The total amount of time in the recovery room needed by these patients is $3(\frac{1}{2}) + 4(1) + 18(2) = 41.5$ hours. ∎

Now Try Exercise 5

	A	B	C	D	E	F	G	H	I	J	K
1	1/2	0.1		1	2	2	2	2		Bin	Frequency
2	1	0.3		2	0.5	2	1	2		1/2	3
3	2	0.6		2	2	2	2	1		1	4
4	Prob. Dist.			2	2	1	0.5	2		2	18
5				2	0.5	2	2	2			

Figure 8. Example 3 solved with a spreadsheet.

EXAMPLE 4

Simulation of a queue Customers steadily arrive at a bank during the hour from 9 A.M. to 10 A.M. so that the line of customers is never empty. There are three tellers, and each customer requires a varying amount of time with a teller. For simplicity, we assume that 40% of the customers need 3 minutes, 50% need 5 minutes, and 10% need 8 minutes. Each customer enters the queue at the end and goes to the first available teller when reaching the front of the queue. Simulate the service process.

(a) Show how many of the first 20 customers each of the tellers is able to service on a random day and in that hour.

(b) If all 20 customers were at the bank when it opened at 9 A.M., what was the average time spent at the bank once it opened?

INCORPORATING TECHNOLOGY

Solution **(a)** (*Graphing Calculator*) We generate 20 random whole numbers from 1 to 10. We consider numbers 1 to 4 as representing customers requiring 3 minutes, numbers 5 to 9 as customers requiring 5 minutes, and 10 as customers needing 8 minutes. We do not sort them, because we want to preserve the randomness of their arrival. Here is a typical list:

Cust. #:	1, 2, 3, 4, 5, 6, 7, 8, 9, 10, 11, 12, 13, 14, 15, 16, 17, 18, 19, 20
Random #:	10, 7, 2, 3, 1, 6, 4, 3, 1, 10, 6, 5, 2, 3, 7, 7, 10, 10, 5, 5.

To determine the schedule, let the tellers be A, B, and C. Then the first customer goes to teller A. Since her random number is 10, she requires 8 minutes, occupying teller A until 9:08. Meanwhile, the second customer, with random number 7, goes to teller B, where he needs 5 minutes. He occupies teller B until 9:05. Then customer #3, with random number 2, goes to teller C until 9:03. Since teller C finishes first, customer #4 steps up to C at 9:03. That customer (with random number 3) requires 3 minutes and leaves teller C at 9:06. In case two tellers are free at the same moment, let us use the convention that the tellers are chosen in alphabetical order, with A first. From Table 1, we see that teller A served 6 of the first 20 customers, teller B served 6, and C served 8 customers. They completed the first 20 transactions at 9:34 A.M.

(*Electronic Spreadsheet*) In Fig. 9, the Random Number Generation routine from the Data Analysis tool could have used the probability distribution in A1:B3 to generate the random sample in E1:X2, the same sequence of random numbers presented in the third column of Table 1. Table 1 can be used as before (with the second column removed) to obtain the same answer.

	A	B	C	D	E	F	G	H	I	J	K	L	M	N	O	P	Q	R	S	T	U	V	W	X
1	3	0.4		Cust. #:	1	2	3	4	5	6	7	8	9	10	11	12	13	14	15	16	17	18	19	20
2	5	0.5		Random #:	8	5	3	3	3	5	3	3	3	8	5	5	3	3	5	5	8	8	5	5
3	8	0.1																						
4	**Prob. Dist.**																							

Figure 9.   The random sample in Example 4(a) generated with a spreadsheet.

(b) We can find the average amount of time spent after the bank opened by totaling the time spent by all customers (use the number of minutes after 9 A.M. in the "End time" column) and dividing by 20, the number of customers. This gives $(8+5+3+6+8+11+11+11+14+19+16+19+19+22+24+24+30+32+29+34)/20 = 17.25$ minutes. Thus, on the average, a person who was at the bank at 9 A.M. required 17.25 minutes after the bank opened to be served and to complete his transaction. ∎

Now Try Exercise 7

The simulation should be repeated many times to determine the typical outcome. So you might simulate 50 days from 9 A.M. to 10 A.M. to see how long it takes to service the first 20 customers and, on the average, how long a customer spends in the bank if he or she is one of the first 20 people there when the bank opens. It might be useful to see the effect of using four tellers or see what happens when the probabilities of the service times are defined differently.

In practice, the arrival times of the customers are also random and can be built into the simulation. A time-and-motion study would be used to determine the appropriate probabilistic model of the arrival process.

TABLE 1

Customer #	Random #	Time req.	Teller	Start time	End time
1	10	8	A	9:00	9:08
2	7	5	B	9:00	9:05
3	2	3	C	9:00	9:03
4	3	3	C	9:03	9:06
5	1	3	B	9:05	9:08
6	6	5	C	9:06	9:11
7	4	3	A	9:08	9:11
8	3	3	B	9:08	9:11
9	1	3	A	9:11	9:14
10	10	8	B	9:11	9:19
11	6	5	C	9:11	9:16
12	5	5	A	9:14	9:19
13	2	3	C	9:16	9:19
14	3	3	A	9:19	9:22
15	7	5	B	9:19	9:24
16	7	5	C	9:19	9:24
17	10	8	A	9:22	9:30
18	10	8	B	9:24	9:32
19	5	5	C	9:24	9:29
20	5	5	C	9:29	9:34

EXERCISES 6.8

1. **Rolling a Die** Simulate 36 rolls of a fair die. Give the relative frequency and the corresponding theoretical probability of each of the outcomes and compare them.

2. **Rolling Dice** Simulate 96 rolls of a pair of dice where the sum is observed. Give the relative frequency and the corresponding theoretical probability of each of the outcomes. Make a table showing your results. Repeat the experiment 6 times and consider the total as if 576 rolls were simulated. [*Note*: $(6)(96) = 576$.]

3. **Free-Throws** Simulate 10 free-throws for Kobe Bryant, whose free throw average in 2008 was 81%. How many of the shots were successful?

4. **Baseball** A baseball player is a .331 hitter. Simulate 10 at-bats for this player and tell how many hits he gets. (Being a .331 hitter means that 33.1% of his at-bats result in a hit.)

5. **Test Taking** A student who has not studied for a 10-question multiple-choice test, with 4 choices among the answers (a, b, c, d) for each question, decides to simulate such a test and answer the questions according to a simulation in which each choice of answer has the same probability. Use a calculator to generate a simulated answer sheet. Assume the correct answers are a, b, b, c, d, d, a, c, b, a. What is the student's score?

6. **Balls in an Urn** In sampling 4 balls at random from an urn containing 30 balls, *without replacement* after each draw, we consider the balls as numbered 1 to 30. In selecting random whole numbers from 1 to 30, we ignore any number that has already been selected and continue the selection until we obtain a sample of size 4. Assume there are 20 red balls and 10 green balls in the urn. Draw 10 samples of size 4 and tabulate the number of red balls in each sample. Compare your results with the theoretical probability.

7. **Registration Queue** Students are queued up at the registrar's office when the registration windows open at 8 A.M. There are four open windows; students approach the first open window as they advance to the front of the queue. Assume that 10% of the students require 5 minutes of service time, 30% of the students require 7 minutes of service time, 40% require 10 minutes, and 20% require 15 minutes. Simulate the service of the first 20 students in a random queue. Show the schedule of service at the four windows (A, B, C, D), determine how long it takes to process these students, and give the average time from 8 A.M. to leaving the service window.

8. **Bank Queue** Simulate the bank queue of Example 4 using four tellers. Give the time needed to process the

first 20 customers and the average time spent by each customer in the bank after 9 A.M.

9. **Gas Queue** A gas station with four self-serve pumps has determined that 80% of all customers completely fill their gas tanks and the remaining 20% fill their tank with a fixed dollar amount's worth of fuel. Suppose that it takes an average of 5 minutes for a complete fill-up and 3 minutes for a partial fill-up. Suppose also

that from 5 PM until 6 PM customers arrive steadily so that there is always a line and that the next customer in line proceeds to the next available pump. Simulate this process for 30 customers.

10. **Rolling Three Dice** Simulate 108 rolls of three dice, and show the frequency of each possible sum of the faces: $3, 4, \ldots, 18$.

CHAPTER SUMMARY

1. The *sample space* of an experiment is the set of all possible outcomes of the experiment. Each subset of the sample space is called an *event*. We say that an event *occurs* when the outcome is an element of the event.

2. The event $E \cup F$ occurs when either E or F (or both) occurs. The event $E \cap F$ occurs when both E and F occur. The event E' occurs when E does not occur.

3. Two events are *mutually exclusive* if they cannot both occur at the same time.

4. A *probability distribution* for a finite sample space associates a probability with each outcome of the sample space. Each probability is a number between 0 and 1, and the sum of the probabilities is 1. The probability of an event is the sum of the probabilities of the outcomes in the event.

5. The inclusion-exclusion principle states that the probability of the union of two events is the sum of the probabilities of the events minus the probability of their intersection. If the two events are mutually exclusive, the probability of the union is just the sum of the probabilities of the events.

6. We say that the *odds* in favor of an event are a to b if the probability of the event is $a/(a + b)$. Intuitively, the event is expected to occur a times for every b times it does not occur.

7. For a sample space with a finite number of equally likely outcomes, the probability of an event is the number of elements in the event divided by the number of elements in the sample space.

8. The probability of the complement of an event is 1 minus the probability of the event.

9. $\Pr(E|F)$, the conditional probability that E occurs given that F occurs, is computed as $\Pr(E \cap F)/\Pr(F)$. For a sample space with a finite number of equally likely outcomes, it can be computed as $n(E \cap F)/n(F)$.

10. The product rule states that if $\Pr(F) \neq 0$, then $\Pr(E \cap F) = \Pr(F) \cdot \Pr(E|F)$.

11. E and F are *independent* events if $\Pr(E \cap F) = \Pr(E) \cdot \Pr(F)$. Equivalently, E and F [with $\Pr(F) \neq 0$] are independent events if $\Pr(E|F) = \Pr(E)$.

12. A collection of events is said to be *independent* if for each collection of events chosen from them, the probability that all the events occur equals the product of the probabilities that each occurs.

13. Tree diagrams provide a useful device for determining probabilities of combined outcomes in a sequence of experiments.

14. Bayes' theorem states that if $B_1, B_2, \ldots, B_n$ are mutually exclusive events whose union is the entire sample space and A is an event, then for each event B_i,

$$\Pr(B_i|A) = \frac{\Pr(B_i)\Pr(A|B_i)}{\Pr(B_1)\Pr(A|B_1) + \cdots + \Pr(B_n)\Pr(A|B_n)}.$$

15. The ability to generate random numbers allows us to simulate the outcomes of experiments.

REVIEW OF FUNDAMENTAL CONCEPTS

1. Describe how to form a sample space for an experiment.

2. Using the language of sets and assuming that A and B are events in a sample space S, write the following events in set notation: $(A$ or $B)$; $(A$ and $B)$; not A.

3. In a sample space, what is the probability of the empty set?

4. What subset in a sample space corresponds to the certain event?

5. Draw Venn diagrams for the events $(A$ or $B)$, $(A$ and $B)$, (not A).

6. Write a formula for the probability of the event $A \cup B$ assuming that you know $\Pr(A)$, $\Pr(B)$, and $\Pr(A \cap B)$.

7. Explain the difference between mutually exclusive events and independent events.

8. State the addition principle.

9. Suppose the probability of an event is k/n. What are

the odds that the event will occur?

10. Suppose the odds that an event occurs are a to b. What is the probability that the event will occur?

11. State the inclusion–exclusion principle for two events.

12. What is the definition of $\Pr(E|F)$?

13. What is Bayes' Theorem?

14. What is a tree diagram?

KEY FORMULAS

Addition Principle:

$$\Pr(E) = \Pr(s) + \Pr(t) + \Pr(u) + \cdots + \Pr(z),$$

where the event E consists of the finite number of outcomes $s, t, u, \ldots, z$

Inclusion–Exclusion Principle:

$$\Pr(E \cup F) = \Pr(E) + \Pr(F) - \Pr(E \cap F)$$

Mutually Exclusive Events: $\Pr(E \cup F) = \Pr(E) + \Pr(F)$, when E and F are mutually exclusive.

Converting Odds to a Probability: If the odds in favor of an event E are a to b, then $\Pr(E) = \dfrac{a}{a+b}$.

Conditional Probability for Equally Likely Outcomes:

$$\Pr(E|F) = \frac{n(E \cap F)}{n(F)}$$

Product Rule: If $\Pr(F) \neq 0$, then $\Pr(E \cap F) = \Pr(F) \cdot \Pr(E|F)$.

Independent Events: If E and F are independent events with nonzero probabilities, then $\Pr(E|F) = \Pr(E)$ and $\Pr(F|E) = \Pr(F)$.

Bayes' Theorem: If $B_1, B_2, \ldots, B_n$ are mutually exclusive events, and if $B_1 \cup B_2 \cup \cdots \cup B_n = S$, then for any event A in S,

$$\Pr(B_k|A) = \frac{\Pr(B_k) \cdot \Pr(A|B_k)}{\Pr(B_1) \cdot \Pr(A|B_1) + \cdots + \Pr(B_n) \cdot \Pr(A|B_n)}$$

for $k = 1, 2, \ldots, n$.

SUPPLEMENTARY EXERCISES

1. **Coin Tosses** A coin is to be tossed five times. What is the probability of obtaining at least one head?

2. **Coin Tosses** Suppose that we toss a coin three times and observe the sequence of heads and tails. Let E be the event that "the first toss lands heads" and F the event that "there are more heads than tails." Are E and F independent?

3. **Prizes** Each box of a certain brand of candy contains either a toy airplane or a toy gun. If one-third of the boxes contain an airplane and two-thirds contain a gun, what is the probability that a person who buys two boxes of candy will receive both an airplane and a gun?

4. **Committee Selection** A committee consists of five men and five women. If three people are selected at random from the committee, what is the probability that they all will be men?

5. **Public and Private Colleges** Out of the 50 colleges in a certain state, 25 are private, 15 offer engineering majors, and 5 are private colleges offering engineering majors. If a college is selected at random, what is the conditional probability that it offers an engineering major given that it is a public college?

6. **Tax Audits** An auditing procedure for income tax returns has the following characteristics: If the return is incorrect, the probability is 90% that it will be rejected; if the return is correct, the probability is 95% that it will be accepted. Suppose that 80% of all income tax returns are correct. If a return is audited and rejected, what is the probability that the return was actually correct?

7. **Numbers** A number is chosen at random from the numbers 1 to 100. What is the probability that the number is divisible by 5?

8. **Numbers** A number is chosen at random from the numbers 1 to 10,000. What is the probability that the number is divisible by 5?

9. **Numbers** A number is chosen at random from the numbers 1 to 10,000. What is the probability that the number is divisible by 3 or 5?

10. **Numbers** A number is chosen at random from the numbers 1 to 10,000. What is the probability that the number is divisible by 3 or 12?

11. **Seating Arrangements** Jack and Hugo attend a party at which there are two tables of 8 for dinner. If guests are assigned to seats at random, what is the probability that Jack and Hugo will be seated at the same table?

12. **Student Honors** Five students are to receive special honors at commencement. Of the five, two are engineering majors.

    (a) What is the probability that the two engineering majors will be called up as the first two students to receive their awards?

(b) What is the probability that the two engineering majors will be called up consecutively to receive their awards?

13. **Exam Questions** Prior to taking an essay examination, students are given 10 questions to prepare. Six of the 10 will appear on the exam. One student decides to prepare only eight of the questions. Assume that the questions are equally likely to be chosen by the professor.

(a) What is the probability that she has prepared every question appearing on the test?

(b) What is the probability that both questions she did not prepare appear on the test?

14. **Code Words** A collection of code words consists of all strings of seven characters, where each of the first three characters can be any letter or digit and each of the last four characters must be a digit. For example, 7A32765 is allowed but 7A3B765 is not.

(a) What is the probability that a code word chosen at random begins with ABC?

(b) What is the probability that a code word chosen at random ends with 6578?

(c) What is the probability that a code word chosen at random ends with a four-digit number divisible by 3?

(d) What is the probability that a code word chosen at random consists of three letters followed by four even digits?

15. **Archery** Two archers shoot at a moving target. One can hit the target with probability $\frac{1}{4}$ and the other with probability $\frac{1}{3}$. Assuming that their efforts are independent events, what is the probability that

(a) Both will hit the target?

(b) At least one will hit the target?

16. If the odds in favor of an event are 7 to 5, what is the probability that the event will occur?

17. **Olympic Swimmers** In an Olympic swimming event, two of the seven contestants are American. The contestants are randomly assigned to lanes 1 through 7. What is the probability that the Americans are assigned to the first two lanes?

18. **Balls in an Urn** An urn contains three balls numbered 1, 2, and 3. Balls are drawn one at a time without replacement until the sum of the numbers drawn is four or more. Find the probability of stopping after exactly two balls are drawn.

19. **Dice** A red die and a green die are rolled as a pair. Let E be the event that "the red die shows a 2" and let F be the event that "the sum of the numbers is 8." Are the events E and F independent?

20. Let E and F be events with $Pr(E) = .4$, $Pr(F) = .3$, and $Pr(E \cup F) = .5$. Find $Pr(E|F)$.

21. **Weighing Produce** A supermarket has three employees who package and weigh produce. Employee A records the correct weight 98% of the time. Employees B and C record the correct weight 97% and 95% of the time, respectively. Employees A, B, and C handle 40%, 40%, and 20% of the packaging, respectively. A customer complains about the incorrect weight recorded on a package he has purchased. What is the probability that the package was weighed by employee C?

22. **Days of Week** Three people are chosen at random. What is the probability that at least two of them were born on the same day of the week?

23. Let B and A be independent events for which the probability that at least one of them occurs is $\frac{1}{2}$ and the probability that B occurs but A does not occur is $\frac{1}{3}$. Find $Pr(A)$.

24. **Balls in an Urn** An urn contains 10 balls numbered 1 through 10. Seven balls are drawn one at a time at random without replacement. Find the probability that exactly three odd-numbered balls are drawn and they occur on odd-numbered draws from the urn.

25. **Bills in Envelopes** Each of three sealed opaque envelopes contains two bills. One envelope contains two \$1 bills, another contains two \$5 bills, and the third contains a \$1 bill and a \$5 bill. An envelope is selected at random and a bill is taken from the envelope at random. If it is a \$5 bill, what is the probability that the other bill in the envelope is also a \$5 bill?

26. **Carnival Game** A carnival huckster has placed a coin under one of three cups and asks you to guess which cup contains the coin. After you select a cup, he removes one of the unselected cups, which he guarantees does not contain the coin. You may now either stay with your original choice or switch to the other remaining cup. What decision will give you the greater probability of winning?

27. **Commuting Time** The odds of an American worker living within 20 minutes of work are 13 to 12. What is the probability that a worker selected at random lives within 20 minutes of work?

28. **Demographics** Twenty-six percent of all Americans are under 18 years old. What are the odds that a person selected at random is under 18?

29. **Letters** If the nine letters A, C, D, E, I, N, O, T, and U are arranged to form a word, what is the probability that it will be one of the meaningful words EDUCATION, AUCTIONED, or CAUTIONED?

30. **Dragons** An island contains an equal number of one-headed, two-headed, and three-headed dragons. If a dragon head is picked at random, what is the likelihood of its belonging to a one-headed dragon?

31. **Coin Tosses** Two players each toss a coin three times. What is the probability that they get the same number of tails?

32. Dice Suppose that a pair of dice is rolled. Given that a double does not occur, what is the probability that one die shows a three?

33. Left-Handedness According to *Bottom Line Personal* of March 30, 1991, the chances of having a left-handed child are 4 in 10 if both parents are left-handed, 2 in 10 if one parent is left-handed, and only 1 in 10 if neither parent is left-handed. Suppose a left-handed child is chosen at random from a population in which 25% of the adults are left-handed. What is the probability that the child's parents are both left-handed?

34. Languages Of the 120 students in a class, 30 speak Chinese, 50 speak Spanish, 75 speak French, 12 speak Spanish and Chinese, 30 speak Spanish and French, and 15 speak Chinese and French. Seven students speak all three languages. A student is chosen at random. What is the probability that he speaks none of these languages?

35. What is the probability that a whole number between 100 and 400 contains the digit 2?

36. Committee Composition PE A committee is composed of w women and m men. If three women and two men are added to the committee, and if one person is selected at random from the enlarged committee, then the probability that a woman is selected can be represented by

(a) $\dfrac{w}{m}$ (b) $\dfrac{w}{w+m}$ (c) $\dfrac{w+3}{m+2}$

(d) $\dfrac{w+3}{w+m+3}$ (e) $\dfrac{w+3}{w+m+5}$

37. Political Poll PE Of a group of people surveyed in a political poll, 60% said they would vote for candidate R. Of those who said they would vote for R, 90% actually voted for R, and of those who did not say they would vote for R, 5% actually voted for R. What percent of the group voted for R?

(a) 56% (b) 59% (c) 62% (d) 65% (e) 74%

38. Coin Tosses When three coins are tossed, what is the probability of at least one tail appearing given that at least one head appeared?

39. Rolling a Die What is the probability of having each of the numbers one through six appear in six consecutive rolls of a die?

40. Balls in an Urn An urn contains 10 red balls and 20 green balls. If four balls are drawn one at a time without replacement, what is the probability that the sequence of colors will be red, green, green, red?

41. Drawing Cards A card is drawn at random from a deck of cards. Then the card is replaced and the deck is thoroughly shuffled. This process is repeated two more times.

(a) What is the probability that all three cards are aces?

(b) What is the probability that at least one of the cards is an ace?

42. March Madness Each March, sixty-four men's college basketball teams compete in the NCAA championship tournament. They are divided into four regions of sixteen teams each. The winners of each region advance to the Final Four. If a fan selects four teams at random, what are the odds against those teams being in the Final Four? *Note*: Of course, the fan will select only one team per region.

43. Matching Socks A drawer contains two red socks and two blue socks. If two socks are drawn randomly from the drawer, what is the probability that the two socks have the same color?

44. Physical Fitness Of 50 fitness buffs surveyed, 15 like bicycling, 20 like jogging, and 5 like bicycling and jogging. What is the probability that a fitness buff selected at random likes only one of the two sports?

45. Tossing Dice Find the odds in favor of getting four different numbers when tossing four dice.

46. Birthdays What is the probability that out of a group of 5 people, exactly two people have the same birthday? *Note*: Assume there are 365 days in a year.

In Exercises 47–49, use a graphing calculator or spreadsheet to calculate the probabilities.

47. Medical Screening A drug company wants to test a drug for a chronic disease. The company wants a sample of 500 people who have the disease. It tests 12,735 people for the disease, which generally affects 5% of the population. The test is known to have a 2% false positive rate and a 4% false negative rate. Six hundred and fifty people test positive for the disease. Based on the test results, how many of the total population actually can be expected to have the disease?

48. Rolling a Die Simulate an experiment in which either you roll a die until you get a 6 or you have rolled the die 15 times. Record the number of times you roll the die until the first 6. Find the relative frequency of each outcome in the set $\{1, 2, 3, \ldots, 15\}$. Perform the experiment at least 20 times.

49. Drawing Cards Simulate an experiment in which you draw 3 cards from a deck of 52 cards, with replacement after each draw. Determine the number of spades in the sample and repeat the experiment 20 times. Find the relative frequency of at least 2 spades in a sample of size 3. What is the theoretical probability of at least 2 spades in a sample of size 3?

Conceptual Exercises

50. Give an example of two events that are mutually exclusive. Give an example of two sets that are not mutually exclusive.

51. Give an example of two independent events.

52. Describe the difference between disjoint events and independent events in your own words.

53. Explain why two mutually exclusive events with nonzero probabilities cannot be independent.

54. Give an example of two events that are mutually exclusive and not independent.

55. Explain why it is intuitively clear that if E and F are independent events, then so are E and F'.

56. What additional information would you need to know in order to compute $\Pr(E \cap F)$ if you already know $\Pr(E)$ and $\Pr(F)$?

CHAPTER TEST

1. Coins A box contains a penny, a nickel, a dime, a quarter, and a half dollar. You select two coins at random from the box.

(a) Construct a sample space for this situation.

(b) List the elements of the event E in which the total value of the coins you have selected is an even number of cents.

2. Convert the following odds to probabilities.

(a) 3 to 5   (b) 1,000,000 to 1

3. Checkers When Tommy plays checkers against his father, he wins 40% of the time. When he plays against his mother, he wins 30% of the time. What are the odds of him beating his father? losing to his mother?

4. Candidates for Office Some of the candidates for president of the computer club at Riverdale High are seniors, and the rest are juniors. Let J be the event in which a junior is elected, and let F be the event in which a female is elected. Describe the following events:

(a) $J \cap F'$ (b) $(J \cap F)'$ (c) $F' \cup J$

5. Heads and Tails Emilio tosses a fair coin five times. What is the probability that he gets at least one head and at least one tail?

6. Measles Vaccine Fifteen percent of children attending kindergarten have not had a measles vaccine. In a class of 20 students, what is the probability that at least one has not had a measles vaccine?

7. Suppose E and F are events in a sample space, with $\Pr(E) = \frac{1}{4}$, $\Pr(F') = \frac{3}{8}$, and $\Pr(E' \cap F) = \frac{1}{2}$. Determine the following:

(a) $\Pr(F)$ (b) $\Pr(E \cup F)$ (c) $\Pr(F|E')$

(d) Are E and F mutually exclusive?

(e) Are E and F independent?

8. Quality Control Ten of a certain kind of gadget are tested. The probability that any given such gadget is defective is .1. What is the probability that at least one of the 10 gadgets is defective? What is the probability that exactly one of the 10 gadgets is defective?

9. Cards and Marbles Wanda has a deck of 52 cards, a box, and an urn. The box contains 5 red marbles and 10 green marbles, while the urn contains 12 red marbles and 8 green marbles. Wanda picks a card at random from the deck. If it is a face card (jack, queen, or king), she then picks a marble from the box. Otherwise, she picks a marble from the urn.

(a) Determine the probability that she picks a red marble, given that she drew a face card from the deck.

(b) What is the probability that she ends up with a red marble?

(c) If E is the event in which Wanda picks a face card and F is the event in which she picks a red marble, are E and F independent? mutually exclusive?

(d) If Wanda ends up with a green marble, what is the probability that she drew a face card?

10. Loaded Die The probability distribution for the result of rolling a loaded die is given in Table 1.

TABLE 1

Outcome	1	2	3	4	5	6
Probability	.15	.20	.10	.25	.25	.05

(a) Determine the probability that the outcome is an odd number.

(b) Given that the outcome is odd, what is the probability that the outcome is greater than 4?

11. Class Rank and Gender A finite mathematics class of 50 students is composed of freshmen and sophomores according to Table 2. A student from the class is selected at random.

TABLE 2

	Freshmen	Sophomores
Females	12	8
Males	14	16

(a) What is the probability that the selected student is either female or a sophomore?

(b) What is the probability that the selected student is male, given that the student is a freshman?

CHAPTER 6 | PROJECT

Two Paradoxes

First Paradox: *Under certain circumstances you have your best chance of winning a tennis tournament if you play most of your games against the best possible opponent.*

Alice and her two sisters, Betty and Carol, are avid tennis players. Betty is the best of the three sisters, and Carol plays at the same level as Alice. Alice defeats Carol 50% of the time but only defeats Betty 40% of the time.

Alice's mother offers to give her $100 if she can win two consecutive games when playing three alternating games against her two sisters. Since the games will alternate, Alice has two possibilities for the sequence of opponents. One possibility is to play the first game against Betty, followed by a game with Carol, and then another game with Betty. We will refer to this sequence as BCB. The other possible sequence is CBC.

1. Make a guess of the best sequence for Alice to choose; the one having the majority of the games against the weaker opponent or the one having the majority of the games against the stronger opponent.

2. Calculate the probability of Alice getting the $100 reward if she chooses the sequence CBC.

3. Calculate the probability of Alice getting the $100 reward if she chooses the sequence BCB.

4. Which sequence should Alice choose?

5. How would you explain to someone who didn't know probability why the sequence you chose is best?

Second Paradox: *The probability of a male applicant being admitted to a graduate school can be higher than the probability for a female applicant even though for each department the probability of a female being admitted is higher.* (This apparent contradiction is known as **Simpson's paradox**.)

To simplify matters, consider a university with two professional graduate programs, medicine and law. Suppose that last year 1000 men and 1000 women applied and the outcome was as shown in Table 1.

TABLE 1						
	Men			**Women**		
	Applied	**Accepted**	**Rejected**	**Applied**	**Accepted**	**Rejected**
Law	700	560	140	400	340	60
Medicine	300	40	260	600	160	440

6. What is the probability that a male applicant was accepted to a professional program? female?

7. Which gender does the university appear to be favoring?

8. What is the probability that a male applicant was accepted to law school? female?

9. What is the probability that a male applicant was accepted to medical school? female?

10. Which gender do the individual professional schools appear to be favoring?

11. Without using probability, justify the apparent contradiction between the answers for part 7 and part 10.

PROBABILITY
AND STATISTICS

Statistics is the branch of mathematics that deals with data: their collection, description, analysis, and use in prediction. In this chapter we present some topics in statistics that can be used as a springboard to further study. Since we are presenting a series of topics rather than a comprehensive survey, we will bypass large areas of statistics without saying anything about them. However, the discussion should give you some feeling for the subject. Section 7.1 shows how bar charts, pie charts, histograms, and box plots help us turn raw data into a visual form that often allows us to see patterns in the data quickly. Section 7.2 discusses the problem of describing data by means of a distribution and a histogram. It also introduces the concept of random variables. Section 7.3 presents the binomial distribution, one of the most commonly used distributions in statistical applications. Sections 7.4 and 7.5 introduce the mean and the standard deviation, the two most frequently used descriptive statistics, and illustrate how Chebychev's inequality can be used in making estimations. Sections 7.6 and 7.7 explore the binomial distribution further and introduce the normal distribution, which has special importance in statistical analysis.

7.1 Visual Representations of Data

Data can be presented in raw form or organized and displayed in tables or charts. In this section we use various types of charts to visualize and analyze data.

In the fall of 2007, freshmen at 356 baccalaureate colleges and universities in the United States answered an extensive questionnaire.[1] One question asked each student to give the highest degree they planned to pursue. See Table 1. (*Note*: The Medical category includes Dental and Veterinary degrees.) Such a table is often referred to as a **frequency table** since it presents the frequency with which each response occurs.

TABLE 1		
Highest Degree Planned	**Number**	**Percent**
Bachelor's	60,392	22.2
Master's	116,159	42.7
Doctorate	47,606	17.5
Medical	26,387	9.7
Law	12,786	4.7
Other	8,705	3.2
Total	272,035	100.0

Bar Charts The numbers from the example in Table 1 are displayed in the *bar chart* of Fig. 1. This pictorial display gives a good feel for the relative number of students planning to earn each degree.

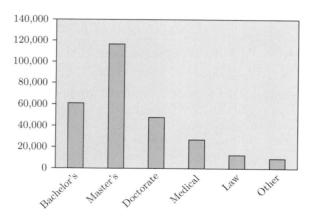

Figure 1. Bar chart for highest degree planned.

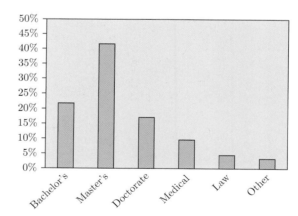

Figure 2. Bar chart for highest degree planned.

The percentages in the right column of Table 1 give the percent of the students out of this group of 272,035 students who plan to pursue each degree. The bar chart for the percentages is shown in Fig. 2. It looks exactly like the bar chart in Fig. 1. The only difference is the labeling of the tick marks along the *y*-axis.

Pie Charts Another popular type of chart that can be used to display data consisting of several categories is the *pie chart*. It consists of a circle subdivided into sectors (slices of pie), where each sector corresponds to a category. The area of

[1]The detailed results of the questionnaire are given in *The American Freshman: National Norms for Fall 2007* (Los Angeles: American Council on Education, 2008, UCLA).

each sector is proportional to the percentage of items in that category. This is accomplished by making the central angle of each sector equal to 360° times the percentage associated with the segment.

EXAMPLE 1   **Freshman aspirations**   Create a pie chart for the "highest degree planned" data. Label each sector with its category and percentage.

Solution   Step 1.   Use the rightmost column of Table 1 to obtain the central angles for the sectors. See Table 2.

TABLE 2		
Highest Degree Planned	**Percent**	**360° × Percent**
Bachelor's	22.2	79.9°
Master's	42.7	153.7°
Doctorate	17.5	63.0°
Medical	9.7	34.9°
Law	4.7	16.9°
Other	3.2	11.5°

Step 2.   Draw a circle, draw a vertical radius line extending from the center of the circle, and then draw an angle of measure approximately 79.9° with the radius line as the initial side of the angle. See Fig. 3(a).

Step 3.   Draw an angle of approximately 153.7°, using the terminal side of the angle drawn in step 2 as the initial side. See Fig. 3(b).

Step 4.   Continue as in step 3 to draw each sector, and then label the sectors with their categories and percentages.   ■

Now Try Exercise 7

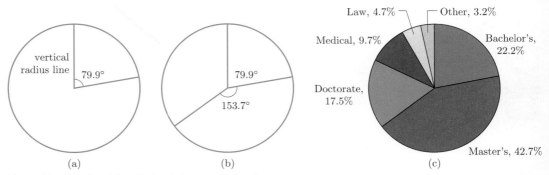

Figure 3.   Pie chart for highest degree planned.

Histograms   In the "highest degree planned" example, the responses to the question were words. The data to be organized consisted of six different words, where each occurred with a high frequency. In many cases to be analyzed, the data are a collection of numbers. For instance, the data could consist of ages, weights, or test scores of individuals. In such cases, the x-axis in a bar chart is labeled with numbers, as in an ordinary x-y coordinate system, and the data are referred to as *numerical data*.

EXAMPLE 2   **Tabulating quiz scores**   Figure 4 on the next page gives the quiz scores for a class of 25 students.

(a) Organize the data into a frequency table.

(b) Create a histogram for the data.

Figure 4   8   7   6   10   5   10   7   1   8   0   10   5   9   3   8   6   10   4   9   10   7   0   9   5   8

Solution **(a)** An easy way to count the number of exams for each score is to write down the numbers from 0 through 10, and considering the quiz papers one at a time, make a slash mark alongside the score for each paper. Such a tabulation produces Table 3(a). In Table 3(b) the slash marks have been totaled.

(b) The histogram (Fig. 5) is drawn on an x-y coordinate system. Note that each bar is centered over its corresponding score. This is accomplished by having the base of each bar extend one-half unit on each side of its score. For instance, the base of the bar corresponding to a score of 10 extends from 9.5 to 10.5.

TABLE 3 Tabulation of quiz scores

0	//		0	2
1	/		1	1
2			2	0
3	/		3	1
4	/		4	1
5	///		5	3
6	//		6	2
7	///		7	3
8	////		8	4
9	///		9	3
10	卌		10	5

(a)　　　　　(b)

Now Try Exercise 13

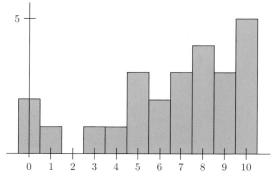

Figure 5.   Histogram for quiz scores.

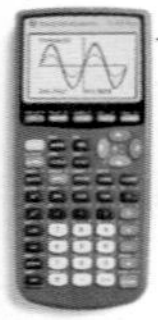

INCORPORATING TECHNOLOGY

GC   The steps required to create a histogram with a TI-83/84 Plus calculator are shown in Figs. 6 through 9. The details of carrying out the task are presented in Appendix B.

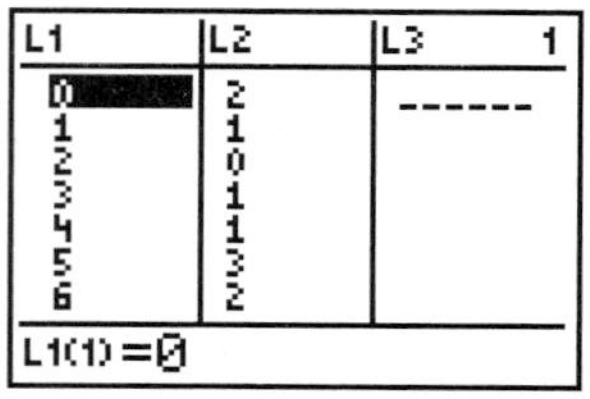

Figure 6

Figure 7

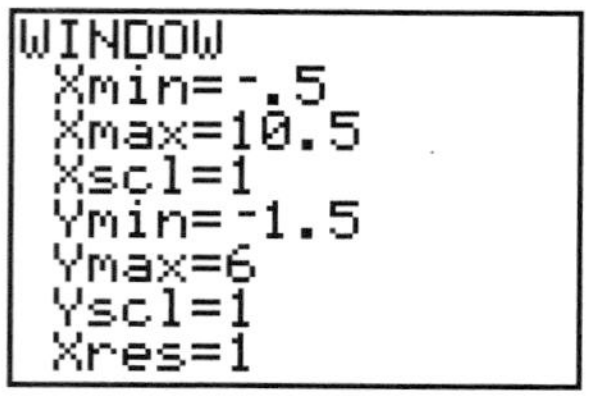

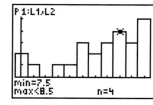

Figure 8

Figure 9

ES   The histogram in Figure 10 can be produced with the following steps.

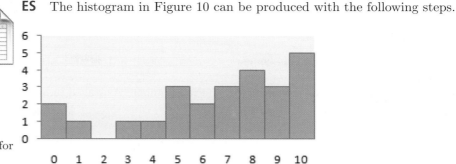

Figure 10. Excel histogram for Example 2.

1. Place the data from the right column of Table 3(b) in a column of a spreadsheet and select the data.

2. (Excel 2007) On the **Insert** tab, in the **Charts** group, click on **Column**.
   (Excel 97-2003) Click the **Chart Wizard** button (holds a picture of a histogram) on the toolbar, and click on **Columns** in the **Chart type** list box.

3. (Excel 2007) Under **2-D Column** click **Clustered Column**. *Note:* You can rest the mouse on any chart type to see its name.
   (Excel 97-2003) Double-click on the first histogram in the **Chart sub-type** box, and then click on the **Finish** button.

4. (Excel 2007) Right-click on the numbers below the x-axis and click on **Select Data**.
   (Excel 97-2003) Right-click on the histogram, and click on **Source Data**.

5. (Excel 2007) Click the right **Edit** button in the **Select Source Data** window that appears, enter {0, 1, 2, 3, 4, 5, 6, 7, 8, 9, 10} into the **Axis label range** box, click the box's **OK** button, and click the window's **OK** button.
   (Excel 97-2003) Type {0, 1, 2, 3, 4, 5, 6, 7, 8, 9, 10} into the **Category (X) axis labels** box, click the box's **OK** button, and click the window's **OK** button.

6. (Excel 2007) On the **Design** tab, in the **Chart Layouts** group, click on **Layout 8**.
   (Excel 97-2003) Right-click on one of the rectangle of the histogram, click on **Format Data Series**, select the **Options** tab, set **Gap width** to 0, and click on the **OK** button.

7. (Excel 2007) On the **Design** tab, in the **Chart Styles** group, select **Style 37**.
   (Excel 97-2003) Right-click on the histogram, click on **Chart Options**, select the **Gridlines** tab, uncheck all boxes, and click on the **OK** button.

8. Click on each legend and press the **Del** key.

Median, Quartiles, and Box Plots   When an instructor returns exam papers, he or she usually gives students some indication of how they did overall. Occasionally the instructor gives the average of the grades, and perhaps the standard deviation. (These two topics are discussed extensively in the remainder of this chapter.) However, most instructors state the **median** of the grade distribution. The median grade is the grade that divides the bottom 50% of the grades from the top 50%. To find the median of a set of N numbers, first arrange the numbers in increasing or decreasing order. The median is the middle number if N is odd and the average of the two middle numbers if N is even.

EXAMPLE 3   **Medians**   Find the medians of the following two sets of data.

(a) Tiger Woods's scores on four rounds of golf in the 2008 U.S. Masters tournament: 72 71 68 72

(b) The 25 quiz scores discussed in Example 2

Solution (a) Here $N = 4$, an even number. Arranged in increasing order, the four scores are

$$68, \ 71, \ 72, \ 72.$$

The middle two scores are 71 and 72. The median is their average. Therefore,

$$\text{median} = \frac{71 + 72}{2} = \frac{143}{2} = 71.5.$$

(b) Here $N = 25$, an odd number. The position of the middle number is $\frac{25 + 1}{2} =$ 13. The tabulation of quiz scores in Table 3 can be used instead of an ordering of the scores. The median will be the thirteenth highest score. Adding up the numbers of scores of 10's, 9's, and 8's gives 12 scores. Therefore, the thirteenth score must be a 7. That is, the median is 7. ■

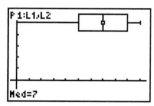

Figure 11

Graphing calculators can display a picture, called a **box plot**, that analyzes a set of data and shows not only the median, but also the **quartiles**. The quartiles are the medians of the sets of data below and above the median. The median of the numbers less than the median is called the first quartile and is denoted Q_1. The median of the numbers greater than the median is called the third quartile and is denoted Q_3. A box plot also is useful in showing pictorially the spread of the data. Figure 11 gives the box plot on a TI-83/84 Plus for the set of 25 quiz scores presented in Example 2. The steps for obtaining the box plot are the same as for the histogram as shown in Figs. 6 through 9, with the exception that in Fig. 7 the fifth icon is selected. Figure 12, which shows the median, appears when $\boxed{\text{TRACE}}$ is pressed. Pressing the arrow keys reveals the smallest quiz score (minX), the largest quiz score (maxX), and the first and third quartiles. See Figs. 13–16. Box plots similar to those in Figs. 11 through 16 can be displayed on the TI-89. The steps are the same as those given in Appendix D for the histogram except that `Plot Type` should be set to `Box Plot`.

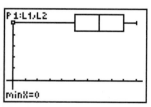

Figure 12

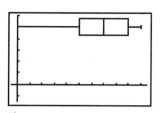

Figure 13

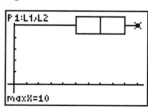

Figure 14

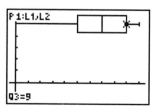

Figure 16

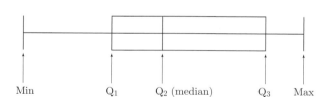

Figure 17.   A general box plot.

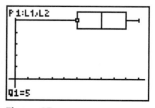

Figure 15

Figure 17 shows the five pieces of information given by a box plot. This information is referred to as the **five-number summary** of the data. The median is also called the second quartile and is denoted Q_2. Essentially, the three quartiles divide the data into four approximately equal parts, each part consisting of roughly 25% of the numbers. The length of the rectangular part of the box plot, which is $Q_3 - Q_1$, is called the **interquartile range**. The quartiles provide information about the dispersion of the data. The interquartile range is the length of the interval in which approximately the middle 50% of the data lie.

EXAMPLE 4   **Five-number summary and interquartile range** Find the five-number summary and the interquartile range for the following set of numbers: 1 3 6 10 15 21 28 36 45 55.

Solution The numbers are given in ascending order, and there are 10 numbers. Immediately we see that min = 1 and max = 55. The next number to be found is the median. Since 10 is an even number, the median is the average of the middle two numbers.

$$1 \quad 3 \quad 6 \quad 10 \quad \mathbf{15} \quad \mathbf{21} \quad 28 \quad 36 \quad 45 \quad 55$$

That is,

$$Q_2 = \text{median} = \frac{15 + 21}{2} = 18.$$

The numbers to the left of the median are 1 3 6 10 15, and the numbers to the right of the median are 21 28 36 45 55. These lists have medians 6 and 36, respectively. Therefore, $Q_1 = 6$, $Q_3 = 36$, and the interquartile range is $Q_3 - Q_1 = 30$.

Now Try Exercise 19

Practice Problems 7.1

Suppose a list consists of 17 numbers in increasing order. Clearly the first number is the min and the last number is the max.

1. Which number in the list is the median?

2. Which numbers in the list are used to obtain the first quartile?

3. Which numbers in the list are used to obtain the third quartile?

EXERCISES 7.1

In Exercises 1–4, display the data in a bar chart that shows frequencies on the y-axis.

1. 2007 School Enrollments (in millions)

Type	Enrollment
Elementary	39.4
Secondary	16.4
College	18.0

Source: U.S. Dept. of Education, National Center for Education Statistics, *Digest of Education Statistics*.

2. 2008 U.S. Defense Employees

Branch	Officers and Enlistees
Army	525,482
Navy	331,383
Marine Corps	190,651
Air Force	327,589

Source: U.S. Dept. of Defense.

3. Areas of the Great Lakes

Lake	Area (sq mi)
Superior	31,700
Michigan	22,300
Huron	23,100
Erie	9,910
Ontario	7,550

Source: Encyclopedia Britannica.

4. Bachelor's Degrees Earned in 2006, by Field

Field of Study	Number of Degrees
Business	318,042
Social Sciences	161,485
Education	107,238
Health Sciences	91,973
Psychology	88,134
Engineering	67,045
Other	651,325

Source: U.S. National Center for Education Statistics, *Digest of Education Statistics*.

5. **School Enrollments** Display the data from the table in Exercise 1 in a bar chart showing percentages on the y-axis.

6. **U.S. Defense Employees** Display the data from the table in Exercise 2 in a bar chart showing percentages on the y-axis.

7. **Interest on Public Debt** PE In 2008, the interest on the public debt accounted for about 8.9% of the federal budget. If the federal budget is displayed in a pie chart, what should be the size of the central angle of the sector corresponding to the interest on the public debt?
   (a) $7.5°$ (b) $32°$ (c) $60°$ (d) $90°$ (e) $120°$

8. **U.S. Defense Employees** Display the data from the table in Exercise 2 in a pie chart.

9. **Great Lakes** Display the data from the table in Exercise 3 in a pie chart.

10. **Bachelor's Degrees** Display the data from the table in Exercise 4 in a pie chart.

Freshman Aspirations *Exercises 11 and 12 refer to the pie chart in Fig. 3(c).*

11. What is the probability that a freshman selected at random in the fall of 2007 planned to obtain a Master's or Doctorate degree?

12. What is the probability that a freshman selected at random in the fall of 2007 planned to obtain a medical or law degree?

13. **Vice-Presidential Tie Breakers** The number of tie-breaking votes cast by each of the 21 vice presidents of the United States who served during the twentieth century are shown. Draw a histogram for these data.

   0, 0, 4, 10, 0, 2, 3, 3, 4, 1, 7,
   8, 0, 4, 2, 0, 0, 1, 7, 0, 4

14. **Presidential Ages** The ages at inauguration of the 43 presidents from George Washington to George W. Bush are shown. Draw a histogram for the ages.

   57, 61, 57, 57, 58, 57, 61, 54, 68, 51, 49, 64, 50,
   48, 65, 52, 56, 46, 54, 49, 50, 47, 55, 55, 54, 42,
   51, 56, 55, 51, 54, 51, 60, 62, 43, 55, 56, 61, 52,
   69, 64, 46, 54

15. PE For what value of n will the median of the numbers $\{2, 3, 5, 20\}$ be the same as the median of the numbers $\{n, 1, 3, 5, 15\}$?
   (a) 2 (b) 3 (c) 4 (d) 5 (e) 6

16. PE If n is a whole number between 0 and 7, then the median of the numbers $\{1, 3, 5, n, 2, 4, 6\}$ must be
   (a) n (b) 3.5 (c) either 2 or 3
   (d) either 3 or 4 (e) either 5 or 6

In Exercises 17 and 18, draw the box plot corresponding to the given five-number summary.

17. min $= 2$, $Q_1 = 5$, $Q_2 = 7$, $Q_3 = 10$, max $= 15$

18. min $= 10$, $Q_1 = 13$, $Q_2 = 17$, $Q_3 = 20$, max $= 25$

In Exercises 19–22, find the five-number summary and the interquartile range for the given set of numbers, and then draw the box plot.

19. 10, 11, 13, 14, 16, 17, 19, 20, 21, 23, 24

20. 3, 6, 8, 9, 11, 14, 18

21. 20, 25, 31, 38, 42, 47, 51, 54, 56

22. 7, 17, 26, 34, 41, 47, 52, 56, 59, 61

23. Match each of the histograms in column I with the corresponding box plot in column II.

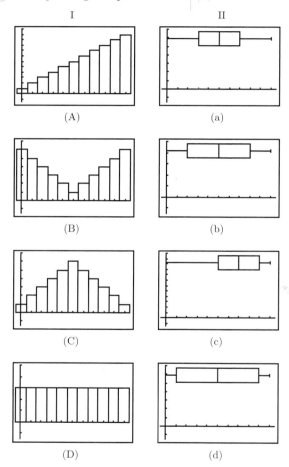

I

II

(A) (a)

(B) (b)

(C) (c)

(D) (d)

24. **Food Cost** The box plot for the price (in cents) of a can of tomato soup is shown.

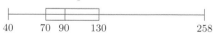

(a) Approximately what percentage of the soups are priced below 70 cents?

(b) Approximately what percentage of the soups are priced above 130 cents?

(c) Approximately what percentage of the soups are priced below 90 cents?

(d) Approximately what percentage of the soups are priced between 90 and 130 cents?

(e) What is the median price of a can of soup?

25. Test Scores Consider the following box plot of scores on a standardized test.

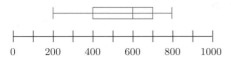

(a) Give the five-number summary of the data.

(b) Approximately what percentage of the scores is below 400?

(c) Approximately what percentage of the scores is between 400 and 600?

(d) Approximately what percentage of the scores is higher than 600?

(e) Approximately what percentage of the scores is between 200 and 700?

26. Batting Averages The data below give the top 10 batting averages at the end of the 2007 season for the American League and the National League. Compare the data using a box plot and discuss which of the leagues seems to have the better players.

American League: .363, .351, .341, .338, .332, .330, .324, .324, .322, .317

National League: .340, .337, .332, .332, .332, .327, .325, .320, .320, .320

27. Batting Averages The Atlanta Braves played a game against the Milwaukee Brewers. The batting averages of each team's players (except for pitchers and designated hitters) on that day were as follows:

Braves: .229, .243, .317, .281, .296, .200, .345, .227, .350, .286

Brewers: .317, .150, .270, .333, .250, .200, .359, .280, .091

Draw a box plot for each team and comment on which team seems to be more likely to win. Explain your answer.

Solutions to Practice Problems 7.1

1. Since there are an odd number of numbers in the list, the middle number (that is, the ninth number) is the median. *Note:* When N, the number of numbers, is odd, the median is the $\frac{N+1}{2}$th number.

2. There are 8 numbers in the truncated list consisting of the numbers to the left of the median. Since 8 is even, the median of this truncated list is the average of the middle two numbers. That is, the first quartile is the average of the fourth and fifth numbers. *Note:* When N is even, the median of a list of N numbers is the average of the $\frac{N}{2}$th number and the number following the $\frac{N}{2}$th number.

3. There are 8 numbers in the truncated list consisting of the numbers to the right of the median. Since 8 is even, the median of this truncated list is the average of the middle two numbers of the truncated list. So the third quartile is the average of the fourth and fifth numbers of the truncated list; that is, the average of the thirteenth and fourteenth numbers of the original list.

7.2 Frequency and Probability Distributions

Our goal in this section is to describe a given set of data in terms that allow for interpretation and comparison. As we shall see, both graphical and tabular displays of data can be useful for this purpose.

Our modern technological society has a compulsion about gathering statistical data. It is hardly possible to glance at a newspaper or a magazine and not be confronted with massive arrays of statistics gathered from studies of schools, churches, the economy, and so forth. One of the chief tasks confronting us is to interpret in a meaningful way the data collected and to make decisions based on our interpretations. The mathematical tools for doing this belong to that part of mathematics called **statistics**.

To get an idea of the problems considered in statistics, let us consider a concrete example. Mr. Jones, a businessman, is interested in purchasing a car dealership. Two dealerships are for sale, and each dealer has provided him with data describing past sales. Dealership A provided 1 year's worth of data, dealership B, 2 years' worth. The data are summarized in Table 1. The problem confronting Mr. Jones is that of analyzing the data to determine which car dealership to buy.

TABLE 1

	Number of occurrences	
Weekly sales	Dealership A	Dealership B
5	2	20
6	2	0
7	13	0
8	20	10
9	10	12
10	4	50
11	1	12

These data are presented in a form often used in statistical surveys. For each possible value of a statistical variable (in this case the number of cars sold weekly) we have tabulated the number of occurrences. Such a tabulation is called a **frequency distribution**. Although a frequency distribution is a very useful way of displaying and summarizing survey data, it is by no means the most efficient form in which to analyze such data. For example, it is difficult to compare dealership A with dealership B using only Table 1.

Comparisons are much more easily made if we use proportions rather than actual numbers of occurrences. For example, instead of recording that dealership A had weekly sales of 5 cars during 2 weeks of the year, let us record that the proportion of the observed weeks in which dealership A had weekly sales of 5 was $\frac{2}{52} \approx .04$. Similarly, by dividing each of the entries in the right column by 52, we obtain a new table describing the sales of dealership A (Table 2).[1] We similarly can construct a new table for dealership B (Table 3).

These tables are called **relative frequency distributions**. In general, consider an experiment with the numerical outcomes $x_1, x_2, \ldots, x_r$. Suppose that the number of occurrences of x_1 is f_1, the number of occurrences of x_2 is f_2, and so forth (Table 4). The frequency distribution lists all the outcomes of the experiment and the number of times each occurred. (For the sake of simplicity, we usually arrange $x_1, x_2, \ldots, x_r$ in increasing order.)

TABLE 2

Weekly sales	Proportion of occurrences, dealership A
5	$\frac{2}{52} \approx .04$
6	$\frac{2}{52} \approx .04$
7	$\frac{13}{52} = .25$
8	$\frac{20}{52} \approx .38$
9	$\frac{10}{52} \approx .19$
10	$\frac{4}{52} \approx .08$
11	$\frac{1}{52} \approx .02$

TABLE 3

Weekly sales	Proportion of occurrences, dealership B
5	$\frac{20}{104} \approx .19$
6	0
7	0
8	$\frac{10}{104} \approx .10$
9	$\frac{12}{104} \approx .12$
10	$\frac{50}{104} \approx .48$
11	$\frac{12}{104} \approx .12$

TABLE 4

Outcome	Frequency	Relative frequency
x_1	f_1	f_1/n
x_2	f_2	f_2/n
$\vdots$	$\vdots$	$\vdots$
x_r	f_r	f_r/n
Total	n	1

Suppose that the total number of occurrences is n. Then the **relative frequency** of outcome x_1 is f_1/n, the relative frequency of outcome x_2 is f_2/n, and

---

[1] For simplification we shall round off the data of this example to two decimal places.

so forth. The relative frequency distribution pairs each outcome with its relative frequency. The sum of the frequencies in a frequency distribution is n. The sum of the relative frequencies in a relative frequency distribution is 1.

The frequency or relative frequency distribution is obtained directly from the performance of an experiment and the collection of data observed at each trial of the experiment. For example, we might imagine a coin-tossing experiment in which a coin is tossed five times and the number of occurrences of heads is observed. On each performance of the experiment we might observe 0, 1, 2, 3, 4, or 5 heads. We could repeat the experiment, say 90 times, and record the outcomes. We have collected data like that in Table 5. While doing the experiment we would record the frequencies $f_0, f_1, f_2, \ldots, f_5$ of the various outcomes and then divide by 90 to obtain the relative frequencies $f_0/90, f_1/90, f_2/90, \ldots, f_5/90$. The sum of the frequency column is the number of trials of the experiment (here, 90), and the sum of the relative frequency column is 1.

TABLE 5

Number of heads	Frequency	Relative frequency
0	3	$\frac{3}{90} \approx .03$
1	14	$\frac{14}{90} \approx .16$
2	23	$\frac{23}{90} \approx .26$
3	27	$\frac{27}{90} = .30$
4	17	$\frac{17}{90} \approx .19$
5	6	$\frac{6}{90} \approx .07$
Total	90	$\frac{90}{90} = 1.00$

It is often possible to gain useful insight into an experiment by representing its relative frequency distribution in graphical form. For instance, let us graph the relative frequency distribution for car dealership A. Begin by drawing a number line (Fig. 1).

Figure 1

The numbers that represent possible outcomes of the experiment (weekly car sales) are 5, 6, 7, 8, 9, 10, 11. Locate each of these numbers on the number line. Above each number erect a rectangle whose base is one unit wide and whose height is the relative frequency of that number. Above the number 5, for example, we draw a rectangle of height .04. The completed graph is shown in Fig. 2 on the next page. For the sake of comparison we have also drawn a graph of the relative frequency distribution for dealership B.

As we mentioned earlier, graphs of the type just drawn are called histograms. They vividly illustrate the data being considered. For example, comparison of the histograms of Fig. 2 reveals significant differences between the two dealerships. On the one hand, dealership A is very consistent. Most weeks its sales are in the middle range of 7, 8, or 9. On the other hand, dealership B can often achieve very high sales (it had sales of 10 in 48% of the weeks) at the expense of a significant number of weeks of low sales (sales of 5 in 19% of the weeks). The histogram for the coin-tossing experiment recorded previously appears in Fig. 3.

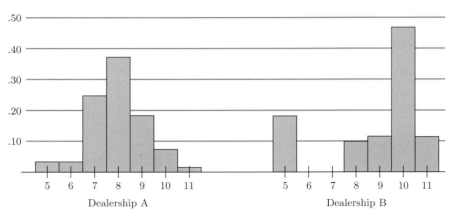

Figure 2

Dealership A   Dealership B

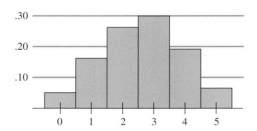

Figure 3. Relative frequency
distribution for number of
heads in 5 tosses—experi-
mental results.

It is possible to use histograms to represent the relative frequencies of events
as areas. To illustrate the procedure, consider the histogram corresponding to
dealership A. Each rectangle has width 1 and height equal to the relative frequency
of a particular outcome of the experiment. For instance, the highest rectangle is
centered over the number 8 and has height .38, the relative frequency of the outcome
8. Note that the area of the rectangle is

$$\text{area} = (\text{height})(\text{width}) = (.38)(1) = .38.$$

In other words, the area of the rectangle equals the relative frequency of the corresponding outcome. We have verified this in the case of the outcome 8, but it is true
in general. In a similar fashion, we may represent the relative frequency of more
complicated events as areas. Consider, for example, the event $E = $"sales between 7
and 10, inclusive." This event consists of the set of outcomes $\{7, 8, 9, 10\}$, and so its
relative frequency is the sum of the respective relative frequencies of the outcomes
7, 8, 9, and 10. Therefore, the relative frequency of the event E is the area of the
blue region of the histogram in Fig. 4.

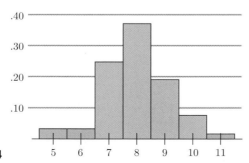

Figure 4

An important thing to notice is that so far we have made the tables and the
histograms for actual, as opposed to theoretical, experiments. That is, the tables

and the histograms were produced from collections of sample data that were obtained by actually recording the outcomes of experiments. We shall now look at theoretical experiments and continue to explore the important notion of **probability distribution**. In many cases, data of an actual experiment are best interpreted when we can construct a theoretical model for the experiment.

Let us reconsider the coin-tossing experiment in which a coin was tossed five times and the number of occurrences of heads recorded. If the coins are fair coins, then we can set up a model for the experiment by noting once again that the possible outcomes are 0, 1, 2, 3, 4, or 5 heads. We will construct the probability distribution for this experiment by listing the outcomes in the sample space with their probabilities. The probabilities of 0, 1, 2, 3, 4, 5 heads can be obtained with the methods of Chapter 6. The number of distinct sequences of 5 tosses is 2^5, or 32. The number of sequences having k heads (and $5 - k$ tails) is

$$C(5, k) = \binom{5}{k}.$$

Thus

$$\Pr(k \text{ heads}) = \frac{\binom{5}{k}}{2^5} \qquad (k = 0, 1, 2, 3, 4, 5).$$

The probability distribution for the experiment is shown in Table 6.

The histogram for a probability distribution is constructed in the same way as the histogram for a relative frequency distribution. Each outcome is represented on the number line, and above each outcome we erect a rectangle of width 1 and of height equal to the probability corresponding to that outcome (see Fig. 5).

We note that the histogram in Fig. 5 is based on a theoretical model of coin tossing, whereas the histogram in Fig. 3 was drawn from experimental results only available after the experiment was actually performed and observed.

TABLE 6

Number of heads	Probability
0	$\dfrac{\binom{5}{0}}{2^5} = \dfrac{1}{32}$
1	$\dfrac{\binom{5}{1}}{2^5} = \dfrac{5}{32}$
2	$\dfrac{\binom{5}{2}}{2^5} = \dfrac{10}{32}$
3	$\dfrac{\binom{5}{3}}{2^5} = \dfrac{10}{32}$
4	$\dfrac{\binom{5}{4}}{2^5} = \dfrac{5}{32}$
5	$\dfrac{\binom{5}{5}}{2^5} = \dfrac{1}{32}$

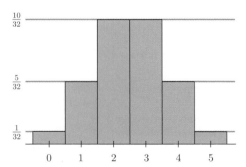

Figure 5. Probability distribution for number of heads in 5 tosses—theoretical results.

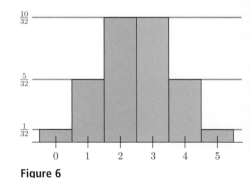

Figure 6

Just as we used the histogram for the relative frequency distribution to picture the relative frequency of an event, we may also use the histogram of a probability distribution to picture the probability of an event. For instance, to find the probability of at least 3 heads on 5 tosses of a fair coin, we need only add the probabilities of the outcomes: 3 heads, 4 heads, 5 heads. That is,

$$\Pr(\text{at least 3 heads}) = \Pr(3 \text{ heads}) + \Pr(4 \text{ heads}) + \Pr(5 \text{ heads}).$$

Since each of these probabilities is equal to the area of a rectangle in the histogram of Fig. 5, the area of the blue region in Fig. 6 equals the probability of the event. This result is a special case of the following fact:

In a histogram of a probability distribution, the probability of an event E is the sum of the areas of the rectangles corresponding to the outcomes in E.

EXAMPLE 1

Probabilities and histograms   The histogram of a probability distribution is as given in Fig. 7. Indicate the portion of the histogram whose area is the probability of the event "more than 50."

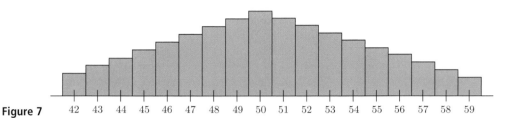

Figure 7

Solution The event "more than 50" is the set of outcomes $\{51, 52, 53, 54, 55, 56, 57, 58, 59\}$. So we indicate in blue the portion of the histogram corresponding to these outcomes (Fig. 8). The area of the blue region is the probability of the event "more than 50."

Now Try Exercise 11   ∎

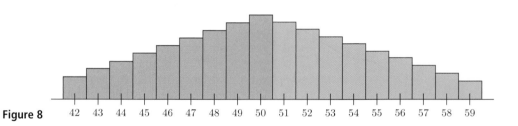

Figure 8

Random Variables Consider a theoretical experiment with numerical outcomes. Denote the outcome of the experiment by the letter X. For example, if the experiment consists of observing the number of heads in five tosses of a fair coin, then X assumes one of the six values 0, 1, 2, 3, 4, 5. Since the values of X are determined by the unpredictable random outcomes of the experiment, X is called a **random variable** or, more specifically, the *random variable associated with the experiment*.

The random variable notation is often convenient and is commonly used in probability and statistics texts. In considering several different experiments, it is sometimes necessary to use letters other than X to stand for random variables. It is customary, however, to use only capital letters, such as X, Y, Z, W, U, V, for random variables.

If k is one of the possible outcomes of the experiment with associated random variable X, then we denote the probability of the outcome k by

$$\Pr(X = k).$$

For example, in the coin-tossing experiment described previously, if X is the number of heads in the five tosses, then

$$\Pr(X = 3)$$

denotes the probability of getting 3 heads. The probability distribution of the random variable X is shown in Table 7.

TABLE 7

k	$\Pr(X = k)$
0	$\frac{1}{32}$
1	$\frac{5}{32}$
2	$\frac{10}{32}$
3	$\frac{10}{32}$
4	$\frac{5}{32}$
5	$\frac{1}{32}$

Rather than speak of the probability distribution associated with the model of an experiment, we can speak of the *probability distribution associated with the corresponding random variable.* Such a probability distribution is a table listing the various values of X (i.e., outcomes of the experiment) and their associated probabilities with $p_1 + p_2 + \cdots + p_r = 1$:

k	$\Pr(X = k)$
x_1	p_1
x_2	p_2
$\vdots$	$\vdots$
x_r	p_r

EXAMPLE 2

Selecting balls from an urn   Consider the urn of Examples 1 and 2 of Section 6.4, in which there are eight white balls and two green balls. A sample of three balls is chosen at random from the urn. Let X denote the number of green balls in the sample. Find the probability distribution of X.

Solution   There are $C(10, 3) = 120$ equally likely outcomes and X can be 0, 1, or 2. Reasoning as in Section 6.4, we have

$$\Pr(X = 0) = \frac{C(2, 0) \cdot C(8, 3)}{120} = \frac{1 \cdot 56}{120} = \frac{56}{120} = \frac{7}{15}$$

$$\Pr(X = 1) = \frac{C(2, 1) \cdot C(8, 2)}{120} = \frac{2 \cdot 28}{120} = \frac{56}{120} = \frac{7}{15}$$

$$\Pr(X = 2) = \frac{C(2, 2) \cdot C(8, 1)}{120} = \frac{1 \cdot 8}{120} = \frac{8}{120} = \frac{1}{15}$$

The probability distribution for X is given by the following table.

k	$\Pr(X = k)$
0	$\frac{7}{15}$
1	$\frac{7}{15}$
2	$\frac{1}{15}$

Now Try Exercise 7

■

EXAMPLE 3

Rolling a pair of dice   Let X denote the random variable defined as the sum of the upper faces appearing when two dice are rolled. Determine the probability distribution of X and draw its histogram.

Solution   The experiment of rolling two dice leads to 36 possibilities, each having probability $\frac{1}{36}$.

$$(1, 1) \quad (1, 2) \quad (1, 3) \quad (1, 4) \quad (1, 5) \quad (1, 6)$$
$$(2, 1) \quad (2, 2) \quad (2, 3) \quad (2, 4) \quad (2, 5) \quad (2, 6)$$
$$(3, 1) \quad (3, 2) \quad (3, 3) \quad (3, 4) \quad (3, 5) \quad (3, 6)$$
$$(4, 1) \quad (4, 2) \quad (4, 3) \quad (4, 4) \quad (4, 5) \quad (4, 6)$$
$$(5, 1) \quad (5, 2) \quad (5, 3) \quad (5, 4) \quad (5, 5) \quad (5, 6)$$
$$(6, 1) \quad (6, 2) \quad (6, 3) \quad (6, 4) \quad (6, 5) \quad (6, 6)$$

The sum of the numbers in each pair gives the value of X. For example, the pair $(3, 1)$ corresponds to $X = 4$. Note that the pairs corresponding to a given value of X lie on a diagonal, as shown in the preceding chart, where we have indicated all pairs corresponding to $X = 4$. It is now easy to calculate the number of pairs corresponding to a given value k of X and from it the probability $\Pr(X = k)$. For example, there are three pairs adding to 4, so

$$\Pr(X = 4) = \tfrac{3}{36} = \tfrac{1}{12}.$$

Performing this calculation for all k from 2 to 12 gives the probability distribution and the histogram shown in Fig. 9.

Now Try Exercise 5

k	$\Pr(X = k)$	k	$\Pr(X = k)$
2	$\frac{1}{36}$	8	$\frac{5}{36}$
3	$\frac{1}{18}$	9	$\frac{1}{9}$
4	$\frac{1}{12}$	10	$\frac{1}{12}$
5	$\frac{1}{9}$	11	$\frac{1}{18}$
6	$\frac{5}{36}$	12	$\frac{1}{36}$
7	$\frac{1}{6}$		

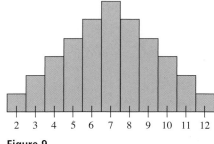

Figure 9

The advantage of the random variable notation is that the variable X can be treated algebraically and we can consider expressions such as X^2. This is just the random variable corresponding to the experiment whose outcomes are the squares of the outcomes of the original experiment. Similarly, we can consider random variables such as $X + 3$ and $(X - 2)^2$. One important example of algebraic manipulation of random variables appears in Section 7.5. There are many others.

EXAMPLE 4

Probability distribution of X^2 Suppose that a random variable X has probability distribution given by the following table:

k	$\Pr(X = k)$
-1	.2
0	.3
1	.1
2	.4

Determine the probability distribution of the random variable X^2.

Solution The outcomes of X^2 are the squares of the outcomes of X. The probabilities of the outcomes of X^2 are determined by the probabilities of the outcomes of X. The possible outcomes of X^2 are $k = 1$ (which results from the case $X = -1$ or from the case $X = 1$), $k = 0$, and $k = 4$. Since

$$\Pr(X^2 = 1) = \Pr(X = -1) + \Pr(X = 1),$$

the probability distribution of X^2 is as follows.

k	$\Pr(X^2 = k)$
0	.3
1	.3
4	.4

Now Try Exercise 13

INCORPORATING TECHNOLOGY

GC   Appendices B and D show how to draw histograms with a graphing calculator.

ES   Appendix C shows how to use Excel to create histograms. ■

Practice Problems 7.2

1. **Carnival Game** In a certain carnival game a wheel is divided into five equal parts, of which two are red and three are white. The player spins the wheel until the marker lands on "red" or until three spins have occurred. The number of spins is observed. Determine the probability distribution for this experiment.

2. **Carnival Game** Refer to the carnival game of Problem 1. Suppose that the player pays $1 to play this game and receives 50 cents for each spin. Determine the probability distribution for the experiment of playing the game and observing the player's earnings.

EXERCISES 7.2

1. **Final Grades** Table 8 gives the frequency distribution for the final grades in a course. (Here A = 4, B = 3, C = 2, D = 1, F = 0.) Determine the relative frequency distribution associated with these data and draw the associated histogram.

2. **Gas Queue** The number of cars waiting to be served at a gas station was counted at the beginning of every minute during the morning rush hour. The frequency distribution is given in Table 9. Determine the relative frequency distribution associated with these data and draw the histogram.

3. **Weather Requests** The telephone company counted the number of people dialing the weather each minute on a rainy morning from 5 A.M. to 6 A.M. The frequency distribution is given in Table 10. Determine the relative frequency distribution associated with these data.

4. **Production Level** A production manager counted the number of items produced each hour during a 40-hour workweek. The frequency distribution is given in Table 11. Determine the relative frequency distribution associated with these data.

5. **Coin Tosses** A fair coin is tossed three times and the number of heads is observed. Determine the probability distribution for this experiment and draw its histogram.

6. **Archery** An archer can hit the bull's-eye of the target with probability $\frac{1}{3}$. She shoots until she hits the bull's-eye or until four shots have been taken. The number of shots is observed. Determine the probability distribution for this experiment.

7. **Selecting Balls from an Urn** An urn contains three red balls and four white balls. A sample of three balls is selected at random and the number of red balls observed. Determine the probability distribution for this experiment and draw its histogram.

8. **Rolling a Die** A die is rolled and the number on the top face is observed. Determine the probability distribution for this experiment and draw its histogram.

TABLE 8	
Grade	Number of occurrences
0	2
1	3
2	10
3	6
4	4

TABLE 9	
Number of cars waiting	Number of occurrences
0	0
1	9
2	21
3	15
4	12
5	3

TABLE 10	
Number of calls during minute	Number of occurrences
20	3
21	3
22	0
23	6
24	18
25	12
26	0
27	9
28	6
29	3

TABLE 11	
Number produced during hour	Number of occurrences
50	2
51	0
52	4
53	6
54	14
55	8
56	4
57	0
58	0
59	2

9. Carnival Game In a certain carnival game the player selects two balls at random from an urn containing two red balls and four white balls. The player receives $5 if he draws two red balls and $1 if he draws one red ball. He loses $1 if no red balls are in the sample. Determine the probability distribution for the experiment of playing the game and observing the player's earnings.

10. Carnival Game In a certain carnival game a player pays $1 and then tosses a fair coin until either a "head" occurs or he has tossed the coin four times. He receives 50 cents for each toss. Determine the probability distribution for the experiment of playing the game and observing the player's earnings.

11. Figure 10 is the histogram for a probability distribution. What is the probability that the outcome is between 5 and 7, inclusive?

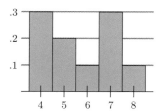

Figure 10

12. Figure 11 is the histogram for a probability distribution. To what event do the blue rectangles correspond?

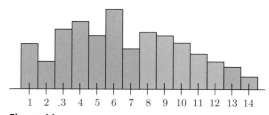

Figure 11

Let the random variables X and Y have the probability distributions listed in Table 12. Determine the probability distributions of the random variables in Exercises 13–20.

TABLE 12

k	$\Pr(X = k)$	k	$\Pr(Y = k)$
0	.1	5	.3
1	.2	10	.4
2	.3	15	.1
3	.2	20	.1
4	.2	25	.1

13. X^2 **14.** Y^2 **15.** $X - 1$

16. $Y - 15$ **17.** $\frac{1}{5}Y$ **18.** $2X^2$

19. $(X + 1)^2$ **20.** $\left(\frac{1}{5}Y + 1\right)^2$

21. Grade Distributions Two classes take the same examination and the grades are recorded in Table 13. We assigned the integers 0 through 4 to the grades F through A, respectively. Table 13 gives the frequency distribution of grades in each class. Find the relative frequency distribution and the histogram for each class. Describe the difference in the grade distributions for the two classes.

TABLE 13

		Number of students	
Grade		9 A.M. **class**	10 A.M. **class**
F	(0)	10	16
D	(1)	15	23
C	(2)	20	15
B	(3)	10	21
A	(4)	5	25

22. Grade Distributions Using Table 13, answer the following questions.

(a) What percentage of the students in the 9 A.M. class have grades of C or less?

(b) What percentage of the 10 A.M. class have grades of C or less?

(c) What percentage of the 9 A.M. class have grades of D or F?

(d) What percentage of the students in both classes combined have grades of C or more?

Exercises 23–27 refer to the tables associated with Exercises 1–4.

23. Grade Distribution For the data in Table 8, determine the percentage of students who get C or higher.

24. Gas Queue The data in Table 9 have been tabulated for every minute of the (60-minute) rush hour. What percentage of the time is the waiting line 4 or more cars?

25. Weather Requests Use the data in Table 10.

(a) For what percentage of the 60 minutes from 5 A.M. to 6 A.M. are there either less than 22 or more than 27 calls to the weather number?

(b) For what percentage of the hour are there between 23 and 25 calls (inclusive)?

(c) Draw the histogram.

(d) What would be your estimate of the average number of calls coming in during a minute of the hour for which the data have been tabulated? Explain.

26. Production Level Draw a histogram for the relative frequency distribution of Table 11.

27. Production Level For the data in Table 11, answer the following questions.

(a) What is the highest number of items produced in any one hour?

(b) What percentage of the time is that maximum number of items produced?

(c) What number of items is produced with the highest frequency?

(d) In what percentage of the 40 hours do production levels exceed 54 items?

(e) Estimate the average number of items produced per hour in this week. Explain.

28. Assume that X and Y are random variables with the given probability distributions.

k	$\Pr(X = k)$	$\Pr(Y = k)$
1	.30	.20
2	.40	.20
3	.20	.20
4	.10	.40

(a) Draw the histogram for X.

(b) Draw the histogram for Y.

(c) Find $\Pr(X = 2 \text{ or } 3)$.

(d) Find $\Pr(Y = 2 \text{ or } 3)$.

(e) Find the probability that X is at least 2.

(f) Find the probability that $X + 3$ is at least 5.

(g) Find the probability that Y^2 is at most 9.

(h) Find the probability that Y is at most 10.

(i) Find the probability distribution of $2X$.

(j) Find the probability distribution of $(Y + 2)^2$.

(k) Which of X or Y has the higher average value? Why would you think so?

29. Here is the probability distribution of the random variable U.

k	$\Pr(U = k)$
0	$\frac{3}{15}$
1	$\frac{2}{15}$
2	$\frac{4}{15}$
3	$\frac{5}{15}$
4	?

(a) Determine the probability that $U = 4$.

(b) Find $\Pr(U \geq 2)$.

(c) Find the probability that U is at most 3.

(d) Find the probability that $U + 2$ is less than 4.

(e) Draw the histogram of the distribution of U.

Solutions to Practice Problems 7.2

1. Since the outcomes are the numbers of spins, there are three possible outcomes: one, two, and three spins. The probabilities for each of these outcomes can be computed from a tree diagram (Fig. 12). For instance, the outcome two (spins) occurs if the first spin lands on white and the second spin on red. The probability of this outcome is $\frac{3}{5} \cdot \frac{2}{5} = \frac{6}{25}$.

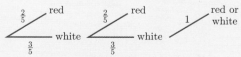

Figure 12

k	$\Pr(X = k)$
1	$\frac{2}{5}$
2	$\frac{6}{25}$
3	$\frac{9}{25}$

2. The same game is being played as in Problem 1, except that now the outcome we are concentrating on is the player's financial situation at the end of the game. The player's earnings depend on the number of spins as follows: one spin results in $-\$.50$ earnings (i.e., a loss of 50 cents); two spins result in \$0 earnings (i.e., breaking even); and three spins result in \$.50 earnings (i.e., the player ends up ahead by 50 cents). The probabilities for these three situations are the same as before.

Earnings	Probability
$-\$.50$	$\frac{2}{5}$
0	$\frac{6}{25}$
$\$.50$	$\frac{9}{25}$

7.3 Binomial Trials

In this section we fix our attention on the simplest experiments: those with just two outcomes. These experiments, called **binomial trials** (or *Bernoulli trials*), occur in many applications. Here are some examples of binomial trials.

1. Toss a coin and observe the outcome, heads or tails.

2. Administer a drug to a sick individual and classify the reaction as "effective" or "ineffective."

3. Manufacture a light bulb and classify it as "nondefective" or "defective."

The outcomes of a binomial trial are usually called "success" and "failure." Of course, the labels "success" and "failure" need have no connection with the usual meanings of these words. For example, in experiment 2 we might label the outcome "ineffective" as "success" and "effective" as "failure." Throughout our discussion of binomial trials we will always denote the probability of "success" by p and probability of "failure" by q. Since a binomial trial has only two outcomes, we have $p + q = 1$, or

$$q = 1 - p.$$

Consider a particular binomial trial and the following experiment. Repeat the binomial trial n times and observe the number of successes that occur. Assume that the n successive trials are independent of one another. The fundamental problem of the theory of binomial trials is to calculate the probabilities of the outcomes of this experiment.

Let X be a random variable associated with the experiment. X is the number of "successes" in the n trials of the experiment. For example, if we toss a coin 20 times and assume that "heads" is a "success," then $X = 3$ means that the experiment resulted in 3 "heads" and 17 "tails." In an experiment of n trials, the number of "successes" can be any one of the numbers $0, 1, 2, \ldots, n$. These are the possible values of X.

We write $\Pr(X = k)$ to denote the probability that $X = k$, namely, the probability that k of the n trials result in success. As we saw in the coin-tossing experiment in Section 7.2, we can find the probability distribution of X using the methods of counting and basic probability principles developed earlier in the book.

If X is the number of "successes" in n independent trials, where in each trial the probability of a "success" is p, then (with $q = 1 - p$)

$$\Pr(X = k) = \binom{n}{k} p^k q^{n-k} \tag{1}$$

for $k = 0, 1, 2, \ldots, n$. *Note:* $\binom{n}{k}$ is the same as $C(n, k)$.

Note that the right side of (1) is one of the terms in the binomial expansion of $(p + q)^n$ (see Section 5.7). We say that X is a **binomial random variable** with parameters n and p. The derivation of (1) is given at the end of this section.

Let X be the number of heads in five tosses of a fair coin. Then X is a binomial random variable with parameters $p = \frac{1}{2}$ and $n = 5$. The calculation for this particular variable appears in Section 7.2. The probability distribution is

k	$\Pr(X = k)$
0	$\frac{1}{32}$
1	$\frac{5}{32}$
2	$\frac{10}{32}$
3	$\frac{10}{32}$
4	$\frac{5}{32}$
5	$\frac{1}{32}$

By (1)

$$\Pr(X = k) = \binom{5}{k}\left(\frac{1}{2}\right)^k \left(\frac{1}{2}\right)^{5-k}.$$

Substitution of the values of k (0, 1, 2, 3, 4, 5) gives the probabilities in the table.

EXAMPLE 1

Baseball Each time at bat the probability that a baseball player gets a hit is .300. He comes up to bat four times in a game. Assume that his times at bat are independent trials. Find the probability that he gets (a) exactly two hits and (b) at least two hits.

Solution Each at-bat is considered an independent binomial trial. A "success" is a hit. So $p = .300$, $q = 1 - p = .700$, and $n = 4$. Therefore, X is the number of hits in four at-bats or the number of "successes" in 4 trials.

(a) We need to determine $\Pr(X = 2)$. From formula (1) with $k = 2$, we have

$$\Pr(X = 2) = \binom{4}{2}(.300)^2(.700)^{4-2} = 6(.09)(.49) = .2646.$$

(b) "At least two hits" means $X \geq 2$. Applying formula (1) with $k = 2$, 3, and 4, we have

$$\Pr(X \geq 2) = \Pr(X = 2) + \Pr(X = 3) + \Pr(X = 4)$$

$$= \binom{4}{2}(.300)^2(.700)^2 + \binom{4}{3}(.300)^3(.700)^1 + \binom{4}{4}(.300)^4(.700)^0$$

$$= 6(.09)(.49) + 4(.027)(.700) + 1(.0081)(1)$$

$$= .2646 + .0756 + .0081 = .3483.$$

So the batter can be expected to get at least two hits out of four at-bats in about 35% of the games.

Now Try Exercise 1

EXAMPLE 2

Women in the labor force Statistics[1] show that 61% of all married women in the United States are in the labor force. Five married U.S. women are randomly selected. Find the probability that at least one of them is in the labor force. Assume that each selection is an independent binomial trial.

Solution Let "success" be "in the labor force." Then

$$p = .61 \qquad q = 1 - p = .39 \quad \text{and} \quad n = 5.$$

[1] Statistical Abstract of the United States; U.S. Census Bureau, 2008.

Therefore, X is the number of women (out of the five selected) that are in the labor force. Then

$$\Pr(X \geq 1) = 1 - \Pr(X = 0) = 1 - \binom{5}{0}(.61)^0(.39)^5$$

$$\approx 1 - .009 = .991.$$

Thus, in a group of five randomly selected married U.S. women, there is about a 99.1% chance that at least one of them is in the labor force. ∎

Now Try Exercise 17

EXAMPLE 3

Quality control A plumbing-supplies manufacturer produces faucet washers, which are packaged in boxes of 300. Quality control studies have shown that 2% of the washers are defective. What is the probability that a box of washers contains exactly 9 defective washers?

Solution Deciding whether a single washer is or is not defective is a binomial trial. Since we wish to consider the number of defective washers in a box, let "success" be the outcome "defective." Then

$$p = .02 \qquad q = 1 - .02 = .98 \qquad n = 300.$$

The probability that 9 out of 300 washers are defective equals

Now Try Exercise 7

$$\Pr(X = 9) = \binom{300}{9}(.02)^9(.98)^{291} \approx .07. \qquad ∎$$

EXAMPLE 4

Veterinary medicine The recovery rate for a certain cattle disease is 25%. If 40 cattle are afflicted with the disease, what is the probability that exactly 10 will recover?

Solution In this example the binomial trial consists of observing a single cow, with recovery as "success." Then

$$p = .25 \qquad q = 1 - .25 = .75 \qquad n = 40.$$

The probability of 10 successes is

Now Try Exercise 11

$$\Pr(X = 10) = \binom{40}{10}(.25)^{10}(.75)^{30} \approx .14. \qquad ∎$$

Calculations arising in binomial trial problems can be tedious to carry out. For instance suppose that in Example 4 we wanted to find the probability that 16 or more cattle recover. Using formula (1) to compute the probabilities that $16, 17, \ldots, 40$ cattle recover, the desired probability is

$$\Pr(X = 16) + \Pr(X = 17) + \cdots + \Pr(X = 40)$$

$$= \binom{40}{16}(.25)^{16}(.75)^{24} + \binom{40}{17}(.25)^{17}(.75)^{23} + \cdots + \binom{40}{40}(.25)^{40}(.75)^0.$$

Each of the terms in this sum is difficult to compute. The thought of computing all of them should be sufficient motivation to seek an alternative approach. Fortunately, there is a reasonably simple method of approximating a sum of this type. We will illustrate the technique in Section 7.7.

Verification of Formula (1) We first consider the case where $n = 3$ and then generalize. Consider a three-trial binomial experiment with two possible results (S or F) on each trial. Assume that the trials are independent and the probability of "S" on each trial is p. It follows that the probability of "F" on each trial is $1 - p$, which we denote by q. The tree in Fig. 1 represents the possible outcomes of the experiment.

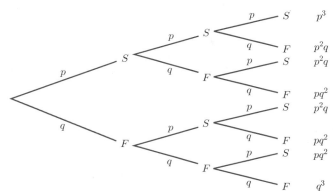

Figure 1

The probability of each individual branch is obtained by multiplying the probabilities along the branch. Then, the probability of two successes in three trials, for example, is the sum of the probabilities of each branch representing two S's and one F. There are three such branches, each with probability p^2q. For the general case, suppose we want the probability of k successes in n trials. Each branch having k S's and $(n-k)$ F's has the associated probability $p^k q^{n-k}$. How many such branches are there in the tree? We can use the methods of Chapter 5 to count the number of branches with k S's and $(n-k)$ F's. What we want to know is the number of ways in which we can arrange k S's and $(n-k)$ F's. This is just $\binom{n}{k}$. So

$$\Pr(X = k) = \binom{n}{k} p^k q^{n-k}. \qquad \blacksquare$$

Figure 2

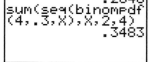

INCORPORATING TECHNOLOGY

GC Binomial probabilities are easily calculated on most graphing calculators. Let's solve Example 1, first on the TI-83/84 Plus and then on the TI-89.

TI-83/84 Plus The value of **binompdf(n,p,x)** is the probability of x successes in n trials, where the probability of success is p. (To display **binompdf(**, press 2nd [DISTR] **0**.) The sum of consecutive probabilities from X = r to X = s successes is the value of **sum(seq(binompdf(n,p,X),X,r,s))**. (To display the word **sum**, press 2nd[LIST], move the cursor to MATH, and press **5**. To display the word **seq(**, press 2nd[LIST], move the cursor to OPS, and press **5**.) Figure 2 uses these two commands to solve Example 1.

TI-89 A convenient way to calculate the binomial probabilities for Example 1, is to invoke the **Y=** editor and then assign to **y1** the expression

$$\mathbf{nCr(4,x)*.3^x*.7^(4-x)}.$$

The sum of consecutive probabilities from $x = r$ to $x = s$ successes is the value of **sum(seq(y1(x),x,r,s))**. The command **seq** creates a list, and the command **sum** adds together specified values from the list. (The words **sum(** and **seq(** are both found on the MATH/List menu.) Figure 3 gives the solution to Example 1. $\blacksquare$

Figure 3

ES In an Excel spreadsheet, the value of $\Pr(X = k)$ for a binomial random variable X is calculated with the function **BINOMDIST$(k, n, p, 0)$** where k is the number of successes, n is the number of trials, and p is the probability of success. The value of $\Pr(X \le k)$ is given by the function **BINOMDIST$(k, n, p, 1)$**. Consecutive probabilities, for instance $\Pr(X = r)$ through $\Pr(X = s)$, can be summed with the expression

$$\textbf{BINOMDIST}(s, n, p, 1) - \textbf{BINOMDIST}(r - 1, n, p, 1).$$

Practice Problems 7.3

1. A number is selected at random from the numbers 0 through 9999. What is the probability that the number is a multiple of 5?

2. If the experiment in Problem 1 is repeated 20 times, with replacement, what is the probability of getting four numbers that are multiples of 5?

EXERCISES 7.3

1. **Rolling a Die** A single die is rolled four times. Find the probability that exactly two of the rolls show a "one."

2. **Coin Tosses** Find the probability of obtaining exactly three heads when tossing a fair coin six times.

3. **Sales** A salesperson determines that the probability of making a sale to a customer is $\frac{1}{4}$. What is the probability of making a sale to three of the next four customers?

4. **Basketball** A basketball player makes free throws with probability .7. What is the probability of making exactly two out of five free throws?

5. **Voter Preferences** Suppose that 60% of the voters in a state intend to vote for a certain candidate. What is the probability that a survey polling five people reveals that two or fewer intend to vote for that candidate?

6. **Exam Questions** An exam consists of six "true or false" questions. What is the probability that a person can get five or more correct by just guessing?

7. **Chemistry Majors** Ten percent of all undergraduates at a university are chemistry majors. In a random sample of eight students, find the probability that exactly two are chemistry majors.

8. **Committee Selection** Sixty percent of all students at a university are female. A committee of five students is selected at random. Only one is a woman. Find the probability that no more than one woman is selected. What might be your conclusion about the way the committee was chosen?

9. **Commuter Stickers** Thirty percent of all cars crossing a toll bridge have a commuter sticker. What is the probability that among 10 randomly selected cars waiting to cross the bridge at least 2 have commuter stickers?

10. **Rolling a Die** A die is rolled 12 times. What is the probability of at least two 5's appearing?

11. **Silver Cars** Forty percent of a particular model of car are silver. What is the probability that in the next 10 observations of this model you observe 5 silver cars?

12. **Remedial English** Fifteen percent of the students who take a screening test are assigned to a remedial English class. In a group of eight students, what is the probability that three will be placed in the remedial class?

13. **Consumer Preferences** Nine customers at a supermarket are asked independently if they use brand X laundry soap. In general, 20% of the population use this brand. What is the probability that among the nine, more than two people use brand X?

14. Write the probability distribution for a binomial random variable with parameters $n = 6$, $p = \frac{1}{4}$.

15. Calculate the probability distribution for a binomial random variable with $n = 8$, $p = .40$.

16. **Darts** The probability is .64 that a dartist scores a bull's-eye on a single toss of a dart. What is the most probable number of bull's-eyes for him to score in his next ten tosses? (*Note:* First make a guess in order to test your intuition. Then calculate the probabilities of 6 successes and 7 successes.)

17. **Coin Tosses PE** A coin is tossed 4 times. What is the probability that at least one head appears?
    (a) $\frac{1}{4}$ (b) $\frac{1}{2}$ (c) $\frac{7}{8}$ (d) $\frac{15}{16}$ (e) $\frac{31}{32}$

18. (a) Explain why

$$\binom{n}{k} = \binom{n}{n-k}$$

for $k = 0, 1, 2, \ldots, n$.

(b) Let X be the random variable associated with binomial trials with $n = 10$ and $p = \frac{1}{2}$. Show that

$$\Pr(X = k) = \Pr(X = 10 - k)$$

for $k = 0, 1, 2, \ldots, 10$.

19. Jury Verdict A jury has 12 jurors. A vote of at least 10 of 12 for "guilty" is necessary for a defendant to be convicted of a crime. Assume that each juror acts independently of the others and that the probability that any one juror makes the correct decision on a defendant is .80. If the defendant is guilty, what is the probability that the jury makes the correct decision?

20. Genetics Every offspring inherits a gene for hair color from each parent. We denote the dominant gene by A and the recessive gene by a. If a person has AA or Aa, then the person exhibits the dominant characteristic. We call a person with the genes Aa a hybrid. A person with aa exhibits the recessive characteristic. Two hybrid parents have three children. Find the probability that at least one child exhibits the recessive characteristic.

21. Coin Tosses A coin is tossed until four heads occur. What is the probability that the fourth head occurs on the tenth toss?

22. Rolling a Die A single die is rolled 10 times and the number of sixes is observed. What is the probability that a six appears 9 times, given that it appears at least 9 times?

23. Selecting Teams The students in a small class are divided into three teams—A, B, and C. Each week two of the teams are selected at random to participate in a competition. What is the probability that team C is selected at least twice during the next three weeks?

24. Rolling Dice When six dice are rolled, what is the probability that exactly five of the dice show a 5 or a 6?

25. Free Throws A basketball player makes 82% of his free throws. What is the most likely number of free throws for him to make in his next 10 tries? (*Note:* First make a guess in order to test your intuition. Then calculate the probabilities of 8 free throws and 9 free throws.)

26. Multiple-Choice Exam An exam consists of ten multiple-choice questions where each question has four choices. If you guess the answers completely at random, what is the probability that you answer at least two questions correctly?

27. Tennis Suppose that in a single game of tennis, the server wins each point with a probability of .6. The game ends when one player accumulates at least four points and is ahead by at least two points. For instance, denoting the players by A and B, player A would win with any of the following outcomes; ABAAA, AABB-BAAA, ABAABA. What is the probability that the server wins and the game ends after 6 points?

28. Baseball A .300 hitter comes to bat four times in a game. What is the probability of getting no hits? 1 hit? 2 hits? 3 hits? 4 hits?

29. Gender of Children A family chosen at random has four children.

(a) What is the probability that there are two boys and two girls?

(b) What is the probability that there are three children of one gender and one of the other?

(c) What is the probability that all four children are of the same gender?

30. Theft of Gold A small country owns 10,000 gold ingots that are stored in 100 guarded bins, each holding 100 ingots. One of the guards has stolen an ingot from each bin and replaced it with a bar of pyrite (fool's gold). The captain of the guards is suspicious that thievery has taken place and is considering two methods for detecting the theft. The first method is to select and examine one ingot from each bin. The second method is to select 25 bins, and then select four ingots from each bin. Which method has the best chance of detecting the theft?

31. Rolling Dice Which of the following is most likely: (a) getting at least one three in six rolls of a die or (b) getting at least two threes in twelve rolls of a die?

32. Baseball The World Series of Baseball consists of a sequence of at most seven games that terminates when one team wins its fourth game. Suppose that the stronger team (the *favorite*) has probability p (where $p > \frac{1}{2}$) of winning any particular game. Then the probability of the weaker team (the *underdog*) winning any particular game is $1 - p$.

(a) Explain why the probability that the underdog wins the series in five games is $\binom{4}{3}(1-p)^4 p$.

(b) Determine the probability that the underdog wins the World Series in four games. Six games. Seven games.

(c) Show that if $p = .6$, then the probability that the underdog wins the World Series is .289792.

(d) Explain why the probability in part (c) is the same as $\binom{7}{0}(1-p)^7 + \binom{7}{1}p(1-p)^6 + \binom{7}{2}p^2(1-p)^5 + \binom{7}{3}p^3(1-p)^4$.

33. Centenarians The probability that a twenty-one year old woman will live to be 100 is 2.17%. What is the probability that at least two out of a group of 77 twenty-one-year old women will live to be 100?

34. Left-handedness Ten percent of the population is left-handed. What is the probability that in a group of 10 people, at least two will be left-handed?

35. Drug Reaction Suppose the probability of a person having an adverse reaction to a certain drug is 2%. If the drug is administered to 56 people, what is the probability that three or more people will have an adverse reaction?

36. Manufacturing Three percent of the widgets produced by a certain machine are defective. What is the probability that a box of 30 widgets contains two or more defective widgets?

In Exercises 37–43, use a graphing calculator or spreadsheet to calculate the probabilities.

37. **Baseball** Refer to Exercise 32.

   (a) Use the formula in part (d) to calculate the probability that the underdog wins the World Series when $p = .6$.

   (b) If the World Series consisted of more than seven games, the favorite would be more likely to win. How long a World Series would be required for the probability of the favorite (with $p = .6$) winning the series to be $\geq 90\%$? *Note:* The series must consist of an odd number of games. For a series of $2n - 1$ games, the winning team must win n games.

38. **Quality Control** Consider Example 3.

   (a) Calculate the probability that a box of washers contains exactly 12 defective washers.

   (b) What is the probability that at most 9 washers will be defective?

39. **Veterinary Medicine** Consider Example 4.

   (a) Calculate the probability that exactly 20 cattle will recover.

   (b) Calculate the sum $\Pr(X = 16) + \Pr(X = 17) + \cdots + \Pr(X = 40)$ discussed in the paragraph following Example 4.

40. **Jury Duty** Suppose there is a .40% chance of being selected for jury duty in September. A school system has 900 teachers.

   (a) What is the probability that 8 teachers will be chosen for jury duty in September?

   (b) Create a table showing the probabilities of having 0 through 6 teachers chosen.

   (c) What is the probability that at most 9 teachers will be chosen?

41. **Dice** When a pair of dice is rolled, the probability of obtaining seven is $\frac{1}{6}$. Suppose a pair of dice is rolled 25 times.

   (a) Calculate the probability that 8 sevens occur.

   (b) Create a table showing the probabilities of having 0 through 6 sevens occur.

   (c) What is the probability that 10 or more sevens will occur?

42. **Genetics** Suppose individuals with a certain gene have a 60% probability of eventually contracting a certain disease. If 100 individuals with the gene participate in a lifetime study, what is the probability that 60 or more of them eventually contract the disease?

43. **Centenarians** Refer to Exercise 33. How large a group of twenty-one year old women is required so that the probability of at least two of them becoming centenarians is over 90%?

7.4 The Mean

It is important at this point to recognize the difference between a *population* and a *sample*. A **population** is a set of all elements about which information is desired. A **sample** is a subset of a population that is analyzed in an attempt to estimate certain properties of the entire population. For instance, suppose that we are interested in finding out some characteristics of the automobile industry but do not have access to the entire population of dealerships in the United States. We must choose a random sample of these dealerships and concentrate on gathering information from it. For instance, suppose we are interested in the average sales for all the car dealerships in the United States for the month of October 2009. We could choose a random sample of $n = 200$ car dealerships across the country, determine the average October 2009 sales for these dealerships, and then use this value to estimate the average October 2009 sales for all car dealerships in the United States.

The average value of the numbers in a sample is called the **sample mean** and is denoted by the symbol $\bar{x}$. It is calculated by adding together the numbers in the sample and then dividing by the number of numbers in the sample.

> **DEFINITION** The **sample mean** (or *average*) of the sample of n numbers $x_1, x_2, \ldots, x_n$ is
> $$\bar{x} = \frac{x_1 + x_2 + \cdots + x_n}{n}.$$

EXAMPLE 1   **Average weekly car sales**   Compute the sample mean of the weekly sales of dealership A of Section 7.2.

Solution   Recall that the weekly sales of dealership A are given in Table 1. Thus we may form the sample mean of the weekly sales figures as follows:

TABLE 1

Weekly sales	Number of occurrences
5	2
6	2
7	13
8	20
9	10
10	4
11	1

$$\frac{1}{52}[(5+5) + (6+6) + \underbrace{(7+\cdots+7)}_{13 \text{ times}} + \underbrace{(8+\cdots+8)}_{20 \text{ times}}$$

$$+ \underbrace{(9+\cdots+9)}_{10 \text{ times}} + \underbrace{(10+\cdots+10)}_{4 \text{ times}} + 11]$$

$$= \frac{5 \cdot 2 + 6 \cdot 2 + 7 \cdot 13 + 8 \cdot 20 + 9 \cdot 10 + 10 \cdot 4 + 11 \cdot 1}{52} \qquad (1)$$

$$= 5 \cdot \tfrac{2}{52} + 6 \cdot \tfrac{2}{52} + 7 \cdot \tfrac{13}{52} + 8 \cdot \tfrac{20}{52} + 9 \cdot \tfrac{10}{52} + 10 \cdot \tfrac{4}{52} + 11 \cdot \tfrac{1}{52}$$

$$\approx 7.96.$$

Thus the sample mean of the weekly sales is approximately 7.96 cars. ■

NOTE ▶   We considered the data from dealership A to be a sample since it was only one year's data and we are interested in making comparisons and using them to predict the future sales of the two dealerships. ■

Let us reexamine the calculation above. The sample mean is given by expression (1). We did this calculation by adding together the observed sales for the 52 weeks of the year and then dividing by 52. To make the calculation more efficient, we noticed that we could group all of the weeks in which we observed five sales, all of the weeks in which there were six sales, and so on. Instead of adding 52 numbers, we simply multiplied each observed value of "sales" by its frequency of occurrence and then divided by 52. Another alternative is to multiply each observed value of "sales" by the relative frequency with which it occurred (e.g., $5 \times \tfrac{2}{52}$), and then add. That is, to compute the mean weekly sales we need only add up the products [number of sales] · [relative frequency of occurrence] over all possible sales figures. If the data for any sample are displayed in a frequency table or a relative frequency table, the sample mean can be calculated in a similar fashion. Since the calculation of $\bar{x}$ depends on the sample values, $\bar{x}$ is a *statistic*.

Sample Mean Suppose that an experiment has as outcomes the numbers $x_1, x_2, \ldots, x_r$. Suppose the frequency of x_1 is f_1, the frequency of x_2 is f_2, and so forth, and that

$$f_1 + f_2 + \cdots + f_r = n.$$

Then

$$\overline{x} = \frac{x_1 f_1 + x_2 f_2 + \cdots + x_r f_r}{n},$$

or

$$\overline{x} = x_1 \left(\frac{f_1}{n}\right) + x_2 \left(\frac{f_2}{n}\right) + \cdots + x_r \left(\frac{f_r}{n}\right).$$

Similar calculations are made when we work with entire populations. Assume the population size is N and that $x_1, x_2, \ldots, x_N$ are the population values. The **population mean**, denoted by the Greek letter μ (mu), is given by the formula

$$\mu = \frac{x_1 + x_2 + \cdots + x_N}{N}.$$

If the data have been grouped into a frequency or relative frequency table, a formula analogous to the one for samples is used:

$$\mu = x_1 \left(\frac{f_1}{N}\right) + x_2 \left(\frac{f_2}{N}\right) + \cdots + x_r \left(\frac{f_r}{N}\right).$$

A numerical descriptive measurement made on a sample is called a **statistic**. Such a measurement made on a population is called a **parameter** of the population. For instance, the sample mean $\overline{x}$ is a statistic and the population mean μ is a parameter. Usually, since we cannot have access to entire populations, we rely on a sample to obtain statistics, and we attempt to use the statistics to estimate the parameters of the population. To help distinguish the parameter from the statistic, all parameters are denoted by Greek letters and all statistics by English letters. We use the common convention of denoting a sample size by lowercase n and a population size by uppercase N.

EXAMPLE 2   **Average life expectancy of deer** An ecologist observes the life expectancy of a certain species of deer held in captivity. Based on a population of 1000 deer, he observes the data shown in Table 2. What is the mean life expectancy of this population of deer?

Solution We convert the given data into a relative frequency distribution by replacing observed frequencies by relative frequencies [= (observed frequency)/1000] (Table 3). The mean of these data is

$$\mu = 1 \cdot 0 + 2 \cdot (.06) + 3 \cdot (.18) + 4 \cdot (.25) + 5 \cdot (.20) + 6 \cdot (.12)$$
$$+ 7 \cdot (.05) + 8 \cdot (.12) + 9 \cdot (.02) = 4.87.$$

Now Try Exercise 3   So the mean life expectancy of this population of deer is 4.87 years. ∎

EXAMPLE 3   **Average weekly car sales** Which car dealership should Mr. Jones buy if he wants the one that will, on the average, sell more cars?

Solution We have seen in Example 1 that the mean of the sample data for dealership A is $\overline{x}_A \approx 7.96$. On the other hand, associated to the data for dealership B (Table 4),

TABLE 2	
Age at death (years)	Number observed
1	0
2	60
3	180
4	250
5	200
6	120
7	50
8	120
9	20

TABLE 3	
Age at death (years)	Relative frequency
1	0
2	.06
3	.18
4	.25
5	.20
6	.12
7	.05
8	.12
9	.02

TABLE 4	
Weekly sales	Relative frequency
5	$\frac{20}{104}$
6	0
7	0
8	$\frac{10}{104}$
9	$\frac{12}{104}$
10	$\frac{50}{104}$
11	$\frac{12}{104}$

we find the sample mean:

$$\overline{x}_B = 5 \cdot \left(\tfrac{20}{104}\right) + 6 \cdot 0 + 7 \cdot 0 + 8 \cdot \left(\tfrac{10}{104}\right) + 9 \cdot \left(\tfrac{12}{104}\right) + 10 \cdot \left(\tfrac{50}{104}\right) + 11 \cdot \left(\tfrac{12}{104}\right)$$
$$\approx 8.85.$$

Thus the average sales of dealership A are 7.96 cars per week, whereas those of dealership B are 8.85 cars per week. If we make the assumption that past sales history predicts future sales, Mr. Jones should buy dealership B. ■

Now Try Exercise 5

Expected Value The sample and population mean have analogs in the theoretical setting of random variables. Suppose that X is a random variable with the following probability distribution:

x_i	$\Pr(X = x_i)$
x_1	p_1
x_2	p_2
$\vdots$	$\vdots$
x_N	p_N

Then the values of X (namely $x_1, x_2, \ldots, x_N$) are the possible outcomes of an experiment. The expected value of X, denoted $E(X)$, is defined as follows:

DEFINITION The **expected value** of the random variable X is given by

$$E(X) = x_1 p_1 + x_2 p_2 + \cdots + x_N p_N.$$

Since the value of p_i represents the theoretical relative frequency of the outcome x_i, the formula for $E(X)$ is similar to the formula for the mean of a relative frequency distribution. Thus the expected value of the random variable X is also called the *mean* of the random variable X or of the probability distribution of X and may be denoted either by $E(X)$ or by μ_X. Frequently, $E(X)$ is used interchangeably with the Greek letter μ when the context is clear.

The expected value of a random variable is the center of the probability distribution in the sense that it is the balance point of the histogram. For example, let X = the number of heads in 5 tosses of a fair coin. The probability distribution appears in Table 5 and the histogram in Fig. 1 on the next page. We can calculate the mean of X:

$$\mu_X = 0\left(\tfrac{1}{32}\right) + 1\left(\tfrac{5}{32}\right) + 2\left(\tfrac{10}{32}\right) + 3\left(\tfrac{10}{32}\right) + 4\left(\tfrac{5}{32}\right) + 5\left(\tfrac{1}{32}\right) = \tfrac{80}{32} = 2.5.$$

TABLE 5	X = number of heads in 5 tosses of a fair coin	
k	$\Pr(X = k)$	$k \cdot \Pr(X = k)$
0	$\frac{1}{32}$	0
1	$\frac{5}{32}$	$\frac{5}{32}$
2	$\frac{10}{32}$	$\frac{20}{32}$
3	$\frac{10}{32}$	$\frac{30}{32}$
4	$\frac{5}{32}$	$\frac{20}{32}$
5	$\frac{1}{32}$	$\frac{5}{32}$
Totals	1	$\mu = \frac{80}{32} = 2.5$

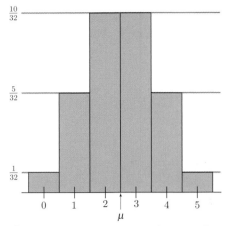

Figure 1. Probability distribution of number of heads.

The mean is shown at the bottom of the histogram (Fig. 1). In contrast, we note that the sample mean, $\overline{x}$, for the coin-tossing experiment tabulated in Section 7.2 was 2.66 (see Table 6). We rarely find that the sample mean $\overline{x}$ is exactly the theoretical value μ_X.

TABLE 6	Observed frequency of heads		
Number of heads x_i	Frequency f_i	Relative frequency (f_i/n)	$x_i \cdot (f_i/n)$
0	3	$\frac{3}{90}$	0
1	14	$\frac{14}{90}$	.16
2	23	$\frac{23}{90}$	.51
3	27	$\frac{27}{90}$	.90
4	17	$\frac{17}{90}$	.76
5	6	$\frac{6}{90}$	.33
Totals	$n = 90$	1	$2.66 = \overline{x}$

We use binomial random variables so often that it is helpful to know that we have an easy formula for $E(X)$ in such cases.

If X is a binomial random variable with parameters n and p, then

$$E(X) = np. \qquad (2)$$

If X is the number of heads in five tosses of a fair coin, then using the formula, we see that $E(X) = 5\left(\frac{1}{2}\right) = 2.5$, which is consistent with our previous calculation. Formula (2) will be verified at the end of this section.

EXAMPLE 4   **Quality control** Consider the plumbing-supplies manufacturer of Example 3 of Section 7.3. Find the average number of defective washers per box.

Solution The number of defective washers in each box is a binomial random variable with $n = 300$ and $p = .02$. The average number of defective washers per box is the expected value of X. $\mathrm{E}(X) = np = 300 \cdot (.02) = 6$. ∎

Now Try Exercise 15

EXAMPLE 5

Average result from rolling a pair of dice Let the random variable X denote the sum of the faces appearing after rolling two dice. Determine $\mathrm{E}(X)$.

TABLE 7

k	$\mathbf{Pr}\,(X = k)$	k	$\mathbf{Pr}\,(X = k)$
2	$\frac{1}{36}$	8	$\frac{5}{36}$
3	$\frac{1}{18}$	9	$\frac{1}{9}$
4	$\frac{1}{12}$	10	$\frac{1}{12}$
5	$\frac{1}{9}$	11	$\frac{1}{18}$
6	$\frac{5}{36}$	12	$\frac{1}{36}$
7	$\frac{1}{6}$		

Solution We determined the probability distribution of X in Example 3 of Section 7.2 (Table 7). Therefore,

$$\mathrm{E}(X) = 2 \cdot \tfrac{1}{36} + 3 \cdot \tfrac{1}{18} + 4 \cdot \tfrac{1}{12} + 5 \cdot \tfrac{1}{9} + 6 \cdot \tfrac{5}{36} + 7 \cdot \tfrac{1}{6}$$

$$+ 8 \cdot \tfrac{5}{36} + 9 \cdot \tfrac{1}{9} + 10 \cdot \tfrac{1}{12} + 11 \cdot \tfrac{1}{18} + 12 \cdot \tfrac{1}{36} = 7.$$

Now Try Exercise 13 Clearly, 7 is the balance point of the histogram shown in Section 7.2. ∎

The expected value of a random variable may be used to analyze games of chance, as the next two examples show.

EXAMPLE 6

Expected winnings from a dice game Two people play a dice game. A single die is rolled. If the outcome is 1 or 2, then A pays B \$2. If the outcome is 3, 4, 5, or 6, then B pays A \$4. What are the long-run expected winnings for A?

Solution Let X be the random variable representing the payoff to A. Then X assumes the possible values -2 and 4. Moreover, since the probability of 1 or 2 on the die is $\frac{1}{3}$, we have

$$\mathrm{Pr}(X = -2) = \tfrac{1}{3}.$$

Similarly,

$$\mathrm{Pr}(X = 4) = \tfrac{2}{3}.$$

Therefore,

$$\mathrm{E}(X) = (-2) \cdot \tfrac{1}{3} + 4 \cdot \tfrac{2}{3} = 2.$$

In other words, the expected payoff to A is \$2 per play. If the game is repeated a large number of times, then on the average A should profit \$2 per play. For example, in 1000 games, we expect that A will profit \$2000. ∎

Now Try Exercise 9

In evaluating a game of chance we use the expected value of the winnings to determine how fair the game is. The expected value of a completely fair game is zero. Let us compute the expected value of the winnings for two variations of the game roulette. American and European roulette games differ in both the nature of the wheel and the rules for playing.

American roulette wheels have 38 numbers (1 through 36 plus 0 and 00), of which 18 are red, 18 are black, and 2 are green. Many different types of bets are possible. We shall consider the "red" bet. When you bet \$1 on red, you win \$1 if a red number appears and you lose \$1 otherwise.

European roulette wheels have 37 numbers (1 through 36 plus 0). The rules of European roulette differ from the American rules. One variation is as follows: When you bet \$1 on "red," you win \$1 if the ball lands on a red number and lose \$1 if the ball lands on a black number. However, if the ball lands on the green number (0), then your bet stays on the table (the bet is said to be "imprisoned") and the payoff is determined by the result of the next spin. If a red number appears, you receive your \$1 bet back, and if a black number appears, you lose your \$1 bet. However, if the green number (0) appears, you get back half of your bet, \$.50. The tree diagrams for American and European roulette are given in Fig. 2.

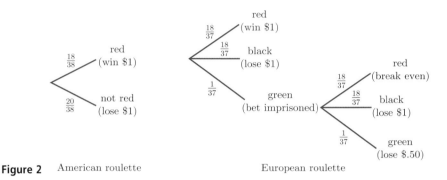

Figure 2   American roulette   European roulette

EXAMPLE 7

Expected winnings from roulette

(a) Set up the probability distribution tables for the earnings in American roulette and European roulette for the \$1 bet on red.

(b) Compute the expected values for the probability distributions in part (a).

Solution (a) For American roulette there are only two possibilities: earnings of \$1 or of $-\$1$. These occur with probabilities $\frac{18}{38}$ and $\frac{20}{38}$, respectively.

For European roulette the possible earnings are \$1, \$0, $-\$.50$, or $-\$1$. There are two ways in which to lose \$1, one with probability $\frac{18}{37}$ and the other with probability $\frac{1}{37} \cdot \frac{18}{37} = \frac{18}{1369}$. Therefore,

$$\Pr(\text{lose } \$1) = \frac{18}{37} + \frac{18}{1369} = \frac{684}{1369}.$$

These probability distributions are tabulated in Table 8.

TABLE 8				
American roulette			**European roulette**	
Earnings	Probability		Earnings	Probability
1	$\frac{18}{38}$		1	$\frac{18}{37}$
-1	$\frac{20}{38}$		0	$\frac{18}{1369}$
			$-\frac{1}{2}$	$\frac{1}{1369}$
			-1	$\frac{684}{1369}$

(b) American roulette:

$$\mu = 1 \cdot \tfrac{18}{38} + (-1) \cdot \tfrac{20}{38} = -\tfrac{2}{38} \approx -.0526.$$

European roulette:

$$\mu = 1 \cdot \tfrac{18}{37} + 0 \cdot \tfrac{18}{1369} + \left(-\tfrac{1}{2}\right)\tfrac{1}{1369} + (-1)\tfrac{684}{1369}$$

$$= -\tfrac{1}{74} \approx -.0135.$$

Now Try Exercise 7 ▮

The secrets of Nicholas Dandolas, one of the famous gamblers of the twentieth century, are revealed by Ted Thackrey, Jr., in *Gambling Secrets of Nick the Greek* (Rand-McNally, 1968). The chapter entitled "Roulette" is subtitled "For Europeans Only." Looking at the probabilities of winning does not reveal any significant advantage of European roulette over American roulette: $\tfrac{18}{37}$ is not much bigger than $\tfrac{18}{38}$. Also, the chance in European roulette to break even is very small. The real difference between the two games is revealed by the expected values. Someone playing American roulette will lose, on the average, about $5\tfrac{1}{4}$ cents per \$1 bet, whereas for European roulette the average loss is about $1\tfrac{1}{3}$ cents. In both cases you expect to lose money in the long run, but in American roulette you lose nearly four times as much.

NOTE ▶ Casinos refer to the percent of each bet they expect to keep as the *house percentage* or the *house advantage*. The house percentage is 5.26% on all but one American roulette bet. ▮

In summary, there are three types of mean: sample mean ($\overline{x}$), population mean (μ), and expected value of a random variable ($\mathrm{E}(X)$, μ, or μ_X).

Verification of Formula (2)   Note that

$$\mu = 0 \cdot \Pr(X = 0) + 1 \cdot \Pr(X = 1) + \cdots + n \cdot \Pr(X = n)$$

$$= 0 \cdot \binom{n}{0} p^0 q^{n-0} + 1 \cdot \binom{n}{1} p^1 q^{n-1} + \cdots + n \cdot \binom{n}{n} p^n q^{n-n}.$$

Moreover, note that

$$k \binom{n}{k} = k \cdot \frac{n(n-1) \cdot \cdots \cdot (n-k+1)}{k(k-1) \cdot \cdots \cdot 2 \cdot 1} = n \cdot \frac{(n-1) \cdot \cdots \cdot (n-k+1)}{(k-1) \cdot \cdots \cdot 2 \cdot 1}$$

$$= n \binom{n-1}{k-1} \qquad (k = 1, 2, 3, \ldots, n).$$

Therefore,

$$\mu = 1 \cdot \binom{n}{1} p^1 q^{n-1} + 2 \cdot \binom{n}{2} p^2 q^{n-2} + \cdots + n \cdot \binom{n}{n} p^n q^0$$

$$= n \binom{n-1}{0} p^1 q^{n-1} + n \binom{n-1}{1} p^2 q^{n-2} + \cdots + n \binom{n-1}{n-1} p^n q^0$$

$$= np \left[\binom{n-1}{0} p^0 q^{n-1} + \binom{n-1}{1} p^1 q^{n-2} + \cdots + \binom{n-1}{n-1} p^{n-1} q^0 \right]$$

$$= np(p+q)^{n-1} \qquad \text{(by the binomial theorem)}$$

$$= np \qquad \text{(since } p + q = 1\text{).}$$

▮

Practice Problems 7.4

1. **Life Insurance** A 74-year-old man pays $100 for a one-year life insurance policy, which pays $2000 in the event that he dies during the next year. According to life insurance tables, the probability of a 74-year-old man living one additional year is .95. Write down the probability distribution for the possible financial outcome and determine its expected value.

2. **Life Insurance** According to life insurance tables, the probability that a 74-year-old man will live an additional five years is .7. How much should a 74-year-old be willing to pay for a policy that pays $2000 in the event of death any time within the next 5 years?

EXERCISES 7.4

1. Find the expected value for the probability distribution in Table 9.

TABLE 9

Value	Probability
0	.15
1	.2
2	.1
3	.25
4	.3

2. Find the expected value for the probability distribution in Table 10.

TABLE 10

Value	Probability
-1	.1
$-\frac{1}{2}$	.4
0	.25
$\frac{1}{2}$	.2
1	.05

3. **Grades** A college student received the following course grades for 10 (three-credit) courses during his freshman year: 4, 4, 4, 3, 3, 3, 3, 2, 2, 1.
   (a) Find his grade point average by adding the grades and dividing by 10.
   (b) Write down the relative frequency table.
   (c) Find the mean of the relative frequency distribution in part (b).

4. **Gymnastic Scores** An Olympic gymnast received the following scores from six judges: 9.8, 9.8, 9.4, 9.2, 9.2, 9.0.
   (a) Find the average score by adding the scores and dividing by 6.
   (b) Write down the relative frequency table.
   (c) Find the mean of the relative frequency distribution in part (b).

5. **Comparing Toothpastes** Table 11 gives the relative frequency of the number of cavities for two groups of children trying different brands of toothpaste. Calculate the sample means to determine which group had fewer cavities.

TABLE 11

Number of cavities	Relative frequency Group A	Relative frequency Group B
0	.3	.2
1	.3	.3
2	.2	.3
3	.1	.1
4	0	.1
5	.1	0

6. **Investments** Table 12 gives the possible returns of two different investments and their probabilities. Calculate the means of the probability distributions to determine which investment has the greater expected return.

TABLE 12

Investment A	
Return	Probability
$1000	.2
$2000	.5
$3000	.3

Investment B	
Return	Probability
$-$3000	.1
0	.3
$4000	.6

7. **Roulette** In American roulette, a bettor may place a $1 bet on any one of the 38 numbers on the roulette wheel. He wins $35 (plus the return of his bet) if the ball lands on his number; otherwise, he loses his bet. Write down

the probability distribution for the earnings from this type of bet and find the expected value.

8. **Roulette** In American roulette, a dollar may be bet on a pair of numbers. The expected earnings for this type of bet is $-\$\frac{1}{19}$. How much money does the bettor receive if the ball lands on one of the two numbers?

9. **Carnival Game** In a carnival game, the player selects balls one at a time, without replacement, from an urn containing two red and four white balls. The game proceeds until a red ball is drawn. The player pays $1 to play the game and receives $\$\frac{1}{2}$ for each ball drawn. Write down the probability distribution for the player's earnings and find its expected value.

10. **Carnival Game** In a carnival game, the player selects two coins from a bag containing two silver dollars and six slugs. Write down the probability distribution for the winnings and determine how much the player would have to pay so that he would break even, on the average, over many repetitions of the game.

11. **Life Insurance** Using life insurance tables, a retired man determines that the probability of living 5 more years is .9. He decides to take out a life insurance policy that will pay $10,000 in the event that he dies during the next 5 years. How much should he be willing to pay for this policy? (Do not take account of interest rates or inflation.)

12. **Life Insurance** Using life insurance tables, a retired couple determines that the probability of living 5 more years is .9 for the man and .95 for the woman. They decide to take out a life insurance policy that will pay $10,000 if either one dies during the next 5 years and $15,000 if both die during that time. How much should they be willing to pay for this policy? (Assume that their life spans are independent events.)

13. **Dice** A pair of dice is rolled and the larger of the two numbers showing is recorded. Find the expected value of this experiment.

14. **Baseball** Ted is a consistent .275 hitter. How many hits is he expected to have in his next 40 at-bats?

15. **Rolling a Die** A die is rolled 30 times. What is the expected number of times that a 5 or a 6 will appear?

16. What is the probability of success for a binomial random variable with 20 trials whose expected value is 3?

17. **Basketball** A basketball player makes 40% of his three-point shots and 60% of his free throws. If he is fouled while taking a three-point shot, he is given three free throws. Which is greater: the expected number of points from taking a three-point shot or the expected number of points from taking three free throws?

18. The *range* of a set of numbers is the difference between the highest and the lowest number. Suppose a set of five distinct positive integers has a median, mean, and range of 6. What are the possibilities for the five numbers?

19. Give a set of five different single-digit numbers for which

   (a) the median equals the mean.

   (b) the median is less than the mean.

   (c) the median is greater than the mean.

20. **Grades** José wants to earn a 90% overall average in his mathematics class. His current grades are 83%, 92%, and 89%. What grade does José need to average on the next three assessments to earn a 90% overall average?

21. **Weather** The average daily temperature during April in Washington, D.C. is 56.1°. Suppose that in a certain year, the average daily temperature for the first 16 days of April is 54°. What temperature must the remaining 14 days average in order for the overall average to reach the historic average of 56.1°?

22. **Exam Scores PE** A student's exam scores are 95, 88, and 79. What score must the student earn on the fourth exam to have an average (arithmetic mean) score of 90?

   (a) 96 (b) 97 (c) 98 (d) 99 (e) 100

23. **PE** If 5, 6, and x have the same average (arithmetic mean) as 2, 7, and 9, then x equals

   (a) 4 (b) 5 (c) 6 (d) 7 (e) 8

24. **Candle Sales PE** A store sold an average (arithmetic mean) of x candles per day for k days, and then sold y candles on the next day. What is the average number of candles sold daily for the $(k + 1)$-day period?

   (a) $x + \dfrac{y}{k}$ (b) $\dfrac{kx + y}{k + 1}$ (c) $\dfrac{k(x + y)}{k + 1}$

   (d) $\dfrac{x + ky}{k + 1}$ (e) $x + \dfrac{y}{k + 1}$

25. **Ticket Sales PE** Last weekend a movie theater sold x adult tickets at $7 each and y children's tickets at $4 each. The average (arithmetic mean) revenue per ticket was

   (a) $\dfrac{28xy}{x + y}$ (b) $\dfrac{7x + 4y}{x + y}$ (c) $\dfrac{7x + 4y}{11}$

   (d) $\dfrac{28xy}{11}$ (e) $\dfrac{7x + 4y}{xy}$

26. **PE** If three distinct positive integers have an average (arithmetic mean) of 70, and if the smallest of the three integers is 50, then the largest of the three integers can be at most

   (a) 70 (b) 99 (c) 100 (d) 109 (e) 159

27. **PE** If three distinct positive integers have an average (arithmetic mean) of 200, and if the smallest of the three integers is 120, then the largest of the three integers can be at most

   (a) 200 (b) 350 (c) 359 (d) 459 (e) 460

28. **Weekly Revenue PE** A small business had an average (arithmetic mean) weekly revenue of $14,000 over the past three weeks. The revenue for the first week was twice the revenue of the third week, and the revenue

for the second week was half the revenue of the third week. What was the revenue for the first week?

(a) $6000   (b) $12,000   (c) $18,000

(d) $20,000   (e) $24,000

29. Baseball Cards PE Tom, Dick, and Harry have an average (arithmetic mean) of 120 baseball cards. Tom has $1\frac{1}{2}$ times as many cards as Dick, and Harry has $\frac{1}{2}$ as many cards as Dick. How many baseball cards does Tom have?

(a) 60   (b) 90   (c) 120   (d) 180   (e) 240

30. Exam Scores PE Three members of a study group each earned a score of 91 on an exam, and the other five members of the group each earned a score of 87. The average (arithmetic mean) score earned by the members of this study group is

(a) 88.0   (b) 88.5   (c) 89.0   (d) 89.5   (e) 90.0

31. Batting Averages PE Five members of a baseball team have batting averages of .300, and the other four members of the team have batting averages of .350. The overall batting average among members of the team is closest to

(a) .311   (b) .322   (c) .325   (d) .330   (e) .333

32. Magazine Sales PE Half of the magazines at a newsstand sell for an average (arithmetic mean) of $2.00 and the other half sell for an average of $2.50. If the total retail value of the magazines is $135.00, how many magazines are there at the newsstand?

(a) 56   (b) 57   (c) 58   (d) 59   (e) 60

33. Truck Capacity PE A truck can carry a maximum of 75,000 pounds of cargo. How many cases of cargo can it carry if half of the cases have an average (arithmetic mean) weight of 20 pounds and the other half have an average weight of 30 pounds?

(a) 3000   (b) 3200   (c) 3500   (d) 3750   (e) 4000

34. Theft Insurance PE Bob wishes to insure a priceless family heirloom against theft. The annual premium for policy A is $150, and it will pay $75,000 if the heirloom is stolen. Policy B will pay $100,000, but the annual premium for policy B is $250. Bob estimates the probability that the heirloom will be stolen in any given year and remains undecided between the two policies. What is this estimated probability?

(a) .001   (b) .002   (c) .003   (d) .004   (e) .005

35. Rain Insurance PE The promoter of a football game is concerned that it will rain. She has the option of spending $8000 on insurance that will pay $40,000 if it rains. She estimates that the revenue from the game will be $60,000 if it does not rain and $25,000 if it does rain. What must the chance of rain be if she is ambivalent about this insurance?

(a) 20%   (b) 25%   (c) 30%   (d) 35%   (e) 40%

Solutions to Practice Problems 7.4

1. There are two possibilities. If the man lives until the end of the year, he loses $100. If he dies during the year, his estate gains $1900 (the $2000 settlement minus the $100 premium).

Outcome	Probability
−$100	.95
$1900	.05

$$\mu = (-100)(.95) + (1900)(.05) = 0$$

(Thus, if the insurance company insures a large number of people, it should break even. Its profits will result from the interest that it earns on the money being held.)

2. Let x denote the cost of the policy. The probability distribution is as follows.

Outcome	Probability
−x	.7
$2000 - x$	.3

$$\mu = (-x)(.7) + (2000 - x)(.3)$$
$$= -.7x + 600 - .3x$$
$$= 600 - x$$

The expected value will be zero if $x = 600$. Therefore, the man should be willing to pay up to $600 for his policy.

7.5 The Variance and Standard Deviation

In Section 7.4 we introduced three related concepts: the mean of a sample ($\overline{x}$); the mean of a population (μ); and the mean or expected value of a random variable [E(X)]. The mean is probably the single most important number that can be used to describe a sample, a population, or a probability distribution of a random variable. The next most important number is the **variance**.

Roughly speaking, the variance measures the dispersal or spread of a distribution about its mean. The more closely concentrated the distribution about its mean, the smaller the variance; the more spread out, the larger the variance. Thus, for example, the probability distribution whose histogram is drawn in Fig. 1(a) has a smaller variance than that in Fig. 1(b).

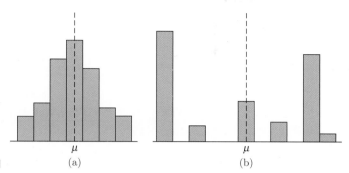

Figure 1   (a)   (b)

Let us now define the variance of a probability distribution of a random variable. Suppose X is a random variable with values $x_1, x_2, \ldots, x_N$ and respective probabilities $p_1, p_2, \ldots, p_N$. Suppose that the mean is μ. Then the deviations of the various outcomes from the mean are given by the N differences

$$x_1 - \mu, \quad x_2 - \mu, \quad \ldots, \quad x_N - \mu.$$

Since we want to give weight to the various deviations according to their likelihood of occurrence, it is tempting to multiply each deviation by its probability of occurrence. However, this will not lead to a very satisfactory measure of deviation from the mean. This is because some of the differences will be positive and others negative. In the process of addition, deviations from the mean (both positive and negative deviations) will combine to yield a zero total deviation. To correct this, we consider instead the squares of the differences:

$$(x_1 - \mu)^2, \quad (x_2 - \mu)^2, \quad \ldots, \quad (x_N - \mu)^2,$$

which are all ≥ 0. To obtain a measure of deviation from the mean, we multiply each of these expressions by the probability of the corresponding outcome. The number thus obtained is called the *variance of the probability distribution* (or of the associated random variable) and is denoted Var(X). That is, the variance of a probability distribution is given by the formula

DEFINITION

$$\mathrm{Var}(X) = (x_1 - \mu)^2 p_1 + (x_2 - \mu)^2 p_2 + \cdots + (x_N - \mu)^2 p_N.$$

EXAMPLE 1

Computing variance Compute the variance of the following probability distribution:

Outcome	Probability
0	.1
1	.3
2	.5
3	.1

Solution The mean is given by

$$\mu = 0 \cdot (.1) + 1 \cdot (.3) + 2 \cdot (.5) + 3 \cdot (.1) = 1.6.$$

In the notation of random variables, the calculations of the variance may be summarized as follows:

k	$\Pr(X = k)$	$k - \mu$	$(k - \mu)^2$	$(k - \mu)^2 \Pr(X = k)$
0	.1	$0 - 1.6 = -1.6$	2.56	.256
1	.3	$1 - 1.6 = -.6$	.36	.108
2	.5	$2 - 1.6 = .4$	.16	.080
3	.1	$3 - 1.6 = 1.4$	1.96	.196

$$\text{Var}(X) = .256 + .108 + .080 + .196 = .64.$$

Now Try Exercise 1

There is an alternate formula for the variance that can simplify its calculation.

Alternate Formula for Variance[1]   If X is a random variable, then

$$\text{Var}(X) = \text{E}(X^2) - [\text{E}(X)]^2$$

EXAMPLE 2   **Using the alternate formula for variance**   Use the alternate formula to find the variance of the random variable in Example 1.

Solution By Example 1, we know that $\text{E}(X) = 1.6$. The probability distribution of X^2 is as follows

k	$\Pr(X^2 = k)$
0	.1
1	.3
4	.5
9	.1

$$\text{E}(X^2) = 0 \cdot (.1) + 1 \cdot (.3) + 4 \cdot (.5) + 9 \cdot (.1) = 3.2.$$

Therefore,

Now Try Exercise 21

$$\text{Var}(X) = \text{E}(X^2) - [\text{E}(X)]^2 = 3.2 - 1.6^2 = 3.2 - 2.56 = .64.$$

An advantage of this alternate formula is that if the expected value is an unwieldy number, we are spared the tedious task of subtracting it from the values of the variable, which sometimes produces even more unwieldy numbers that must be squared and summed.

Actually, a much more commonly used measure of dispersal about the mean is the **standard deviation**, which is just the square root of the variance and is denoted σ_X. (σ is the Greek letter sigma, and σ_X is pronounced "sigma sub X.")

DEFINITION $\sigma_X = \sqrt{\text{Var}(X)}$

---
[1]The alternate formula for the variance can be derived from the fact that $\text{Var}(X) = \text{E}[(X - \mu)^2]$.

Thus, for example, for the probability distribution of Example 1 we have
$$\sigma_X = \sqrt{.64} = .8.$$

The reason for using the standard deviation as opposed to the variance is that the former is expressed in the same units of measurement as X, whereas the latter is not.

In Section 7.3, we saw that if X is a binomial random variable with parameters n and p, then $E(X) = np$. The variance and standard deviation of a binomial random variable also have simple formulas.

> **Variance and Standard Deviation of a Binomial Random Variable**   If X is a binomial random variable with parameters n and p, then with $q = 1 - p$,
> $$\text{Var}(X) = npq$$
> $$\sigma_X = \sqrt{npq}.$$

EXAMPLE 3   Compute the mean and standard deviation for the binomial random variable X, the number of *ones* appearing in 180 rolls of a die.

Solution   Here $n = 180$, $p = \frac{1}{6}$, and $q = 1 - \frac{1}{6} = \frac{5}{6}$. Therefore,
$$\mu = np = 180 \cdot \frac{1}{6} = 30$$

Now Try Exercise 9

$$\sigma_X = \sqrt{npq} = \sqrt{180 \cdot \frac{1}{6} \cdot \frac{5}{6}} = \sqrt{25} = 5. \qquad \blacksquare$$

In Section 7.3, we developed formulas for the mean of a population (μ). Similar formulas are available for the variance and standard deviation of a population. In this case, the standard deviation is denoted σ and the variance is denoted σ^2.

> **DEFINITION Population Variance and Standard Deviation** Consider a population of N numbers $x_1, x_2, \ldots, x_N$ having mean μ. Then the variance is defined as
> $$\sigma^2 = \frac{(x_1 - \mu)^2 + (x_2 - \mu)^2 + \cdots + (x_N - \mu)^2}{N}.$$
> If the numbers have been grouped into the values $x_1, x_2, \ldots, x_r$ with frequencies $f_1, f_2, \ldots, f_r$, then
> $$\sigma^2 = \frac{1}{N} \left[(x_1 - \mu)^2 f_1 + (x_2 - \mu)^2 f_2 + \cdots + (x_r - \mu)^2 f_r \right]$$
> or
> $$\sigma^2 = (x_1 - \mu)^2 \left(\frac{f_1}{N} \right) + (x_2 - \mu)^2 \left(\frac{f_2}{N} \right) + \cdots + (x_r - \mu)^2 \left(\frac{f_r}{N} \right).$$
> The **standard deviation**, σ, is defined as the square root of the variance.

EXAMPLE 4   **Computing variance and standard deviation**   Compute the variance and the standard deviation for the population of scores on a five-question quiz as tabulated in Table 1 on the next page.

Solution   We first find μ.
$$\mu = \frac{1}{60}[0(4) + 1(9) + 2(6) + 3(14) + 4(18) + 5(9)] = \frac{180}{60} = 3.$$

TABLE 1	
Score	Frequency
0	4
1	9
2	6
3	14
4	18
5	9
Total	60

TABLE 2				
x_i	f_i	$x_i - \mu$	$(x_i - \mu)^2$	$(x_i - \mu)^2(f_i)$
0	4	-3	9	36
1	9	-2	4	36
2	6	-1	1	6
3	14	0	0	0
4	18	1	1	18
5	9	2	4	36
Totals	60			132

We find σ^2 by subtracting 3 from each of the test scores, squaring the differences, weighting each with its frequency, and dividing the resulting sum by $N = 60$. The computation is shown in Table 2. Therefore, $\sigma^2 = \frac{132}{60} = 2.2$. The standard deviation, which is found by taking the square root of the variance, is $\sigma \approx 1.48$. ■

As we discussed in Section 7.4, we sometimes have only sample values at our disposal. If so, we must use sample statistics to estimate the population parameters. For example, we can use the sample mean $\overline{x}$ as an estimate of the population mean μ, and the sample variance as an estimate of the population variance, σ^2. In fact, if samples of size n were chosen repeatedly from a population and the sample mean were computed for each sample, then the average of these means should be close to the value of the population mean, μ. This is a desirable property for any statistic used to estimate a parameter—the averages of the statistic get arbitrarily close to the actual value of the parameter as the number of samples increases. Such an estimate is said to be **unbiased**. Thus $\overline{x}$ is an unbiased estimate of μ.

The situation with the variance is a little trickier. In order to have an unbiased estimate of the population variance σ^2, we must define the **sample variance**, s^2, in a slightly peculiar way.

> **DEFINITION Sample Variance and Standard Deviation** Consider a sample of n numbers $x_1, x_2, \ldots, x_n$ having mean $\overline{x}$. Then the **variance** is
>
> $$s^2 = \frac{(x_1 - \overline{x})^2 + (x_2 - \overline{x})^2 + \cdots + (x_n - \overline{x})^2}{n - 1}.$$
>
> If the numbers have been grouped into the values $x_1, x_2, \ldots, x_r$ with frequencies $f_1, f_2, \ldots, f_r$, then
>
> $$s^2 = \frac{1}{n - 1} \left[(x_1 - \overline{x})^2 f_1 + (x_2 - \overline{x})^2 f_2 + \cdots + (x_r - \overline{x})^2 f_r \right].$$
>
> The **standard deviation**, s, is defined as the square root of the variance.

This is the usual definition and the way in which most statistical calculators do the computation of the sample variance. Note that the divisor is one less than the sample size. With this definition, s^2 is an unbiased estimate of σ^2.

EXAMPLE 5

Computing sample standard deviation Compute the sample standard deviations for the frequency distributions of sales in car dealerships A and B.

Solution The frequency distribution for dealership A is given by Table 3. In Example 1 of Section 7.4, we found the sample mean of the weekly sales to be $\overline{x}_A = 7.96$. Recall that we are treating the data collected from these dealerships as samples (one year's data from dealership A and two year's data from dealership B). Therefore, the sample variance for dealership A is given by

TABLE 3

Weekly sales	Frequency
5	2
6	2
7	13
8	20
9	10
10	4
11	1
Total	$n = 52$

$$s_A^2 = \frac{1}{51}\big[(5 - 7.96)^2 \cdot 2 + (6 - 7.96)^2 \cdot 2 + (7 - 7.96)^2 \cdot 13$$
$$+ (8 - 7.96)^2 \cdot 20 + (9 - 7.96)^2 \cdot 10 + (10 - 7.96)^2 \cdot 4$$
$$+ (11 - 7.96)^2 \cdot 1\big] \approx 1.45.$$

The sample standard deviation, s_A, for dealership A is given by

$$s_A = \sqrt{s_A^2} = \sqrt{1.45} \approx 1.20 \text{ cars.}$$

In a similar way, we find that the sample standard deviation of dealership B is $s_B \approx 2.03$ cars. Since s_A is smaller than s_B, dealership B exhibited greater variation than dealership A during the time the sales were observed. On average, dealership B had higher weekly sales, but those of dealership A showed greater consistency. The sample statistics might help Mr. Jones decide which dealership to buy. He will have to decide if consistency is more important than the size of long-term average sales per week.

Now Try Exercise 5

We can use the value of the sample mean to estimate the population mean. The sample standard deviation helps us to determine the degree of accuracy of our estimate. If the sample standard deviation is small, indicating that the population is not widely dispersed about its mean, the estimated value of μ is likely to be close to the actual value of μ.

What does the standard deviation tell us about the dispersal of the data about the mean of a probability distribution? *Chebychev's inequality* helps us to see that the larger the standard deviation, the more likely it is that we find extreme values in the data. The probability that an outcome falls more than c units away from the mean is at most σ^2/c^2.

Chebychev's Inequality   Suppose that a probability distribution with numerical outcomes has expected value μ and standard deviation σ. Then the probability that a randomly chosen outcome lies between $\mu - c$ and $\mu + c$ is at least $1 - (\sigma^2/c^2)$.

A verification of the Chebychev inequality can be found in most elementary statistics texts.

EXAMPLE 6   **Applying Chebychev's inequality**   Suppose that a probability distribution has mean 5 and standard deviation 1. Use the Chebychev inequality to estimate the probability that an outcome lies between 3 and 7.

Solution   Here $\mu = 5$, $\sigma = 1$. Since we wish to estimate the probability of an outcome lying between 3 and 7, we set $\mu - c = 3$ and $\mu + c = 7$. Thus $c = 2$. Then by the Chebychev inequality, the desired probability is at least

$$1 - \frac{\sigma^2}{c^2} = 1 - \frac{1}{4} = .75.$$

That is, if the experiment is repeated a large number of times, we expect at least 75% of the outcomes to be between 3 and 7. Also, we expect at most 25% of the outcomes to fall below 3 or above 7.

Now Try Exercise 13(a)

The Chebychev inequality has many practical applications, one of which is illustrated in the next example.

EXAMPLE 7

Quality control Apex Drug Supply Company sells bottles containing 100 capsules of penicillin. Due to the bottling procedure, not every bottle contains exactly 100 capsules. Assume that the average number of capsules in a bottle is indeed 100 ($\mu = 100$) and the standard deviation is 2 ($\sigma = 2$). If the company ships 5000 bottles, estimate the number having between 95 and 105 capsules inclusive.

Solution By Chebychev's inequality, the proportion of bottles having between $100 - 5$ and $100 + 5$ capsules should be at least

$$1 - (2^2/5^2) = \tfrac{21}{25} = .84.$$

That is, we expect at least 84% of the 5000 bottles, or 4200 bottles, to be in the desired range.

Now Try Exercise 15

Note that the estimate provided by Chebychev's inequality is crude. In more advanced statistics books, you can find sharper estimates. Also, in the case of the normal distribution, we shall provide a much more precise way of estimating the probability of falling within c units of the mean, based on using a table of areas under the normal curve (see Section 7.6).

INCORPORATING TECHNOLOGY

GC In Figs. 2 and 3, the mean $\bar{x}$, sample standard deviation **Sx**, and population standard deviation **σx** are calculated for the car dealership data from Table 3. The weekly sales were entered into list **L1** and the frequencies into list **L2**. Figure 3 was invoked by entering **1-Var Stats L1,L2** from the home screen. (To display **1-Var Stats**, press STAT ► 1.)

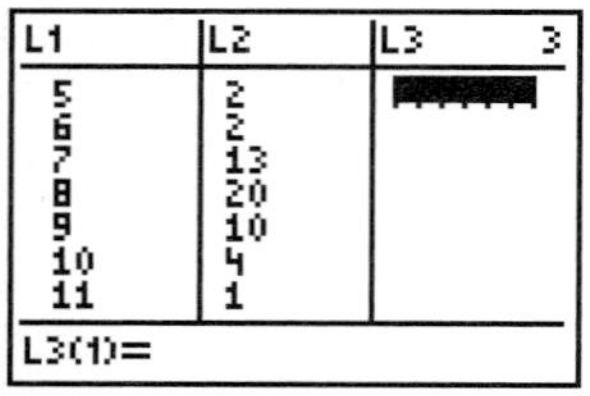

L1	L2	L3 3
5	2	
6	2	
7	13	
8	20	
9	10	
10	4	
11	1	
L3(1)=		

Figure 2

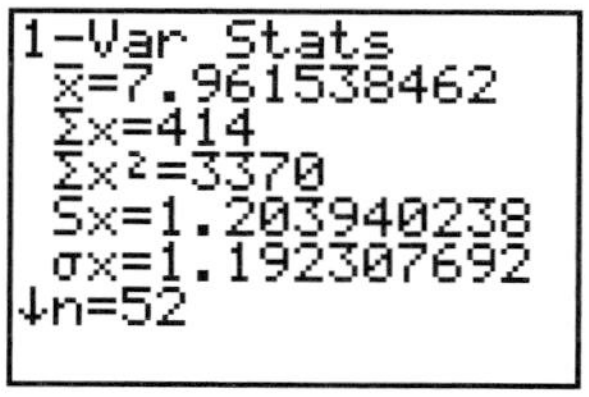

```
1-Var Stats
x̄=7.961538462
Σx=414
Σx²=3370
Sx=1.203940238
σx=1.192307692
↓n=52
```

Figure 3

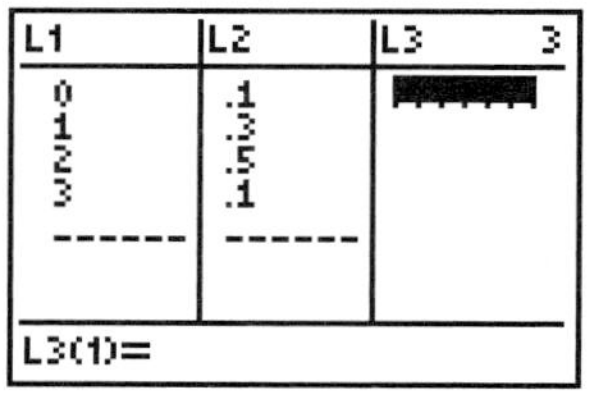

L1	L2	L3 3
0	.1	
1	.3	
2	.5	
3	.1	
--	--	
L3(1)=		

Figure 4

```
1-Var Stats
x̄=1.6
Σx=1.6
Σx²=3.2
Sx=
σx=.8
↓n=1
```

Figure 5

The mean and standard deviation of a probability distribution can be calculated in the same way by placing the probabilities in list **L2**. Figures 4 and 5 analyze the probability distribution in Example 1. Note that **n** is the sum of the entries in **L2**.

Obtaining Means and Standard Deviations with an Excel Spreadsheet After the numbers in a sample have been placed into a range, the sample mean, variance, and standard deviation can be calculated by evaluating the functions AVERAGE, VAR, and STDEV of the range. The functions VARP and STDEVP calculate the population variance and standard deviation.

Practice Problems 7.5

1. (a) Compute the variance of the probability distribution in Table 4.

(b) Using Table 4, find the probability that the outcome is between 22 and 24, inclusive.

2. Refer to the probability distribution of Problem 1. Use the Chebychev inequality to approximate the probability that the outcome is between 22 and 24.

TABLE 4	
Outcome	Probability
21	$\frac{1}{16}$
22	$\frac{1}{8}$
23	$\frac{5}{8}$
24	$\frac{1}{8}$
25	$\frac{1}{16}$

EXERCISES 7.5

1. Compute the variance of the probability distribution in Table 5.

TABLE 5	
Outcome	Probability
70	.5
71	.2
72	.1
73	.2

2. Compute the variance of the probability distribution in Table 6.

TABLE 6	
Outcome	Probability
-1	$\frac{1}{8}$
$-\frac{1}{2}$	$\frac{3}{8}$
0	$\frac{1}{8}$
$\frac{1}{2}$	$\frac{1}{8}$
1	$\frac{2}{8}$

3. Determine by inspection which one of the probability distributions, A or B, in Fig. 6 has the greater variance.

4. Determine by inspection which one of the probability distributions, B or C, in Fig. 6 has the greater variance.

5. Investment Returns Table 7 gives the probability distribution for the possible returns from two different investments.

(a) Compute the mean and the variance for each investment.

(b) Which investment has the higher expected return (i.e., mean)?

(c) Which investment is less risky (i.e., has lesser variance)?

TABLE 7	
Investment A	
Return ($ millions)	Probability
-10	$\frac{1}{5}$
20	$\frac{3}{5}$
25	$\frac{1}{5}$
Investment B	
Return ($ millions)	Probability
0	.3
10	.4
30	.3

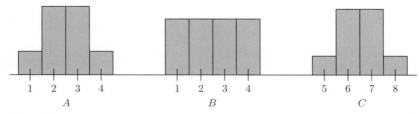

Figure 6

6. Golf Scores Two golfers recorded their scores for 20 nine-hole rounds of golf. Golfer A's scores were

$$39, 39, 40, 40, 40, 40, 40, 40,$$
$$41, 41, 41, 41, 41, 41, 41, 42, 43, 43, 43, 44.$$

Golfer B's scores were

$$40, 40, 40, 41, 41, 41, 41, 42, 42, 42, 42, 42,$$
$$43, 43, 43, 43, 43, 43, 44, 44.$$

(a) Compute the sample mean and the variance of each golfer's scores.

(b) Who is the better golfer? (*Note:* The lower the score, the better.)

(c) Who is the more consistent golfer?

7. Weekly Sales Table 8 gives the relative frequency distribution for the weekly sales of two businesses.

(a) Compute the population mean and the variance for each business.

(b) Which business has the better sales record?

(c) Which business has the more consistent sales record?

TABLE 8

| Sales | Relative frequency | |
	Business A	Business B
100	.1	0
101	.2	.2
102	.3	0
103	0	.2
104	0	.1
105	.2	.2
106	.2	.3

8. Course Grades Student A received the following course grades during her first year of college:

$$4, 4, 4, 4, 3, 3, 2, 2, 2, 0.$$

Student B received the following course grades during her first year:

$$4, 4, 4, 4, 4, 4, 3, 1, 1, 1.$$

(a) Compute the population means and variances.

(b) Which student had the better grade point average?

(c) Which student was more consistent?

9. Coin Tosses Suppose a coin is tossed 12 times. Find the mean and standard deviation for the number of heads.

10. Dice Suppose a pair of dice is rolled 720 times. Find the mean and standard deviation for the number of times the sum of seven appears.

11. Quality Control A manufacturer produces widgets that are packaged in boxes of 200. The probability of a widget being defective is .015. Find the mean and standard deviation for the number of defective widgets in a box.

12. Basketball A basketball player makes each free throw with probability $\frac{3}{5}$. Find the mean and standard deviation for the number of successes in 15 tries.

13. Suppose that a probability distribution has mean 35 and standard deviation 5. Use the Chebychev inequality to estimate the probability that an outcome will lie between

(a) 25 and 45.   (b) 20 and 50.   (c) 29 and 41.

14. Suppose that a probability distribution has mean 8 and standard deviation .4. Use the Chebychev inequality to estimate the probability that an outcome will lie between

(a) 6 and 10.   (b) 7.2 and 8.8.

(c) 7.5 and 8.5.

15. Bulb Lifetimes For certain types of fluorescent lights the number of hours a bulb will burn before requiring replacement has a mean of 3000 hours and a standard deviation of 250 hours. Suppose that 5000 such bulbs are installed in an office building. Estimate the number that will require replacement between 2000 and 4000 hours from the time of installation.

16. Quality Control An electronics firm determines that the number of defective transistors in each batch averages 15 with standard deviation 10. Suppose that 100 batches are produced. Estimate the number of batches having between 0 and 30 defective transistors.

17. Suppose that a probability distribution has mean 75 and standard deviation 6. Use the Chebychev inequality to find the value of c for which the probability that the outcome lies between $75 - c$ and $75 + c$ is at least $\frac{7}{16}$.

18. Suppose that a probability distribution has mean 17 and standard deviation .2. Use the Chebychev inequality to find the value of c for which the probability that the outcome lies between $17 - c$ and $17 + c$ is at least $\frac{15}{16}$.

19. Dice The probability distribution for the sum of numbers obtained from rolling a pair of dice is given in Table 9.

(a) Compute the mean and the variance of this probability distribution.

(b) Using the table, give the probability that the number is between 4 and 10, inclusive.

(c) Use the Chebychev inequality to estimate the probability that the number is between 4 and 10, inclusive.

TABLE 9	
Number	Probability
2	$\frac{1}{36}$
3	$\frac{2}{36}$
4	$\frac{3}{36}$
5	$\frac{4}{36}$
6	$\frac{5}{36}$
7	$\frac{6}{36}$
8	$\frac{5}{36}$
9	$\frac{4}{36}$
10	$\frac{3}{36}$
11	$\frac{2}{36}$
12	$\frac{1}{36}$

TABLE 10	
Number of "ones"	Probability
0	.112
1	.269
2	.296
3	.197
4	.089
5	.028
6	.007
7	.001
8	.000
9	.000
10	.000
11	.000
12	.000

TABLE 11	
k	$\Pr(X = k)$
-2	.2
-1	.2
0	.2
1	.2
2	.2

20. Dice The probability distribution for the number of "ones" obtained from rolling 12 dice is given in Table 10. This probability distribution has mean 2 and standard deviation 1.291 ($\sigma^2 = \frac{5}{3}$).

(a) Using the table, give the probability that the number of "ones" is between 0 and 4, inclusive.

(b) Use the Chebychev inequality to estimate the probability that the number of "ones" is between 0 and 4, inclusive.

21. Use the alternate definition of variance to calculate the variance of the random variable in Table 11.

22. If X is a random variable, then the variance of X equals the variance of $X - a$ for any number a. Redo Exercise 1 using this result with $a = 70$.

23. If X is a random variable, then the variance of aX equals a^2 times the variance of X. Verify this result for the random variable in Exercise 2 with $a = 2$.

24. If X is a random variable, then

$$E(X - a) = E(X) - a \quad \text{and} \quad E(aX) = aE(X)$$

for any number a. Give intuitive justifications of these results.

In Exercises 25–28, use a graphing calculator or spreadsheet to calculate the answers.

25. College Enrollments Table 12 gives the fall 2005 enrollments of the 8 largest colleges in the United States. Determine the population mean and standard deviation for these enrollments.

26. Priciest Colleges Table 13 gives the tutition and fees for the eight priciest colleges in the United States for the academic year 2007–08. Determine the population mean and standard deviation of these costs.

27. Ph.D. Degrees Table 14 on the next page summarizes the production of Ph.D. degrees in statistics at a certain university during the past 25 years. For instance, three Ph.D. degrees were awarded during 5 of the last 25 years. Determine the population mean and standard deviation for the number of degrees awarded each year.

TABLE 12 Eight largest U.S. colleges	
College	Enrollment
Miami-Dade College	54,169
Arizona State Univ. at Tempe	51,612
Univ. of Minnesota, Twin Cities	51,175
Western International University	50,663
Ohio State Univ., Main Campus	50,504
University of Texas at Austin	49,696
University of Florida	49,693
Michigan State University	45,166

TABLE 13 Eight priciest U.S. colleges	
College	Tuition & Fees
George Washington Univ.	$39,210
Kenyon College	$38,140
Bucknell Univ.	$38,134
Sarah Lawrence College	$38,090
Univ. of Richmond	$37,610
Vassar College	$37,570
Columbia Univ.	$37,223
Bennington College	$36,800

TABLE 14

Number of degrees	Number of years
3	5
4	7
5	8
6	2
7	1
8	2

TABLE 15

Earnings	Probability
−5	.23
−1	.32
1	.35
5	.07
10	.03

28. Game of Chance Table 15 gives the probability distribution for the possible earnings from a certain game of chance. Determine the mean and the standard deviation for the earnings.

Solutions to Practice Problems 7.5

1. (a)

k	$\Pr(X=k)$	$k-\mu$	$(k-\mu)^2$	$(k-\mu)^2\Pr(X=k)$
21	$\frac{1}{16}$	-2	4	$\frac{4}{16}$
22	$\frac{1}{8}$	-1	1	$\frac{1}{8}$
23	$\frac{5}{8}$	0	0	0
24	$\frac{1}{8}$	1	1	$\frac{1}{8}$
25	$\frac{1}{16}$	2	4	$\frac{4}{16}$

$$\mu = 21 \cdot \tfrac{1}{16} + 22 \cdot \tfrac{1}{8} + 23 \cdot \tfrac{5}{8} + 24 \cdot \tfrac{1}{8} + 25 \cdot \tfrac{1}{16}$$

$$= \tfrac{21}{16} + \tfrac{44}{16} + \tfrac{230}{16} + \tfrac{48}{16} + \tfrac{25}{16} = \tfrac{368}{16} = 23$$

$$\text{Var}(X) = \tfrac{4}{16} + \tfrac{1}{8} + 0 + \tfrac{1}{8} + \tfrac{4}{16}$$

$$= \tfrac{2}{8} + \tfrac{1}{8} + 0 + \tfrac{1}{8} + \tfrac{2}{8} = \tfrac{6}{8} = \tfrac{3}{4}$$

(b) $\frac{7}{8}$. The probability that the outcome is between 22 and 24 is

$$\Pr(22) + \Pr(23) + \Pr(24) = \tfrac{1}{8} + \tfrac{5}{8} + \tfrac{1}{8} = \tfrac{7}{8}.$$

2. Probability $\geq \frac{1}{4}$. Here $\mu = 23$, $\sigma^2 = \frac{3}{4}$, and $c = 1$. By the Chebychev inequality, the probability that the outcome is between $23-1$ and $23+1$ is at least $1 - \left(\frac{3}{4}/1^2\right) = 1 - \frac{3}{4} = \frac{1}{4}$. [From 1(b) we obtained the actual probability of $\frac{7}{8}$, which is much greater than $\frac{1}{4}$. In the next section we will study a technique that gives better estimates. However, this technique holds only for a special type of probability distribution.]

7.6 The Normal Distribution

In this section we will see that the histogram for a binomial random variable can be approximated by a region under a smooth curve called a *normal curve*. Actually, these curves have value in their own right in that they represent some random variables associated with experiments having infinitely many possible outcomes.

Toss a coin 20 times and observe the number of heads. By using formula (1) of Section 7.3 with $n = 20$ and $p = .5$, we can calculate the probability of k heads. The results are displayed in Table 1. The data of Table 1 can be displayed in histogram form, as in Fig. 1.

TABLE 1 Probability of k heads (to four decimal places)

k	Probability of k heads	k	Probability of k heads
0	.0000	10	.1762
1	.0000	11	.1602
2	.0002	12	.1201
3	.0011	13	.0739
4	.0046	14	.0370
5	.0148	15	.0148
6	.0370	16	.0046
7	.0739	17	.0011
8	.1201	18	.0002
9	.1602	19	.0000
		20	.0000

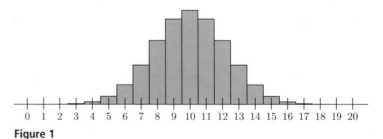

Figure 1

As we have seen, various probabilities may be interpreted as areas. For example, the probability that at most 9 heads occur is equal to the sum of the areas of all the rectangles to the left of the central one (Fig. 2). The shape of the histogram in Figs. 1 and 2 suggests that we might be able to approximate such areas by using a smooth bell-shaped curve. The curve shown in Fig. 3 on the next page is a good candidate. It is called a **normal curve** and plays an important role in statistics and probability. (Tables giving the areas under normal curves have been constructed and can be used to approximate binomial probabilities.) For instance, the area of the blue rectangles in Fig. 2 is approximately the same as the area under the normal curve to the left of 9.5 shown in Fig. 4. As another example, the probability of obtaining exactly 10 heads in 20 tosses of a coin is the area of the blue rectangle

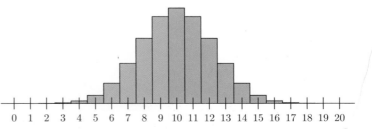

Figure 2

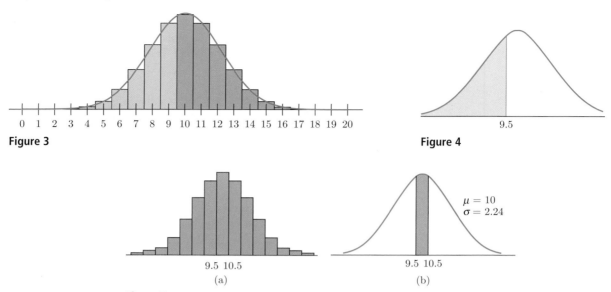

Figure 3

Figure 4

Figure 5

in Fig. 5(a), which is approximated by the area under the normal curve shown in Fig. 5(b).

To be able to use normal curves in our computations, we need to study them more closely. Let us now take a glimpse into the realm of so-called continuous probability by studying appropriate experiments—namely, experiments with **normally distributed outcomes**. For such experiments, the probabilities of events are computed as areas under normal curves. It is no exaggeration to say that experiments with normally distributed outcomes are among the most significant in probability theory. Such experiments abound in the world around us. Here are a few examples:

1. Choose an individual at random and observe his or her IQ.

2. Choose a 1-day-old infant and observe his or her weight.

3. Choose an 8-year-old male at random and observe his height.

4. Choose a leaf at random from a particular tree and observe its length.

5. A lumber mill is cutting planks that are supposed to be 8 feet long; choose a plank at random and observe its actual length.

Associated to each of the foregoing experiments is the normal curve, as shown in Fig. 6. The curve is symmetric about a vertical line drawn through its highest point. This line of symmetry indicates the mean value of the corresponding experiment.

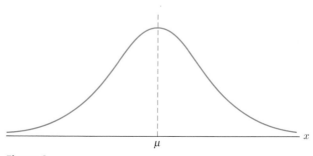

Figure 6

The mean value is denoted as usual by the Greek letter μ. For example, if in experiment 4 on the previous page the average length of the leaves on the tree is 5 inches, then $\mu = 5$ and the corresponding bell-shaped curve is symmetric about the line $x = 5$.

The connection between an experiment with normally distributed outcomes and its associated normal curve is as follows: The probability that the experimental outcome is between a and b equals the area under the associated normal curve from $x = a$ to $x = b$. (This is the shaded region in Fig. 7.)

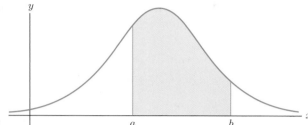

Figure 7

The total area under a normal curve is always 1. This is due to the fact that the probability that the variable X corresponding to the distribution takes on some numerical value on the x-axis is 1.

EXAMPLE 1

Shading regions under a normal curve   A certain experiment has normally distributed outcomes with mean $\mu = 1$. Shade the region corresponding to the probabilities of the following outcomes.

(a) The outcome lies between 1 and 3.

(b) The outcome lies between 0 and 2.

(c) The outcome is less than .5.

(d) The outcome is greater than 2.

Solution   The outcomes are plotted along the x-axis. We then shade the appropriate region under the curve.

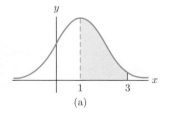
(a)

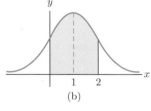
(b)

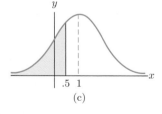
(c)

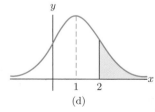
(d)

There are many different normal curves with the same mean. For instance, in Fig. 8 we have drawn three normal curves, all with $\mu = 0$. Roughly speaking, the difference between these normal curves is in the width of the center "hump."

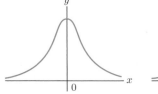

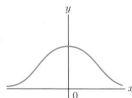

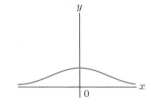

Figure 8

A sharper hump indicates that the outcomes are more likely to be close to the mean. A flatter hump indicates a greater likelihood for the outcomes to be spread out. As we have seen, the spread of the outcomes about the mean is described by the standard deviation, denoted by the Greek letter σ. In the case of a normal curve, the standard deviation has a simple geometric meaning: The normal curve "twists" (or, in calculus terminology, "inflects") at a distance σ on either side of the mean (Fig. 9). More specifically, a normal curve may be thought of as made up of two pieces: a "cap," which looks like an upside-down bowl; and a pair of legs, which curve in the opposite direction. The places at which the cap and legs are joined are at a distance σ from the mean. Thus it is clear that the size of σ controls the sharpness of the hump.

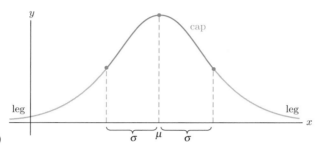

Figure 9

A normal curve is completely described by its mean μ and standard deviation σ. In fact, given μ and σ, we may write down the equation of the associated normal curve:

$$y = \frac{1}{\sigma\sqrt{2\pi}}\, e^{-\left(\frac{1}{2}\right)\left(\frac{x-\mu}{\sigma}\right)^2},$$

where $\pi \approx 3.1416$ and $e \approx 2.7183$. Fortunately, we will not need this rather complicated formula in what follows. But it is only fair to say that all theoretical work on the normal curve ultimately rests on this equation.

For our purposes we will compute areas of regions under normal curves by consulting a table. One might expect that a separate table would be needed for each normal curve, but such is not the case. Only one table is needed: the table corresponding to the **standard normal curve**, which is the one for which $\mu = 0$ and $\sigma = 1$. So let us begin our discussion of areas under normal curves by considering the standard normal curve.

We usually use the letter Z to denote a random variable having the standard normal distribution. Let z be any number and let $A(z)$ denote the area under the standard normal curve to the left of z (Fig. 10). Table 2 gives $A(z)$ for various values of z, with the values of $A(z)$ rounded to four decimal places. Thus, $A(z) = \Pr(Z \le z)$.[1] A more extensive table can be found in Appendix A. The efficient use of these tables depends on the following three facts:

1. The standard normal curve is symmetric about $z = 0$.

2. The total area under the standard normal curve is 1.

3. The probability that the standard normal variable Z lies to the left of the number z is the area $A(z)$ in Fig. 10.

These facts allow us to use the tables to find the areas of various types of regions.

---

[1] We could have said that $A(z) = \Pr(Z < z)$. However, since the region strictly to the left of z and that region with the line segment at z adjoined have the same area, $\Pr(Z < z)$ and $\Pr(Z \le z)$ are the same. We always use the $\le$ symbol.

TABLE 2

z	A(z)	z	A(z)	z	A(z)
−4.00	.0000	−1.25	.1056	1.50	.9332
−3.75	.0001	−1.00	.1587	1.75	.9599
−3.50	.0002	−.75	.2266	2.00	.9772
−3.25	.0006	−.50	.3085	2.25	.9878
−3.00	.0013	−.25	.4013	2.50	.9938
−2.75	.0030	0	.5000	2.75	.9970
−2.50	.0062	.25	.5987	3.00	.9987
−2.25	.0122	.50	.6915	3.25	.9994
−2.00	.0228	.75	.7734	3.50	.9998
−1.75	.0401	1.00	.8413	3.75	.9999
−1.50	.0668	1.25	.8944	4.00	1.0000

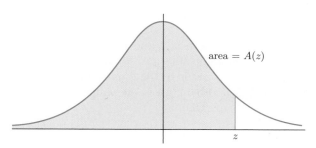

area = $A(z)$

Figure 10

EXAMPLE 2

Determining areas of regions under the standard normal curve   Use Table 2 to determine the areas of the regions under the standard normal curve pictured in Fig. 11.

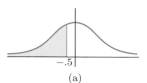 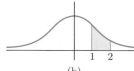 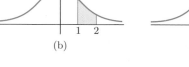 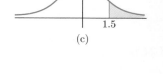

−.5

(a)

1   2

(b)

1.5

(c)

Figure 11

Solution **(a)** This region is just the portion of the curve to the left of −.5. So its area is $A(-.5)$. Looking down the middle pair of columns of the table, we find that $A(-.5) = .3085$. This means that

$$\Pr(Z \leq -.5) = .3085.$$

(b) This region results from beginning with the region to the left of 2 and subtracting the region to the left of 1. We obtain an area of

$$A(2) - A(1) = .9772 - .8413 = .1359.$$

Thus

$$\Pr(1 \leq Z \leq 2) = .1359.$$

(c) This region can be thought of as the entire region under the curve, with the region to the left of 1.5 removed. Therefore, the area is

$$1 - A(1.5) = 1 - .9332 = .0668.$$

So

$$\Pr(Z \geq 1.5) = .0668.$$

Now Try Exercises 1, 3, and 5

EXAMPLE 3 **Finding a region under the standard normal curve** Find the value of z for which $\Pr(Z \geq z) = .1056$ (see Fig. 12).

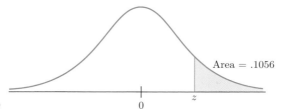

Area = .1056

Figure 12

Solution Since the area under the standard normal curve is 1 and the curve is symmetric about $z = 0$, the area of the portion to the right of 0 must be .5. We draw a sketch of the standard normal curve, placing z on the axis to the right of 0. (This way, the area to the right of z will be less than .5.) Table 2 gives the values of $A(z)$, which are left tail areas. The area to the left of our z is

$$A(z) = 1 - .1056 = .8944.$$

Now Try Exercise 9 From Table 2 we find that the value of z for which $A(z) = .8944$ is 1.25. ∎

Percentiles In large-scale testing, scores are frequently reported as percentiles rather than as raw scores. What does it mean to say that a score is "the 90th percentile"? It means that, roughly speaking, the score separates the bottom 90% of the scores from the top 10%.

> **DEFINITION** If a score S is the **pth percentile** of a normal distribution, then $p\%$ of all scores fall below S, and $(100 - p)\%$ of all scores fall above S.

EXAMPLE 4 **Determining a percentile of the standard normal distribution** What is the 50th percentile of the standard normal distribution?

Solution The standard normal curve is symmetric about $z = 0$, and the total area under the curve is 1. Thus, 50% of the values of the standard normal variable fall below 0, and $(100 - 50)\% = 50\%$ of its values fall above 0. So 0 is the 50th percentile of the standard normal distribution. ∎

EXAMPLE 5 **Determining a percentile of the standard normal distribution** What is the 95th percentile of the standard normal distribution?

Solution We shall call the value that we seek z_{95} to remind us that it is a score and that the probability that an outcome is to the left of it is 95% (see Fig. 13).

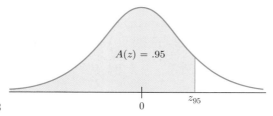

$A(z) = .95$

z_{95}

Figure 13

Since Appendix A gives areas to the left of values of z, we should search the column marked $A(z)$ for the area we need—.95. We find that the closest value to .95 is .9505, and $A(1.65) = .9505$. Hence $z_{95} \approx 1.65$. This means that 95% of the time the standard normal variable falls below 1.65. Since $\mu = 0$ and $\sigma = 1$, another way of stating the result is that in the standard normal distribution, 95% of the values are less than 1.65 standard deviations above the mean.

> Now Try Exercise 13

The problem of finding the area of a region under *any* normal curve can be reduced to finding the area of a region under the standard normal curve. To illustrate the computation procedure, let us consider a numerical example.

EXAMPLE 6

Finding areas of regions under normal curves Find the area under the normal curve with $\mu = 3$, $\sigma = 2$ from $x = 1$ to $x = 5$. This represents $\Pr(1 \leq X \leq 5)$ for a random variable X having the given normal distribution.

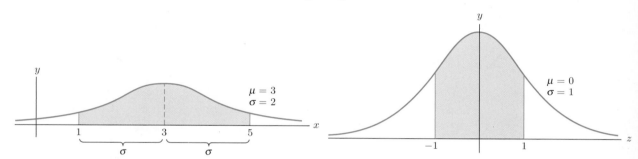

Figure 14

Figure 15

Solution We have sketched the described region in Fig. 14. It extends from one standard deviation below the mean to one standard deviation above. Draw the corresponding region under the standard normal curve. That is, draw the region from one standard deviation below to one standard deviation above the mean (Fig. 15). It is a theorem that this new region has the same area as the original one. But the area in Fig. 15 may be computed from Table 2 as $A(1) - A(-1)$. So our desired area is

> Now Try Exercise 25

$$A(1) - A(-1) = .8413 - .1587 = .6826.$$

EXAMPLE 7

Finding areas of regions under a normal curve Consider the normal curve with $\mu = 12$, $\sigma = 1.5$. Find the area of the region under the curve between $x = 11.25$ and $x = 15$. (Fig. 16).

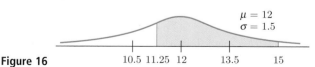

Figure 16

Solution Expressed as a probability, we want to find $\Pr(11.25 \leq X \leq 15)$ for a random variable X having a normal distribution with $\mu = 12$ and $\sigma = 1.5$. The number 11.25 is .75 below the mean 12. And .75 is $.75/1.5 = .5$ standard deviations. The number 15 is 3 above the mean. And 3 is $3/1.5 = 2$ standard deviations. Therefore, the region has the same area as the region under the standard normal curve from $-.5$ to 2, which is

> Now Try Exercise 23

$$A(2) - A(-.5) = .9772 - .3085 = .6687.$$

Suppose that a normal curve has mean μ and standard deviation σ. Then the area under the curve from $x = a$ to $x = b$ is

$$A\left(\frac{b-\mu}{\sigma}\right) - A\left(\frac{a-\mu}{\sigma}\right).$$

The numbers $b - \mu$ and $a - \mu$, respectively, measure the distances of b and a from the mean. The numbers $(b - \mu)/\sigma$ and $(a - \mu)/\sigma$ express these distances as multiples of the standard deviation σ. So the area under the normal curve from $x = a$ to $x = b$ is computed by expressing x in terms of standard deviations from the mean and then treating the curve as if it were the standard normal curve.

We summarize the procedure.

If X is a random variable having a normal distribution with mean μ and standard deviation σ, then

$$\Pr(a \le X \le b) = \Pr\left(\frac{a-\mu}{\sigma} \le Z \le \frac{b-\mu}{\sigma}\right) = A\left(\frac{b-\mu}{\sigma}\right) - A\left(\frac{a-\mu}{\sigma}\right)$$

and

$$\Pr(X \le x) = \Pr\left(Z \le \frac{x-\mu}{\sigma}\right) = A\left(\frac{x-\mu}{\sigma}\right),$$

where Z has the standard normal distribution and $A(z)$ is the area under that distribution to the left of z.

Let us now use our knowledge of areas under normal curves to calculate probabilities arising in some applied problems.

EXAMPLE 8   **Birth weights of infants**   Suppose that for a certain population the birth weights of infants in pounds are normally distributed with $\mu = 7.75$ and $\sigma = 1.25$. Find the probability that an infant's birth weight is more than 9 pounds, 10 ounces. (*Note:* 9 pounds, 10 ounces $= 9\frac{5}{8}$ pounds.)

Solution   Let $X =$ infant's birth weight. Then X is a random variable having a normal distribution with $\mu = 7.75$ and $\sigma = 1.25$ pounds. $\Pr\left(X \ge 9\frac{5}{8}\right)$ is given by the area under the appropriate normal curve to the right of $9\frac{5}{8}$—that is, the area shaded in Fig. 17. Since $9\frac{5}{8} = 9.625$, the number $9\frac{5}{8}$ lies $9.625 - 7.75 = 1.875$ units above the mean. In turn, this is $1.875/1.25 = 1.5$ standard deviations. We can find the corresponding z-value in one calculation by finding

$$z = \frac{x-\mu}{\sigma} = \frac{9.625 - 7.75}{1.25} = 1.5.$$

Thus 9.625 is 1.5 standard deviations above the mean. The area we seek is sketched under the standard normal curve in Fig. 18 and is

$$1 - A(1.5) = 1 - .9332 = .0668.$$

Now Try Exercise 31   So the probability that an infant weighs more than 9 pounds, 10 ounces is .0668. ∎

EXAMPLE 9   **Produce sales**   A wholesale produce dealer finds that the number of boxes of bananas sold each day is normally distributed with $\mu = 1200$ and $\sigma = 100$. Find the probability that the number sold on a particular day is less than 1000.

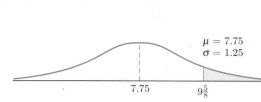

Figure 17

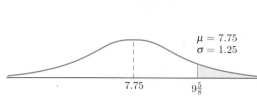

Figure 18

Solution Let X = the number of boxes of bananas sold each day. Since daily sales are normally distributed, the desired probability, $\Pr(X \leq 1000)$, is the area to the left of 1000 in the normal curve drawn in Fig. 19. The number 1000 is 2 standard deviations below the mean; that is, $x = 1000$ corresponds to a z-value of

$$z = \frac{x - \mu}{\sigma} = \frac{1000 - 1200}{100} = -2.$$

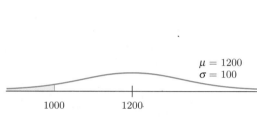

Figure 19

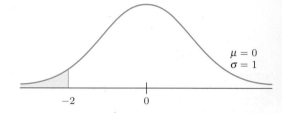

Figure 20

Now Try Exercise 35

Therefore, the area we seek is $A(-2) = .0228$, shown in Fig. 20. The probability that less than 1000 boxes will be sold in a day is .0228. ■

EXAMPLE 10

Inventory size   The wholesale produce dealer of Example 9 wants to be 99% sure that she has enough boxes of bananas on hand each day to meet the demand. How many should she stock each day?

Solution Let x be the number of boxes of bananas that the produce dealer should stock. Since she wants to be 99% sure that the demand for boxes of bananas does not exceed x, we must find the 99th percentile of a normal distribution with $\mu = 1200$ and $\sigma = 100$. To help us remember what x really is, we will rename it x_{99}. The corresponding value for the standard normal random variable is z_{99}. Figures 21 and 22 on the next page show the appropriate areas—first under the given normal curve and then under the standard normal curve.

   The area, $A(z)$, that we seek under the standard normal curve is .99. Referring to Appendix A, we get closest with $A(z) = .9906$, corresponding to $z_{99} = 2.35$. The value z_{99} is 2.35 standard deviations above the mean of its distribution. We conclude that x_{99} is also 2.35 standard deviations above its mean. Hence,

$$x_{99} = 1200 + (2.35)(100) = 1435 \text{ boxes.}$$

Therefore, we expect that on 99% of the days, 1435 boxes of bananas will meet the demand. More than 1435 boxes should be needed 1% of the time (one day out of 100). ■

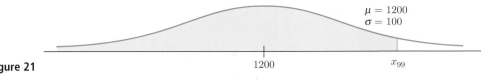

Figure 21

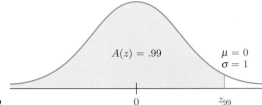

Figure 22

We summarize the technique for finding percentiles of normal distributions.

If x_p is the pth percentile of a normal distribution with mean μ and standard deviation σ, then

$$x_p = \mu + z_p \cdot \sigma,$$

where z_p is the pth percentile of the standard normal distribution.

INCORPORATING TECHNOLOGY

GC Normal curves can easily be graphed and normal probabilities calculated on most graphing calculators. Consider Example 6. Figure 23 contains the graph of the normal curve, and Fig. 24 gives the desired probability.

TI-83/84 Plus The graph of the normal curve in Fig. 23 was obtained by setting **Y₁=normalpdf(X,3,2)** in the **Y=** editor, and pressing GRAPH. (To display **normalpdf(**, press 2nd[DISTR] **1**. The general form of this function is **Y₁=normalpdf(X,μ,σ)**.) To obtain the result in Fig. 24, press 2nd[CALC] **7** and answer the questions by entering the appropriate numbers. Specifically, respond to **"Lower Limit?"** by typing in the number **1** and pressing ENTER, and respond to **"Upper Limit?"** by typing in the number **5** and pressing ENTER. To erase the shading under the curve, press 2nd[DRAW] **1**. To find the area of an infinite region, just give a large negative value for the lower bound or a large positive value for the upper bound.

Figure 23.
$[-6.4, 12.4]$ by $[-.2, .5]$.

The area under a normal curve also can be evaluated on the home screen with the command **fnInt(Y₁,X,a,b)** where Y₁ has been set to a normalpdf function. For instance, the area of the shaded region in Example 6 can be evaluated by typing **fnInt(Y₁,X,1,5)** and pressing ENTER. (From the home screen, **fnInt(** is displayed with MATH **9**.)

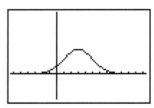

Figure 24

TI-89 The graph of the normal curve similar to the one in Fig. 23 can be obtained by setting **y1=1/(2√(2π))e^(-.5((x-3)/2)^2)** in the **Y=** editor, and pressing ◆[GRAPH]. To obtain a result similar to the one in Fig. 24, press F5 **7** and answer the questions by entering the appropriate numbers. Specifically, respond to **"Lower Limit?"** by typing in the number **1** and pressing ENTER, and respond to **"Upper Limit?"** by typing in the number **5** and pressing ENTER. To erase the shading under the curve, press 2nd[F6] **1**. To find the area of an infinite region, just give a large negative value for the lower bound or a large positive value for the upper bound.

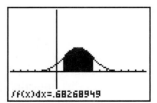

ES If z and x are any numbers, then the value of $A(z)$ is given by the Excel function NORMSDIST(z), and the area to the left of x under the normal curve having mean μ and standard deviation σ is NORMDIST(x, μ, σ,TRUE). If y is a number between 0 and 1, then NORMSINV(y) is the value of z for which $A(z) = y$, and NORMINV(y, μ, σ) is the value of x for which the area to the left of x under the normal curve having mean μ and standard deviation σ is y. In Fig. 25, the answers to four examples from this section are computed in an Excel spreadsheet.

	A	B	C	D
1	**Example**	**Answer**		**Formula Used**
2	2(b)	0.135905122		NORMSDIST(2)-NORMSDIST(1)
3	5	1.644853627		NORMSINV(0.95)
4	9	0.022750132		NORMDIST(1000,1200,100,TRUE)
5	10	1432.634787		NORMINV(0.99,1200,100)

Figure 25

Practice Problems 7.6

1. Refer to Fig. 26(a). Find the value of z for which the area of the shaded region is .0802.

2. Refer to the normal curve in Fig. 26(b). Express the following numbers in terms of standard deviations from the mean.

   (a) 90   **(b)** 82   **(c)** 94   **(d)** 104

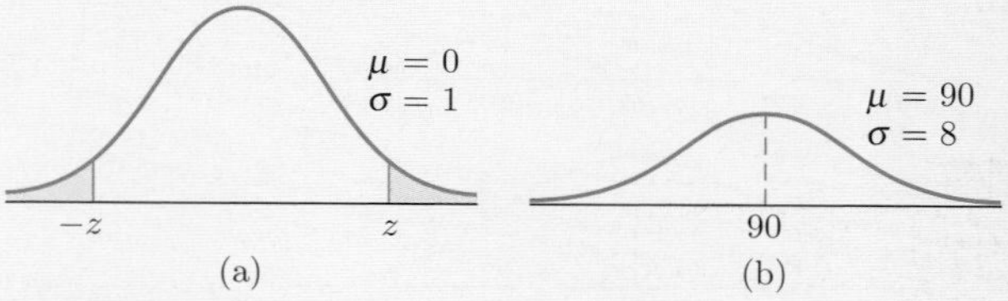

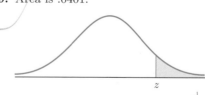

(a)

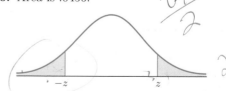

(b)

Figure 26

EXERCISES 7.6

In Exercises 1–8, use the table for $A(z)$ (Table 2) to find the areas of the shaded regions under the standard normal curve.

1.

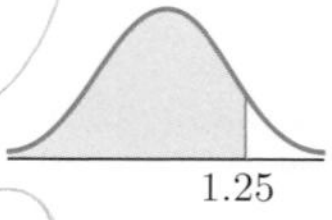

1.25

2.

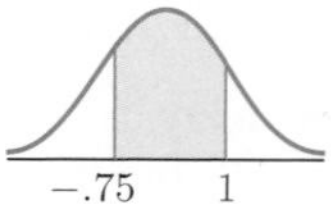

−.75   1

3.

.25

4.

−1   1

5.

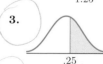

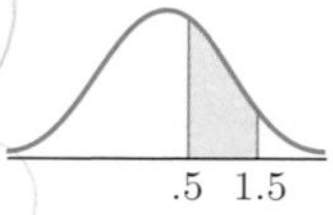

.5 1.5

6.

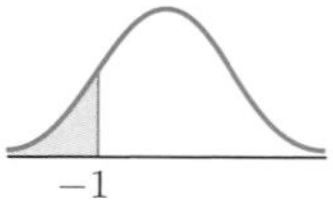

−1

7.

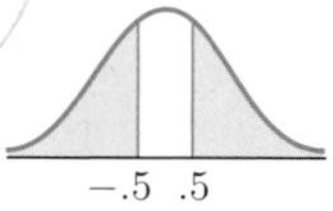

−.5 .5

8.

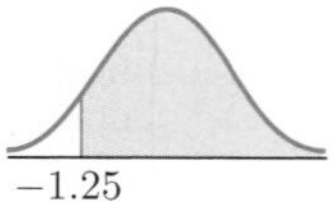

−1.25

In Exercises 9–12, find the value of z for which the area of the shaded region under the standard normal curve is as specified.

9. Area is .0401.

10. Area is .0456.

−z z

11. Area is .5468.

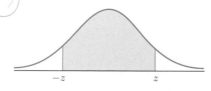

−z z

12. Area is .6915.

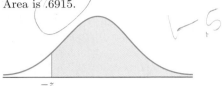

13. What is the 90th percentile of the standard normal distribution?

14. What is the 65th percentile of the standard normal distribution?

In Exercises 15–18, determine μ and σ by inspection.

15.

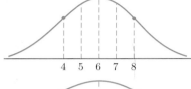

16.

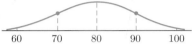

17.

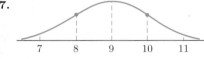

18.

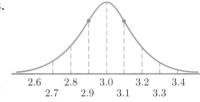

Exercises 19–22 refer to the normal curve with $\mu = 8$, $\sigma = \frac{3}{4}$.

19. Convert 6 into standard deviations from the mean.

20. Convert $9\frac{1}{4}$ into standard deviations from the mean.

21. **PE** What value is exactly 10 standard deviations above the mean?

(a) $15\frac{1}{2}$ (b) $\frac{1}{2}$ (c) 18 (d) $7\frac{1}{2}$ (e) $6\frac{3}{4}$

22. **PE** What value is exactly 2 standard deviations below the mean?

(a) $9\frac{1}{2}$ (b) 10 (c) 6 (d) $7\frac{1}{4}$ (e) $6\frac{1}{2}$

In Exercises 23–26, find the areas of the shaded regions under the given normal curves.

23.

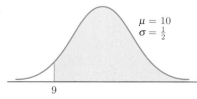

$\mu = 10$
$\sigma = \frac{1}{2}$

24.

$\mu = 30$
$\sigma = 4$

25.

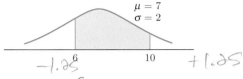

$\mu = 7$
$\sigma = 2$

26.

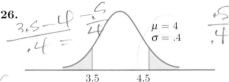

$\mu = 4$
$\sigma = .4$

27. What is the probability that an outcome of a normal random variable is within two standard deviations of the mean?

28. What is the probability that an outcome of a normal random variable is within three standard deviations of the mean?

29. Find the value of σ for a normal random variable X having $\mu = 5$, if $\Pr(X \leq 6) = .9772$.

30. Find the value of σ for a normal random variable X having $\mu = 10$, if $\Pr(14.5 \leq X) = .0013$.

31. **Elephant Heights** Suppose that the height (at the shoulder) of adult African bull bush elephants is normally distributed with $\mu = 3.3$ meters and $\sigma = .2$ meter. The elephant on display at the Smithsonian Institution has height 4 meters and is the largest elephant on record. What is the probability that an adult African bull bush elephant has height 4 meters or more?

32. **Bottling Reliability** At a soft-drink bottling plant, the amount of cola put into the bottles is normally distributed with $\mu = 16\frac{3}{4}$ ounces and $\sigma = \frac{1}{2}$. What is the probability that a bottle will contain less than 16 ounces?

33. **Manufacturing Reliability** Bolts produced by a machine are acceptable provided that their length is within the range from 5.95 to 6.05 centimeters. Suppose that the lengths of the bolts produced are normally distributed with $\mu = 6$ centimeters and $\sigma = .02$. What is the probability that a bolt will be of an acceptable length?

34. **IQ Scores** As measured with the Stanford-Binet Intelligence Scale, IQ scores are normally distributed with mean 100 and standard deviation 16.

(a) What percent of the population has an IQ score of 140 or more?

(b) Find the 90th percentile of IQ scores.

35. Gasoline Sales The amount of gas sold weekly by a certain gas station is normally distributed with $\mu = 30{,}000$ gallons and $\sigma = 4000$. If the station has 39,000 gallons on hand at the beginning of the week, what is the probability of its running out of gas before the end of the week?

36. Light Bulb Lifetimes Suppose that the lifetimes of a certain light bulb are normally distributed with $\mu = 1200$ hours and $\sigma = 160$. Find the probability that a light bulb will burn out in less than 1000 hours.

37. SAT Scores Assume that SAT verbal scores for a first-year class at a university are normally distributed with mean 520 and standard deviation 75.

   (a) The top 10% of the students are placed into the honors program for English. What is the lowest score for admittance into the honors program?

   (b) What is the range of the middle 90% of the SAT verbal scores at this university?

   (c) Find the 98th percentile of the SAT verbal scores.

38. Mailing Bags A mail-order house uses an average of 300 mailing bags per day. The number of bags needed each day is approximately normally distributed with $\sigma = 50$. How many bags must the company have on hand at the beginning of a day to be 99% certain that all orders can be filled?

39. Tire Lifetimes The lifetime of a certain brand of tires is normally distributed with mean $\mu = 30{,}000$ miles and standard deviation $\sigma = 5000$ miles. The company has decided to issue a warranty for the tires but does not want to replace more than 2% of the tires that it sells. At what mileage should the warranty expire?

40. Let X be a random variable with $\mu = 4$ and $\sigma = .5$.

   (a) Use the Chebychev inequality to estimate $\Pr(3 \le X \le 5)$.

   (b) If X were normally distributed, what would be the exact probability that X is between 3 and 5 inclusive?

   (c) Reconcile the difference between the answers to (a) and (b).

41. Soft-Drink Dispenser Let X be the amount of soda released by a soft-drink dispensing machine into a 6-ounce cup. Assume that X is normally distributed with $\sigma = .25$ ounces and that the average "fill" can be set by the vendor.

   (a) At what quantity should the average "fill" be set so that no more than .5% of the releases overflow the cup?

   (b) Using the average "fill" found in part (a), determine the minimal amount that will be dispensed in 99% of the cases.

In Exercises 42–45, use a graphing calculator or spreadsheet to obtain the information.

42. Draw the graph of the normal curve with $\mu = 10$, $\sigma = 2$ and the normal curve with $\mu = 10$, $\sigma = 3$ on the same coordinate system. Describe the effect on a normal curve of increasing σ.

43. Draw the graph of the normal curve with $\mu = 11$, $\sigma = 2$ and the normal curve with $\mu = 15$, $\sigma = 2$ on the same coordinate system. Describe the effect on a normal curve of increasing μ.

44. Heights In a certain population, heights (in inches) are normally distributed with $\mu = 67$ and $\sigma = 3$. Find the probability that a person selected at random has a height between 63 and 71 inches.

45. Manufacturing Reliability In a certain manufacturing process, lengths (in cm) of widgets are normally distributed with $\mu = 5.4$ and $\sigma = .6$. Find the probability that a widget selected at random has a length greater than 5.832 cm.

Solutions to Practice Problems 7.6

1. 1.75. Due to the symmetry of normal curves, each piece of the shaded region has area $\frac{1}{2}(.0802) = .0401$. Therefore, $A(-z) = .0401$ and so by Table 2, $-z = -1.75$. Thus $z = 1.75$.

2. (a) 0. Since 90 *is* the mean, it is 0 standard deviations from the mean.

   (b) -1. Since 82 is $90-8$, it is 8 units or 1 standard deviation below the mean.

   (c) .5. Here $94 = 90 + 4$ is 4 units or .5 standard deviations above the mean.

   (d) 1.75. Here $104 = 90+14$ is 14 units or $\frac{14}{8} = 1.75$ standard deviations above the mean.

7.7 Normal Approximation to the Binomial Distribution

In Section 7.3 we saw that complicated and tedious calculations can arise from the binomial probability distribution. For instance, determining the probability of getting at least 20 threes in 100 rolls of a die requires the computation

$$\binom{100}{20}\left(\frac{1}{6}\right)^{20}\left(\frac{5}{6}\right)^{80} + \binom{100}{21}\left(\frac{1}{6}\right)^{21}\left(\frac{5}{6}\right)^{79} + \cdots + \binom{100}{100}\left(\frac{1}{6}\right)^{100}\left(\frac{5}{6}\right)^{0}.$$

Mathematicians have shown that such probabilities can be closely approximated by using normal curves.

Consider the histograms of the binomial distributions in Figs. 1 and 2. The number of trials, n, increases from 5 to 40, with p fixed at .3. As n increases, the shape of the histogram more closely conforms to the shape of the region under a normal curve.

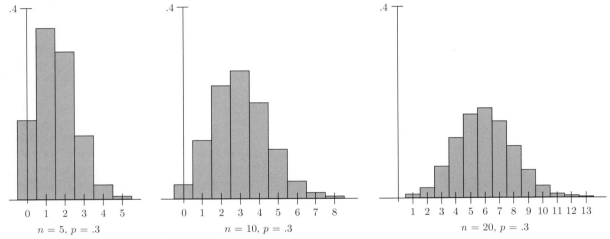

Figure 1. Binomial distribution.

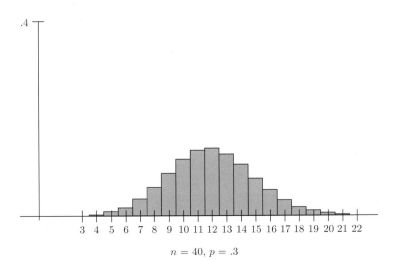

Figure 2. Binomial distribution.

We have the following result:

Suppose that we perform a sequence of n binomial trials with probability of success p and probability of failure q and observe the number of successes. Then the histogram for the resulting probability distribution may be approximated by the normal curve with $\mu = np$ and $\sigma = \sqrt{npq}$.

> **NOTE** This approximation is very accurate when both $np > 5$ and $nq > 5$. ∎

EXAMPLE 1

Quality control Refer to Example 3 of Section 7.3. A plumbing-supplies manufacturer produces faucet washers that are packaged in boxes of 300. Quality control studies have shown that 2% of the washers are defective. What is the probability that more than 10 of the washers in a single box are defective?

Solution Let $X =$ the number of defective washers in a box. Then X is a binomial random variable with $n = 300$ and $p = .02$. We will use the approximating normal curve with

$$\mu = np = 300(.02) = 6$$
$$\sigma = \sqrt{npq} = \sqrt{300(.02)(.98)} \approx 2.425.$$

The probability that more than 10 of the washers in a single box are defective is the sum of the areas of the blue rectangles centered at $11, 12, \ldots, 300$ in the histogram for the random variable X (see Fig. 3). The corresponding region under the approximating normal curve is shaded in Fig. 4. This is the area under the standard normal curve to the right of

$$z = \frac{10.5 - \mu}{\sigma} = \frac{10.5 - 6}{2.425} \approx 1.85.$$

The area of the region is $1 - A(1.85) = 1 - .9678 = .0322$. Therefore, approximately 3.22% of the boxes should contain more than 10 defective washers. ∎

> Now Try Exercise 1(c)

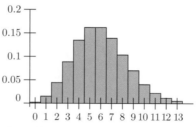

Figure 3

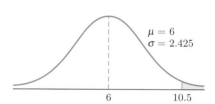

$\mu = 6$
$\sigma = 2.425$

Figure 4

> **NOTE** In Fig. 4 we shaded the region to the right of 10.5 rather than to the right of 10. This gives a better approximation to the corresponding area under the histogram, since the rectangle corresponding to 11 "successes" has its left endpoint at 10.5. ∎

Let us consider an application to medical research.

EXAMPLE 2

Veterinary medicine Consider the cattle disease of Example 4 of Section 7.3, from which 25% of the cattle recover. A veterinarian discovers a serum to combat the disease. In a test of the serum she observes that 16 of a herd of 40 recover. Suppose that the serum had not been used. What is the likelihood that at least 16 cattle would have recovered?

Solution Let X be the number of cattle that recover. Then X is a binomial random variable with $n = 40$ independent trials. If the serum is not used, $p = .25$. The approximating normal curve has

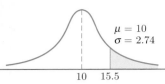

$$\mu = np = 40(.25) = 10, \qquad \sigma = \sqrt{npq} = \sqrt{40(.25)(.75)} \approx 2.74.$$

The likelihood that at least 16 cattle would have recovered is $\Pr(X \geq 16)$. This corresponds to the area under the normal curve to the right of 15.5 (Fig. 5). The area to the right of 15.5 under a normal curve with $\mu = 10$ and $\sigma = 2.74$ is the same as the area under the standard normal curve to the right of

Figure 5

$$z = \frac{15.5 - \mu}{\sigma} = \frac{15.5 - 10}{2.74} \approx 2.01.$$

We find $1 - A(2.01) \approx 1 - A(2.00) = 1 - .9772 = .0228$. Thus, if the serum were not used, the veterinarian would expect about a 2% chance that 16 or more cattle recover. Thus the 16 observed recoveries probably did not occur by chance. The veterinarian can reasonably conclude that the serum is effective against the disease.

Now Try Exercise 3   ■

EXAMPLE 3

Heads and tails Assume that a fair coin is tossed 100 times. Find the probability of observing exactly 50 heads.

Solution Let X be the number of heads on $n = 100$ binomial trials with $p = .5$ probability of "success" on each trial. We are to find the area of the rectangle extending from 49.5 to 50.5 on the x-axis in the histogram for X. The actual probability is

$$\binom{100}{50}(.5)^{50}(.5)^{50} = \binom{100}{50}(.5)^{100}.$$

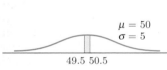

We approximate the probability with an area under the normal curve with $\mu = np = 100(.5) = 50$ and $\sigma = \sqrt{npq} = \sqrt{100(.5)(.5)} = 5$. The area we seek is sketched in Fig. 6. It is the area under the standard normal curve from

Figure 6

$$z = \frac{49.5 - 50}{5} = -.10 \quad \text{to} \quad z = \frac{50.5 - 50}{5} = .10.$$

Using Appendix A, we find that

$$A(.10) - A(-.10) = .5398 - .4602 = .0796.$$

So the likelihood of getting exactly 50 heads in 100 tosses of a fair coin is quite small—about 8%.

Now Try Exercise 1(a)   ■

EXAMPLE 4

Rolling a die Find the probability that in 100 rolls of a fair die we observe at least 20 threes.

Solution Let X be the number of threes observed in $n = 100$ trials, with $p = \frac{1}{6}$ the probability of a three on each trial. Then we need to find the area to the right of 19.5 under the normal curve with

$$\mu = np = 100\left(\tfrac{1}{6}\right) \approx 16.7 \quad \text{and} \quad \sigma = \sqrt{npq} = \sqrt{100\left(\tfrac{1}{6}\right)\left(\tfrac{5}{6}\right)} \approx 3.73.$$

This area is

$$1 - A\left(\frac{19.5 - 16.7}{3.73}\right) \approx 1 - A(.75) = 1 - .7734 = .2266.$$

Now Try Exercise 7   Therefore, the probability of observing at least 20 threes is about .2266.   ■

1. **Drug Testing** A new drug is being tested on laboratory mice. The mice have been given a disease for which the recovery rate is $\frac{1}{2}$.

   (a) In the first experiment the drug is given to 5 of the mice and all 5 recover. Find the probability that the success of this experiment was due to luck. That is, find the probability that 5 out of 5 mice recover in the event that the drug has no effect on the illness.

   (b) In a second experiment the drug is given to 25 mice and 18 recover. Find the probability that 18 or more recover in the event that the drug has no effect on the illness.

2. **Drug Testing** What conclusions can be drawn from the results in Problem 1?

EXERCISES 7.7

In Exercises 1–18, use the normal curve to approximate the probability.

1. An experiment consists of 25 binomial trials, each having probability $\frac{1}{5}$ of success. Use an approximating normal curve to estimate the probability of

   (a) exactly 5 successes.

   (b) between 3 and 7 successes, inclusive.

   (c) less than 10 successes.

2. An experiment consists of 18 binomial trials, each having probability $\frac{2}{3}$ of success. Use an approximating normal curve to estimate the probability of

   (a) exactly 10 successes.

   (b) between 8 and 16 successes, inclusive.

   (c) more than 12 successes.

3. **Drug Testing** Laboratory mice are given an illness for which the usual recovery rate is $\frac{1}{6}$. A new drug is tested on 20 of the mice, and 8 of them recover. What is the probability that 8 or more would have recovered if the 20 mice had not been given the drug?

4. **ESP** A person claims to have ESP (extrasensory perception). A coin is tossed 16 times, and each time the person is asked to predict in advance whether the coin will land heads or tails. The person predicts correctly 75% of the time (i.e., on 12 tosses). What is the probability of being correct 12 or more times by pure guessing?

5. **Roulette** In American roulette, the probability of winning when betting "red" is $\frac{9}{19}$. What is the probability of being ahead after betting the same amount 90 times?

6. **Wine Tasting** A wine-taster claims that she can usually distinguish between domestic and imported wines. As a test, she is given 100 wines to test and correctly identifies 63 of them. What is the probability that she accomplished that good a record by pure guessing? That is, what is the probability of being correct 63 or more times out of 100 by pure guessing?

7. **Basketball** A basketball player makes each free throw with probability $\frac{3}{4}$. What is the probability of making 68 or more shots out of 75 trials?

8. **Bookstore Customers** A bookstore determines that two-fifths of the people who come into the store make a purchase. What is the probability that of the 54 people who come into the store during a certain hour, less than 14 make a purchase?

9. **Baseball** A baseball player gets a hit with probability .310. Find the probability that he gets at least 6 hits in 20 times at bat.

10. **Advertising Campaign** An advertising agency, which reached 25% of its target audience with its old campaign, has devised a new advertising campaign. In a sample of 1000 people, it finds that 290 have been reached by the new advertising campaign. What is the probability that at least 290 people would have been reached by the old campaign? Does the new campaign seem to be more effective?

11. **Equipment Reliability** A washing machine manufacturer finds that 2% of its washing machines break down within the first year. Find the probability that less than 15 out of a lot of 1000 washers break down within 1 year.

12. **Color Blindness** The incidence of color blindness among the men in a certain country is 20%. Find the expected number of color-blind men in a random sample of 70 men. What is the probability of finding exactly that number of color-blind men in a sample of size 70?

13. **Product Reliability** The probabilities of failure for each of three independent components in a device are .01, .02, and .01, respectively. The device fails only if all three components fail. Out of a lot of 1 million devices, how many would be expected to fail? Find the probability that more than three devices in the lot fail.

14. **iPhones** In a random sample of 250 college students, 50 of them own an iPhone. Estimate the probability that a college student chosen at random owns an iPhone. If

actually 25% of all college students own iPhones, what is the probability that in a random survey of 250 students, at most 50 of them own the devices?

15. Marksman A marksman hits a target with probability .35. Estimate the probability of hitting the target between 30 and 40 times in 100 attempts.

16. Airline Reservations An airline accepts 150 reservations for a flight on an airplane that holds 140 passengers. If the probability of a passenger for this flight cancelling is .14, estimate the probability that some passengers will have to be bumped.

17. Ski Tour A travel agent is arranging a tour for the local 1000-member ski club. He needs a minimum of 29 people to register and thinks that the probability of a member registering for the tour is .03. Estimate the probability that enough members will register.

18. Coin Toss A fair coin is tossed 100 times. Estimate the probability that more than 65 heads or more than 65 tails appear.

In Exercises 19–22, use a graphing calculator or spreadsheet to calculate the probabilities.

19. Coin Tosses In 100 tosses of a fair coin, let X be the number of heads. Find the exact value of $\Pr(49 \leq X \leq 51)$, and also find the normal approximation to that probability.

20. Rolling a Die Let X be the number of 4's in 120 rolls of a fair die. Calculate the exact probability $\Pr(17 \leq X \leq 21)$, and also find the normal approximation to that probability.

21. Name Recognition Say that there is a 20% chance that a person chosen at random from the population has never heard of John Steinbeck. Find the exact probability that in 150 people we find exactly 30 people who have not heard of Steinbeck. Compare your result with the normal approximation to that probability.

22. Male Heights About 5% of American males are 6 feet 2 inches or taller. Calculate the exact probability that of 150 men at a business meeting, no more than five are 6 feet 2 inches or taller, and also find the normal approximation to that probability.

Solutions to Practice Problems 7.7

1. **(a)** Giving the drug to a single mouse is a binomial trial with "recovery" as "success" and "death" as "failure." If the drug has no effect, then the probability of success is $\frac{1}{2}$. The probability of five successes in five trials is given by formula (2) of Section 7.3, with $n = 5$, $p = \frac{1}{2}$, $q = \frac{1}{2}$, $k = 5$.

$$\Pr(X = 5) = \binom{5}{5}\left(\frac{1}{2}\right)^5\left(\frac{1}{2}\right)^0$$

$$= \left(\frac{1}{2}\right)^5$$

$$= \frac{1}{32} = .03125$$

(b) As in part (a), this experiment is a binomial experiment with $p = \frac{1}{2}$. However, now $n = 25$. The probability that 18 or more mice recover is

$$\Pr(X = 18) + \Pr(X = 19) + \cdots + \Pr(X = 25).$$

This probability is the area of the blue portion of the histogram in Fig. 7(a). The histogram can be approximated by the normal curve with

$$\mu = 25 \cdot \frac{1}{2} = 12.5$$

and

$$\sigma = \sqrt{25 \cdot \frac{1}{2} \cdot \frac{1}{2}} = \sqrt{\frac{25}{4}} = \frac{5}{2} = 2.5$$

[Fig. 7(b)]. Since the blue portion of the histogram begins at the point 17.5, the desired probability is approximately the area of the shaded region under the normal curve. The number 17.5 is

$$\frac{17.5 - 12.5}{2.5} = \frac{5}{2.5} = 2$$

standard deviations to the right of the mean. Hence, the area under the curve is $1 - A(2) = 1 - .9772 = .0228$. Therefore, the probability that 18 or more mice recover is approximately .0228.

2. Both experiments offer convincing evidence that the drug is helpful in treating the illness. The likelihood of obtaining the results by pure chance is slim. The second experiment might be considered more conclusive than the first, since the result, if due to chance, has a lower probability.

(Continued)

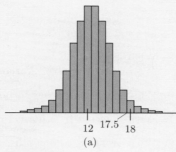

(a)

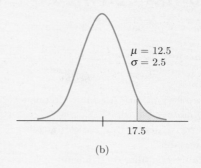

(b)

Figure 7

CHAPTER SUMMARY

1. *Bar charts*, *pie charts*, *histograms*, and *box plots* help us turn raw data into visual forms that often allow us to see patterns in the data quickly.

2. The *median* of an ordered list of data is a number with the property that the same number of data items lie above it as below it. For an ordered list of N numbers, it is the middle number when N is odd, and the average of the two middle numbers when N is even.

3. For an ordered list of data, the *first quartile* Q_1 is the median of the list of data items below the median, and the *third quartile* Q_3 is the median of the list of data items above the median. The difference of the third and first quartiles is called the *interquartile range*. The sequence of numbers consisting of the lowest number, Q_1, the median, Q_3, and the highest number is called the *five-number summary*.

4. The probability distribution for a random variable can be displayed in a table or a histogram. With a histogram, the probability of an event is the sum of the areas of the rectangles corresponding to the outcomes in the event.

5. If the probability of success in each trial of a binomial experiment is p, then the probability of k successes in n trials is $\binom{n}{k}p^k(1-p)^{n-k}$.

6. The *sample mean* of a sample of n numbers is the sum of the numbers divided by n.

7. The *expected value* of a random variable is the sum of the products of each outcome and its probability.

8. The *variance* of a random variable is the sum of the products of the square of each outcome's distance from the expected value and the outcome's probability. The variance of the random variable X can also be computed as $E(X^2) - [E(X)]^2$.

9. A binomial random variable with parameters n and p has expected value np and variance $np(1-p)$.

10. The square root of the variance is called the *standard deviation*.

11. Chebychev's inequality states that the probability that an outcome of an experiment is within c units of the mean is at least $1 - (\sigma^2/c^2)$, where σ is the standard deviation.

12. A normal curve is identified by its mean (μ) and its standard deviation (σ). The standard normal curve has $\mu = 0$ and $\sigma = 1$. Areas of regions under the standard normal curve can be obtained with the aid of a table or graphing calculator.

13. A random variable is said to be normally distributed if the probability that an outcome lies between a and b is the area of the region under a normal curve from $x = a$ to $x = b$. After the numbers a and b are converted to standard deviations from the mean, the sought-after probability can be obtained as an area under the standard normal curve.

14. Probabilities associated with a binomial random variable with parameters n and p can be approximated with a normal curve having $\mu = np$ and $\sigma = \sqrt{np(1-p)}$.

REVIEW OF FUNDAMENTAL CONCEPTS

1. What is a bar chart? A pie chart? A histogram? A box plot?

2. What is the median of a list of numbers? The first quartile? The third quartile? The interquartile range? The five-number summary?

3. What is a frequency distribution? A relative frequency distribution? A probability distribution?

4. How is a histogram constructed from a distribution?

5. What is a random variable?

6. What is meant by the probability distribution of a discrete random variable?

7. What are the identifying features of a binomial random variable?

8. What is the formula for the probability of k successes in n independent binomial trials?

9. What is meant by the expectation (or expected value) of a random variable? Variance? Standard deviation?

10. What is the Chebychev inequality, and how is it used?

11. What is meant by a normal random variable?

12. What is meant by the pth percentile of a normal random variable?

13. How are binomial probabilities approximated with the normal distribution?

KEY FORMULAS

Binomial Probabilities: If X is the number of "successes" in n independent trials, where in each trial the probability of a "success" is p, then $\Pr(X = k) = \binom{n}{k}p^k q^{n-k}$, for $k = 0, 1, 2, \ldots, n$, where $q = 1 - p$.

Sample Mean: If $x_1, x_2, \ldots, x_n$ is a sample of n numbers, then

$$\overline{x} = \frac{x_1 + x_2 + \cdots + x_n}{n}.$$

Sample Mean: If $x_1, x_2, \ldots, x_r$ is a sample of n numbers where the frequency of x_1 is f_1, the frequency of x_2 is f_2, and so forth, where $f_1 + f_2 + \cdots + f_r = n$, then

$$\overline{x} = \frac{x_1 f_1 + x_2 f_2 + \cdots + x_r f_r}{n}$$
$$= x_1\left(\frac{f_1}{n}\right) + x_2\left(\frac{f_2}{n}\right) + \cdots + x_r\left(\frac{f_r}{n}\right).$$

Population Variance: If $x_1, x_2, \ldots, x_r$ is a population of n numbers where the frequency of x_1 is f_1, the frequency of x_2 is f_2, and so forth, where $f_1 + f_2 + \cdots + f_r = n$, then

$$\sigma^2 = \frac{1}{N}\left[(x_1 - \mu)^2(f_1) + (x_2 - \mu)^2(f_2) \right.$$
$$\left. + \cdots + (x_r - \mu)^2(f_r)\right].$$

Sample Variance: If $x_1, x_2, \ldots, x_r$ is a sample of n numbers where the frequency of x_1 is f_1, the frequency of x_2 is f_2, and so forth, where $f_1 + f_2 + \cdots + f_r = n$, then

$$s^2 = \frac{1}{n-1}\left[(x_1 - \overline{x})^2(f_1) + (x_2 - \overline{x})^2(f_2) \right.$$
$$\left. + \cdots + (x_r - \overline{x})^2(f_r)\right].$$

Mean and Variance of a Random Variable: If X is a random variable with values $x_1, x_2, \ldots, x_N$ and associated probabilities $p_1, p_2, \ldots, p_N$, then

$$\mu = E(X) = x_1 p_1 + x_2 p_2 + \cdots + x_N p_N$$
$$\text{Var}(X) = (x_1 - \mu)^2 p_1 + (x_2 - \mu)^2 p_2 + \cdots + (x_N - \mu)^2 p_N.$$

Alternate Formula for Variance: $\text{Var}(X) = E(X^2) - [E(X)]^2$

Mean and Variance of a Binomial Random Variable: $\mu = np$, $\text{Var}(X) = npq$, and $\sigma_X = \sqrt{npq}$, where X has parameters n and p, and $q = 1 - p$.

Chebychev's Inequality: $\Pr(\mu - c \leq X \leq \mu + c) \geq 1 - \dfrac{\sigma^2}{c^2}$, where X has mean μ and standard deviation σ.

Normal Random Variable:

$$\Pr(a \leq X \leq b) = \Pr\left(\frac{a - \mu}{\sigma} \leq Z \leq \frac{b - \mu}{\sigma}\right)$$
$$= A\left(\frac{b - \mu}{\sigma}\right) - A\left(\frac{a - \mu}{\sigma}\right)$$

and

$$\Pr(X \leq x) = \Pr\left(Z \leq \frac{x - \mu}{\sigma}\right) = A\left(\frac{x - \mu}{\sigma}\right),$$

where X is a normal random variable with mean μ and standard deviation σ, Z has the standard normal distribution, and $A(z)$ is the area under that distribution to the left of z.

Percentiles for a Normal Distribution: $x_p = \mu + z_p \cdot \sigma$, where x_p is the pth percentile of a normal distribution with mean μ and standard deviation σ, and z_p is the pth percentile of the standard normal distribution.

Normal Approximation to the Binomial Distribution: The histogram for the binomial distribution with parameters n and p is approximated by the normal curve with $\mu = np$ and $\sigma = \sqrt{npq}$, where $q = 1 - p$.

SUPPLEMENTARY EXERCISES

1. **U.S. Population** Display the data from Table 1 in a bar chart that shows frequencies on the y-axis. Then display the data in a pie chart.

TABLE 1	U.S. population by region (in millions)
Region	**Population**
Northeast	66.2
Midwest	54.7
South	109.1
West	69.4

Source: U.S. Census Bureau, 2006.

2. Find the five-number summary and the interquartile range for the following set of numbers, and then draw the box plot.

$$1, 2, 3, 4, 5, 9, 14, 23$$

3. An experiment consists of three binomial trials, each having probability $\frac{1}{3}$ of success.
   (a) Determine the probability distribution table for the number of successes.
   (b) Use the table to compute the mean and the variance of the probability distribution.

4. Find the area of the shaded region under the standard normal curve shown in Fig. 1(a).

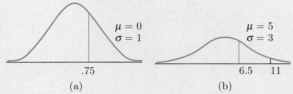

$\mu = 0$	$\mu = 5$
$\sigma = 1$	$\sigma = 3$
.75	6.5 11
(a)	(b)

Figure 1

5. Find the area of the shaded region under the normal curve with $\mu = 5$, $\sigma = 3$ shown in Fig. 1(b).

6. **Archery** An archer has probability .3 of hitting a certain target. What is the probability of hitting the target exactly two times in four attempts?

7. Suppose that a probability distribution has mean 10 and standard deviation $\frac{1}{3}$. Use the Chebychev inequality to estimate the probability that an outcome will lie between 9 and 11.

8. Table 2 gives the probability distribution of the random variable X. Compute the mean and the variance of the random variable.

TABLE 2	
k	$\Pr(X = k)$
0	.2
1	.3
5	.1
10	.4

9. **Heights of Adult Males** The height of adult males in the United States is normally distributed with $\mu = 5.75$ feet and $\sigma = .2$ feet. What percent of the adult male population has height of 6 feet or greater?

10. **Balls in an Urn** An urn contains four red balls and four white balls. An experiment consists of selecting at random a sample of four balls and recording the number of red balls in the sample. Set up the probability distribution and compute its mean and variance.

11. **Jury Selection** In a certain city two-fifths of the registered voters are women. Out of a group of 54 voters allegedly selected at random for jury duty, 13 are women. A local civil liberties group has charged that the selection procedure discriminated against women. Use the normal curve to estimate the probability of 13 or fewer women being selected in a truly random selection process.

12. **Quality Control** In a complicated production process, $\frac{1}{4}$ of the items produced have to be readjusted. Use the normal curve to estimate the probability that out of a batch of 75 items, between 8 and 22 (inclusive) of the items require readjustment.

13. Figure 2(a) is a normal curve with $\mu = 80$ and $\sigma = 15$. Find the value of h for which the area of the shaded region is .8664.

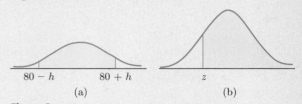

$80 - h$ $80 + h$	z
(a)	(b)

Figure 2

14. Figure 2(b) is a standard normal curve. Find the value of z for which the area of the shaded region is .7734.

15. **IQ Scores** As measured with the Wechsler Adult Intelligence Scale, IQ scores are normally distributed with mean 100 and standard deviation 15.
    (a) What percent of the adult population has an IQ score of 133 or more?
    (b) Find the 95th percentile of IQ scores.

16. **Guessing on an Exam** A true–false exam consists of ten 10-point questions. The instructor informs the students that six of the answers are *true* and four are

false. An unprepared student decides to guess the answer to each question with the use of the spinner in Fig. 3, which gives *true* 60% of the time. Determine the student's expected score. Can you think of a better strategy?

Figure 3

Conceptual Exercises

17. Give an example of a grade distribution for a class of students in which

   (a) scoring in the 3rd quartile is not very good.

   (b) scoring in the 3rd quartile corresponds to a perfect grade.

18. Give an example of a distribution of ten grades for which

   (a) the mean and median are equal.

   (b) the mean is less than the median.

   (c) the median is less than the mean.

19. What is the difference between a population mean and a sample mean?

20. Explain in your own words the meaning of "expected value."

21. If each number in a set of numbers is increased by 5, will the mean increase by 5?

22. If each number in a set of numbers is doubled, will the standard deviation be doubled?

23. Explain the type of probability situations for which the binomial distribution applies.

24. Give an example of a sequence of repeated trials that does not produce a binomial distribution.

CHAPTER TEST

1. Supermarket Queue The manager of a supermarket counts the number of customers waiting in the express checkout line at random times throughout the week. Her observations are summarized in the following frequency table.

Number Waiting in Line	Frequency
0	2
1	5
2	9
3	13
4	11
5	7
6	3

Construct the corresponding relative frequency table, and use it to estimate the probability that at most three customers are waiting in line.

2. Find the five-number summary and the interquartile range for the following set of numbers, and then draw the box plot.

$$20, 25, 26, 27, 29, 30, 33, 34, 37, 40, 42$$

3. Coin Tosses A fair coin is tossed twice. Let X be the number of heads.

   (a) Determine the probability distribution of X.

   (b) Determine the probability distribution of $2X + 5$.

4. Dice A pair of fair dice is rolled 12 times. *Note:* For each roll, the probability of getting a 7 is 1/6.

   (a) What is $\Pr($the result is 7 exactly twice$)$?

   (b) What is $\Pr($the result is 7 at least twice$)$?

   (c) What is the expected number of times that the result is 7?

5. The probability distribution of a random variable X is given in the following table. Determine the mean, variance, and standard deviation of X.

k	$\Pr(X = k)$
-2	.3
0	.1
1	.4
3	.2

6. Dice Game Lucy and Ethel play a game of chance in which a pair of fair dice is rolled once. If the result is 7 or 11, then Lucy pays Ethel $10.00. Otherwise, Ethel pays Lucy $3.00. In the long run, which player comes out ahead, and by how much?

7. Let Z be the standard normal random variable. Determine the following.

   (a) $\Pr(Z \leq 1)$

   (b) $\Pr(Z \geq -2.25)$

   (c) $\Pr(-1 \leq Z \leq 1.15)$

8. Blood Sugar Levels for Diabetics Assume the fasting blood glucose level among diabetics is normally distributed with mean 106 mg/100 ml and standard deviation 10 mg/100 ml.

(a) What is the probability that a randomly selected diabetic will have a fasting blood glucose level of more than 116 mg/100 ml?

(b) What is the probability that the fasting blood glucose level of a randomly selected diabetic will be between 96 and 121 mg/100 ml?

(c) For what value of c will 24.2% of diabetics have a fasting blood glucose level of less than c mg/100 ml? more than c mg/100 ml?

9. **Opinion Polling** A new shopping mall is to be built, and 20% of the community's residents oppose the construction. A random sample of 25 residents is polled.

(a) Approximate the probability that more than 5 but at most 10 of the selected residents oppose the construction.

(b) Determine the exact probability that exactly 10 of the selected residents oppose the construction, and compare your answer with the normal approximation of that probability.

(c) Determine the exact probability that at least one of the selected residents opposes the construction, and compare your answer with the normal approximation of that probability.

CHAPTER 7 | PROJECT

An Unexpected Expected Value[1]

An urn contains four red balls and six white balls. Suppose two balls are drawn at random from the urn, and let X be the number of red balls drawn. The probability of obtaining two red balls depends on whether the balls are drawn with or without replacement. The purpose of this project is to show that the expected number of red balls drawn is not affected by whether or not the first ball is replaced before the second ball is drawn.

1. Do you think the probability that both balls are red is higher if the first ball is replaced before the second ball is drawn, or if the first ball is not replaced?

2. Suppose the first ball is replaced before the second ball is drawn. Find the probability that both balls are red.

3. Suppose the first ball is not replaced before the second ball is drawn. Find the probability that both balls are red.

4. Was your intuitive guess in part 1 correct?

5. Do you think that the expected number of red balls drawn is higher if the balls are drawn with replacement or without replacement?

6. Suppose the first ball is replaced before the second ball is drawn. Find the expected number of red balls that will be drawn.

7. Suppose the first ball is not replaced before the second ball is drawn. Find the expected number of red balls that will be drawn.

8. Was your intuitive guess in part 5 correct?

9. Pretend that the balls are ping-pong balls that have been finely ground up, and that the red and white specks have been thoroughly mixed. Forty percent of the specks will be red and 60% will be white. Suppose you stir the specks and use a tablespoon to scoop out 10% of the specks. That is, suppose the tablespoon holds a quantity of specks corresponding to one ball.

   (a) What percentage of a red ball is contained in the spoon?

   (b) What percentage of the remaining specks in the urn are red?

   (c) If the spoonful of specks is replaced, does the percentage of red specks in the urn change?

   (d) Use the results from parts (b) and (c) to explain why the expected number of red balls as calculated in parts 6 and 7 is the same with and without replacement.

---

[1]The idea for this project was taken from the article "An Unexpected Expected Value," by Stephen Schwartzman, which appeared in the February 1993 issue of *The Mathematics Teacher*.

MARKOV PROCESSES

Suppose that we perform, one after the other, a sequence of experiments that have the same set of outcomes. The probabilities of the various outcomes of a particular experiment of the sequence may depend in some way on the outcomes of preceding experiments. The nature of such a dependency may be very complicated. In the extreme, the outcome of the current experiment may depend on the entire history of the outcomes of preceding experiments. However, there is a simple type of dependency that occurs frequently in applications and that we can analyze with fair ease. Namely, we suppose that the probabilities of the various outcomes of the current experiment depend (at most) on the outcome of the preceding experiment. In this case the sequence of experiments is called a **Markov process**. In this chapter we present some of the most elementary ideas concerning Markov processes and their applications.

8.1 The Transition Matrix

Here are some Markov processes that arise in applications.

EXAMPLE 1   **Investment**   A particular utility stock is very stable and, in the short run, the probability that it increases or decreases in price depends only on the result of the preceding day's trading. The price of the stock is observed at 4 P.M. each day and is recorded as "increased," "decreased," or "unchanged." The sequence of observations forms a Markov process.   ■

EXAMPLE 2   **Medicine**   A doctor tests the effect of a new drug on high blood pressure. Based on the effects of metabolism, a given dose is eliminated from the body in 24 hours. Blood pressure is measured once a day and is recorded as "high," "low," or "normal." The sequence of measurements forms a Markov process.   ■

EXAMPLE 3   **Sociology**   A sociologist postulates that the likelihood that, in certain countries, a woman will enter the labor force depends primarily on whether the woman's mother worked. He designs an experiment to test this hypothesis by viewing the sequence of career choices of a woman, her daughters, her granddaughters, her great-granddaughters, and so on as a Markov process.   ■

Let us now introduce some vocabulary and mathematical machinery with which to study Markov processes. The experiments are performed at regular time intervals and have the same set of outcomes. These outcomes are called *states*, and the outcome of the current experiment is referred to as the *current state* of the process. After each time interval, the process may change its state. The transition from state to state can be described by tree diagrams, as is shown in the next example.

EXAMPLE 4   **Using a tree diagram to represent transitions**   Refer to the utility stock of Example 1. Suppose that if the stock increases one day, the probability that on the next day it increases is .3, remains unchanged .2, decreases .5. On the other hand, if the stock is unchanged one day, the probability that on the next day it increases is .6, remains unchanged .1, decreases .3. If the stock decreases one day, the probability that it increases the next day is .3, is unchanged .4, decreases .3. Represent the possible transitions between states and their probabilities by tree diagrams.

Solution   The Markov process has three states: "increases," "unchanged," and "decreases." The transitions from the first state ("increases") to the other states are

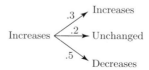

Note that each branch of the tree has been labeled with the probability of the corresponding transition. Similarly, the tree diagrams corresponding to the other

two states are

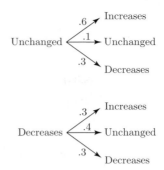

The three tree diagrams of Example 4 may be summarized in a single matrix. We insert the probabilities from a given tree down a column of the matrix, so that each column of the matrix records the information about transitions from one particular state. So the first column of the matrix is

$$\begin{bmatrix} .3 \\ .2 \\ .5 \end{bmatrix},$$

corresponding to transitions from the state "increases." The complete matrix is

		Current state		
		Increases	Unchanged	Decreases
Next state	Increases	.3	.6	.3
	Unchanged	.2	.1	.4
	Decreases	.5	.3	.3

This matrix, which records all data about transitions from one state to another, is called the **transition matrix** of the Markov process.

EXAMPLE 5

Women in the labor force Census studies from the 1960s reveal that in the United States 80% of the daughters of working women also work and that 30% of the daughters of nonworking women work. Assume that this trend remains unchanged from one generation to the next. Determine the corresponding transition matrix.

Solution There are two states, which we label "work" and "don't work." The first column corresponds to transitions from the first state—that is, from "work." The probability that the daughter of a working woman chooses *not* to work is $1 - .8 = .2$. Therefore, the first column is

$$\begin{bmatrix} .8 \\ .2 \end{bmatrix}.$$

In similar fashion, the second column is

$$\begin{bmatrix} .3 \\ .7 \end{bmatrix}.$$

The transition matrix is, therefore,

		Current generation	
		Work	Don't work
Next generation	Work	.8	.3
	Don't work	.2	.7

Now Try Exercise 25(a)

Here is the form of a general transition matrix for a Markov process:

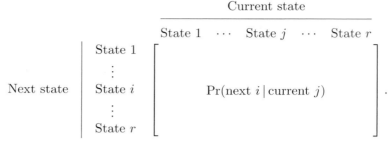

Note that this matrix satisfies the following two properties:

1. All entries are greater than or equal to 0.
2. The sum of the entries in each column is 1.

Any square matrix satisfying properties 1 and 2 is called a **stochastic matrix**. (The word "stochastic" derives from the Greek word "stochastices," which means a person who predicts the future.)

Let us examine further the Markov process of Example 5. In 1960 about 40% of U.S. women worked and 60% did not. This distribution is described by the column matrix

$$\begin{bmatrix} .4 \\ .6 \end{bmatrix}_0,$$

which is called a **distribution matrix**. The subscript 0 is added to denote that this matrix describes generation 0. Their daughters constitute generation 1, and their granddaughters generation 2. There is a distribution matrix for each generation. The distribution matrix for generation n is

$$\begin{bmatrix} p_W \\ p_{DW} \end{bmatrix}_n,$$

where p_W is the percentage of women in generation n who work and p_{DW} is the percentage who don't work. Of course, the numbers p_W and p_{DW} are also probabilities. The number p_W is the probability that a woman selected at random from generation n works. Similarly, p_{DW} is the probability that a woman selected at random from generation n does not work. Shortly we shall give a method for calculating the distribution matrix for generation n.

In general, whenever a Markov process applies to a group with members in r possible states, a distribution matrix of the form

$$\begin{bmatrix} p_1 \\ p_2 \\ \vdots \\ p_r \end{bmatrix}_0$$

gives the initial percentages of members in each of the r states. Similarly, a matrix of the same type (with the subscript n) gives the percentages of members in each of the r states after n time periods. Note that each of the percentages in the distribution matrix is also a probability—the probability that a randomly selected member will be in the corresponding state.

EXAMPLE 6

Projecting women in the labor force In 1960, census figures showed that 40% of American women worked. Use the stochastic matrix of Example 5 to determine the percentage of working women in each of the next two generations.

Solution Let us denote by A the stochastic matrix of Example 5:

$$\begin{array}{cc} & \text{Current generation} \\ \hline & \begin{array}{cc} \text{Work} & \text{Don't work} \end{array} \\ \text{Next generation} \begin{array}{c} \text{Work} \\ \text{Don't work} \end{array} & \begin{bmatrix} .8 & .3 \\ .2 & .7 \end{bmatrix}. \end{array}$$

The initial distribution matrix is

$$\begin{bmatrix} .4 \\ .6 \end{bmatrix}_0.$$

Our goal is to compute the distribution matrices for generations 1 and 2. With an eye toward performing similar calculations for other countries, let us use letters rather than specific numbers in these distribution matrices. Let

$$\begin{bmatrix} \ \ \end{bmatrix}_0 = \begin{bmatrix} x_0 \\ y_0 \end{bmatrix}, \qquad \begin{bmatrix} \ \ \end{bmatrix}_1 = \begin{bmatrix} x_1 \\ y_1 \end{bmatrix}, \qquad \begin{bmatrix} \ \ \end{bmatrix}_2 = \begin{bmatrix} x_2 \\ y_2 \end{bmatrix}.$$

The state transitions from generation 0 to generation 1 may be displayed in a tree diagram.

Adding together the probabilities for the two paths leading to "work" in generation 1 gives

$$x_1 = .8x_0 + .3y_0. \tag{1}$$

Similarly, adding together the probabilities for the two paths leading to "don't work" in generation 1 gives

$$y_1 = .2x_0 + .7y_0. \tag{2}$$

Thus, (1) and (2) show that x_1 and y_1 can be computed from this pair of equations.

$$x_1 = .8x_0 + .3y_0$$
$$y_1 = .2x_0 + .7y_0$$

This system of equations is equivalent to the one matrix equation

$$\begin{bmatrix} .8 & .3 \\ .2 & .7 \end{bmatrix} \begin{bmatrix} x_0 \\ y_0 \end{bmatrix} = \begin{bmatrix} x_1 \\ y_1 \end{bmatrix}. \tag{3}$$

Or, to write equation (3) symbolically,

$$A \begin{bmatrix} \ \ \end{bmatrix}_0 = \begin{bmatrix} \ \ \end{bmatrix}_1. \tag{4}$$

Now it is easy to do the arithmetic to compute the distribution matrix for generation 1 of American women:

$$A \begin{bmatrix} \ \ \end{bmatrix}_0 = \begin{bmatrix} .8 & .3 \\ .2 & .7 \end{bmatrix} \begin{bmatrix} .4 \\ .6 \end{bmatrix}_0 = \begin{bmatrix} .5 \\ .5 \end{bmatrix}_1.$$

That is, 50% of American women in generation 1 will work, and 50% will not.

To compute the distribution matrix for generation 2, we use the same reasoning as before, when we showed that to get

$$\begin{bmatrix} \\ \end{bmatrix}_1 \quad \text{from} \quad \begin{bmatrix} \\ \end{bmatrix}_0,$$

just multiply by A.

Similarly,

$$A \begin{bmatrix} \\ \end{bmatrix}_1 = \begin{bmatrix} \\ \end{bmatrix}_2 .$$

However, by (4), we have a formula for $\begin{bmatrix} \\ \end{bmatrix}_1$, which we can insert into the last equation, getting[1]

$$\begin{bmatrix} \\ \end{bmatrix}_2 = A \begin{bmatrix} \\ \end{bmatrix}_1 = A \left(A \begin{bmatrix} \\ \end{bmatrix}_0 \right) = A^2 \begin{bmatrix} \\ \end{bmatrix}_0 .$$

In other words,

$$A^2 \begin{bmatrix} \\ \end{bmatrix}_0 = \begin{bmatrix} \\ \end{bmatrix}_2 . \tag{5}$$

A simple calculation gives

$$A^2 = \begin{bmatrix} .70 & .45 \\ .30 & .55 \end{bmatrix},$$

so that we can now compute the distribution for generation 2 of American women:

$$\begin{bmatrix} .70 & .45 \\ .30 & .55 \end{bmatrix} \begin{bmatrix} .4 \\ .6 \end{bmatrix}_0 = \begin{bmatrix} .55 \\ .45 \end{bmatrix}_2 .$$

Now Try Exercise 19 That is, after two generations 55% of American women work and 45% do not. ∎

An argument similar to that used to derive equation (5) can be used to show that

$$A^3 \begin{bmatrix} \\ \end{bmatrix}_0 = \begin{bmatrix} \\ \end{bmatrix}_3 , \quad A^4 \begin{bmatrix} \\ \end{bmatrix}_0 = \begin{bmatrix} \\ \end{bmatrix}_4 , \quad A^5 \begin{bmatrix} \\ \end{bmatrix}_0 = \begin{bmatrix} \\ \end{bmatrix}_5 , \quad \ldots .$$

A condensed notation is

$$A^n \begin{bmatrix} \\ \end{bmatrix}_0 = \begin{bmatrix} \\ \end{bmatrix}_n \qquad (n = 1, 2, 3, \ldots). \tag{6}$$

That is, to compute the distribution matrix for generation n, merely compute the product of A^n times the distribution matrix for generation 0. Equation (6) can be used to predict the distribution matrix for any number of generations into the future, starting from any given distribution matrix. Let us now look at an entirely different type of situation that can be described by a Markov process.

EXAMPLE 7

Taxi zones Taxis pick up and deliver passengers in a city that is divided into three zones. Records kept by the drivers show that of the passengers picked up in zone I, 50% are taken to a destination in zone I, 40% to zone II, and 10% to zone III. Of the passengers picked up in zone II, 40% go to zone I, 30% to zone II, and 30% to zone III. Of the passengers picked up in zone III, 20% go to zone I, 60% to zone II, and 20% to zone III. Suppose that at the beginning of the day 60% of the taxis are in zone I, 10% in zone II, and 30% in zone III. What is the distribution of taxis in the various zones after all have had one passenger? Two passengers?

---

[1] Just as in elementary algebra, we define the powers $A^2, A^3, \ldots$ of the matrix A by $A^2 = A \cdot A$, $A^3 = A \cdot A \cdot A, \ldots$.

Solution This situation is an example of a Markov process. The states are the zones. The initial distribution of the taxis gives the zeroth distribution matrix:

$$\begin{bmatrix} .6 \\ .1 \\ .3 \end{bmatrix}_0 .$$

The stochastic matrix associated to the process is the one giving the probabilities of taxis starting in any one zone and ending up in any other. There is one column for each zone:

From zone:

		I	II	III
	I	.5	.4	.2
To zone:| II	.4	.3	.6	= A.
	III	.1	.3	.2

After all taxis have had one passenger, the distribution matrix is just

$$A \begin{bmatrix} .6 \\ .1 \\ .3 \end{bmatrix}_0 = \begin{bmatrix} .5 & .4 & .2 \\ .4 & .3 & .6 \\ .1 & .3 & .2 \end{bmatrix} \begin{bmatrix} .6 \\ .1 \\ .3 \end{bmatrix}_0 = \begin{bmatrix} .40 \\ .45 \\ .15 \end{bmatrix}_1 .$$

That is, 40% of the taxis are in zone I, 45% in zone II, and 15% in zone III. After all taxis have had two passengers, the distribution matrix is

$$A^2 \begin{bmatrix} .6 \\ .1 \\ .3 \end{bmatrix}_0 ,$$

which, after some arithmetic, can be shown to be

$$\begin{bmatrix} .410 \\ .385 \\ .205 \end{bmatrix}_2 .$$

That is, after two passengers, 41% of the taxis are in zone I, 38.5% are in zone II, and 20.5% are in zone III.

Now Try Exercise 21

The crucial formula used in both Examples 6 and 7 is

$$A \begin{bmatrix} \\ \end{bmatrix}_0 = \begin{bmatrix} \\ \end{bmatrix}_1 . \tag{7}$$

From this one follows the more general formula

$$A^n \begin{bmatrix} \\ \end{bmatrix}_0 = \begin{bmatrix} \\ \end{bmatrix}_n .$$

We carefully proved (7) in the special case of Example 6. Let us do the same for Example 7. Suppose that the initial distribution of taxis is

$$\begin{bmatrix} x_0 \\ y_0 \\ z_0 \end{bmatrix} .$$

How many taxis end up in zone I after one passenger? The taxis in zone I come from three sources—zones I, II, and III. And the first row of the stochastic matrix

A gives the percentages of taxis starting out in each of the zones and ending up in zone I:

$$[\text{percent of taxis going to zone I}] = [.5] \cdot [\text{percent of taxis in zone I}]$$
$$+ [.4] \cdot [\text{percent of taxis in zone II}]$$
$$+ [.2] \cdot [\text{percent of taxis in zone III}]$$
$$= .5x_0 + .4y_0 + .2z_0.$$

Indeed, the first entry, x_1, in the product

$$\begin{bmatrix} .5 & .4 & .2 \\ .4 & .3 & .6 \\ .1 & .3 & .2 \end{bmatrix} \begin{bmatrix} x_0 \\ y_0 \\ z_0 \end{bmatrix} = \begin{bmatrix} x_1 \\ \\ \end{bmatrix}$$

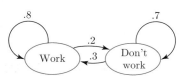

is just $.5x_0 + .4y_0 + .2z_0$. Similarly, the proportions of taxis in zones II and III coincide with the other two entries in the matrix product. So equation (7) really holds.

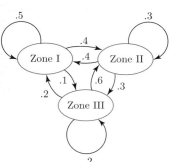

Interpretation of the Entries of A^n   Label the columns and rows of the transition matrix A and A^n with the states as in the paragraph following Example 5. Then the entry in the ith row and jth column of A is the probability of the transition from state j to state i after one time period.

> The entry in the ith row and jth column of the matrix A^n is the probability of the transition from state j to state i after n time periods.

Transition Diagrams   The probabilities for a Markov process can be visually displayed in a transition diagram. Figure 1 shows the transition diagrams for the working women and taxi zone examples. Each arrow going between states is labeled with the probability of the corresponding transition.

Figure 1

INCORPORATING TECHNOLOGY

GC   Let

$$A = \begin{bmatrix} .8 & .3 \\ .2 & .7 \end{bmatrix}$$

be the 2×2 matrix of Examples 5 and 6, and let

$$B = \begin{bmatrix} .4 \\ .6 \end{bmatrix}$$

be the initial distribution matrix. Successive distribution matrices are easy to obtain with a graphing calculator. The most recently displayed list, number, or matrix becomes the value of the variable **Ans** (on the TI-83/84 Plus) or the variable **ans(1)** (on the TI-89). (To obtain **Ans** or **ans(1)**, press 2nd[ANS].) In Figs. 2 and 4, after matrix B is displayed, it becomes the value of the variable **Ans** or **ans(1)**. Therefore, the value of **[A]*Ans** (or **a*ans(1)**) is the matrix product AB. Each time ENTER is pressed, the instruction **[A]*Ans** (or **a*ans(1)**) is repeated. That is, the preceding matrix is multiplied on the left by the matrix A. Figures 3 and 5, which result after ENTER is pressed two more times, show the additional matrices A^2B and A^3B. ∎

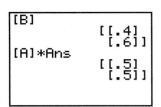

Figure 2

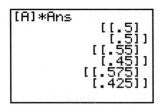

Figure 3

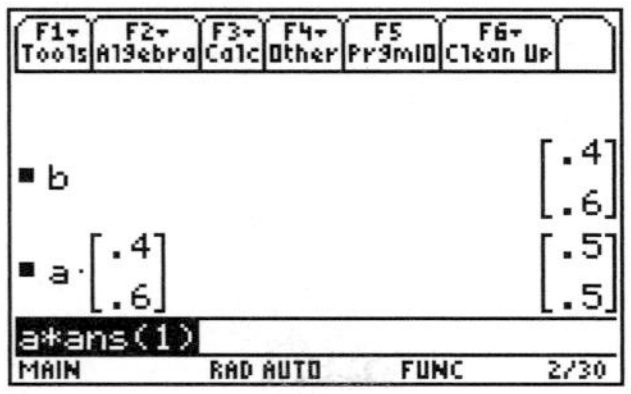

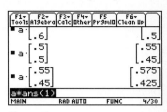

Figure 4

Figure 5

ES Figure 6, which shows successive distribution matrices, can be created as follows:

1. Give the name **A** to the 2 × 2 matrix on the left.
2. Enter **.4** and **.6** into cells D2 and D3.
3. Select the range E2:E3, type in **=MMULT(A,D2:D3)**, and press Ctrl+Shift+Enter.
4. Select the range E2:E3, and drag its fill handle right to column I.

NOTE In Step 3, the column matrix $\begin{bmatrix} 0.4 \\ 0.6 \end{bmatrix}$ was referred to as the range of cells D2:D3 rather than by a name. This allowed AutoFill to use the pattern specified in E2:E3 as a basis for filling additional cells. ■

	A	B	C	D	E	F	G	H	I
1	**Matrix A**		**Generation**	**0**	**1**	**2**	**3**	**4**	**5**
2	0.8	0.3		0.4	0.5	0.55	0.575	0.5875	0.59375
3	0.2	0.7		0.6	0.5	0.45	0.425	0.4125	0.40625

Figure 6

Practice Problems 8.1

1. Is $\begin{bmatrix} \frac{2}{5} & 1 \\ \frac{3}{5} & .2 \\ \frac{2}{5} & -.3 \end{bmatrix}$ a stochastic matrix?

2. **Learning Process** An elementary learning process consists of subjects participating in a sequence of events. Experiment shows that of the subjects not conditioned to make the correct response at the beginning of any event, 40% will be conditioned to make the correct response at the end of the event. Once a subject is conditioned to make the correct response, he stays conditioned.

   (a) Set up the 2 × 2 stochastic matrix with columns and rows labeled N (not conditioned) and C (conditioned) that describes this situation.

   (b) Compute A^3.

   (c) If initially all the subjects are not conditioned, what percent of them will be conditioned after three events?

EXERCISES 8.1

In Exercises 1–6, determine whether or not the matrix is stochastic.

1. $\begin{bmatrix} 1 & .8 \\ 0 & .2 \end{bmatrix}$

2. $\begin{bmatrix} \frac{1}{3} & \frac{1}{3} \\ \frac{2}{3} & \frac{2}{3} \end{bmatrix}$

3. $\begin{bmatrix} .4 & .3 & .2 \\ .6 & .7 & .8 \end{bmatrix}$

4. $\begin{bmatrix} .4 & .5 & .1 \\ .3 & .4 & 0 \\ .3 & .2 & .9 \end{bmatrix}$

5. $\begin{bmatrix} \frac{1}{6} & \frac{5}{12} & 0 \\ \frac{1}{2} & \frac{1}{4} & .5 \\ \frac{1}{3} & \frac{1}{3} & .5 \end{bmatrix}$ **6.** $\begin{bmatrix} 1 & 0 & 0 \\ 0 & 1 & 0 \\ 0 & 0 & 1 \end{bmatrix}$

In Exercises 7–12, write a stochastic matrix corresponding to the transition diagram.

7.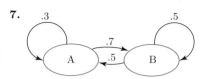

8.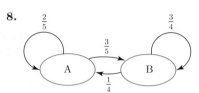

9.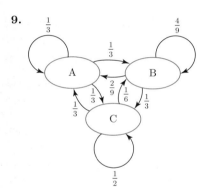

10.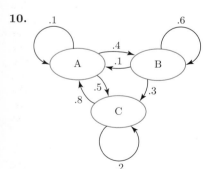

11.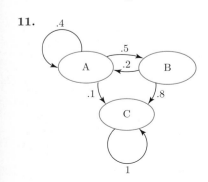

12.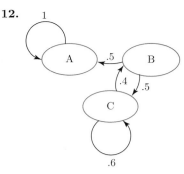

In Exercises 13–18, draw a transition diagram corresponding to the stochastic matrix.

13.
$\begin{array}{c} \\ A \\ B \end{array}\begin{array}{cc} A & B \\ \begin{bmatrix} \frac{2}{7} & \frac{1}{8} \\ \frac{5}{7} & \frac{7}{8} \end{bmatrix} \end{array}$

14.
$\begin{array}{c} \\ A \\ B \end{array}\begin{array}{cc} A & B \\ \begin{bmatrix} 1 & .3 \\ 0 & .7 \end{bmatrix} \end{array}$

15.
$\begin{array}{c} \\ A \\ B \\ C \end{array}\begin{array}{ccc} A & B & C \\ \begin{bmatrix} .4 & .1 & .5 \\ 0 & .7 & .1 \\ .6 & .2 & .4 \end{bmatrix} \end{array}$

16.
$\begin{array}{c} \\ A \\ B \\ C \end{array}\begin{array}{ccc} A & B & C \\ \begin{bmatrix} 0 & \frac{2}{3} & \frac{1}{8} \\ \frac{1}{5} & 0 & \frac{1}{4} \\ \frac{4}{5} & \frac{1}{3} & \frac{5}{8} \end{bmatrix} \end{array}$

17.
$\begin{array}{c} \\ A \\ B \\ C \end{array}\begin{array}{ccc} A & B & C \\ \begin{bmatrix} .2 & 0 & .4 \\ 0 & 1 & .5 \\ .8 & 0 & .1 \end{bmatrix} \end{array}$

18.
$\begin{array}{c} \\ A \\ B \\ C \end{array}\begin{array}{ccc} A & B & C \\ \begin{bmatrix} .2 & .7 & 0 \\ .3 & 0 & 1 \\ .5 & .3 & 0 \end{bmatrix} \end{array}$

19. **Women in the Labor Force** Referring to Example 5, consider a typical group of French women, of whom 47% currently work. Assume that the same percentage of daughters follow in their mothers' footsteps as with the American women—that is, that given by the matrix

$$A = \begin{bmatrix} .8 & .3 \\ .2 & .7 \end{bmatrix}.$$

Use A and A^2 to determine the proportion of working French women in the next two generations. (Round off to the nearest whole percent.)

20. **Women in the Labor Force** Repeat Exercise 19 for the women of Belgium, of whom 44% currently work. (Round off the percentage of women to the nearest whole percent.)

21. **Taxi Zones** Refer to Example 7 (taxi zones). If originally 40% of the taxis start in zone I, 40% in zone II, and 20% in zone III, how will the taxis be distributed after each has taken one passenger?

22. **Health Plan Option** A university faculty health plan offers an optional dental plan. During the open enrollment period each year, 90% of the people who currently have the dental plan re-enroll for it and 10% opt out. Of the people who do not have the dental plan 40% enroll for it and 60% stay out of the plan.

(a) Draw a transition diagram with ovals labeled "Dental plan" and "No dental plan" for this Markov process.

(b) Set up the 2×2 stochastic matrix (with columns and rows labeled D and N) for the Markov process.

(c) Compute the second power of the matrix in part (b).

(d) Suppose that for the year 2008, 70% of the faculty are in the dental plan and 30% are not in the plan. That is, the initial distribution is given by the column matrix $\begin{bmatrix} .7 \\ .3 \end{bmatrix}$. Use the matrices in parts (b) and (c) to find the distribution matrices for 2009 and 2010.

23. Population Movement According to the U.S. Census Bureau, the South was the fastest growing region in the country from 2004 to 2005. Figure 7 shows the percentages of people who moved in and out of the South during that time period. In 2004, about 36% of the U.S. population lived in the South.

Figure 7

(a) Set up the stochastic matrix that displays the transitions.

(b) Assuming that these transition rates persisted for several years, use the matrix from part (a) to estimate the percent of the U.S. living in the South in 2005 and in 2006.

24. Voter Patterns For a certain group of states, it was observed that 70% of the Democratic governors were succeeded by Democrats and 30% by Republicans. Also, 40% of the Republican governors were succeeded by Democrats and 60% by Republicans.

(a) Set up the 2×2 stochastic matrix with columns and rows labeled D and R that displays these transitions.

(b) Compute A^2 and A^3.

(c) Suppose that all the current governors are Democrats. Assuming that the current trend holds for three elections, what percent of the governors will then be Democrats?

25. T-Maze Each day mice are put into a T-maze (a maze shaped like a "T"; Fig. 8). In this maze they have the choice of turning to the left (rewarded with cheese) or to the right (receive cheese along with mild shock). After the first day their decision whether to turn left or right is influenced by what happened on the previous day. Of those that go to the left on a certain day, 90% go to the left on the next day and 10% go to the right. Of those that go to the right on a certain day, 70% go to the left on the next day and 30% go to the right.

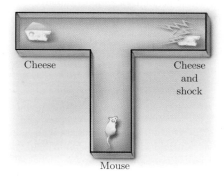

Figure 8

(a) Set up the 2×2 stochastic matrix with columns and rows labeled L and R that describes this situation.

(b) Compute the second power of the matrix in part (a).

(c) Suppose that on the first day (day 0) 50% go to the left and 50% go to the right. So, the initial distribution is given by the column matrix $\begin{bmatrix} .5 \\ .5 \end{bmatrix}_0$. Using the matrices in parts (a) and (b), find the distribution matrices for the next two days, days 1 and 2.

(d) Make a guess as to the percentage of mice that will go to the left after 50 days. (Do not compute.)

26. Fitness A group of physical fitness devotees works out in the gym every day. The workouts vary from strenuous to moderate to light. When their exercise routine was recorded, the following observation was made: Of the people who work out strenuously on a particular day, 40% will work out strenuously on the next day and 60% will work out moderately. Of the people who work out moderately on a particular day, 50% will work out strenuously and 50% will work out lightly on the next day. Of the people working out lightly on a particular day, 30% will work out strenuously on the next day, 20% moderately, and 50% lightly.

(a) Set up the 3×3 stochastic matrix with columns and rows labeled S, M, and L that describes these transitions.

(b) Suppose that on a particular Monday 80% have a strenuous, 10% a moderate, and 10% a light workout. What percent will have a strenuous workout on Wednesday?

27. Political Views According to the Higher Education Research Institute,[2] 32% of students at baccalaureate granting colleges who entered college in 2007 characterize their political views as Liberal, 43% as Middle-of-the-road, and 25% as Conservative. Suppose that

---

[2] *The American Freshman: National Norms for Fall 2007*; American Council on Education, University of California-Los Angeles.

each year these students changed their political views as described by the following matrix.

		From view:		
		L	M	C
To view:	L	.94	.02	.01
	M	.05	.96	.04
	C	.01	.02	.95

(a) What percentage of the students who held conservative political views as freshmen held middle-of-the-road views as sophomores?

(b) Explain the meaning of the percentage .96 appearing in the center of the matrix.

(c) Draw the transition diagram for this Markov process.

(d) What percentage of the students held middle-of-the-road political views as sophomores? Juniors?

28. Student Residences According to the Higher Education Research Institute,[3] 80% of students at baccalaureate granting colleges who entered college in 2007 lived in College residence halls, 13% lived with Relatives, and 7% lived in Other types of housing. Suppose that each year these students changed their residences as described by the following matrix.

		From residence:		
		C	F	O
To residence:	C	.9	.1	.2
	F	.05	.8	.1
	O	.05	.1	.7

(a) What percentage of the students who lived with family as freshmen lived in college residence halls as sophomores?

(b) Explain the meaning of the percentage .8 appearing in the center of the matrix.

(c) Draw the transition diagram for this Markov process.

(d) What percentage of the students lived in college resience halls as sophomores? Juniors?

29. Population Movement A sociologist studying living patterns in a certain region determines that each year the population shifts between urban, suburban, and rural areas as shown in Fig. 9.

(a) Set up a stochastic matrix that displays these transitions.

(b) What percentage of people who live in urban areas in 2009 will live in rural areas in 20011?

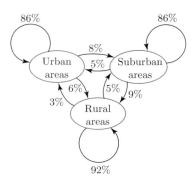

Figure 9

30. Market Share A retailer stocks three brands of breakfast cereal. A survey is taken of 5000 people who purchase cereal weekly from this retailer. Each week Crispy Flakes loses 12% of its customers to Crunchy Nuggets and 19% to Toasty Cinnamon Twists. Crunchy Nuggets loses 16% of its customers to Crispy Flakes and 10% of its customers to Toasty Cinnamon Twists, and Toasty Cinnamon Twists loses 20% of its customers to Crispy Flakes and 14% to Crunchy Nuggets.

(a) Set up a stochastic matrix displaying these transitions.

(b) Suppose that this week 1500 people buy Crispy Flakes, 1500 buy Crunchy Nuggets, and 2000 people buy Toasty Cinnamon Twists. How many people will buy Crispy Flakes next week? How many will buy Toasty Cinnamon Twists in two weeks?

31. Analysis of a Poem In 1913, Markov analyzed a long poem written by a Russian author.[4] He found that vowels were followed by consonants 87.2% of the time (either in the same word or the next word), and that consonants were followed by vowels 66.3% of the time.

(a) Set up the 2×2 stochastic matrix, with columns and rows labeled V and C, that describes this situation.

(b) Find the probability that the second letter following a vowel is also a vowel.

In Exercises 32 and 33, find the third and fourth distribution matrices for the given stochastic matrix and initial distribution. (Round entries to two decimal places.)

32. $\begin{bmatrix} .3 & .9 \\ .7 & .1 \end{bmatrix}, \begin{bmatrix} .5 \\ .5 \end{bmatrix}_0$

33. $\begin{bmatrix} .5 & .4 \\ .5 & .6 \end{bmatrix}, \begin{bmatrix} .3 \\ .7 \end{bmatrix}_0$

[3] *The American Freshman: National Norms for Fall 2007*; American Council on Education, University of California-Los Angeles.

[4] Markov, A.A.: An example of statistical analysis of the text of *Eugene Onegin*. *Bulletin de l'Académie Imperiale des Sciences de St Petersburg*, 7, series 6, pp. 153–62.

In Exercises 34–38, compute the first five powers of each matrix (round off to two decimal places).

34. $\begin{bmatrix} 1 & \frac{1}{2} \\ 0 & \frac{1}{2} \end{bmatrix}$ **35.** $\begin{bmatrix} \frac{1}{3} & \frac{1}{3} \\ \frac{2}{3} & \frac{2}{3} \end{bmatrix}$ **36.** $\begin{bmatrix} 0 & 1 \\ 1 & 0 \end{bmatrix}$

37. $\begin{bmatrix} .1 & .3 \\ .9 & .7 \end{bmatrix}$ **38.** $\begin{bmatrix} .2 & .2 & .2 \\ .3 & .3 & .3 \\ .5 & .5 & .5 \end{bmatrix}$

Stochastic matrices for which some power contains no zero entries are called regular *matrices. In Exercises 39 and 40, conjecture whether or not the given matrix is regular by looking at the first few powers of the matrix.*

39. $\begin{bmatrix} .5 & 0 \\ .5 & 1 \end{bmatrix}$ **40.** $\begin{bmatrix} .7 & 1 \\ .3 & 0 \end{bmatrix}$

In Exercises 41–46, use a graphing calculator or a spreadsheet to calculate the answers.

41. Let A be the stochastic matrix $\begin{bmatrix} .1 & .6 \\ .9 & .4 \end{bmatrix}$, and let the initial distribution be $B = \begin{bmatrix} .5 \\ .5 \end{bmatrix}_0$.

(a) Generate the next four distribution matrices.

(b) Calculate $A^4 B$ and confirm that it is the same as the fourth distribution matrix.

42. Repeat Exercise 41 for the matrices $\begin{bmatrix} .4 & .2 \\ .6 & .8 \end{bmatrix}$ and $\begin{bmatrix} .7 \\ .3 \end{bmatrix}_0$.

43. Consider the matrices of Exercise 41. Beginning with the initial distribution matrix, generate 10 more distributions. Continue to generate 10 more. The matrices will get closer and closer to a certain 2×1 matrix. What is that matrix?

44. Repeat Exercise 43 for the matrices of Exercise 42.

45. Generate 35 successive powers of the matrix A from Exercise 41. (With a graphing calculator, the instructions **[A]*Ans** and **a*ans(1)** can be used to compute successive powers of a square matrix.) The matrices will get closer and closer to a certain 2×2 matrix. What is that matrix? How is that matrix related to the 2×1 matrix found in Exercise 43?

46. Repeat Exercise 45 for the square matrix of Exercise 42.

Solutions to Practice Problems 8.1

1. No. It fails on all three conditions. The matrix is not square, the entry $-.3$ is not ≥ 0, and the sum of the entries in the first (and second) column is not equal to 1.

2. (a) $\begin{array}{cc} & \text{N} \quad \text{C} \\ \begin{array}{c} \text{N} \\ \text{C} \end{array} & \begin{bmatrix} .6 & 0 \\ .4 & 1 \end{bmatrix} \end{array}$. Since there are only two possibilities and 40% of those not conditioned become conditioned, the remaining 60% stay not conditioned. After each event 100% of the conditioned stay conditioned, and therefore 0% become not conditioned.

(b) $A^2 = \begin{bmatrix} .6 & 0 \\ .4 & 1 \end{bmatrix} \begin{bmatrix} .6 & 0 \\ .4 & 1 \end{bmatrix} = \begin{bmatrix} .36 & 0 \\ .64 & 1 \end{bmatrix}$,

$A^3 = A^2 \cdot A = \begin{bmatrix} .36 & 0 \\ .64 & 1 \end{bmatrix} \begin{bmatrix} .6 & 0 \\ .4 & 1 \end{bmatrix}$

$= \begin{bmatrix} .216 & 0 \\ .784 & 1 \end{bmatrix}$.

(c) Here $\begin{bmatrix} \\ \end{bmatrix}_0 = \begin{bmatrix} 1 \\ 0 \end{bmatrix}$. Therefore,

$\begin{bmatrix} \\ \end{bmatrix}_3 = A^3 \begin{bmatrix} 1 \\ 0 \end{bmatrix} = \begin{bmatrix} .216 & 0 \\ .784 & 1 \end{bmatrix} \begin{bmatrix} 1 \\ 0 \end{bmatrix} = \begin{bmatrix} .216 \\ .784 \end{bmatrix}$.

So 78.4% will be conditioned after three events.

8.2 Regular Stochastic Matrices

In the preceding section we studied the percentages of working women in various generations in America. We showed that if $\begin{bmatrix} \\ \end{bmatrix}_0$ is the initial distribution matrix, then the distribution matrix $\begin{bmatrix} \\ \end{bmatrix}_n$ for the nth generation is given by

$$\begin{bmatrix} \\ \end{bmatrix}_n = A^n \begin{bmatrix} \\ \end{bmatrix}_0, \tag{1}$$

where A is the stochastic matrix

$$A = \begin{bmatrix} .8 & .3 \\ .2 & .7 \end{bmatrix}.$$

In this section we are interested in determining long-term trends in Markov processes. To get an idea of what is meant, consider the example of Jordanian women in the labor force.

EXAMPLE 1

Women in the labor force In Jordan 25% of the women currently work. The effect of maternal influence of mothers on their daughters is given by the matrix

$$\begin{bmatrix} .6 & .2 \\ .4 & .8 \end{bmatrix}.$$

(a) How many women will work after $1, 2, 3, \ldots, 11$ generations?

(b) Estimate the long-term trend.

(c) Answer the same questions (a) and (b) for China, assuming that 40% of all Chinese women currently work and that the effect of maternal influence is the same as for Jordan.

Solution (a) The percentages of women working in generation n (for $n = 1, 2, 3, \ldots$) can be determined from equation (1):

$$\begin{bmatrix} \quad \\ \quad \end{bmatrix}_n = \begin{bmatrix} .6 & .2 \\ .4 & .8 \end{bmatrix}^n \begin{bmatrix} .25 \\ .75 \end{bmatrix}_0.$$

After the mildly tedious job of raising the stochastic matrix to various powers, we obtain the results shown in Table 1.

TABLE 1

Generation	Percent of women working	Generation	Percent of women working
0	25	6	33.30
1	30	7	33.32
2	32	8	33.33
3	32.8	9	33.33
4	33.12	10	33.33
5	33.25	11	33.33

(b) It appears from the accompanying table that the long-term trend is for one-third or $33\frac{1}{3}\%$ of all Jordanian women to work.

(c) The corresponding results for China can be computed by replacing the initial distribution matrix $\begin{bmatrix} .25 \\ .75 \end{bmatrix}_0$ by $\begin{bmatrix} .40 \\ .60 \end{bmatrix}_0$, reflecting that initially 40% of all Chinese women work. The results of the calculations are shown in Table 2. Again, the long-term trend is for one-third of the women to work. ∎

From Example 1 one might begin to suspect the following: The long-term trend is always for one-third of the women to work, independent of the initial distribution.

TABLE 2

Generation	Percent of women working	Generation	Percent of women working
0	40	6	33.36
1	36	7	33.34
2	34.4	8	33.34
3	33.76	9	33.34
4	33.50	10	33.33
5	33.40	11	33.33

Verification To see why this rather surprising fact should hold, it is useful to examine the powers of A:

$$A^2 = \begin{bmatrix} .44 & .28 \\ .56 & .72 \end{bmatrix} \qquad A^3 = \begin{bmatrix} .376 & .312 \\ .624 & .688 \end{bmatrix} \qquad A^4 = \begin{bmatrix} .3504 & .3248 \\ .6496 & .6752 \end{bmatrix}$$

$$A^5 = \begin{bmatrix} .3402 & .3299 \\ .6598 & .6701 \end{bmatrix} \qquad A^6 = \begin{bmatrix} .3361 & .3320 \\ .6639 & .6680 \end{bmatrix} \qquad A^7 = \begin{bmatrix} .3344 & .3328 \\ .6656 & .6672 \end{bmatrix}$$

$$A^8 = \begin{bmatrix} .3338 & .3331 \\ .6662 & .6669 \end{bmatrix} \qquad A^9 = \begin{bmatrix} .3335 & .3332 \\ .6665 & .6668 \end{bmatrix} \qquad A^{10} = \begin{bmatrix} .3334 & .3333 \\ .6666 & .6667 \end{bmatrix}.$$

As A is raised to further powers, the matrices approach

$$\begin{bmatrix} \frac{1}{3} & \frac{1}{3} \\ \frac{2}{3} & \frac{2}{3} \end{bmatrix}. \tag{2}$$

Now suppose that initially the proportion of women working is x_0. That is, the initial distribution matrix is

$$\begin{bmatrix} x_0 \\ 1 - x_0 \end{bmatrix}.$$

Then, after n generations, the distribution matrix is

$$\begin{bmatrix} \quad \\ \quad \end{bmatrix}_n = A^n \begin{bmatrix} \quad \\ \quad \end{bmatrix}_0 = A^n \begin{bmatrix} x_0 \\ 1 - x_0 \end{bmatrix}.$$

But after many generations n is large, so that A^n is approximately the matrix (2). Thus,

$$\begin{bmatrix} \quad \\ \quad \end{bmatrix}_n \approx \begin{bmatrix} \frac{1}{3} & \frac{1}{3} \\ \frac{2}{3} & \frac{2}{3} \end{bmatrix} \begin{bmatrix} x_0 \\ 1 - x_0 \end{bmatrix} = \begin{bmatrix} \frac{1}{3}x_0 + \frac{1}{3}(1 - x_0) \\ \frac{2}{3}x_0 + \frac{2}{3}(1 - x_0) \end{bmatrix} = \begin{bmatrix} \frac{1}{3} \\ \frac{2}{3} \end{bmatrix}.$$

In other words, after n generations approximately one-third of the women work and two-thirds do not. ∎

From the preceding calculations we see that the stochastic matrix A possesses a number of very special properties. First, as n gets large, A^n approaches the matrix

$$\begin{bmatrix} \frac{1}{3} & \frac{1}{3} \\ \frac{2}{3} & \frac{2}{3} \end{bmatrix}.$$

Second, any initial distribution approaches the distribution $\begin{bmatrix} \frac{1}{3} \\ \frac{2}{3} \end{bmatrix}$ after many generations. The limiting matrix

$$\begin{bmatrix} \frac{1}{3} & \frac{1}{3} \\ \frac{2}{3} & \frac{2}{3} \end{bmatrix}$$

is called the **stable matrix** of A, and the limiting distribution

$$\begin{bmatrix} \frac{1}{3} \\ \frac{2}{3} \end{bmatrix}$$

is called the **stable distribution** of A. Finally, note that all the columns of the stable matrix are the same and are equal to the stable distribution.

The matrices that share the aforementioned properties with A are very important. For these matrices one can predict a long-term trend, and this trend is independent of the initial distribution. An important class of matrices with these properties is the class of *regular stochastic matrices*.

> **DEFINITION** A stochastic matrix is said to be **regular** if some power has all positive entries.

EXAMPLE 2

Identifying regular stochastic matrices Which of the following stochastic matrices are regular?

(a) $\begin{bmatrix} .6 & .2 \\ .4 & .8 \end{bmatrix}$ (b) $\begin{bmatrix} 0 & .5 \\ 1 & .5 \end{bmatrix}$ (c) $\begin{bmatrix} 0 & 1 \\ 1 & 0 \end{bmatrix}$

Solution (a) All entries are positive, so the matrix is regular.

(b) Here a zero occurs in the first power. However,

$$\begin{bmatrix} 0 & .5 \\ 1 & .5 \end{bmatrix}^2 = \begin{bmatrix} .5 & .25 \\ .5 & .75 \end{bmatrix},$$

which has all positive entries. So the original matrix is regular.

(c) Note that

$$\begin{bmatrix} 0 & 1 \\ 1 & 0 \end{bmatrix}^2 = \begin{bmatrix} 1 & 0 \\ 0 & 1 \end{bmatrix} \quad \begin{bmatrix} 0 & 1 \\ 1 & 0 \end{bmatrix}^3 = \begin{bmatrix} 0 & 1 \\ 1 & 0 \end{bmatrix}$$

$$\begin{bmatrix} 0 & 1 \\ 1 & 0 \end{bmatrix}^4 = \begin{bmatrix} 1 & 0 \\ 0 & 1 \end{bmatrix} \quad \begin{bmatrix} 0 & 1 \\ 1 & 0 \end{bmatrix}^5 = \begin{bmatrix} 0 & 1 \\ 1 & 0 \end{bmatrix}.$$

The even powers of the matrix are the 2×2 identity matrix, and the odd powers are the original matrix. Every power has a zero in it, so the matrix is not regular. ■

Now Try Exercises 1, 3, and 5

Regular matrices share all the properties observed in the special case. Moreover, there is a simple technique for computing the stable distribution (see property 4 in the following box) that spares us from having to multiply matrices.

Let A be a regular stochastic matrix.

1. The powers A^n approach a certain matrix as n gets large. This limiting matrix is called the **stable matrix** of A.

2. For any initial distribution $\begin{bmatrix} \\ \\ \end{bmatrix}_0$, $A^n \begin{bmatrix} \\ \\ \end{bmatrix}_0$ approaches a certain distribution $\begin{bmatrix} \\ \\ \end{bmatrix}$. This limiting distribution is called the **stable distribution** of A.

3. All columns of the stable matrix are the same; they equal the stable distribution.

4. The stable distribution $X = [\;]$ can be determined by solving the system of linear equations

$$\begin{cases} \text{sum of the entries of } X = 1 \\ AX = X. \end{cases}$$

EXAMPLE 3

Finding the stable distribution of a regular stochastic matrix   Use property 4 to determine the stable distribution of the regular stochastic matrix

$$A = \begin{bmatrix} .6 & .2 \\ .4 & .8 \end{bmatrix}.$$

Solution Let $X = \begin{bmatrix} x \\ y \end{bmatrix}$ be the stable distribution. The condition "sum of the entries of $X = 1$" yields the equation

$$x + y = 1.$$

The condition $AX = X$ gives the equations

$$\begin{bmatrix} .6 & .2 \\ .4 & .8 \end{bmatrix} \begin{bmatrix} x \\ y \end{bmatrix} = \begin{bmatrix} x \\ y \end{bmatrix} \qquad \text{or} \qquad \begin{cases} .6x + .2y = x \\ .4x + .8y = y. \end{cases}$$

So we have the system

$$\begin{cases} x + y = 1 \\ .6x + .2y = x \\ .4x + .8y = y. \end{cases}$$

Combining terms in the second and third equations and eliminating the decimals by multiplying by 10, we have

$$\begin{cases} x + y = 1 \\ -4x + 2y = 0 \\ 4x - 2y = 0. \end{cases}$$

Note that the second and third equations are the same, except for a factor -1, so the last equation may be omitted. Now the system reads

$$\begin{cases} x + y = 1 \\ -4x + 2y = 0. \end{cases}$$

The diagonal form is obtained by the Gauss–Jordan elimination method:

$$\begin{bmatrix} 1 & 1 & | & 1 \\ -4 & 2 & | & 0 \end{bmatrix} \xrightarrow{\ R_2 + 4R_1 \ } \begin{bmatrix} 1 & 1 & | & 1 \\ 0 & 6 & | & 4 \end{bmatrix}$$

$$\xrightarrow{\ \frac{1}{6}R_2 \ } \begin{bmatrix} 1 & 1 & | & 1 \\ 0 & 1 & | & \frac{2}{3} \end{bmatrix}$$

$$\xrightarrow{\ R_1 + (-1)R_2 \ } \begin{bmatrix} 1 & 0 & | & \frac{1}{3} \\ 0 & 1 & | & \frac{2}{3} \end{bmatrix}$$

Thus

$$x = \tfrac{1}{3}, \qquad y = \tfrac{2}{3}.$$

So the stable distribution is

$$\begin{bmatrix} x \\ y \end{bmatrix} = \begin{bmatrix} \frac{1}{3} \\ \frac{2}{3} \end{bmatrix},$$

as we observed before. Note that once the stable distribution is determined, the stable matrix is easy to find. Just place the stable distribution in every column:

$$\begin{bmatrix} \frac{1}{3} & \frac{1}{3} \\ \frac{2}{3} & \frac{2}{3} \end{bmatrix}.$$

Now Try Exercise 7

■

EXAMPLE 4

Finding the stable taxi distribution In Section 8.1 we studied the distribution of taxis in three zones of a city. The movement of taxis from zone to zone was described by the regular stochastic matrix

$$A = \begin{bmatrix} .5 & .4 & .2 \\ .4 & .3 & .6 \\ .1 & .3 & .2 \end{bmatrix}.$$

In the long run, what percentage of taxis will be in each of the zones?

Solution Let $X = \begin{bmatrix} x \\ y \\ z \end{bmatrix}$ be the stable distribution of A. Then x is the long-term percentage of taxis in zone I, y the percentage in zone II, and z the percentage in zone III. X is determined by the equations

$$\begin{cases} x + y + z = 1 \\ \quad\quad AX = X, \end{cases}$$

or, equivalently,

$$\begin{cases} x + y + z = 1 \\ .5x + .4y + .2z = x \\ .4x + .3y + .6z = y \\ .1x + .3y + .2z = z. \end{cases}$$

Rewriting the equations with all the terms involving the variables on the left, we get

$$\begin{cases} x + y + z = 1 \\ -.5x + .4y + .2z = 0 \\ .4x - .7y + .6z = 0 \\ .1x + .3y - .8z = 0. \end{cases}$$

Applying the Gauss–Jordan elimination method to this system, we get the solution $x = .4$, $y = .4$, $z = .2$. Thus, after many trips, approximately 40% of the taxis are in zone I, 40% in zone II, and 20% in zone III. ∎

Now Try Exercise 11

We have come full circle. We began Chapter 2 by solving systems of linear equations. Matrices were developed as a tool for solving such systems. Then we found matrices to be interesting in their own right. Finally, in the current chapter, we have used systems of linear equations to answer questions about matrices.

INCORPORATING TECHNOLOGY

GC If A is a square matrix, then graphing calculators can compute A^n. (With the TI-83/84 Plus, n can be as large as 255. However, even higher powers can be obtained with instructions such as **Ans^255**.) For a regular stochastic matrix A, A^{255} should be an excellent approximation to the stable matrix of A. In Figures 1 and 3, A is the matrix of Example 3 and C is the matrix of Example 4. (*Note:* ▶ **Frac**, which stands for "display as a fraction," is obtained on the TI-83/84 Plus by pressing MATH 1.)

Calculators or computers also can be used to obtain a stable distribution by solving the system of linear equations or can be used to confirm a stable distribution by carrying out a matrix multiplication. The system of linear equations from Example 3 is solved in Figs. 2 and 4. ∎

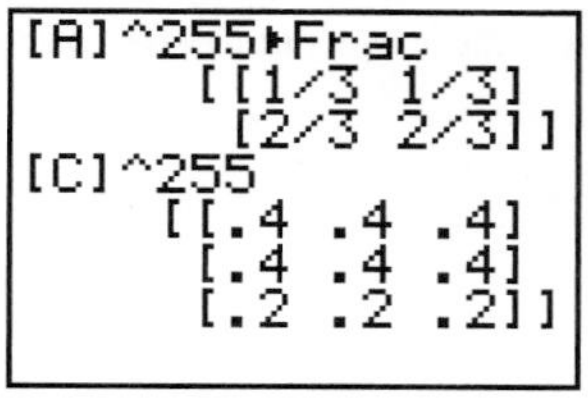

```
[A]^255▶Frac
      [[1/3 1/3]
       [2/3 2/3]]
[C]^255
      [[.4 .4 .4]
       [.4 .4 .4]
       [.2 .2 .2]]
```

Figure 1

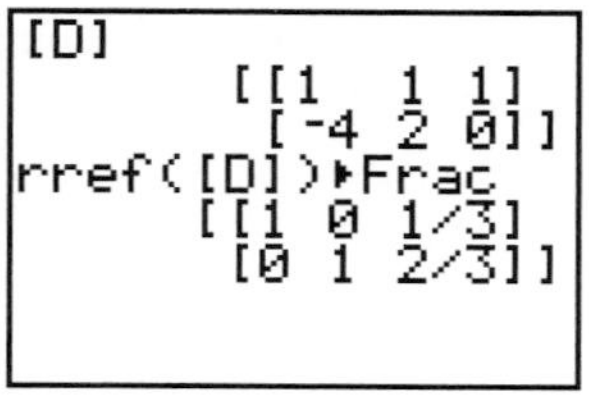

```
[D]
      [[1  1 1]
       [-4 2 0]]
rref([D])▶Frac
      [[1 0 1/3]
       [0 1 2/3]]
```

Figure 2

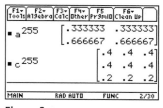

Figure 3

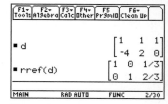

Figure 4

ES Successive powers of a matrix can be generated on a spreadsheet in much the same way that successive distribution matrices were generated in Fig. 6 of Section 8.1. The stable distribution can be found by using Solver to solve the appropriate system of linear equations.

APPENDIX **Verification of Method for Obtaining the Stable Distribution**

In this appendix we verify that the stable distribution X can be obtained by solving the system of equations

$$\begin{cases} \text{sum of the entries of } X = 1 \\ AX = X \end{cases}$$

Let A be a regular stochastic matrix. Suppose that we take as the initial distribution its stable distribution X. Then the nth distribution matrix, or $A^n X$, approaches the stable distribution (by property 2), so that

$$X \approx A^n X \quad \text{for large } n.$$

Therefore,

$$AX \approx A \cdot A^n X = A^{n+1} X.$$

But $A^{n+1} X$ is the $(n + 1)$st distribution matrix, which is also approximately X. Thus AX is approximately X. But the approximation can be made closer and closer by taking n large. Therefore, AX is arbitrarily close to X, or

$$AX = X. \tag{3}$$

This is a matrix equation in X. There is one other condition on X: X is a distribution matrix. Therefore,

$$\text{sum of the entries of } X = 1. \tag{4}$$

So, by (3) and (4), we find this system of linear equations for the entries of X:

$$\begin{cases} \text{sum of the entries of } X = 1 \\ AX = X. \end{cases}$$

Practice Problems 8.2

1. Is $\begin{bmatrix} 0 & .2 & .5 \\ .5 & 0 & .5 \\ .5 & .8 & 0 \end{bmatrix}$ a regular stochastic matrix? Explain your answer.

2. Find the stable matrix for the regular stochastic matrix in Problem 1.

3. **Cigarette Smokers** In a study of cigarette smokers it was determined that of the people who smoked menthol cigarettes on a particular day, 10% smoked menthol the next day and 90% smoked nonmenthol. Of the people who smoked nonmenthol cigarettes on a particular day, the next day 30% smoked menthol and 70% smoked nonmenthol. In the long run, what percent of the people will be smoking nonmenthol cigarettes on a particular day?

EXERCISES 8.2

In Exercises 1–6, determine whether or not the matrix is a regular stochastic matrix.

1. $\begin{bmatrix} \frac{1}{4} & \frac{2}{7} \\ \frac{3}{4} & \frac{5}{7} \end{bmatrix}$

2. $\begin{bmatrix} .6 & 0 \\ .4 & 1 \end{bmatrix}$

3. $\begin{bmatrix} .3 & 1 \\ .7 & 0 \end{bmatrix}$

4. $\begin{bmatrix} 1 & 0 & .7 \\ 0 & 1 & .2 \\ 0 & 0 & .1 \end{bmatrix}$

5. $\begin{bmatrix} 0 & .8 & 0 \\ 1 & .1 & .5 \\ 0 & .1 & .5 \end{bmatrix}$

6. $\begin{bmatrix} .6 & .6 & .6 \\ .3 & .3 & .3 \\ .1 & .1 & .1 \end{bmatrix}$

In Exercises 7–11, find the stable distribution for the given regular stochastic matrix.

7. $\begin{bmatrix} .5 & .1 \\ .5 & .9 \end{bmatrix}$

8. $\begin{bmatrix} .4 & 1 \\ .6 & 0 \end{bmatrix}$

9. $\begin{bmatrix} .8 & .3 \\ .2 & .7 \end{bmatrix}$

10. $\begin{bmatrix} .3 & .1 & .2 \\ .4 & .8 & .6 \\ .3 & .1 & .2 \end{bmatrix}$

11. $\begin{bmatrix} .1 & .4 & .7 \\ .6 & .4 & .2 \\ .3 & .2 & .1 \end{bmatrix}$

12. **Voter Patterns** Refer to Exercise 24 of Section 8.1. In the long run what proportion of the governors will be Democrats?

13. **T-Maze** Refer to Exercise 25 of Section 8.1. What percentage of the mice will be going to the left after many days?

14. **Computer Reliability** A certain university has a computer room with 219 terminals. Each day there is a 3% chance that a given terminal will break and a 70% chance that a given broken terminal will be repaired. In the long run, about how many terminals in the room will be working?

15. Market Share Suppose that 60% of people who own a General Motors car, buy a GM car as their next car and 90% of people who own a non-GM car, buy a non-GM car as their next car. What will General Motors' market share be in the long run?

16. Transportation Modes Commuters can get into town by car or bus. Surveys have shown that for those taking their car on a particular day, 20% take their car the next day and 80% take a bus. Also, for those taking a bus on a particular day, 50% take their car the next day and 50% take a bus. In the long run what percentage of the people take a bus on a particular day?

17. Weather Patterns The changes in weather from day to day on the planet Xantar form a regular Markov process. Each day is either rainy or sunny. If it rains one day, there is a 90% chance that it will be sunny the following day. If it is sunny one day, there is a 60% chance of rain the next day. In the long run, what is the daily likelihood of rain?

18. Fitness Refer to Exercise 26 of Section 8.1. In the long run what percentage of the people will have a strenuous workout on a particular day?

19. Car Rentals The Day-by-Day car rental agency only rents cars on a daily basis. Rented cars can be returned at the end of the day to any of the agency's three locations; A, B, or C. Figure 5 shows the percentages of cars returned to each of the locations based on where they were picked up. Assume that all the agency's cars are rented each day, and that initially 40% of the cars are at location A, 30% at location B, and 30% at location C.

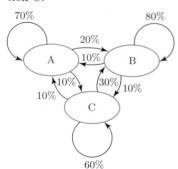

Figure 5

(a) Set up the stochastic matrix that displays these transitions.

(b) Use the matrix from part (a) to estimate the percentage of the cars at location A after one day. After two days.

(c) In the long run, what fraction of the cars will be at each location?

20. Weather Patterns The day-to-day changes in weather for a certain part of the country forms a Markov process. Each day is sunny, cloudy, or rainy. If it is sunny one day, there is a 70% chance that it will be sunny

the following day, a 20% chance it will be cloudy, and a 10% chance of rain. If it is cloudy one day, there is a 30% chance that it will be sunny the following day, a 50% chance it will be cloudy, and a 20% chance of rain. It it rains one day, there is a 60% chance that it will be sunny the following day, a 20% chance it will be cloudy, and a 20% chance of rain. In the long run, what is the daily likelihood of rain?

21. Genetics With respect to a certain gene, geneticists classify individuals as dominant, recessive, or hybrid. In an experiment, individuals are crossed with hybrids, then their offspring are crossed with hybrids, and so on. For dominant individuals, 50% of their offspring will be dominant and 50% will be a hybrid. For the recessive individuals 50% of their offspring will be recessive and 50% hybrid. For hybrid individuals (to be crossed with hybrids) their offspring will be 25% dominant, 25% recessive, and 50% hybrid. In the long run what percent of the individuals in a generation will be dominant?

22. Refer to the stochastic matrix in Example 6 of Section 8.1. In the long run, what percentage of American women will work?

23. As shown in Example 2, $\begin{bmatrix} 0 & 1 \\ 1 & 0 \end{bmatrix}$ is not a regular stochastic matrix. Show that $\begin{bmatrix} .5 \\ .5 \end{bmatrix}$ acts like a stable distribution for this matrix and explain why this fact does not contradict the main premise of this section.

In Exercises 24–28, use a graphing calculator or spreadsheet to calculate the answers.

24. Bird Migrations Figure 6 describes the migration pattern of a species of bird from year to year among three habitats: I, II, and III.

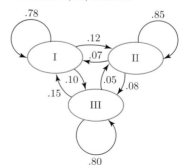

Figure 6

(a) Set up the stochastic matrix that displays these transitions.

(b) If there are 1000 birds in each habitat at the beginning of a year, how many will be in each habitat at the end of the year? At the end of two years?

(c) In the long run, what fraction of the birds will be located at each habitat?

25. Consider the stochastic matrix A, where

$$A = \begin{bmatrix} .85 & .35 \\ .15 & .65 \end{bmatrix}.$$

Approximate the stable matrix of A by raising A to a high power. Then find the exact stable distribution by solving an appropriate system of linear equations. Check your answer by forming the product of A and the stable distribution.

Repeat Exercise 25 for each of the matrices in Exercises 26–28.

26. $\begin{bmatrix} .3 & .1 \\ .7 & .9 \end{bmatrix}$ **27.** $\begin{bmatrix} .1 & .4 & .1 \\ .3 & .2 & .8 \\ .6 & .4 & .1 \end{bmatrix}$

28. $\begin{bmatrix} .4 & .2 & .4 \\ .1 & .3 & .1 \\ .5 & .5 & .5 \end{bmatrix}$

Solutions to Practice Problems 8.2

1. Yes. It is easily seen to be stochastic. Although it has some zero entries, there are no zero entries in

$$A^2 = \begin{bmatrix} .35 & .40 & .10 \\ .25 & .50 & .25 \\ .40 & .10 & .65 \end{bmatrix}.$$

2.
$$\begin{cases} x + y + z = 1 \\ \begin{bmatrix} 0 & .2 & .5 \\ .5 & 0 & .5 \\ .5 & .8 & 0 \end{bmatrix} \begin{bmatrix} x \\ y \\ z \end{bmatrix} = \begin{bmatrix} x \\ y \\ z \end{bmatrix} \end{cases}$$

or

$$\begin{cases} x + y + z = 1 \\ .2y + .5z = x \\ .5x + .5z = y \\ .5x + .8y = z \end{cases}$$

or

$$\begin{cases} x + y + z = 1 \\ -x + .2y + .5z = 0 \\ .5x - y + .5z = 0 \\ .5x + .8y - z = 0 \end{cases}$$

To simplify the arithmetic, multiply each of the last three equations of the system by 10 to eliminate the decimals. Then apply the Gauss–Jordan elimination method.

$$\begin{cases} x + y + z = 1 \\ -10x + 2y + 5z = 0 \\ 5x - 10y + 5z = 0 \\ 5x + 8y - 10z = 0 \end{cases} \begin{cases} x + y + z = 1 \\ 12y + 15z = 10 \\ -15y = -5 \\ 3y - 15z = -5 \end{cases}$$

Next interchange the second and third equations and pivot about $-15y$.

$$\begin{cases} x + y + z = 1 \\ -15y = -5 \\ 12y + 15z = 10 \\ 3y - 15z = -5 \end{cases} \begin{cases} x + z = \frac{2}{3} \\ y = \frac{1}{3} \\ 15z = 6 \\ -15z = -6 \end{cases}$$

Pivoting about $15z$ yields $x = \frac{4}{15}$, $y = \frac{5}{15}$, $z = \frac{6}{15}$, so the stable matrix is

$$\begin{bmatrix} \frac{4}{15} & \frac{4}{15} & \frac{4}{15} \\ \frac{5}{15} & \frac{5}{15} & \frac{5}{15} \\ \frac{6}{15} & \frac{6}{15} & \frac{6}{15} \end{bmatrix}.$$

3. The regular stochastic matrix describing this daily transition is

$$\begin{array}{cc} & \begin{array}{cc} M & N \end{array} \\ \begin{array}{c} M \\ N \end{array} & \begin{bmatrix} .1 & .3 \\ .9 & .7 \end{bmatrix}. \end{array}$$

The stable distribution is found by solving

$$\begin{cases} x + y = 1 \\ \begin{bmatrix} .1 & .3 \\ .9 & .7 \end{bmatrix} \begin{bmatrix} x \\ y \end{bmatrix} = \begin{bmatrix} x \\ y \end{bmatrix} \end{cases}$$

or $\begin{cases} x + y = 1 \\ .1x + .3y = x \\ .9x + .7y = y \end{cases}$ or $\begin{cases} x + y = 1 \\ -.9x + .3y = 0 \\ .9x - .3y = 0. \end{cases}$

Since the last two equations are essentially the same, we need only solve the system consisting of the first two equations. Multiply the second equation by 10:

$$\begin{cases} x + y = 1 \\ -9x + 3y = 0 \end{cases} \rightarrow \begin{cases} x + y = 1 \\ 12y = 9 \end{cases} \rightarrow \begin{cases} x = \frac{1}{4} \\ y = \frac{3}{4}. \end{cases}$$

So the stable distribution is $\begin{bmatrix} \frac{1}{4} \\ \frac{3}{4} \end{bmatrix}$. The stable distribution tells us that in the long run, 25% smoke menthol and 75% smoke nonmenthol cigarettes on any particular day.

8.3 Absorbing Stochastic Matrices

In this section we study long-term trends for a certain class of matrices which are not regular—the absorbing stochastic matrices. By way of introduction, recall some general facts about stochastic matrices.

Stochastic matrices, such as

$$\begin{bmatrix} .3 & .5 & .1 & 0 \\ .2 & .2 & .8 & 0 \\ .1 & .3 & 0 & 0 \\ .4 & 0 & .1 & 1 \end{bmatrix},$$

describe state-to-state changes in certain processes. Each column of a stochastic matrix describes the transitions (or movements) from one specific state. For example, the first column of the preceding stochastic matrix indicates that at the end of one time period the probability is .3 that an object in state 1 stays in state 1, .2 that it goes to state 2, .1 that it goes to state 3, and .4 that it goes to state 4. Similarly, the second column indicates the probabilities for transitions from state 2, the third column from state 3, and the fourth from state 4.

If A is a stochastic matrix, then the columns of A^2 describe the transitions from the various states *after two time periods*. For instance, the third column of A^2 indicates the probabilities of an object starting out in state 3 and ending up in each of the states after two time periods. Similarly, the columns of A^n indicate the transitions from the various states after n periods.

Consider the stochastic matrix just described. Its fourth column illustrates a curious phenomenon. It indicates that if an object starts out in state 4, after one time period the probabilities of going to states 1, 2, or 3 are 0 and the probability of going to state 4 is 1. In other words, all of the objects in state 4 stay in state 4. A state with this property is called an **absorbing state**. More precisely, an absorbing state is a state that is impossible to leave.

EXAMPLE 1

Finding absorbing states of a stochastic matrix Find all absorbing states of the stochastic matrix

$$\begin{bmatrix} 1 & 0 & .3 & 0 \\ 0 & 1 & .1 & 0 \\ 0 & 0 & .5 & 1 \\ 0 & 0 & .1 & 0 \end{bmatrix}.$$

Solution To determine which states are absorbing, one must look at the columns. The first column describes the transitions from state 1. It says that state 1 leads to state 1 100% of the time and to the other states 0% of the time. So state 1 is absorbing. Column 2 describes transitions from state 2. It says that state 2 leads to state 2 100% of the time. So state 2 is absorbing. Clearly, the third column says that state 3 is not absorbing. For example, state 3 leads to state 1 with probability .3. At first glance, column 4 seems to say that state 4 is absorbing. But it is not, because column 4 says that state 4 leads to state 3 100% of the time. ∎

Based on Example 1, we can easily determine the absorbing states of any stochastic matrix: First, the corresponding column has a single 1 and the remaining entries 0. Second, the lone 1 must be located on the main diagonal of the matrix. That is, its row and column number must be the same. So, for example, state i is an absorbing state if and only if the ith entry in the ith column is 1 and all the remaining entries in that column are 0.

> **DEFINITION** An **absorbing stochastic matrix** is a stochastic matrix in which
> 1. there is at least one absorbing state; and
> 2. from any state it is possible to get to at least one absorbing state, either directly or through one or more intermediate states.

Fig. 1 shows the transition diagram for an absorbing stochastic matrix with absorbing state A. Notice that there are no arrows pointing from state A to another state. Also, there is a direct path from state B to state A and an indirect path from state C to state A. The transition diagram in Fig. 2 does not correspond to an absorbing stochastic matrix since there is no way to get from state C or state D to the absorbing state A.

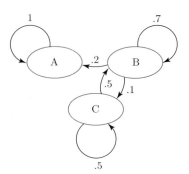

Figure 1   **Figure 2**

EXAMPLE 2

Determining whether a stochastic matrix is absorbing   Is the matrix

$$\begin{bmatrix} 1 & 0 & .3 & 0 \\ 0 & 1 & .1 & 0 \\ 0 & 0 & .5 & 1 \\ 0 & 0 & .1 & 0 \end{bmatrix}$$

an absorbing stochastic matrix?

Solution The absorbing states are easy to recognize by looking at the matrix. In Example 1 we showed that states 1 and 2 are absorbing. The second part of the definition of an absorbing stochastic matrix is easiest to check by looking at the transition diagram corresponding to the Markov process. Fig. 3 shows that there are two direct paths from state 3 to an absorbing state and two indirect paths from state 4 to an absorbing state. Therefore, the matrix is an absorbing stochastic matrix. ■

Now Try Exercises 5 and 7

In general, processes described by stochastic matrices can oscillate indefinitely from state to state in such a way that they exhibit no long-term trend. An example was given in Section 2 using the matrix

$$\begin{bmatrix} 0 & 1 \\ 1 & 0 \end{bmatrix}.$$

The idea of introducing absorbing states is to reduce the degree of oscillation. For when an absorbing state is reached, the process no longer changes. The main result of this section is that absorbing stochastic matrices exhibit a long-term trend. Further, we can determine this trend using a simple computational procedure.

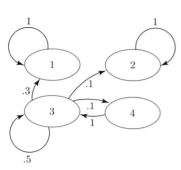

Figure 3

When considering an absorbing stochastic matrix, we will always arrange the states so that the absorbing states come first, then the nonabsorbing states. This is called the **standard form** of the absorbing stochastic matrix.

$$\begin{array}{cc} \overbrace{\text{Absorbing}} & \overbrace{\text{Nonabsorbing}} \\ \left[\quad \Big| \quad \right] \end{array}$$

When an absorbing stochastic matrix is in standard form, it can be partitioned, or subdivided, into four submatrices.

$$\begin{array}{cc} \overbrace{\text{Absorbing}} & \overbrace{\text{Nonabsorbing}} \\ \left[\begin{array}{c|c} I & S \\ \hline 0 & R \end{array} \right] \end{array}$$

The matrix I is an identity matrix, and 0 denotes a matrix having all entries 0. The matrices S and R are the two pieces corresponding to the nonabsorbing states. For example, in the case of the absorbing stochastic matrix of Example 2, this partition is given by

$$\left[\begin{array}{cc|cc} 1 & 0 & .3 & 0 \\ 0 & 1 & .1 & 0 \\ \hline 0 & 0 & .5 & 1 \\ 0 & 0 & .1 & 0 \end{array} \right].$$

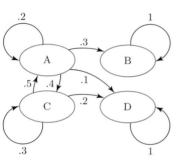

Figure 4

If an absorbing stochastic matrix for a Markov process is not in standard form, you can use its transition diagram to convert it to a standard form.

EXAMPLE 3

Converting an absorbing stochastic matrix to standard form Convert the following absorbing stochastic matrix to standard form and identify the matrices S and R.

$$\begin{array}{c} \quad\ \ A \ \ B \ \ C \ \ D \\ \begin{array}{c} A \\ B \\ C \\ D \end{array} \left[\begin{array}{cccc} .2 & 0 & .5 & 0 \\ .3 & 1 & 0 & 0 \\ .4 & 0 & .3 & 0 \\ .1 & 0 & .2 & 1 \end{array} \right] \end{array}$$

Solution From the transition diagram in Fig. 4 above, we can confirm that the matrix is an absorbing stochastic matrix with absorbing states B and D. To obtain a stochastic matrix in standard form, label the columns and rows of a 4 × 4 matrix B, D, A, C and then read off the probabilities from the transition diagram. We get

$$\begin{array}{c} \quad\ \ B \ \ D \ \ A \ \ C \\ \begin{array}{c} B \\ D \\ A \\ C \end{array} \left[\begin{array}{cc|cc} 1 & 0 & .3 & 0 \\ 0 & 1 & .1 & .2 \\ \hline 0 & 0 & .2 & .5 \\ 0 & 0 & .4 & .3 \end{array} \right] \end{array}$$

Now Try Exercise 9 Therefore, $S = \begin{bmatrix} .3 & 0 \\ .1 & .2 \end{bmatrix}$ and $R = \begin{bmatrix} .2 & .5 \\ .4 & .3 \end{bmatrix}.$ ■

EXAMPLE 4

Progression of a disease The victims of a certain disease are classified into three states: cured, dead from the disease, or sick. Once a person is cured, he is permanently immune. Each year 70% of those sick are cured, 10% die from the disease, and 20% remain ill.

(a) Determine a stochastic matrix describing the progression of the disease.

(b) Determine the absorbing states.

Solution (a) There is one column for each state. Transferring the given data to the matrix gives the result:

$$
\begin{array}{c} \\ \text{Cured} \\ \text{Dead} \\ \text{Sick} \end{array}
\begin{array}{ccc} \text{Cured} & \text{Dead} & \text{Sick} \end{array}
\left[\begin{array}{ccc} 1 & 0 & .7 \\ 0 & 1 & .1 \\ 0 & 0 & .2 \end{array}\right].
$$

(b) The absorbing states are "cured" and "dead," since these are the states that always lead back to themselves. The matrix is an absorbing stochastic matrix, since there is at least one absorbing state and the other state, "sick," can lead to an absorbing state. (In fact, in this case it leads to either of the absorbing states.)

> Now Try Exercise 25(a)

EXAMPLE 5

Long-term trend for the progression of a disease Find the long-term trend of the disease described in Example 4.

Solution The stochastic matrix here is

$$
\left[\begin{array}{cc|c} 1 & 0 & .7 \\ 0 & 1 & .1 \\ 0 & 0 & .2 \end{array}\right].
$$

Its first few powers are given by

$$
A^2 = \left[\begin{array}{cc|c} 1 & 0 & .84 \\ 0 & 1 & .12 \\ 0 & 0 & .04 \end{array}\right] \qquad A^3 = \left[\begin{array}{cc|c} 1 & 0 & .868 \\ 0 & 1 & .124 \\ 0 & 0 & .008 \end{array}\right]
$$

$$
A^4 \approx \left[\begin{array}{cc|c} 1 & 0 & .874 \\ 0 & 1 & .125 \\ 0 & 0 & .002 \end{array}\right] \qquad A^5 \approx \left[\begin{array}{cc|c} 1 & 0 & .875 \\ 0 & 1 & .125 \\ 0 & 0 & .000 \end{array}\right].
$$

```
[A]^255▶Frac
        [[1 0 7/8]
         [0 1 1/8]
         [0 0 0  ]]
```

```
F1▾   F2▾  F3▾ F4▾  F5    F6▾
Tools Algebra Calc Other PrgmIO Clean Up

■ a^255
    [1.  0.  .875      ]
    [0.  1.  .125      ]
    [0.  0.  5.7896E-179]
a^255
MAIN     RAD AUTO   FUNC     1/30
```

It appears that the powers approach the matrix

$$
A = \left[\begin{array}{ccc} 1 & 0 & \frac{7}{8} \\ 0 & 1 & \frac{1}{8} \\ 0 & 0 & 0 \end{array}\right].
$$

Of those initially in state 3, "sick," the probability is seven-eighths of eventually being cured, and one-eighth of eventually dying of the disease.

Example 5 exhibits three important features of the long-term behavior exhibited by all absorbing stochastic matrices. First, as in the case of regular stochastic matrices, the powers approach a particular matrix. This limiting matrix is called a **stable matrix**. Second, for absorbing stochastic matrices the long-term trend depends on the initial state. For example, the stable matrix just computed gives different results depending on the state in which you start. This is reflected by the fact that the three columns are different. (In the case of regular stochastic matrices, the long-term trend does not depend on the initial distribution. All columns of the stable matrix are the same. They all equal the stable distribution.) The third important point to notice is that, no matter what the initial state, all objects eventually go to absorbing states. The absorbing states act like magnets and attract all objects to themselves in the long run.

In Example 5 we computed the stable matrix by raising the given stochastic matrix to various powers. Actually, there is a formal computational procedure for determining the stable matrix. Suppose that we partition an absorbing stochastic matrix into submatrices

$$A = \left[\begin{array}{c|c} I & S \\ \hline 0 & R \end{array}\right].$$

The stable matrix of A is

$$\left[\begin{array}{c|c} I & S(I-R)^{-1} \\ \hline 0 & 0 \end{array}\right].$$

[*Note*: The identity matrix I in $(I-R)^{-1}$ is chosen to be the same size as R in order to make the matrix subtraction permissible.]

EXAMPLE 6

Determining stable matrices Use the preceding formula to determine the stable matrix of

$$\left[\begin{array}{cc|c} 1 & 0 & .7 \\ 0 & 1 & .1 \\ 0 & 0 & .2 \end{array}\right].$$

Solution $S = \begin{bmatrix} .7 \\ .1 \end{bmatrix}$, $R = [.2]$, $I - R = [1] - [.2] = [.8]$, $(I-R)^{-1} = [1/.8]$. Therefore,

$$S(I-R)^{-1} = \begin{bmatrix} .7 \\ .1 \end{bmatrix} [1/.8] = \begin{bmatrix} .7/.8 \\ .1/.8 \end{bmatrix} = \begin{bmatrix} \frac{7}{8} \\ \frac{1}{8} \end{bmatrix}.$$

So the stable matrix is

$$\left[\begin{array}{c|c} I & S(I-R)^{-1} \\ \hline 0 & 0 \end{array}\right] = \left[\begin{array}{cc|c} 1 & 0 & \frac{7}{8} \\ 0 & 1 & \frac{1}{8} \\ 0 & 0 & 0 \end{array}\right].$$

> Now Try Exercise 13
> (stable part only)

EXAMPLE 7

Gambler's ruin Consider a game of chance with the following characteristics: A person repeatedly bets \$1 each play. If he wins, he receives \$1.[1] If he goes broke, he stops playing. Also, if he accumulates \$3, he stops playing. On each play the probability of winning is .4 and of losing .6. What is the probability of eventually accumulating \$3 if he starts with \$1? \$2?

---
[1] That is, he receives his bet of \$1 plus winnings of \$1.

Solution There are four states, corresponding to having \$0, \$3, \$1, or \$2. The first two are absorbing states. The stochastic matrix is

$$
\begin{array}{c} \\ \$0 \\ \$3 \\ \$1 \\ \$2 \end{array}
\begin{array}{cccc} \$0 & \$3 & \$1 & \$2 \end{array} \\
\left[\begin{array}{cc|cc}
1 & 0 & .6 & 0 \\
0 & 1 & 0 & .4 \\
\hline
0 & 0 & 0 & .6 \\
0 & 0 & .4 & 0
\end{array}\right].
$$

The third column is derived in this way: If he has \$1, there is a .6 probability of losing \$1, which would mean going to state \$0. Thus the first entry in the third column is .6. There is no way to get from \$1 to \$3 or from \$1 to \$1 after one play. So the second and third entries are 0. There is a .4 probability of winning \$1—that is, of going from \$1 to \$2. So the last entry is .4. The fourth column is derived similarly.

In this example

$$
S = \begin{bmatrix} .6 & 0 \\ 0 & .4 \end{bmatrix} \qquad R = \begin{bmatrix} 0 & .6 \\ .4 & 0 \end{bmatrix}.
$$

To compute $S(I - R)^{-1}$, observe that

$$
I - R = \begin{bmatrix} 1 & 0 \\ 0 & 1 \end{bmatrix} - \begin{bmatrix} 0 & .6 \\ .4 & 0 \end{bmatrix} = \begin{bmatrix} 1 & -.6 \\ -.4 & 1 \end{bmatrix}.
$$

To compute $(I - R)^{-1}$, recall that

$$
\begin{bmatrix} a & b \\ c & d \end{bmatrix}^{-1} = \begin{bmatrix} d/D & -b/D \\ -c/D & a/D \end{bmatrix}, \qquad D = ad - bc \neq 0.
$$

So, in this example, $D = 1 \cdot 1 - (-.6)(-.4) = 1 - .24 = .76$ and

$$
(I - R)^{-1} = \begin{bmatrix} 1 & -.6 \\ -.4 & 1 \end{bmatrix}^{-1} \approx \begin{bmatrix} 1.32 & .79 \\ .53 & 1.32 \end{bmatrix}
$$

$$
S(I - R)^{-1} \approx \begin{bmatrix} .6 & 0 \\ 0 & .4 \end{bmatrix} \begin{bmatrix} 1.32 & .79 \\ .53 & 1.32 \end{bmatrix} \approx \begin{bmatrix} .79 & .47 \\ .21 & .53 \end{bmatrix}.
$$

Thus the stable matrix is

$$
\left[\begin{array}{c|c} I & S(I-R)^{-1} \\ \hline 0 & 0 \end{array}\right] = \left[\begin{array}{cc|cc}
1 & 0 & .79 & .47 \\
0 & 1 & .21 & .53 \\
0 & 0 & 0 & 0 \\
0 & 0 & 0 & 0
\end{array}\right].
$$

We are interested in the probability that the gambler ends up with \$3. The percentage is different for each of the two starting amounts \$1 and \$2. Recall the meaning of the rows and columns:

$$
\begin{array}{c} \\ \$0 \\ \$3 \\ \$1 \\ \$2 \end{array}
\begin{array}{cccc} \$0 & \$3 & \$1 & \$2 \end{array} \\
\left[\begin{array}{cc|cc}
1 & 0 & .79 & .47 \\
0 & 1 & .21 & .53 \\
\hline
0 & 0 & 0 & 0 \\
0 & 0 & 0 & 0
\end{array}\right].
$$

Looking at the \$1 column, we see that if he starts with \$1, the probability is .21 that he ends up with \$3. Looking at the \$2 column, the probability is .53 that he ends up with \$3.

Now Try Exercise 29(a)

The Fundamental Matrix   The matrix $(I-R)^{-1}$ used to compute the stable matrix is called the **fundamental matrix** and is denoted by the letter F. Its columns and rows should be labeled with the nonabsorbing states. The fundamental matrix directly provides certain useful probabilities for the process. Specifically, the ijth entry of F is the expected number of times the process will be in nonabsorbing state i if it starts in nonabsorbing state j. The sum of the entries of the jth column of F is the expected number of steps before absorption when the process begins in nonabsorbing state j.

The fundamental matrix for the gambler's ruin example is

$$F = \begin{array}{c} \\ \$1 \\ \$2 \end{array} \begin{array}{cc} \$1 & \$2 \\ \begin{bmatrix} 1.32 & .79 \\ .53 & 1.32 \end{bmatrix} \end{array}.$$

The first column of F indicates that when the gambler begins with \$1, he can expect to play $1.32 + .53 = 1.85$ times before quitting. He should have \$1 for an expected number of 1.32 plays and have \$2 for an expected number of .53 plays. The second column gives similar information when the gambler begins with \$2.

INCORPORATING TECHNOLOGY

GC   A graphing calculator can be used to obtain the stable matrix by raising the original stochastic matrix to a high power or by calculating $S(I-R)^{-1}$. In Figs. 5 and 6, **[A]**, **[B]**, and **[C]** are the matrices A, S, and R of Example 7. In Fig. 6, the **MODE Float** option was set to 2. In Figs. 7 and 8, a, s, and r are the matrices A, S, and R of Example 7.   ∎

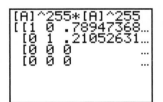

Figure 5

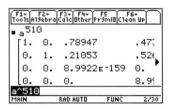

Figure 6

Figure 7

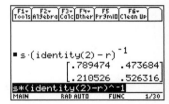

Figure 8

ES   Successive powers of an absorbing stochastic matrix can be generated on a spreadsheet in much the same way that successive distribution matrices were generated in Fig. 6 of Section 8.1. The upper-right quadrant of the stable matrix can be obtained with the formula =**MMULT(S,MINVERSE(I−R))**.

Practice Problems 8.3

1. When an absorbing stochastic matrix is partitioned, the submatrix in the upper left is an identity matrix, denoted by I. Also, when finding the stable matrix, we subtract the submatrix R from an identity matrix, also denoted by I. Are these two identity matrices the same size?

2. Let A be an absorbing stochastic matrix. Interpret the entries of A^2.

3. Is $\begin{bmatrix} 1 & .4 & 0 \\ 0 & .2 & .1 \\ 0 & .4 & .9 \end{bmatrix}$ an absorbing stochastic matrix?

EXERCISES 8.3

In Exercises 1–4 determine whether the transition diagram corresponds to an absorbing stochastic matrix.

1.

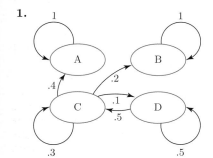

2.

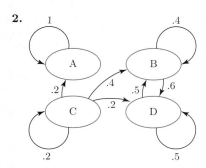

3.

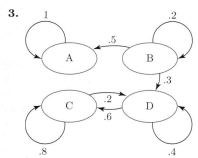

4.

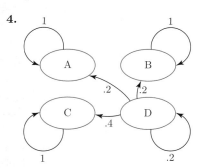

In Exercises 5–8, determine whether the given matrix is an absorbing stochastic matrix.

5. $\begin{bmatrix} 1 & 0 & 0 & 0 \\ 0 & 1 & 0 & 0 \\ 0 & 0 & .8 & .1 \\ 0 & 0 & .2 & .9 \end{bmatrix}$
6. $\begin{bmatrix} 1 & 0 & 0 & .3 \\ 0 & 1 & 0 & .2 \\ 0 & 0 & 1 & .2 \\ 0 & 0 & 0 & .3 \end{bmatrix}$

7. $\begin{bmatrix} 1 & 0 & .4 \\ 0 & .5 & .3 \\ 0 & .5 & .3 \end{bmatrix}$
8. $\begin{bmatrix} 1 & 0 & 0 & 0 \\ 0 & 1 & 0 & 0 \\ 0 & 0 & 0 & 1 \\ 0 & 0 & 1 & 0 \end{bmatrix}$

In Exercises 9–12, convert the absorbing stochastic matrix to standard form.

9. $\begin{array}{c} \\ A \\ B \\ C \end{array} \begin{array}{ccc} A & B & C \\ \begin{bmatrix} .2 & 0 & .5 \\ .3 & 1 & .4 \\ .5 & 0 & .1 \end{bmatrix} \end{array}$
10. $\begin{array}{c} \\ A \\ B \\ C \end{array} \begin{array}{ccc} A & B & C \\ \begin{bmatrix} 1 & .2 & 0 \\ 0 & .3 & 0 \\ 0 & .5 & 1 \end{bmatrix} \end{array}$

11. $\begin{array}{c} \\ A \\ B \\ C \\ D \end{array} \begin{array}{cccc} A & B & C & D \\ \begin{bmatrix} .1 & 1 & .6 & 0 \\ .2 & 0 & .1 & 0 \\ .3 & 0 & .2 & 0 \\ .4 & 0 & .1 & 1 \end{bmatrix} \end{array}$
12. $\begin{array}{c} \\ A \\ B \\ C \\ D \end{array} \begin{array}{cccc} A & B & C & D \\ \begin{bmatrix} 0 & .7 & 0 & 0 \\ 0 & 0 & 0 & .6 \\ 0 & .3 & 1 & .4 \\ 1 & 0 & 0 & 0 \end{bmatrix} \end{array}$

The matrices in Exercises 13–18 are absorbing stochastic matrices in standard form. In each, identify R and S and compute the fundamental matrix and the stable matrix.

13. $\begin{bmatrix} 1 & 0 & .3 \\ 0 & 1 & .2 \\ 0 & 0 & .5 \end{bmatrix}$
14. $\begin{bmatrix} 1 & 0 & \frac{1}{2} \\ 0 & 1 & \frac{1}{6} \\ 0 & 0 & \frac{1}{3} \end{bmatrix}$

15. $\begin{bmatrix} 1 & 0 & .1 & 0 \\ 0 & 1 & .5 & .2 \\ 0 & 0 & .3 & .6 \\ 0 & 0 & .1 & .2 \end{bmatrix}$
16. $\begin{bmatrix} 1 & 0 & \frac{1}{4} & \frac{1}{6} \\ 0 & 1 & \frac{1}{6} & 0 \\ 0 & 0 & \frac{1}{4} & \frac{1}{2} \\ 0 & 0 & \frac{1}{3} & \frac{1}{3} \end{bmatrix}$

17. $\begin{bmatrix} 1 & 0 & 0 & .1 & .2 \\ 0 & 1 & 0 & .3 & 0 \\ 0 & 0 & 1 & 0 & .2 \\ 0 & 0 & 0 & .5 & 0 \\ 0 & 0 & 0 & .1 & .6 \end{bmatrix}$

18. $\begin{bmatrix} 1 & 0 & \frac{1}{4} & 0 & \frac{1}{3} \\ 0 & 1 & \frac{1}{4} & 0 & 0 \\ 0 & 0 & 0 & \frac{1}{3} & \frac{1}{6} \\ 0 & 0 & \frac{1}{2} & \frac{1}{3} & 0 \\ 0 & 0 & 0 & \frac{1}{3} & \frac{1}{2} \end{bmatrix}$

Note: $\begin{bmatrix} 1 & -\frac{1}{3} & -\frac{1}{6} \\ -\frac{1}{2} & \frac{2}{3} & 0 \\ 0 & -\frac{1}{3} & \frac{1}{2} \end{bmatrix}^{-1} = \begin{bmatrix} \frac{3}{2} & 1 & \frac{1}{2} \\ \frac{9}{8} & \frac{9}{4} & \frac{3}{8} \\ \frac{3}{4} & \frac{3}{2} & \frac{9}{4} \end{bmatrix}.$

Gambler's Ruin *Exercises 19 and 20 refer to Example 7.*

19. Interpret the entry .79 in the fundamental matrix.

20. If the gambler begins with $2, what is the expected number of times that he will play before quitting?

21. Job Mobility The lawyers at a law firm are either associates or partners. At the end of each year, 30% of the associates leave the firm, 20% are promoted to partner, and 50% remain associates. Also, 10% of the partners leave the firm at the end of each year. Assume that a lawyer who leaves the firm does not return.

(a) Draw the transition diagram for this Markov process. Label the states A, P, and L.

(b) Set up an absorbing stochastic matrix for the Markov process.

(c) Find the stable matrix.

(d) What is the expected number of years an associate will be in the firm before leaving?

22. Broadband Internet Service Colleges have been rapidly making broadband Internet service available in their residence halls. Of the colleges that offer no broadband Internet service, each year 10% introduce DSL Internet service, 30% introduce cable Internet service, and 60% continue to offer no broadband Internet service. Once a type of broadband Internet service is established, the type of service is never changed.

(a) Draw the transition diagram for the Markov process.

(b) Set up an absorbing stochastic matrix for the Markov process.

(c) Find the stable matrix.

(d) In the long run, what percent of colleges will provide cable Internet service?

(e) What is the expected number of years required for a college to set up a broadband service if it currently does not provide broadband Internet service?

23. Mouse in a Maze A mouse is placed in one of the compartments of the maze shown in Figure 9. After each minute of looking unsuccessfully for food, the mouse exits through one of the doors at random and moves to an adjacent compartment. The Exit door is one-way; that is, the mouse cannot return after he has exited the maze.

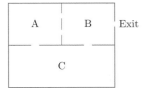

Figure 9

(a) Draw the transition diagram for the Markov process.

(b) Set up an absorbing stochastic matrix for the Markov process.

(c) Find the stable matrix.

(d) If the mouse begins in compartment A, what is the expected amount of time he spends in the maze?

Note:

$$
\begin{bmatrix} 1 & -\frac{1}{2} & -\frac{1}{2} \\ -\frac{2}{3} & 1 & -\frac{1}{2} \\ -\frac{1}{3} & -\frac{1}{4} & 1 \end{bmatrix}^{-1} = \begin{bmatrix} 4.2 & 3 & 3.6 \\ 4 & 4 & 4 \\ 2.4 & 2 & 3.2 \end{bmatrix}.
$$

24. A Card Game Heather and Blake play a card game in which they take turns drawing a card from a shuffled deck of 52 cards. Heather wins the game if she draws a heart and Blake wins the game if he draws a black card. When a player doesn't win on their turn, their card is returned to the deck, the deck is reshuffled, and it becomes the other player's turn. The game has four states: Heather Wins, Blake Wins, Heather's Turn, Blake's Turn.

(a) Draw the transition diagram for the Markov process.

(b) Set up an absorbing stochastic matrix for the Markov process.

(c) Find the stable matrix.

(d) What is the probability that Heather wins if she goes first?

(e) What is the expected number of turns if Heather goes first?

25. Class Standings Suppose that the following data were obtained from the records of a certain two-year college. Of those who were freshmen (F) during a particular year, 80% became sophomores (S) the next year and 20% dropped out (D). Of those who were sophomores during a particular year, 90% graduated (G) by the next year and 10% dropped out.

(a) Set up the absorbing stochastic matrix with states D, G, F, S that describes this transition.

(b) Find the stable matrix.

(c) Determine the probability that an entering freshman will eventually graduate.

(d) Determine the expected number of years a student entering as a freshman will attend the college before either dropping out or graduating.

26. Progression of Mental Illness A research article[2] on the application of stochastic matrices to mental illness considers a person to be in one of four states: state I—chronically insane and hospitalized; state II—dead, with death occurring while unhospitalized; state III—sane; state IV—mildly insane and unhospitalized.

[2]A.W. Marshall and H. Goldhamer, "An Application of Markov Processes to the Study of the Epidemiology of Mental Diseases," *American Statistical Association Journal*, March 1955, pp. 99–129.

States I and II are absorbing states. Suppose that of the people in state III, after one year 1.994% will be in state II, 98% in state III, and .006% in state IV. Also, suppose that of the people in state IV, after one year 2% will be in state I, 3% in state II, and 95% in state IV.

(a) Set up the absorbing stochastic matrix that describes this transition.

(b) Find the stable matrix.

(c) Determine the probability that a person who is currently well will eventually be chronically insane.

(d) For a person in state III, determine the expected number of years for which the person will be in state III.

27. **Accounts Payable** A retailer classifies accounts as having one of four possible states: "paid up," "overdue at most 30 days," "overdue less than 60 days but more than 30 days," and "bad." If no payment is made on an overdue account by the end of the month, the status moves to the next state. When a partial payment is made on an overdue account, its improved status depends on the size of the payment. Experience shows that the following matrix describes the changes in status of accounts.

	Paid	≤ 30	< 60	Bad
Paid	1	.4	.1	0
≤ 30	0	.4	.4	0
< 60	0	.2	.4	0
Bad	0	0	.1	1

(a) What is the probability of an account eventually being paid off if it is currently overdue at most 30 days? Less than 60 days?

(b) If an account is currently overdue at most 30 days, what is the expected number of months until it is either paid or bad?

(c) If the company has $2000 in bills in the "$\leq 30$ day" category and $5000 in bills in the "$< 60$ day" category, how much can the retailer expect will eventually be paid up and how much will eventually be irretrievable bad debt?

28. **Job Mobility** The managers in a company are classified as top managers, middle managers, and first-line managers. Each year, 10% of top managers retire, 10% leave the company, 60% remain top managers, and 20% are demoted to middle managers. Each year, 5% of middle managers retire, 15% leave the company, 10% are promoted to top managers, 60% remain middle managers, and 10% are demoted to first-line managers. Each year, 5% of first-line managers retire, 25% leave the company, 10% are promoted to middle managers, and 60% remain first-line managers.

(a) What is the probability of a top manager eventually retiring? A middle manager? A first-line manager?

(b) If a person is currently a middle manager, what is the expected number of years that he or she will be with the company before either leaving or retiring?

Note:

$$\begin{bmatrix} .4 & -.1 & 0 \\ -.2 & .4 & -.1 \\ 0 & -.1 & .4 \end{bmatrix}^{-1} = \begin{bmatrix} \frac{75}{26} & \frac{10}{13} & \frac{5}{26} \\ \frac{20}{13} & \frac{40}{13} & \frac{10}{13} \\ \frac{5}{13} & \frac{10}{13} & \frac{35}{13} \end{bmatrix}.$$

29. **Gambler's Ruin** As a variation of the gambler's ruin problem, suppose that on each play the probability of winning is $\frac{1}{2}$ and the gambler stops playing if he accumulates $4.

(a) What is the probability of eventually going broke if he starts with $1? $2? $3?

(b) If the gambler begins with $2, what is the expected number of times that he will play before quitting?

Note:

$$\begin{bmatrix} 1 & -\frac{1}{2} & 0 \\ -\frac{1}{2} & 1 & -\frac{1}{2} \\ 0 & -\frac{1}{2} & 1 \end{bmatrix}^{-1} = \begin{bmatrix} \frac{3}{2} & 1 & \frac{1}{2} \\ 1 & 2 & 1 \\ \frac{1}{2} & 1 & \frac{3}{2} \end{bmatrix}.$$

In Exercises 30–32, use a graphing calculator or a spreadsheet to carry out the matrix calculations.

30. Consider the absorbing stochastic matrix A, where

$$A = \begin{bmatrix} 1 & 0 & 0 & 0 & .6 \\ 0 & 1 & 0 & .5 & .1 \\ 0 & 0 & 1 & 0 & .1 \\ 0 & 0 & 0 & .2 & .2 \\ 0 & 0 & 0 & .3 & 0 \end{bmatrix}.$$

Approximate the stable matrix of A by raising A to a high power. Then find the exact stable distribution by calculating $S(I - R)^{-1}$.

31. **Collecting Quotations** A soft drink manufacturer puts one of three different quotations on the inside of each bottle cap. Assuming that each of the quotations is equally likely to appear, what is the probability of receiving all three after purchasing five of the soft drinks? Also, what is the expected number of soft drinks you have to purchase to have all three quotations?

32. Repeat Exercise 30 for the matrix

$$\begin{bmatrix} 1 & 0 & .5 & .4 & .2 \\ 0 & 1 & 0 & .3 & .7 \\ 0 & 0 & 0 & .2 & .1 \\ 0 & 0 & .3 & 0 & 0 \\ 0 & 0 & .2 & .1 & 0 \end{bmatrix}.$$

Solutions to Practice Problems 8.3

1. Sometimes they are, but in general they are not. The size of the first identity matrix equals the number of absorbing states, whereas the size of the second identity matrix is the same as that of the matrix R, which equals the number of nonabsorbing states.

2. Consider the entry in the ith row, jth column of A^2. Suppose that an object begins in state j. Then the entry gives the probability that it ends up in state i after two time periods.

3. Yes. (i) Its first state is absorbing. (ii) From each state it is possible to get to the first state. Note that it is possible to go directly from state 2 to state 1, since $a_{12} = .4 \neq 0$. Since $a_{13} = 0$, it is not possible to go directly from state 3 to state 1. However, this can be accomplished indirectly by going from state 3 to state 2 (possible since $a_{23} = .1 \neq 0$) and then from state 2 to state 1.

CHAPTER SUMMARY

1. A Markov process is a sequence of experiments performed at regular time intervals involving *states*. As a result of each experiment, transitions between states occur with probabilities given by a matrix called the *transition matrix*. The ijth entry in the transition matrix is the conditional probability $\Pr(\text{moving to state } i | \text{in state } j)$.

2. A *stochastic matrix* is a square matrix for which every entry is greater than or equal to 0 and the sum of the entries in each column is 1. Every transition matrix is a stochastic matrix.

3. The nth distribution matrix gives the percentage of members in each state after n time periods.

4. A^n is obtained by multiplying together n copies of A. Its ijth entry is the conditional probability $\Pr(\text{moving to state } i \text{ after } n \text{ time periods } | \text{ in state } j)$. Also, A^n times the initial distribution matrix gives the nth distribution matrix.

5. A stochastic matrix is called *regular* if some power of the matrix has only positive entries.

6. If A is a regular stochastic matrix, as n gets large the powers of the matrix, A^n, approach a certain matrix called the *stable matrix* of A and the distribution matrices approach a certain column matrix called the *stable distribution*. Each column of the stable matrix holds the stable distribution. The stable distribution can be found by solving $AX = X$, where the sum of the entries in X is equal to 1.

7. If the probability of moving from a state to itself is 1, we call that state an *absorbing state*. An *absorbing stochastic matrix* is a stochastic matrix with at least one absorbing state and in which from any state it is possible to eventually get to an absorbing state.

8. In an absorbing process, the transition matrix should be arranged so that absorbing states are listed before nonabsorbing states. The transition matrix will have the form

$$\left[\begin{array}{c|c} I & S \\ \hline 0 & R \end{array}\right],$$

where I is an identity matrix, 0 denotes a matrix of zeros, and S and R represent the transitions from nonabsorbing to absorbing states and from nonabsorbing to nonabsorbing states, respectively.

9. The *stable matrix* of the absorbing matrix in number 8 is

$$\left[\begin{array}{c|c} I & S(I-R)^{-1} \\ \hline 0 & 0 \end{array}\right].$$

10. The *fundamental matrix* of the absorbing matrix in number 8 is the matrix $(I - R)^{-1}$. When its columns and rows are labeled with the nonabsorbing states, its ijth entry is the expected number of times the process will be in nonabsorbing state i given that it started in nonabsorbing state j. The sum of the entries in the jth column is the expected number of steps before absorption when the process begins in state j.

REVIEW OF FUNDAMENTAL CONCEPTS

1. What is a Markov process?

2. What is a transition matrix? A stochastic matrix? A distribution matrix?

3. What is A^n? Give an interpretation of the entries of A^n.

4. How is the nth distribution matrix calculated from the initial distribution matrix?

5. Define *regular* stochastic matrix.

6. Define the stable matrix and the stable distribution of a regular stochastic matrix.

7. Explain how to find the stable distribution of a regular stochastic matrix.

8. What is meant by an absorbing state of a stochastic matrix?

9. What is an absorbing stochastic matrix?

10. Explain how to find the stable matrix of an absorbing stochastic matrix.

11. What is the fundamental matrix of an absorbing stochastic matrix and how is it used?

KEY FORMULAS

Distribution Matrices:
$$\begin{bmatrix} \\ \end{bmatrix}_n = A^n \begin{bmatrix} \\ \end{bmatrix}_0$$

Absorbing Stochastic Matrix: The stable matrix of

$$\left[\begin{array}{c|c} I & S \\ \hline 0 & R \end{array}\right] \quad \text{is} \quad \left[\begin{array}{c|c} I & S(I-R)^{-1} \\ \hline 0 & 0 \end{array}\right].$$

$F = (I - R)^{-1}$ is the Fundamental Matrix, with its columns and rows labeled with the nonabsorbing states. The entry in row i, column j of F gives the expected number of times state i occurs when the process starts in state j. The sum of the entries in column j of F is the expected number of steps until absorption when the process begins in state j.

SUPPLEMENTARY EXERCISES

In Exercises 1–6, determine whether or not the given matrix is stochastic. If so, determine if it is regular, absorbing, or neither.

1. $\begin{bmatrix} 1 & .3 & 0 & 0 \\ 0 & .1 & 0 & 0 \\ 0 & .4 & .7 & .4 \\ 0 & .2 & .3 & .6 \end{bmatrix}$
2. $\begin{bmatrix} .1 & .1 & .1 & .1 \\ .2 & .2 & .2 & .2 \\ .3 & .3 & .3 & .3 \\ .4 & .4 & .4 & .4 \end{bmatrix}$

3. $\begin{bmatrix} 0 & .3 \\ 1 & .7 \end{bmatrix}$
4. $\begin{bmatrix} 1 & 0 & 0 \\ 0 & 1 & \frac{1}{3} \\ 0 & 0 & \frac{2}{3} \end{bmatrix}$

5. $\begin{bmatrix} 1 & \frac{1}{2} & 0 \\ 0 & \frac{1}{2} & 0 \\ 0 & \frac{1}{2} & 1 \end{bmatrix}$
6. $\begin{bmatrix} 1 & 0 & 0 & .3 \\ 0 & 1 & 0 & .3 \\ 0 & 0 & .5 & .3 \\ 0 & 0 & .5 & .1 \end{bmatrix}$

7. Find the stable distribution for the regular stochastic matrix $\begin{bmatrix} .6 & .5 \\ .4 & .5 \end{bmatrix}$.

8. Find the stable matrix for the absorbing stochastic matrix

$$\begin{bmatrix} 1 & 0 & 0 & \frac{1}{8} & \frac{1}{4} \\ 0 & 1 & 0 & \frac{1}{8} & 0 \\ 0 & 0 & 1 & 0 & \frac{1}{4} \\ 0 & 0 & 0 & \frac{1}{4} & \frac{1}{2} \\ 0 & 0 & 0 & \frac{1}{2} & 0 \end{bmatrix}.$$

9. **Economic Mobility** In a certain community currently 10% of the people are H (high income), 60% are M (medium income), and 30% are L (low income). Studies show that for the children of H parents, 50% also become H, 40% become M, and 10% become L. Of the children of M parents, 40% become H, 30% become M,

and 30% become L. Of the children of L parents, 30% become H, 50% become M, and 20% become L.

(a) Set up the 3×3 stochastic matrix that describes this situation.

(b) What percent of the children of the current generation will have high incomes?

(c) In the long run, what proportion of the population will have low incomes?

10. **Quality Control** In a certain factory some machines are properly adjusted and some need adjusting. Technicians randomly inspect machines and make adjustments. Suppose that of the machines that are properly adjusted on a particular day, 80% will also be properly adjusted the following day and 20% will need adjusting. Also, of the machines that need adjusting on a particular day, 30% will be properly adjusted the next day and 70% will still need adjusting.

(a) Set up the 2×2 stochastic matrix with columns labeled P (properly adjusted) and N (need adjusting) that describes this situation.

(b) If initially all the machines are properly adjusted, what percent will need adjusting after 2 days?

(c) In the long run, what percent will be properly adjusted each day?

11. Find the stable matrix for the absorbing stochastic matrix

$$\begin{bmatrix} 1 & 0 & \frac{1}{6} & \frac{1}{2} & \frac{2}{5} \\ 0 & 1 & 0 & 0 & \frac{2}{5} \\ 0 & 0 & 0 & 0 & 0 \\ 0 & 0 & \frac{2}{3} & \frac{1}{2} & 0 \\ 0 & 0 & \frac{1}{6} & 0 & \frac{1}{5} \end{bmatrix}.$$

12. Mouse in a House Figure 1 gives the layout of a house with four rooms connected by doors. Room I contains a mousetrap and room II contains cheese. A mouse, after being placed in one of the rooms, will search for cheese; if unsuccessful after one minute, it will exit to another room by selecting one of the doors at random. (For instance, if the mouse is in room III, after one minute he will go to room II with probability $\frac{1}{3}$ and to room IV with probability $\frac{2}{3}$.) A mouse entering room I will be trapped and therefore no longer move. Also, a mouse entering room II will remain in that room.

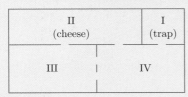

Figure 1

(a) Set up the 4×4 absorbing stochastic matrix that describes this situation.

(b) If a mouse begins in room IV, what is the probability that he will find the cheese after 2 minutes?

(c) If a mouse begins in room IV, what is the probability that he will find the cheese in the long run?

(d) For a mouse beginning in room III, determine the expected number of minutes that will elapse before the mouse either finds the cheese or is trapped.

13. Which of the following is the stable distribution for the regular stochastic matrix $\begin{bmatrix} .4 & .4 & .2 \\ .1 & .1 & .3 \\ .5 & .5 & .5 \end{bmatrix}$?

(a) $\begin{bmatrix} .6 \\ .4 \\ 1 \end{bmatrix}$ (b) $\begin{bmatrix} .2 \\ .3 \\ .5 \end{bmatrix}$ (c) $\begin{bmatrix} .3 \\ .2 \\ .5 \end{bmatrix}$

14. Listening Preferences A city has two competing news stations. From a survey of regular listeners it was determined that of those who listen to station A on a particular day, 90% listen to station A the next day and 10% listen to station B. Of those who listen to station B on a particular day, 20% listen to station A the next day and 80% listen to station B. If today 50% of the regular listeners listen to each station, what percentage of them would you expect to listen to station A 2 days from now?

15. Traffic Conditions Workday traffic conditions from 9 A.M. to 10 A.M. on the Baltimore Beltway can be characterized as Light, Moderate, and Heavy. The following stochastic matrix describes the day-to-day transitions.

$$
\begin{array}{c}
 \\
L \\
M \\
H
\end{array}
\begin{array}{ccc}
 L & M & H \\
\begin{bmatrix} .70 & .20 & .10 \\ .20 & .75 & .30 \\ .10 & .05 & .60 \end{bmatrix}
\end{array}
$$

(a) Interpret the numbers in the second column of the matrix.

(b) In the long run, what percent of the workdays fall into each category?

(c) Of 20 workdays in a month, how many are expected to have Heavy traffic on the Baltimore Beltway from 9 A.M. to 10 A.M.?

16. Mental Health A mental-health facility rates patients on their ability to live on their own. The state of a person's health is "able to work and considered cured (C)," or "long-term hospitalization or death (L)," or "group home (G)," or "short-term hospital care (S)." The following stochastic matrix describes the transitions from month to month. Use the fundamental matrix to determine the expected number of months spent in state G or S before being absorbed into state C or L.

$$
\begin{array}{c}
 \\
C \\
L \\
G \\
S
\end{array}
\begin{array}{cccc}
 C & L & G & S \\
\begin{bmatrix} 1 & 0 & .60 & .05 \\ 0 & 1 & .10 & .40 \\ 0 & 0 & .20 & .50 \\ 0 & 0 & .10 & .05 \end{bmatrix}
\end{array}
$$

17. Reservoir Levels The contents of a reservoir depend on the available rainfall in the region and the demands on the water supply. Suppose a reservoir holds up to 4 units of water (a unit might be a million gallons) and policy for the use of the water for irrigation and drinking water never allows the contents of the reservoir to drop below 1 unit of water. The (rounded) amount of water in the reservoir from week to week seems to follow the transition matrix

$$
\begin{array}{c}
 \\
1 \\
2 \\
3 \\
4
\end{array}
\begin{array}{cccc}
1 & 2 & 3 & 4 \\
\begin{bmatrix} .20 & .10 & .05 & .05 \\ .30 & .20 & .20 & .30 \\ .40 & .40 & .50 & .40 \\ .10 & .30 & .25 & .25 \end{bmatrix}
\end{array}.
$$

(a) Determine and interpret the stable distribution for the matrix.

(b) Suppose the weekly benefits to recreation in the area around the reservoir are estimated to be $4000 when there is 1 unit in the reservoir, $6000 when there are 2 units in the reservoir, $10,000 when there are 3 units, and $3000 when there are 4 units. Determine the average weekly benefits to be realized in the long run.

Conceptual Exercises

18. Explain why the entries in each column of a transition matrix must add up to 1.

19. Suppose A is a transition matrix and

$$A^4 = \begin{bmatrix} .74 & .18 \\ .26 & .82 \end{bmatrix}.$$

Interpret the number .26.

20. Explain why A^2 must be a stochastic matrix if A is a stochastic matrix.

CHAPTER TEST

1. Which of the following matrices are stochastic?

(a) $\begin{bmatrix} \frac{1}{2} & \frac{1}{3} \\ \frac{1}{2} & \frac{2}{3} \end{bmatrix}$

(b) $\begin{bmatrix} .1 & .9 \\ .5 & .5 \end{bmatrix}$

(c) $\begin{bmatrix} 1 & \frac{1}{3} \\ 0 & -\frac{2}{3} \end{bmatrix}$

(d) $\begin{bmatrix} \frac{1}{8} & \frac{1}{2} & 0 \\ \frac{3}{8} & 0 & 1 \\ \frac{1}{2} & \frac{1}{2} & 0 \end{bmatrix}$

2. Which of the following stochastic matrices are regular?

(a) $\begin{bmatrix} 1 & 0 \\ 0 & 1 \end{bmatrix}$

(b) $\begin{bmatrix} .1 & .5 \\ .9 & .5 \end{bmatrix}$

(c) $\begin{bmatrix} .4 & 1 \\ .6 & 0 \end{bmatrix}$

3. Which of the following matrices is the stable distribution for the regular stochastic matrix $\begin{bmatrix} .2 & .2 & .3 \\ .1 & .1 & .4 \\ .7 & .7 & .3 \end{bmatrix}$?

(a) $\begin{bmatrix} .3 \\ .2 \\ .5 \end{bmatrix}$

(b) $\begin{bmatrix} .25 \\ .25 \\ .50 \end{bmatrix}$

(c) $\begin{bmatrix} .35 \\ .35 \\ .30 \end{bmatrix}$

(d) $\begin{bmatrix} .2 \\ .1 \\ .7 \end{bmatrix}$

4. Find the stable distribution and the stable matrix for the regular stochastic matrix $\begin{bmatrix} \frac{1}{5} & \frac{3}{5} \\ \frac{4}{5} & \frac{2}{5} \end{bmatrix}$.

5. Browser Preferences Students at Gotham College regularly use the two browsers Internet Explorer® and Firefox®. Of the students who use Internet Explorer on a certain day, 70% use Internet Explorer the next day and 30% use Firefox. Of the students who use Firefox on a certain day, 60% use Internet Explorer the next day and 40% use Firefox. Suppose that during the first day of a semester 50% of the students use each browser.

(a) Set up the stochastic matrix displaying these transitions.

(b) What is the initial distribution matrix?

(c) What percent of the students will use Internet Explorer two days later?

(d) Show that $\begin{bmatrix} \frac{2}{3} \\ \frac{1}{3} \end{bmatrix}$ is the stable distribution for the stochastic matrix in part (a).

(e) Explain in a sentence the meaning of the number $\frac{2}{3}$ in the stable distribution from part (d).

6. Which of the following are absorbing stochastic matrices? For those that are not absorbing stochastic matrices, explain why.

(a) $\begin{bmatrix} 1 & 0 & .1 \\ 0 & 1 & .8 \\ 0 & 0 & .1 \end{bmatrix}$

(b) $\begin{bmatrix} 1 & 0 & 0 \\ 0 & .4 & .2 \\ 0 & .6 & .8 \end{bmatrix}$

(c) $\begin{bmatrix} 1 & .1 & 0 \\ 0 & .5 & 1 \\ 0 & .4 & 0 \end{bmatrix}$

7. Computer Preferences College math departments have been rapidly establishing their own computer labs. Of the departments with no labs, each year 10% set up labs using Apple® computers, 30% set up labs using PC's, and the remainder do not set up labs that year. Once a lab has been established with a certain type of computer, the lab is never abandoned and the brand of computer is never changed.

(a) Set up the absorbing stochastic matrix that describes these transitions.

(b) Find the stable matrix.

(c) In the long run, what percent of the math departments will have Apple computer labs?

(d) What is the expected number of years required for a math department to decide to set up its own computer lab if it currently does not have a lab?

CHAPTER 8 | PROJECT

Doubly Stochastic Matrices

A square matrix is said to be **doubly stochastic** if the sum of the entries in each column is 1 and the sum of the entries in each row is 1. Some examples of doubly stochastic matrices are

$$\begin{bmatrix} .4 & .6 \\ .6 & .4 \end{bmatrix}, \quad \begin{bmatrix} .1 & .3 & .6 \\ .6 & .1 & .3 \\ .3 & .6 & .1 \end{bmatrix}, \quad \text{and} \quad \begin{bmatrix} .1 & .2 & .3 & .4 \\ .3 & .4 & .1 & .2 \\ .2 & .3 & .4 & .1 \\ .4 & .1 & .2 & .3 \end{bmatrix}.$$

1. Give another example of a 2×2 doubly stochastic matrix.

   (a) Is your matrix symmetric? That is, does it equal its own transpose?

   (b) Prove that every 2×2 doubly stochastic matrix is symmetric.

   (c) Show that the product of your matrix and the matrix

   $$\begin{bmatrix} .4 & .6 \\ .6 & .4 \end{bmatrix}$$

   is doubly stochastic.

   (d) Show that $\begin{bmatrix} \frac{1}{2} \\ \frac{1}{2} \end{bmatrix}$ is a stable distribution for your matrix.

2. Give another example of a 3×3 doubly stochastic matrix.

   (a) Is your matrix symmetric? Are all 3×3 doubly stochastic matrices symmetric?

   (b) Show that the product of your matrix and the matrix

   $$\begin{bmatrix} .1 & .3 & .6 \\ .6 & .1 & .3 \\ .3 & .6 & .1 \end{bmatrix}$$

   is doubly stochastic.

   (c) Show that $\begin{bmatrix} \frac{1}{3} \\ \frac{1}{3} \\ \frac{1}{3} \end{bmatrix}$ is a stable distribution for your matrix.

3. Give another example of a 4×4 doubly stochastic matrix.

   (a) Is your matrix symmetric? Are all 4×4 doubly stochastic matrices symmetric?

   (b) Show that the product of your matrix and the matrix

   $$\begin{bmatrix} .1 & .2 & .3 & .4 \\ .3 & .4 & .1 & .2 \\ .2 & .3 & .4 & .1 \\ .4 & .1 & .2 & .3 \end{bmatrix}$$

   is doubly stochastic.

   (c) Show that $\begin{bmatrix} \frac{1}{4} \\ \frac{1}{4} \\ \frac{1}{4} \\ \frac{1}{4} \end{bmatrix}$ is a stable distribution for your matrix.

We will now show that the product of any two $n \times n$ doubly stochastic matrices is doubly stochastic, and that any doubly stochastic $n \times n$ matrix has

$$\begin{bmatrix} \frac{1}{n} \\ \frac{1}{n} \\ \vdots \\ \frac{1}{n} \end{bmatrix}$$

as a stable distribution. Let E_n be the $n \times n$ matrix for which each entry is 1.

4. Show that A is a doubly stochastic $n \times n$ matrix if and only if $AE_n = E_n$ and $E_n A = E_n$.

5. Show that if A and B are doubly stochastic $n \times n$ matrices, then so is AB. *Hint*: Show that $(AB)E_n = E_n$ and $E_n(AB) = E_n$.

6. Show that if A is a doubly stochastic $n \times n$ matrix, then

$$\begin{bmatrix} \frac{1}{n} \\ \frac{1}{n} \\ \vdots \\ \frac{1}{n} \end{bmatrix}$$

is a stable distribution for A. *Hint*: First show that $A \begin{bmatrix} 1 \\ 1 \\ \vdots \\ 1 \end{bmatrix} = \begin{bmatrix} 1 \\ 1 \\ \vdots \\ 1 \end{bmatrix}$.

7. A collection of $n \times n$ matrices is said to be a *convex set*[1] if whenever A and B are in the set and t is a number between 0 and 1, then $tA + (1 - t)B$ is also in the set. Show that the set of all $n \times n$ doubly stochastic matrices is a convex set. *Note*: For a number r and a matrix A, rA is the matrix obtained by multiplying each entry of A by r.

---

[1] Convex sets are studied in advanced courses in applied matrix theory.

THE THEORY OF GAMES

One of the more interesting developments of twentieth-century mathematics has been the theory of games, a branch of mathematics used to analyze competitive phenomena. This theory has been applied extensively in many fields, including business, economics, psychology, and sociology. The 1994 and 2005 Nobel Prizes in Economics were awarded to economists for their groundbreaking work in integrating game theory into the study of economic behavior. Game theory has become one of the hottest areas of economics, with applications ranging from how the Federal Reserve sets interest rates, to how companies structure incentive pay for employees, to how companies bid on lucrative federal contracts. Mathematically, the theory of games blends the theory of matrices with probability theory. Although an extensive discussion is well beyond the scope of this book, we hope to give the flavor of the subject and some indication of the wide range of its applications.

9.1 Games and Strategies

Let us begin our study of game theory by analyzing a typical competitive situation. Suppose that in a certain town there are two furniture stores, Reliable Furniture Company and Cut-Rate Furniture Company, which compete for all furniture sales in the town. Each of the stores is planning a Labor Day sale and each has the option of marking its furniture down by 10% or 20%. The results of their decisions affect the total percentage of the market that each captures. On the basis of an analysis of past consumer tendencies, it is estimated that if Reliable chooses a 10% discount and so does Cut-Rate, then Reliable will capture 60% of the sales. If Reliable chooses a 10% discount but Cut-Rate chooses 20%, then Reliable will capture only 35% of the sales. On the other hand, if Reliable chooses a 20% discount but Cut-Rate chooses 10%, then Reliable will get 80% of the sales. If Reliable chooses a 20% discount and Cut-Rate also chooses 20%, then Reliable will get 50% of the sales. Each store is able to determine the other store's discount prior to the start of the sale and adjust its own discount accordingly. If you were a consultant to Reliable, what discount would you choose to obtain as large a share of the sales as possible?

To analyze the various possibilities, let us summarize the given data in a matrix. For the sake of brevity, denote Reliable by R and Cut-Rate by C. Then the data can be summarized in a matrix showing R's share in each case as follows:

$$
\begin{array}{cc}
 & C \text{ discount} \\
 & \begin{array}{cc} 10\% & 20\% \end{array} \\
R \text{ discount} \begin{array}{c} 10\% \\ 20\% \end{array} & \left[\begin{array}{cc} .6 & .35 \\ .8 & .5 \end{array} \right].
\end{array}
$$

For example, the number in the second row, first column corresponds to an R discount of 20% and a C discount of 10%. In this case R will capture 80%, or .8, of the sales.

We may view R's choice of discount as choosing one of the rows of the matrix. Similarly, C's choice of discount amounts to choosing one of the columns of the matrix. Suppose that R and C both act rationally. What will be the result? Let us view things from R's perspective first. In scanning his options, he sees a .8 in the second row. So his first reaction might be to take a 20% discount and try for 80% of the sales. However, this route is very risky. As soon as C learns that R has chosen a 20% discount, C will set a 20% discount and lower R's share of the sales to 50%. So the result of choosing row 2 will be for R to capture only 50% of the sales. On the other hand, if R chooses row 1, then C will naturally choose a 20% discount to give R a 35% share of the sales. Of the options open to R, the 50% share is clearly the most desirable. So R will choose a 20% discount.

What about C? In setting his discount, C must choose a column of the matrix. Since the entries represent R's share of the sales, C wishes to make a choice resulting in as *small* a number as possible. If C chooses column 1, then R will immediately respond with a 20% discount in order to acquire 80% of the sales, a disaster for C. On the other hand, if C chooses column 2, then R will choose a 20% discount to obtain 50% of the sales. The best option open to C is to choose a 20% discount.

Thus we see that if both stores act rationally, they will each choose 20% discounts and each will capture 50% of the sales.

The preceding competitive situation is an example of a (mathematical) **game**. In such a game there are two or more players. In the example the players are R and C. Each player is allowed to make a move. In the example the moves are the choices of discount. As the result of a move by each player, there is a payoff to each player. The payoff to each player (store) is the percentage of total sales he captures. In our example, then, we have solved a problem that can be posed for any game:

Fundamental Problem of Game Theory　How should each player decide his move in order to maximize his gain?

Indeed, in our example, R and C chose moves such that each maximized his own share of sales.

Throughout this chapter we consider only games with two players, whom we shall denote by R and C. (R and C stand for row and column, respectively.) Suppose that R can make moves $R_1, R_2, \ldots, R_m$ and that C can make moves $C_1, C_2, \ldots, C_n$. Further suppose that a move R_i by R and C_j by C results in a payoff of a_{ij} to R. Then the game can be represented by the following **payoff matrix**:

$$
R \text{ moves} \quad
\begin{array}{c}
\\
R_1 \\
R_2 \\
\vdots \\
R_m
\end{array}
\begin{array}{c}
\overset{\displaystyle C \text{ moves}}{} \\
\begin{array}{cccc}
C_1 & C_2 & \cdots & C_n
\end{array} \\
\begin{bmatrix}
a_{11} & a_{12} & \cdots & a_{1n} \\
a_{21} & a_{22} & \cdots & a_{2n} \\
\vdots & \vdots & & \vdots \\
a_{m1} & a_{m2} & \cdots & a_{mn}
\end{bmatrix}
\end{array}.
$$

Note that the payoff matrix is an $m \times n$ matrix with a_{ij} as the entry of the ith row, jth column. In our furniture store example the payoff matrix was just the matrix we used in our analysis. Note that a move by R corresponds to a choice of a *row* of the payoff matrix, whereas a move by C corresponds to a choice of a *column*.

Suppose that a given game is played repeatedly. The players can adopt various strategies to attempt to maximize their respective gains (or minimize their losses). In what follows we shall discuss the problem of determining strategies. The simplest type of strategy is one in which a player, on consecutive plays, consistently chooses the same row (or column). Such strategies are called **pure strategies** and are discussed in this section. Strategies involving varied moves are called **mixed strategies** and are discussed in Section 9.2.

In most examples of games, the payoffs to C are related in a simple way to the corresponding payoffs to R. For example, for the furniture stores the payoff to C is 100% minus the payoff to R. In another common type of game a payoff to R of a given amount results in a loss to C of the same amount, and vice versa. For such games the sum of the gains on each play is zero; hence they are called **zero-sum games**. An illustration of such a game is provided in the next example.

EXAMPLE 1

Coin-matching game   Suppose that R and C play a coin-matching game. Each player can show either heads or tails. If R and C both show heads, then C pays R $5. If R shows heads and C shows tails, then R pays C $8. If R shows tails and C shows heads, then C pays R $3. If R shows tails and so does C, then C pays R $1.

(a) Determine the payoff matrix of this game.

(b) Suppose that R and C play the game repeatedly. Determine optimal pure strategies for R and C.

Solution   **(a)** The payoff matrix is given by

$$
\begin{array}{cc}
& C \\
R \quad
\begin{array}{c}
\text{Heads} \\
\text{Tails}
\end{array}
&
\begin{array}{cc}
\text{Heads} & \text{Tails}
\end{array} \\
&
\begin{bmatrix}
5 & -8 \\
3 & 1
\end{bmatrix}
\end{array}.
$$

Each entry specifies a payoff from C to R. The entry "-8" denotes a negative payoff to R, that is, a gain of $8 to C.

(b) R would clearly like to choose heads so as to gain \$5. However, if R consistently chooses heads, C will retaliate by choosing tails, causing R to lose \$8. If R chooses tails, however, then the best C can do is choose tails to give a gain of \$1 to R. So R should clearly choose tails. Now we look at the game from C's point of view. Clearly, C's objective is to minimize the payment to R. If C consistently chooses heads, then R will notice the pattern and choose heads, at a cost to C of \$5. However, if C chooses tails, then the best that R can do is choose tails, thereby costing C \$1. So, clearly, the optimal move for C is to choose tails. ∎

The reasoning just described is rather cumbersome. There is, however, an easy way to summarize what we have done. Let us first describe R's reasoning. R seeks to choose a row of the matrix that will maximize his payoff. However, once a row is chosen consistently, R can expect C to counter by choosing the least element of that row. Thus R should choose his move as follows:

Optimal Pure Strategy for R

1. For each row of the payoff matrix, determine the least element.

2. Choose the row for which this element is as large as possible.

For example, in the game of Example 1 we have circled the least element of each row:

$$\begin{bmatrix} 5 & \boxed{-8} \\ 3 & \boxed{1} \end{bmatrix}.$$

The largest circled element is 1. So R should choose the second row—that is, tails.

In a similar way we may describe the optimal strategy for C. C wishes to choose a column of the payoff matrix so as to minimize the payoff to R. However, C can expect R to adjust his choice to the maximum element of the column. Therefore, we can summarize the optimal strategy for C as follows:

Optimal Pure Strategy for C

1. For each column of the payoff matrix, determine the largest element.

2. Choose the column for which this element is as small as possible.

For example, in the game of Example 1 we have circled the largest element in each column:

$$\begin{bmatrix} \boxed{5} & -8 \\ 3 & \boxed{1} \end{bmatrix}.$$

The smallest circled element is 1, so C should choose the second column, or tails.

EXAMPLE 2   **Optimal pure strategy** Determine optimal pure strategies for R and C for the game whose payoff matrix is

$$\begin{bmatrix} -1 & 5 \\ 1 & 4 \\ 0 & -1 \end{bmatrix}.$$

Solution To determine the strategy for R, we first circle the smallest element in each row:

$$\begin{bmatrix} \text{\textcircled{-1}} & 5 \\ \text{\textcircled{1}} & 4 \\ 0 & \text{\textcircled{-1}} \end{bmatrix}.$$

The largest of these is 1, so R should play the second row. To determine the strategy for C, we circle the largest element in each column:

$$\begin{bmatrix} -1 & \text{\textcircled{5}} \\ \text{\textcircled{1}} & 4 \\ 0 & -1 \end{bmatrix}.$$

Now Try Exercise 5 The smallest of these is 1, so C should play the first column. ∎

All the games considered so far have an important characteristic in common: There is an entry in the payoff matrix which is *simultaneously* the minimum element in its row and the maximum element in its column. Such an entry is called a **saddle point** for the game. As we have seen in the examples considered previously, if a game possesses a saddle point, then an optimal strategy is for R to choose the row containing the saddle point and for C to choose the column containing the saddle point.

A game need not have a saddle point. For example, the matrix

$$\begin{bmatrix} 2 & -2 \\ 0 & 1 \end{bmatrix}$$

is the payoff matrix of a game with no saddle point. The optimal pure strategy for R is to choose the row with the maximum of the circled elements in

$$\begin{bmatrix} 2 & \text{\textcircled{-2}} \\ \text{\textcircled{0}} & 1 \end{bmatrix}.$$

Thus, R chooses row 2. The optimal pure strategy for C is to choose the column with the minimum of the circled elements in

$$\begin{bmatrix} \text{\textcircled{2}} & -2 \\ 0 & \text{\textcircled{1}} \end{bmatrix}.$$

So C chooses column 2. No element is simultaneously the minimum element in its row and the maximum element in its column.

A game that has a saddle point is called a **strictly determined game**. If v is a saddle point for a strictly determined game, then if each player plays the optimal pure strategy, each repetition of the game will result in a payment of v to player R. The number v is called the **value** of the game. Since v is a payoff to player R, the game favors player R when v is positive and favors player C when v is negative. When $v = 0$, the game is said to be a **fair game**.

EXAMPLE 3   **Value of a strictly determined game**   Find the saddle point and the value of the strictly determined game given by the payoff matrix

$$\begin{bmatrix} -1 & -10 & 10 \\ 0 & 7 & 6 \\ 3 & 4 & 11 \\ 2 & 5 & 7 \end{bmatrix}.$$

Solution The least elements in the various rows are

$$
\begin{bmatrix}
-1 & \boxed{-10} & 10 \\
\boxed{0} & 7 & 6 \\
\boxed{3} & 4 & 11 \\
\boxed{2} & 5 & 7
\end{bmatrix}.
$$

The maximum elements in the columns are

$$
\begin{bmatrix}
-1 & -10 & 10 \\
0 & \boxed{7} & 6 \\
\boxed{3} & 4 & \boxed{11} \\
2 & 5 & 7
\end{bmatrix}.
$$

The element 3 in the third row, first column is a minimum in its row and a maximum in its column and so is a saddle point of the game. The value of the game is therefore 3: Each repetition of the game, assuming optimal strategies, results in a payoff of 3 to R.

Now Try Exercise 7

EXAMPLE 4

A child's game R and C play a game in which they show 1 or 2 fingers simultaneously. It is agreed that C pays R an amount equal to the total number of fingers shown less 3 cents. Find the optimal strategy for each player and the value of the game.

Solution The payoff matrix is given by

$$
\begin{array}{cc}
 & \begin{array}{cc} 1 & \quad 2 \end{array} \\
\begin{array}{c} 1 \\ 2 \end{array} & \begin{bmatrix} 2-3 & 3-3 \\ 3-3 & 4-3 \end{bmatrix}
\end{array}
=
\begin{array}{cc}
 & \begin{array}{cc} 1 & 2 \end{array} \\
\begin{array}{c} 1 \\ 2 \end{array} & \begin{bmatrix} -1 & 0 \\ 0 & 1 \end{bmatrix}
\end{array}.
$$

The saddle point is the element that is simultaneously the minimum of its row and the maximum of its column—so an optimal strategy is for R to show 2 fingers and for C to show 1 finger. The value of the game is 0.

Now Try Exercise 9

A game may have more than one saddle point. Consider the game with payoff matrix

$$
\begin{bmatrix}
\boxed{1} & 2 & \boxed{1} \\
\boxed{1} & 5 & \boxed{1} \\
0 & -7 & -1
\end{bmatrix}.
$$

Each circled element is both the minimum element in its row and the maximum element in its column. There are four saddle points representing four optimal strategies. The value of the game, regardless of strategy, is 1. If a game has more than one saddle point, then the value of the game is the same at each of them.

Practice Problems 9.1

Which of the following matrices are the payoff matrices of strictly determined games? For those that are, determine the saddle point and optimal pure strategy for each of the players.

1. $\begin{bmatrix} 1 & -1 & -3 \\ 0 & -2 & 3 \end{bmatrix}$ 2. $\begin{bmatrix} 1 & -1 & 0 \\ 0 & -4 & 5 \end{bmatrix}$

3. $\begin{bmatrix} 1 & -2 & 1 \\ -2 & 1 & 1 \\ 1 & 1 & -2 \end{bmatrix}$

EXERCISES 9.1

Each of the following matrices is the payoff matrix for a strictly determined game. Determine optimal pure strategies for R and C.

1. $\begin{bmatrix} -1 & -2 \\ 0 & 3 \end{bmatrix}$ 2. $\begin{bmatrix} -4 & 0 \\ 2 & 1 \end{bmatrix}$

3. $\begin{bmatrix} -2 & 4 & 1 \\ -1 & 3 & 5 \\ -3 & 5 & 2 \end{bmatrix}$ 4. $\begin{bmatrix} 1 & -1 & 0 \\ 6 & 3 & 2 \\ 2 & -2 & 1 \end{bmatrix}$

5. $\begin{bmatrix} 0 & 3 \\ -1 & 1 \\ -2 & -4 \end{bmatrix}$ 6. $\begin{bmatrix} 0 & -4 & 0 \\ -1 & -2 & 1 \end{bmatrix}$

Each of the following matrices is the payoff matrix for a strictly determined game. (a) Find a saddle point. (b) Determine the value of the game.

7. $\begin{bmatrix} 1 & 0 \\ 0 & -1 \end{bmatrix}$ 8. $\begin{bmatrix} 2 & 3 \\ 4 & 5 \end{bmatrix}$

For each of the following games, give the payoff matrix and decide if the game is strictly determined. If so, determine the optimal strategies for R and C.

9. **Matching Coins** Suppose that R and C play a game by matching coins. On each play, C pays R the number of heads shown (0, 1, or 2) minus twice the number of tails shown.

10. **Scissors, Paper, Stone** In the child's game "scissors, paper, stone," each of two children calls out one of the three words. If they both call out the same word, then the game is a tie. Otherwise, "scissors" beats "paper" (since scissors can cut paper), "paper" beats "stone"

(since paper can cover stone), and "stone" beats "scissors" (since stone can break scissors). Suppose that the loser pays a penny to the winner.

11. **Political Action** Two candidates for political office must decide to be for, against, or neutral on a certain referendum. Pollsters have determined that if candidate R comes out for the referendum, then he will gain 8000 votes if candidate C also comes out for the referendum, will lose 1000 votes if candidate C comes out against, and will gain 1000 votes if candidate C comes out neutral. If candidate R comes out against, then he will lose 7000 votes (respectively gain 4000 votes, lose 2000 votes) if candidate C comes out for (respectively against, neutral on) the referendum. If candidate R is neutral, then he will gain 3000 votes if C is for or against and will gain 2000 votes if C is neutral.

12. **Program Scheduling** TV stations R and C each have a quiz show and a situation comedy to schedule for their 1 o'clock and 2 o'clock time slots. If they both schedule their quiz shows at 1 o'clock, then station R will take $3000 in advertising revenue away from station C. If they both schedule their quiz shows at 2 o'clock, then station C will take $2000 in advertising revenue from R. If they choose different hours for the quiz show, then R will take $5000 in advertising from C by scheduling it at 2 o'clock, and $2000 by scheduling it at 1 o'clock.

13. **Card Game** Player R has two cards: a red 5 and a black 10. Player C has three cards: a red 6, a black 7, and a black 8. They each place one of their cards on the table. If the cards are the same color, R receives the difference of the two numbers. If the cards are of different colors, C receives the minimum of the two numbers.

Solutions to Practice Problems 9.1

1. Not strictly determined. The minimum elements of the rows are

$$\begin{bmatrix} 1 & -1 & \boxed{-3} \\ 0 & \boxed{-2} & 3 \end{bmatrix};$$

the maximum elements of the columns are

$$\begin{bmatrix} \boxed{1} & \boxed{-1} & -3 \\ 0 & -2 & \boxed{3} \end{bmatrix}.$$

No element is simultaneously the minimum in its row and the maximum in its column.

2. Strictly determined. The least elements of the rows are

$$\begin{bmatrix} 1 & \boxed{-1} & 0 \\ 0 & \boxed{-4} & 5 \end{bmatrix}.$$

The largest elements of the columns are

$$\begin{bmatrix} \boxed{1} & \boxed{-1} & 0 \\ 0 & -4 & \boxed{5} \end{bmatrix}.$$

Thus -1 is a saddle point. The optimal strategy for R is to choose row 1; the optimal strategy for C is to choose column 2.

3. Not strictly determined. The minimum elements of the rows are

$$\begin{bmatrix} 1 & \boxed{-2} & 1 \\ \boxed{-2} & 1 & 1 \\ 1 & 1 & \boxed{-2} \end{bmatrix}.$$

The largest element for each column is 1. (Note that there are two choices for each largest element.) But none of the largest column elements is a least row element.

9.2 Mixed Strategies

In Section 9.1 we introduced strictly determined games and gave a method for determining optimal strategies for each player. However, not all games are strictly determined. For example, consider the game with payoff matrix

$$\begin{bmatrix} -1 & 5 \\ 2 & -3 \end{bmatrix}.$$

The minimum entries of the rows are

$$\begin{bmatrix} \boxed{-1} & 5 \\ 2 & \boxed{-3} \end{bmatrix},$$

whereas the maximum entries of the columns are

$$\begin{bmatrix} -1 & \boxed{5} \\ \boxed{2} & -3 \end{bmatrix}.$$

Note that no matrix entry is simultaneously the minimum in its row and the maximum in its column. Note also that no simple strategy of the type considered in Section 9.1 is sufficient to both maximize R's winnings and minimize C's losses. To see this, consider the game from R's point of view. Suppose that R repeatedly plays the strategy "first row," thereby attempting to win 5. After a few plays C will catch on to R's strategy and choose column 1, giving R a loss of 1. Similarly, if R consistently plays the strategy "second row," attempting to win 2, then C can thwart R by choosing the second column, to give R a loss of 3. It is clear that, in order to maximize his payoff, R should sometimes choose row 1 and sometimes row 2. One might expect that by choosing the rows on a probabilistic basis R can prevent C from anticipating his moves and amass enough positive payoffs to counteract the occasional negative ones. Thus we should investigate strategies of the type

$$A: \begin{cases} \text{Choose row 1 with probability .5} \\ \text{Choose row 2 with probability .5} \end{cases}$$

and

$$B: \begin{cases} \text{Choose row 1 with probability .9} \\ \text{Choose row 2 with probability .1.} \end{cases}$$

Such strategies are called **mixed strategies**. Either of the players can pursue such a strategy.

One way that R can carry out strategy A is to alternate between row 1 and row 2 on successive plays of the game. However, if C is at all clever, he will recognize this pattern and determine his play accordingly. What R should do is toss a coin and play row 1 whenever it lands heads and row 2 whenever it lands tails. Then there is no way that C can anticipate R's choice.

Figure 1

To carry out strategy B, R might use a card with a spinner attached at the center of a circle that is 90% red and 10% white. R would then determine his play by spinning the spinner and choosing row 1 if the spinner landed on the red part of the circle and row 2 if it landed on the white part. (See Fig. 1.)

It will be convenient to write mixed strategies in matrix form. Mixed strategies for R will be row matrices, and mixed strategies for C will be column matrices. Thus, for example, mixed strategy A above (for R) corresponds to the matrix

$$A: \begin{bmatrix} .5 & .5 \end{bmatrix},$$

whereas mixed strategy B (for R) corresponds to

$$B: \begin{bmatrix} .9 & .1 \end{bmatrix}.$$

The mixed strategy in which C chooses column 1 with probability .6 and column 2 with probability .4 corresponds to the column matrix

$$\begin{bmatrix} .6 \\ .4 \end{bmatrix}.$$

In comparing different mixed strategies, we use a number called their **expected value**. This number is just the average amount per game paid to R if the players pursue the given mixed strategies. The next example illustrates the computation of the expected value in a special case.

EXAMPLE 1

Expected value of a mixed strategy game   Suppose that a game has payoff matrix

$$\begin{bmatrix} -1 & 5 \\ 2 & -3 \end{bmatrix}.$$

Further suppose that R pursues the mixed strategy $\begin{bmatrix} .9 & .1 \end{bmatrix}$ and that C pursues the mixed strategy $\begin{bmatrix} .6 \\ .4 \end{bmatrix}$. Calculate the expected value of this game.

Solution   Let us view each repetition of the game as an experiment. There are four possible outcomes:

(row 1, column 1)   (row 1, column 2)

(row 2, column 1)   (row 2, column 2).

Let us compute the probability (relative frequency) with which each of the outcomes occurs. For example, consider the outcome (row 1, column 1). According to our assumptions about the strategies of R and C, R chooses row 1 with probability .9 and C chooses column 1 with probability .6. Since R and C make their respective choices independently of one another, the events "row 1" and "column 1" are independent. Therefore, we can compute the probability of the outcome (row 1, column 1) as follows:

$$\text{Pr(row 1, column 1)} = \text{Pr(row 1)} \cdot \text{Pr(column 1)} = (.9)(.6) = .54.$$

That is, the outcome "row 1, column 1" will occur with probability .54. Similarly, we compute the probabilities of the other three outcomes. Table 1 gives the probability and the amount won by R for each outcome. The average amount that R wins per play is then given by

$$(-1)(.54) + (5)(.36) + (2)(.06) + (-3)(.04) = 1.26.$$

Hence the expected value of the given strategies is 1.26.

TABLE 1

Outcome	R wins	Probability
Row 1, column 1	-1	$(.9)(.6) = .54$
Row 1, column 2	5	$(.9)(.4) = .36$
Row 2, column 1	2	$(.1)(.6) = .06$
Row 2, column 2	-3	$(.1)(.4) = .04$

Now Try Exercise 1(a)

We may generalize the preceding computations. To see the pattern, let us first concentrate on 2×2 games. Suppose that a game has payoff matrix

$$\begin{bmatrix} a_{11} & a_{12} \\ a_{21} & a_{22} \end{bmatrix}.$$

Further suppose that R pursues a strategy $\begin{bmatrix} r_1 & r_2 \end{bmatrix}$. That is, R randomly chooses row 1 with probability r_1 and row 2 with probability r_2. Similarly, suppose that C pursues a strategy $\begin{bmatrix} c_1 \\ c_2 \end{bmatrix}$. Then the probabilities of the various outcomes can be tabulated as shown in Table 2. Thus, by following the reasoning used in the special case above, we see that the expected value of the strategies is the sum of the products of the payoffs times the corresponding probabilities:

$$a_{11}(r_1 c_1) + a_{12}(r_1 c_2) + a_{21}(r_2 c_1) + a_{22}(r_2 c_2).$$

TABLE 2

Outcome	Payoff to R	Probability
Row 1, column 1	a_{11}	$r_1 c_1$
Row 1, column 2	a_{12}	$r_1 c_2$
Row 2, column 1	a_{21}	$r_2 c_1$
Row 2, column 2	a_{22}	$r_2 c_2$

On the average, R gains this amount for each play. A somewhat tedious (but easy) calculation shows that

$$\begin{bmatrix} r_1 & r_2 \end{bmatrix} \begin{bmatrix} a_{11} & a_{12} \\ a_{21} & a_{22} \end{bmatrix} \begin{bmatrix} c_1 \\ c_2 \end{bmatrix} = \begin{bmatrix} r_1 & r_2 \end{bmatrix} \begin{bmatrix} a_{11}c_1 + a_{12}c_2 \\ a_{21}c_1 + a_{22}c_2 \end{bmatrix}$$

$$= \begin{bmatrix} a_{11}(r_1 c_1) + a_{12}(r_1 c_2) + a_{21}(r_2 c_1) + a_{22}(r_2 c_2) \end{bmatrix}. \quad (1)$$

Formula (1) is a special case of the following general fact:

Expected Value of a Pair of Strategies   Suppose that a game has payoff matrix

$$\begin{bmatrix} a_{11} & a_{12} & \cdots & a_{1n} \\ a_{21} & a_{22} & \cdots & a_{2n} \\ \vdots & \vdots & & \vdots \\ a_{m1} & a_{m2} & \cdots & a_{mn} \end{bmatrix},$$

where each entry is a payoff to R.   Suppose that R plays the strategy $\begin{bmatrix} r_1 & r_2 & \cdots & r_m \end{bmatrix}$ and that C plays the strategy

$$\begin{bmatrix} c_1 \\ c_2 \\ \vdots \\ c_n \end{bmatrix}.$$

Let e be the expected value of the pair of strategies; that is, the average payoff to R. Then

$$\begin{bmatrix} r_1 & r_2 & \cdots & r_m \end{bmatrix} \begin{bmatrix} a_{11} & a_{12} & \cdots & a_{1n} \\ a_{21} & a_{22} & \cdots & a_{2n} \\ \vdots & \vdots & & \vdots \\ a_{m1} & a_{m2} & \cdots & a_{mn} \end{bmatrix} \begin{bmatrix} c_1 \\ c_2 \\ \vdots \\ c_n \end{bmatrix} = \begin{bmatrix} e \end{bmatrix}.$$

EXAMPLE 2

Choosing the advantageous strategy   Suppose that a game has payoff matrix

$$\begin{bmatrix} 2 & 0 & -1 \\ -1 & 3 & 4 \end{bmatrix}$$

and that R plays the strategy $\begin{bmatrix} .5 & .5 \end{bmatrix}$. Which of the following strategies is more advantageous for C?

$$A = \begin{bmatrix} .6 \\ .3 \\ .1 \end{bmatrix} \quad \text{or} \quad B = \begin{bmatrix} .3 \\ .3 \\ .4 \end{bmatrix}$$

Solution   We compare the expected value with C using strategy A to that with C using strategy B. With strategy A we have

$$\begin{bmatrix} .5 & .5 \end{bmatrix} \begin{bmatrix} 2 & 0 & -1 \\ -1 & 3 & 4 \end{bmatrix} \begin{bmatrix} .6 \\ .3 \\ .1 \end{bmatrix} = \begin{bmatrix} .90 \end{bmatrix}.$$

Using strategy B, we have

$$\begin{bmatrix} .5 & .5 \end{bmatrix} \begin{bmatrix} 2 & 0 & -1 \\ -1 & 3 & 4 \end{bmatrix} \begin{bmatrix} .3 \\ .3 \\ .4 \end{bmatrix} = \begin{bmatrix} 1.20 \end{bmatrix}.$$

Thus strategy A will yield an average payment per play of .90 to R, whereas strategy B will yield an average payment per play of 1.20. Clearly, it is to C's advantage to choose strategy A.   ■

EXAMPLE 3

Chemical company's dumping strategy   The Acme Chemical Corporation has two plants, each situated on the banks of the Blue River, 10 miles from one another. A single inspector is assigned to check that the plants do not dump waste into the river. If he discovers plant A dumping waste, Acme is fined $20,000. If he discovers plant B dumping waste, Acme is fined \$50,000. Suppose that the inspector visits one of the plants each day and that he chooses, on a random basis, to visit plant B 60% of the time. Acme schedules dumping from its two plants on a random basis, one plant per day, with plant B dumping waste on 70% of the days. How much is Acme's average fine per day?

Solution The competition between Acme and the inspector can be viewed as a non-strictly determined game, whose matrix is

$$
\begin{array}{c}
\\
\text{Plant } A \text{ dumps} \\
\text{Plant } B \text{ dumps}
\end{array}
\begin{array}{cc}
\text{Inspect } A & \text{Inspect } B \\
\begin{bmatrix} -20{,}000 & 0 \\ 0 & -50{,}000 \end{bmatrix} .
\end{array}
$$

The strategy of Acme is given by the row matrix $[.3 \quad .7]$. The strategy of the inspector is given by the column matrix $\begin{bmatrix} .4 \\ .6 \end{bmatrix}$. The expected value of the strategies is the matrix product

$$
\begin{bmatrix} .3 & .7 \end{bmatrix} \begin{bmatrix} -20{,}000 & 0 \\ 0 & -50{,}000 \end{bmatrix} \begin{bmatrix} .4 \\ .6 \end{bmatrix} = \begin{bmatrix} -6000 & -35{,}000 \end{bmatrix} \begin{bmatrix} .4 \\ .6 \end{bmatrix}
$$

$$
= \begin{bmatrix} -23{,}400 \end{bmatrix} .
$$

In other words, Acme will be fined an average of \$23,400 per day for polluting the river.

Now Try Exercise 3

In Section 9.3 we will alter payoff matrices by adding a fixed constant to each entry so that all entries become positive numbers. This does not alter the essential character of the game, in that good strategies for the original matrix will also be good strategies for the new matrix. The only difference is that the expected value is increased by the constant added. This procedure enables us to apply the methods of linear programming to the determination of optimal mixed strategies for zero-sum games that are not strictly determined.

EXAMPLE 4

Payoffs with constant increments In Example 1 we saw that for the game with payoff matrix

$$
\begin{bmatrix} -1 & 5 \\ 2 & -3 \end{bmatrix}
$$

and strategies $[.9 \quad .1]$, $\begin{bmatrix} .6 \\ .4 \end{bmatrix}$, the expected value was 1.26. Compute the expected value of those strategies for the matrix obtained by adding 4 to each entry.

Solution The new matrix is

$$
\begin{bmatrix} -1+4 & 5+4 \\ 2+4 & -3+4 \end{bmatrix} \quad \text{or} \quad \begin{bmatrix} 3 & 9 \\ 6 & 1 \end{bmatrix} .
$$

The expected value of the strategies for the new matrix is

$$
\begin{bmatrix} .9 & .1 \end{bmatrix} \begin{bmatrix} 3 & 9 \\ 6 & 1 \end{bmatrix} \begin{bmatrix} .6 \\ .4 \end{bmatrix} = \begin{bmatrix} 3.3 & 8.2 \end{bmatrix} \begin{bmatrix} .6 \\ .4 \end{bmatrix} = \begin{bmatrix} 5.26 \end{bmatrix} .
$$

As it should, the expected value has also increased by 4.

Suppose that the payoff matrix is

$$\begin{bmatrix} -\frac{1}{2} & \frac{5}{2} \\ 1 & -\frac{3}{2} \end{bmatrix}.$$

What is the expected value of the strategies $\begin{bmatrix} .9 & .1 \end{bmatrix}$ and $\begin{bmatrix} .6 \\ .4 \end{bmatrix}$? We see that

$$\begin{bmatrix} .9 & .1 \end{bmatrix} \begin{bmatrix} -\frac{1}{2} & \frac{5}{2} \\ 1 & -\frac{3}{2} \end{bmatrix} \begin{bmatrix} .6 \\ .4 \end{bmatrix} = \begin{bmatrix} .63 \end{bmatrix}.$$

We note that multiplying each element in the payoff matrix by 2 and adding 4 gives the matrix

$$\begin{bmatrix} 3 & 9 \\ 6 & 1 \end{bmatrix},$$

which with the preceding strategies gives the expected value 5.26 (see the solution to Example 4). Multiplying each element of the payoff matrix by 2 and adding 4 to each element produces the same effect on the expected value:

$$5.26 = 2(.63) + 4.$$

Practice Problems 9.2

1. Suppose that the payoff matrix of a game is

$$\begin{bmatrix} 4 & -2 \\ -3 & 1 \end{bmatrix}.$$

Suppose that R plays the strategy $\begin{bmatrix} .6 & .4 \end{bmatrix}$. Which of the two strategies $\begin{bmatrix} .5 \\ .5 \end{bmatrix}$ or $\begin{bmatrix} .7 \\ .3 \end{bmatrix}$ is better for C?

2. Answer the question in Problem 1 for the game whose payoff matrix is

$$\begin{bmatrix} 9 & 3 \\ 2 & 6 \end{bmatrix}.$$

(This matrix is obtained by adding 5 to each entry of the matrix in Problem 1.)

EXERCISES 9.2

1. Suppose that a game has payoff matrix

$$\begin{bmatrix} 3 & -1 \\ -7 & 5 \end{bmatrix}.$$

Calculate the expected values for the following strategies and determine which of the following four situations is most advantageous to R.

(a) R plays $\begin{bmatrix} .5 & .5 \end{bmatrix}$, C plays $\begin{bmatrix} .5 \\ .5 \end{bmatrix}$.

(b) R plays $\begin{bmatrix} 1 & 0 \end{bmatrix}$, C plays $\begin{bmatrix} .5 \\ .5 \end{bmatrix}$.

(c) R plays $\begin{bmatrix} .3 & .7 \end{bmatrix}$, C plays $\begin{bmatrix} .6 \\ .4 \end{bmatrix}$.

(d) R plays $\begin{bmatrix} .75 & .25 \end{bmatrix}$, C plays $\begin{bmatrix} .2 \\ .8 \end{bmatrix}$.

2. Suppose that a game has payoff matrix

$$\begin{bmatrix} 1 & 0 & 2 \\ -1 & 2 & 0 \\ 0 & -1 & -1 \end{bmatrix}.$$

Calculate the expected values for the following strategies and determine which of the following four situations is most advantageous to C.

(a) R plays $\begin{bmatrix} 1 & 0 & 0 \end{bmatrix}$, C plays $\begin{bmatrix} .5 \\ .4 \\ .1 \end{bmatrix}$.

(b) R plays $\begin{bmatrix} .3 & .3 & .4 \end{bmatrix}$, C plays $\begin{bmatrix} .4 \\ .4 \\ .2 \end{bmatrix}$.

(c) R plays $\begin{bmatrix} 0 & .5 & .5 \end{bmatrix}$, C plays $\begin{bmatrix} .4 \\ 0 \\ .6 \end{bmatrix}$.

(d) R plays $\begin{bmatrix} .1 & .1 & .8 \end{bmatrix}$, C plays $\begin{bmatrix} .2 \\ .2 \\ .6 \end{bmatrix}$.

3. **Inspector's Strategy** Refer to Example 3. Suppose that the inspector changes his strategy and visits plant B 80% of the time. How much is Acme's average fine per day?

4. **Inspector's Strategy** Refer to Example 3. Suppose that the inspector visits plant B 30% of the time. How much is Acme's average fine per day?

5. **A Letter Game** Suppose that two players, R and C, write down letters of the alphabet. If both write vowels or both write consonants, then there is no payment to either player. If R writes a vowel and C writes a consonant, then C pays R \$2. If R writes a consonant and C writes a vowel, then R pays C \$1. Suppose that R chooses a consonant 75% of the plays and C chooses a vowel 40% of the plays. What is the average loss (or gain) of R per play?

6. **Flood Insurance** A small business owner must decide whether to carry flood insurance. She may insure her business for \$2 million for \$100,000, \$1 million for \$50,000, or \$.5 million for \$30,000. Her business is worth \$2 million. There is a flood serious enough to destroy her business an average of once every 10 years. In order to save insurance premiums, she decides each year on a probabilistic basis how much insurance to carry. She chooses \$2 million 20% of the time, \$1 million 20% of the time, \$.5 million 20% of the time, and no insurance 40% of the time. What is her average annual loss?

7. Two players, Robert and Carol, play a game with payoff matrix (to Robert)

$$\begin{bmatrix} 3 & -1 \\ -2 & 2 \end{bmatrix}.$$

Is the game strictly determined? Why?
   Suppose Robert has strategy $\begin{bmatrix} .3 & .7 \end{bmatrix}$. The opponents agree that the game should be fair. Is it possible for this to be a fair game? What would Carol's strategy have to be?

8. Two players, Robert and Carol, play a game with payoff matrix (to Robert)

$$\begin{bmatrix} 3 & -1 \\ -2 & 2 \end{bmatrix}.$$

Is the game strictly determined? Why?
   Suppose Robert has strategy $\begin{bmatrix} .7 & .3 \end{bmatrix}$. The opponents agree that the game should be fair. Is it possible for this to be a fair game? What would Carol's strategy have to be?

9. Two players, Robert and Carol, play a game with payoff matrix (to Robert)

$$\begin{bmatrix} 5 & -1 \\ -2 & 2 \end{bmatrix}.$$

Is the game strictly determined? Why?
   Suppose Robert has strategy $\begin{bmatrix} .7 & .3 \end{bmatrix}$. The opponents agree that the game should be fair. Is it possible for this to be a fair game? What would Carol's strategy have to be?

10. Two players, Robert and Carol, play a game with payoff matrix (to Robert)

$$\begin{bmatrix} 5 & -1 \\ -2 & 2 \end{bmatrix}.$$

Is the game strictly determined? Why?
   Suppose Robert has strategy $\begin{bmatrix} .3 & .7 \end{bmatrix}$. The opponents agree that the game should be fair. Is it possible for this to be a fair game? What would Carol's strategy have to be?

11. Assume two players, Renée and Carlos, play a game with the following payoff matrix (to Renée):

$$\begin{bmatrix} 1 & 2 & 4 \\ 1 & 0 & 5 \\ 0 & 1 & -1 \end{bmatrix}.$$

Is the game strictly determined? Determine the strategy for each player. What is the value of the game? Is the game fair?

12. The two players of Exercise 11, Renée and Carlos, play the game again, but this time the payoff matrix (to Renée) is

$$\begin{bmatrix} -3 & -2 & 6 \\ 2 & 0 & 2 \\ 5 & -2 & -4 \end{bmatrix}.$$

(a) Is the game strictly determined? Determine the strategy for each player.

(b) Is the game fair? Why?

Solutions to Practice Problems 9.2

1. If C plays $\begin{bmatrix} .5 \\ .5 \end{bmatrix}$, the expected value (to R) is

$$\begin{bmatrix} .6 & .4 \end{bmatrix} \begin{bmatrix} 4 & -2 \\ -3 & 1 \end{bmatrix} \begin{bmatrix} .5 \\ .5 \end{bmatrix} = \begin{bmatrix} 1.2 & -.8 \end{bmatrix} \begin{bmatrix} .5 \\ .5 \end{bmatrix} = \begin{bmatrix} .2 \end{bmatrix}.$$

If C plays $\begin{bmatrix} .7 \\ .3 \end{bmatrix}$, the expected value (to R) is

$$\begin{bmatrix} .6 & .4 \end{bmatrix} \begin{bmatrix} 4 & -2 \\ -3 & 1 \end{bmatrix} \begin{bmatrix} .7 \\ .3 \end{bmatrix} = \begin{bmatrix} 1.2 & -.8 \end{bmatrix} \begin{bmatrix} .7 \\ .3 \end{bmatrix} = \begin{bmatrix} .6 \end{bmatrix}.$$

Thus in the first case R gains an average of .2 per play, whereas in the second R gains .6. Since C wishes to minimize R's winnings, C should clearly play the first strategy.

2. The answer is the same as in Problem 1, since the new expected values will be 5 more than the original expected values and the first strategy will still be better for C.

9.3 Determining Optimal Mixed Strategies

As we have seen, each choice of strategies by R and C results in an expected value, representing the average payoff to R per play. In this section we shall give a method for choosing the best strategies. Let us begin by clarifying our notion of optimality.

DEFINITION To every choice of a strategy for R there is a best counterstrategy—that is, a strategy for C that results in the least expected value e. An **optimal mixed strategy for R** is one for which the expected value against C's best counterstrategy is as large as possible.

In a similar way we can define the optimal strategy for C.

DEFINITION To every choice of a strategy for C there is a best counterstrategy—that is, a strategy for R that results in the largest expected value e. An **optimal mixed strategy for C** is one for which the expected value against R's best counterstrategy is as small as possible.

It is most surprising that the optimal strategies for R and C in a non-strictly determined game may be determined using linear programming. To see how this is done, let us consider a particular problem.

EXAMPLE 1

Games as linear programs Suppose that a game has payoff matrix

$$\begin{bmatrix} 5 & 3 \\ 1 & 4 \end{bmatrix}.$$

Reduce the determination of an optimal strategy for R to a linear programming problem. *Note*: This game is not strictly determined. (Why?)

Solution Suppose that R plays the strategy $\begin{bmatrix} r_1 & r_2 \end{bmatrix}$. What is C's best counterstrategy? If C plays $\begin{bmatrix} c_1 \\ c_2 \end{bmatrix}$, then the expected value of the game is

$$\begin{bmatrix} r_1 & r_2 \end{bmatrix} \begin{bmatrix} 5 & 3 \\ 1 & 4 \end{bmatrix} \begin{bmatrix} c_1 \\ c_2 \end{bmatrix} = \begin{bmatrix} 5r_1 + r_2 & 3r_1 + 4r_2 \end{bmatrix} \begin{bmatrix} c_1 \\ c_2 \end{bmatrix}$$

$$= \begin{bmatrix} (5r_1 + r_2)c_1 + (3r_1 + 4r_2)c_2 \end{bmatrix}.$$

If C pursues his best counterstrategy, then he will try to minimize the expected value of the game. That is, C will try to minimize

$$(5r_1 + r_2)c_1 + (3r_1 + 4r_2)c_2.$$

Since $c_1 \geq 0$, $c_2 \geq 0$, $c_1 + c_2 = 1$, this expression has as its minimum value the smaller of the terms $5r_1 + r_2$ or $3r_1 + 4r_2$. That is, if $5r_1 + r_2$ is the smaller, then C should choose the strategy $c_1 = 1$, $c_2 = 0$; whereas if $3r_1 + 4r_2$ is the smaller, then C should choose the strategy $c_1 = 0$, $c_2 = 1$. In any case the expected value of the game if C adopts his best counterstrategy is the smaller of $5r_1 + r_2$ and $3r_1 + 4r_2$. The goal of R is to maximize this expected value. In other words, the mathematical problem R faces is this:

Maximize the minimum of $5r_1 + r_2$ and $3r_1 + 4r_2$,

where $r_1 \geq 0$, $r_2 \geq 0$, $r_1 + r_2 = 1$.

Let v denote the minimum of $5r_1 + r_2$ and $3r_1 + 4r_2$. Clearly, $v > 0$. Then

$$\begin{aligned} 5r_1 + r_2 &\geq v \\ 3r_1 + 4r_2 &\geq v \end{aligned} \tag{1}$$

Maximizing v is the same as minimizing $1/v$. Moreover, the inequalities (1) may be rewritten in the form

$$5\frac{r_1}{v} + \frac{r_2}{v} \geq 1$$

$$3\frac{r_1}{v} + 4\frac{r_2}{v} \geq 1 \tag{2}$$

Moreover, since $r_1 \geq 0$, $r_2 \geq 0$, and $r_1 + r_2 = 1$, we see that

$$\frac{r_1}{v} \geq 0, \qquad \frac{r_2}{v} \geq 0, \qquad \frac{r_1}{v} + \frac{r_2}{v} = \frac{1}{v}. \tag{3}$$

This suggests that we introduce new variables:

$$y_1 = \frac{r_1}{v}, \qquad y_2 = \frac{r_2}{v}.$$

Then (3) and (2) may be rewritten as

$$\begin{aligned} y_1 + y_2 &= \frac{1}{v} \\ 5y_1 + y_2 &\geq 1 \\ 3y_1 + 4y_2 &\geq 1 \\ y_1 \geq 0, \quad y_2 &\geq 0 \end{aligned}$$

We wish to minimize $1/v$, so we may finally state our original question in terms of a linear programming problem: Minimize $y_1 + y_2$ subject to the constraints

$$\begin{cases} 5y_1 + y_2 \geq 1 \\ 3y_1 + 4y_2 \geq 1 \\ y_1 \geq 0, \quad y_2 \geq 0. \end{cases}$$

Now Try Exercise 1

In terms of the solution to this linear programming problem we may calculate R's optimal strategy as follows:

$$r_1 = vy_1 \qquad r_2 = vy_2, \qquad \text{where} \quad v = \frac{1}{y_1 + y_2}.$$

In the preceding derivation it was essential that the entries of the matrix were positive numbers, for this is how we derived that $v > 0$. The same reasoning used in Example 1 can be used in general to convert the determination of R's optimal strategy to a linear programming problem, *provided that the payoff matrix has positive entries*. If the payoff matrix does not have positive entries, then just add a large positive constant to each of the entries so as to give a matrix with positive entries. The new matrix will have the same optimal strategy as the original one. However, since all its entries are positive, we may use the previous reasoning to reduce determination of the optimal strategy to a linear programming problem.

Optimal Strategy for R Let the payoff matrix of a game be

$$\begin{bmatrix} a_{11} & a_{12} & \cdots & a_{1n} \\ a_{21} & a_{22} & \cdots & a_{2n} \\ \vdots & \vdots & & \vdots \\ a_{m1} & a_{m2} & \cdots & a_{mn} \end{bmatrix},$$

where all entries of the matrix are positive numbers. Let $y_1, y_2, \ldots, y_m$ be chosen so as to minimize

$$y_1 + y_2 + \cdots + y_m$$

subject to the constraints

$$\begin{cases} y_1 \geq 0, \ y_2 \geq 0, \ \ldots, \ y_m \geq 0 \\ a_{11}y_1 + a_{21}y_2 + \cdots + a_{m1}y_m \geq 1 \\ a_{12}y_1 + a_{22}y_2 + \cdots + a_{m2}y_m \geq 1 \\ \quad\quad\quad \vdots \\ a_{1n}y_1 + a_{2n}y_2 + \cdots + a_{mn}y_m \geq 1. \end{cases}$$

Let

$$v = \frac{1}{y_1 + y_2 + \cdots + y_m}.$$

Then an optimal strategy for R is $\begin{bmatrix} r_1 & r_2 & \cdots & r_m \end{bmatrix}$, where

$$r_1 = vy_1, \quad r_2 = vy_2, \quad \ldots, \quad r_m = vy_m.$$

Furthermore, if C adopts the best counterstrategy, then the expected value is v.

Note that the determination of $y_1, y_2, \ldots, y_m$ is a linear programming problem whose solution can be obtained using either the method of Chapter 3 (if $m = 2$) or the simplex method of Chapter 4 (any m). The next example illustrates the preceding result.

EXAMPLE 2

Finding the optimal strategy for R Suppose that a game has payoff matrix

$$\begin{bmatrix} 5 & 3 \\ 1 & 4 \end{bmatrix}.$$

(a) Determine an optimal strategy for R.

(b) Determine the expected payoff to R if C uses the best counterstrategy.

Solution **(a)** The associated linear programming problem asks us to minimize $y_1 + y_2$ subject to the constraints

$$\begin{cases} y_1 \geq 0, \quad y_2 \geq 0 \\ 5y_1 + y_2 \geq 1 \\ 3y_1 + 4y_2 \geq 1. \end{cases}$$

In Fig. 1 we have sketched the feasible set for this problem and evaluated the objective function at each vertex.

The minimum value of $y_1 + y_2$ is $\frac{5}{17}$ and occurs when $y_1 = \frac{3}{17}$ and $y_2 = \frac{2}{17}$. Further,

$$v = \frac{1}{y_1 + y_2} = \frac{1}{\frac{5}{17}} = \frac{17}{5}$$

$$r_1 = vy_1 = \frac{17}{5} \cdot \frac{3}{17} = \frac{3}{5}$$

$$r_2 = vy_2 = \frac{17}{5} \cdot \frac{2}{17} = \frac{2}{5}$$

Thus the optimal strategy for R is $\begin{bmatrix} \frac{3}{5} & \frac{2}{5} \end{bmatrix}$.

(b) The expected value against the best counterstrategy is $v = \frac{17}{5}$. ∎

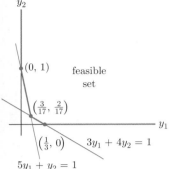

Figure 1

Vertex	$y_1 + y_2$
$(0, 1)$	1
$\left(\frac{3}{17}, \frac{2}{17}\right)$	$\frac{5}{17}$
$\left(\frac{1}{3}, 0\right)$	$\frac{1}{3}$

There is a similar linear programming technique for determining the optimal strategy for C.

Optimal Strategy for C Let the payoff matrix of a game be

$$\begin{bmatrix} a_{11} & a_{12} & \cdots & a_{1n} \\ a_{21} & a_{22} & \cdots & a_{2n} \\ \vdots & \vdots & & \vdots \\ a_{m1} & a_{m2} & \cdots & a_{mn} \end{bmatrix},$$

where all entries of the matrix are positive numbers. Let $z_1, z_2, \ldots, z_n$ be chosen so as to maximize

$$z_1 + z_2 + \cdots + z_n$$

subject to the constraints

$$\begin{cases} z_1 \geq 0, \quad z_2 \geq 0, \quad \ldots, \quad z_n \geq 0 \\ a_{11}z_1 + a_{12}z_2 + \cdots + a_{1n}z_n \leq 1 \\ a_{21}z_1 + a_{22}z_2 + \cdots + a_{2n}z_n \leq 1 \\ \quad\quad\quad \vdots \\ a_{m1}z_1 + a_{m2}z_2 + \cdots + a_{mn}z_n \leq 1. \end{cases}$$

Let $v = 1/(z_1 + z_2 + \cdots + z_n)$. Then an optimal strategy for C is

$$\begin{bmatrix} c_1 \\ c_2 \\ \vdots \\ c_n \end{bmatrix},$$

where $c_1 = vz_1, c_2 = vz_2, \ldots, c_n = vz_n$.

EXAMPLE 3

Finding the optimal strategy for C   Determine the optimal strategy for C for the game with payoff matrix

$$\begin{bmatrix} 5 & 3 \\ 1 & 4 \end{bmatrix}.$$

Solution   We must maximize $z_1 + z_2$ subject to the constraints

$$\begin{cases} z_1 \geq 0, \quad z_2 \geq 0 \\ 5z_1 + 3z_2 \leq 1 \\ z_1 + 4z_2 \leq 1. \end{cases}$$

The solution is as follows: The maximum value is $\frac{5}{17}$ and it occurs when $z_1 = \frac{1}{17}$, $z_2 = \frac{4}{17}$. Therefore, $v = \frac{17}{5}$, and the optimal strategy for C is $\begin{bmatrix} c_1 \\ c_2 \end{bmatrix}$, where

$$c_1 = vz_1 = \frac{17}{5} \cdot \frac{1}{17} = \frac{1}{5}$$

$$c_2 = vz_2 = \frac{17}{5} \cdot \frac{4}{17} = \frac{4}{5}.$$

Now Try Exercise 3   ∎

Notice that in both Examples 2 and 3 we obtained $v = \frac{17}{5}$. This was not just a coincidence. This phenomenon always occurs, and the number v is called the **value** of the game. An easy computation shows that for the matrix of Examples 2 and 3, when R and C each use their optimal strategies, the expected value is $v = \frac{17}{5}$. That is,

$$\begin{bmatrix} \frac{3}{5} & \frac{2}{5} \end{bmatrix} \begin{bmatrix} 5 & 3 \\ 1 & 4 \end{bmatrix} \begin{bmatrix} \frac{1}{5} \\ \frac{4}{5} \end{bmatrix} = \begin{bmatrix} \frac{17}{5} \end{bmatrix}.$$

Let us briefly reconsider the calculations of optimal strategies for R and C. We begin in every case with the matrix for the game, A. Let us assume that A is an $m \times n$ matrix and that each entry of A is a positive number. To find the optimal strategy for C, we find the matrix Z that maximizes the objective function EZ subject to the constraints $AZ \leq B$ and $Z \geq \mathbf{0}$, where

$$E = \underbrace{\begin{bmatrix} 1 & 1 & 1 & \cdots & 1 \end{bmatrix}}_{n \text{ entries}}$$

$$Z = \begin{bmatrix} z_1 \\ z_2 \\ \vdots \\ z_n \end{bmatrix} \quad \text{and} \quad B = \left.\begin{bmatrix} 1 \\ 1 \\ \vdots \\ 1 \end{bmatrix}\right\} m \text{ entries.}$$

The dual of the linear programming problem associated with finding an optimal strategy for C is to find the matrix Y that minimizes the objective function $B^T Y$ subject to the constraints $A^T Y \geq E^T$ and $Y \geq \mathbf{0}$, where

$$Y = \begin{bmatrix} y_1 \\ y_2 \\ \vdots \\ y_m \end{bmatrix}.$$

But this is exactly the problem of finding an optimal strategy for R.

The problem of finding the optimal strategy for R is a linear programming problem whose dual is the problem of finding an optimal strategy for C, and vice versa.

Our previous work with duality leads us to conclude the following:

1. If there exists an optimal strategy for R, then there exists an optimal strategy for C, and vice versa.

2. The minimum of the objective function $y_1 + y_2 + \cdots + y_m$ and the maximum of the objective function $z_1 + z_2 + \cdots + z_n$ are equal—since the linear programming problems are duals of each other. Hence, the value of the optimal strategy for C is the same as the value of the optimal strategy for R, that is,

$$\frac{1}{z_1 + z_2 + \cdots + z_n} = \frac{1}{y_1 + y_2 + \cdots + y_m}.$$

EXAMPLE 4

Optimal strategies when matrix entries are not positive Determine the optimal strategies for R and C for the game with payoff matrix

$$\begin{bmatrix} 1 & -1 \\ -3 & 0 \end{bmatrix}.$$

Solution We cannot apply our technique directly, since only one of the entries of the given matrix is a positive number. However, if we add 4 to each entry, then the new matrix will be

$$\begin{bmatrix} 5 & 3 \\ 1 & 4 \end{bmatrix},$$

which does have all positive entries. These two payoff matrices have the same optimal strategies. The only difference is that the values in the new matrix are 4 more than that of the given matrix. Now, the optimal strategies and the value of a game with the new matrix were found in Examples 2 and 3 to be

$$\begin{bmatrix} \frac{3}{5} & \frac{2}{5} \end{bmatrix}, \qquad \begin{bmatrix} \frac{1}{5} \\ \frac{4}{5} \end{bmatrix}, \qquad \text{and} \qquad \frac{17}{5}.$$

Therefore, the optimal strategies for the given matrix are

$$\begin{bmatrix} \frac{3}{5} & \frac{2}{5} \end{bmatrix} \qquad \text{and} \qquad \begin{bmatrix} \frac{1}{5} \\ \frac{4}{5} \end{bmatrix},$$

Now Try Exercise 5 and the value is $\frac{17}{5} - 4 = -\frac{3}{5}$. ■

EXAMPLE 5

Finding optimal strategies by the simplex method Use the simplex method and the resulting tableau to determine the optimal strategies for the game of Example 4.

Solution As in Example 4, add 4 to each entry to get a matrix with positive entries, and set up the tableau for finding the optimal strategy for C. (We choose this linear programming problem because it is a maximization problem.) The transformed matrix A is

$$\begin{bmatrix} 5 & 3 \\ 1 & 4 \end{bmatrix}.$$

To find the optimal strategy for C, we need to find the values of z_1 and z_2 that maximize $z_1 + z_2$ subject to the constraints

$$\begin{cases} 5z_1 + 3z_2 \le 1 \\ z_1 + 4z_2 \le 1 \\ z_1 \ge 0, \quad z_2 \ge 0. \end{cases}$$

We set up the tableau using slack variables t and u and display the initial and final tableaux:

	z_1	z_2	t	u	M	
t	5	3	1	0	0	1
u	1	4	0	1	0	1
M	-1	-1	0	0	1	0

	z_1	z_2	t	u	M	
z_1	1	0	$\frac{4}{17}$	$-\frac{3}{17}$	0	$\frac{1}{17}$
z_2	0	1	$-\frac{1}{17}$	$\frac{5}{17}$	0	$\frac{4}{17}$
M	0	0	$\frac{3}{17}$	$\frac{2}{17}$	1	$\frac{5}{17}$

Thus the solution is $z_1 = \frac{1}{17}$, $z_2 = \frac{4}{17}$ with $M = z_1 + z_2 = \frac{5}{17}$. Then $v = \frac{17}{5}$, and the optimal strategy for C is

$$\begin{bmatrix} vz_1 \\ vz_2 \end{bmatrix} = \begin{bmatrix} \frac{1}{5} \\ \frac{4}{5} \end{bmatrix}.$$

This agrees with previous solutions, and the value of this game is $\frac{17}{5}$, which is 4 more than the original game. Thus the value of the game is $\frac{17}{5} - 4 = -\frac{3}{5}$.

But the optimal strategy for R can be read from the final tableau since y_1 and y_2 are the values of the variables in the dual of the problem we solved. So $y_1 = t = \frac{3}{17}$, $y_2 = u = \frac{2}{17}$, and $M = \frac{5}{17}$. Then $v = \frac{17}{5}$ and the optimal strategy for R is $\begin{bmatrix} vy_1 & vy_2 \end{bmatrix} = \begin{bmatrix} \frac{3}{5} & \frac{2}{5} \end{bmatrix}$.

Now Try Exercise 11

We actually have a very useful fact.

> **Fundamental Theorem of Game Theory**   Every two-person zero-sum game has a solution.

Verification of the Fundamental Theorem of Game Theory If the given two-person game has a saddle point, then the game is strictly determined, and optimal strategies for R and C are given by the position of the saddle point.

If the game is not strictly determined, then let us assume that the $m \times n$ payoff matrix A has only positive entries. We let B be an $m \times 1$ column matrix in which each entry is 1, and let E be a $1 \times n$ row matrix of 1's. Then

1. There is an optimal feasible solution to the problem:

$$\text{Maximize } M = EZ \text{ subject to } AZ \le B \text{ and } Z \ge \mathbf{0}. \qquad \text{(P)}$$

2. There is an optimal feasible solution to the problem:

$$\text{Minimize } M = B^T Y \text{ subject to } A^T Y \ge E^T \text{ and } Y \ge \mathbf{0}. \qquad \text{(D)}$$

3. The solutions to (P) and (D) give a solution to the game.

To see that characteristics 1 and 2 hold, we note that there is a feasible solution for the inequalities of the primal problem (P). The $n \times 1$ matrix of zeros, $Z = \mathbf{0}$, satisfies $AZ \le B$. Also, there is a feasible solution for the inequalities of the dual problem (D). This can be seen by noting that since every element of the matrix

A is positive, we can find an $m \times 1$ matrix $Y \geq \mathbf{0}$ with sufficiently large entries to guarantee that $A^T Y \geq E^T$. Since the inequalities of both (P) and (D) have a feasible solution, the fundamental theorem of duality (Chapter 4) tells us that both (P) and (D) have optimal feasible solutions.

Let Z^* and Y^* be optimal feasible solutions of (P) and (D), respectively. Say that

$$Z^* = \begin{bmatrix} z_1^* \\ z_2^* \\ \vdots \\ z_n^* \end{bmatrix} \quad \text{and} \quad Y^* = \begin{bmatrix} y_1^* \\ y_2^* \\ \vdots \\ y_m^* \end{bmatrix}.$$

The maximum for (P),

$$M = z_1^* + z_2^* + \cdots + z_n^*,$$

equals the minimum for (D),

$$M = y_1^* + y_2^* + \cdots + y_m^*,$$

and

$$AZ^* \leq B \quad \text{and} \quad A^T Y^* \geq E^T.$$

Recall that B is an $m \times 1$ matrix of 1's and E^T is an $n \times 1$ matrix of 1's.

M must be strictly greater than zero since at least one of the y_i^* must be > 0 in order for $A^T Y \geq E^T$ to hold. Therefore, $1/M$ is defined. We let

$$C = \begin{bmatrix} \dfrac{1}{M} z_1^* \\ \dfrac{1}{M} z_2^* \\ \vdots \\ \dfrac{1}{M} z_n^* \end{bmatrix} = \begin{bmatrix} c_1 \\ c_2 \\ \vdots \\ c_n \end{bmatrix}$$

and

$$R = \begin{bmatrix} \dfrac{1}{M} y_1^* & \dfrac{1}{M} y_2^* & \cdots & \dfrac{1}{M} y_m^* \end{bmatrix} = \begin{bmatrix} r_1 & r_2 & \cdots & r_m \end{bmatrix}.$$

Furthermore, C and R represent optimal strategies for players C and R, respectively. To verify that C and R are legitimate strategies, we note that since $M > 0$, $Z^* \geq \mathbf{0}$, and $Y^* \geq \mathbf{0}$, every entry in C and R is nonnegative. We only need to check that

$$c_1 + c_2 + \cdots + c_n = 1 \quad \text{and} \quad r_1 + r_2 + \cdots + r_m = 1.$$

This follows directly from the definitions of M, C, and R. ∎

Practice Problems 9.3

1. Determine the optimal strategy for C for the game with payoff matrix

$$\begin{bmatrix} 2 & 14 \\ 6 & 12 \\ 8 & 6 \end{bmatrix}.$$

2. Determine by inspection the optimal strategies for C for the games whose payoff matrices are given.

(a) $\begin{bmatrix} 0 & 12 \\ 4 & 10 \\ 6 & 4 \end{bmatrix}$ (b) $\begin{bmatrix} 6 & 0 \\ 4 & 3 \\ 8 & -1 \end{bmatrix}$

EXERCISES 9.3

1. Suppose that a game has payoff matrix

$$\begin{bmatrix} 1 & 6 \\ 4 & 3 \end{bmatrix}.$$

Reduce the determination of an optimal strategy for R into a linear programming problem. Just set up the problem showing the constraints and the objective function.

2. Suppose a game has a payoff matrix

$$\begin{bmatrix} 10 & 6 \\ 5 & 7 \end{bmatrix}.$$

Reduce the determination of an optimal strategy for R into a linear programming problem. Just set up the problem showing the constraints and the objective function.

In Exercises 3–8, determine optimal strategies for R and for C for the games whose payoff matrices are given.

3. $\begin{bmatrix} 2 & 4 \\ 5 & 3 \end{bmatrix}$ **4.** $\begin{bmatrix} 2 & 3 \\ 3 & 2 \end{bmatrix}$

5. $\begin{bmatrix} 3 & -6 \\ -5 & 4 \end{bmatrix}$ **6.** $\begin{bmatrix} 5 & 2 \\ 7 & 1 \end{bmatrix}$

7. $\begin{bmatrix} 4 & 1 \\ 2 & 4 \end{bmatrix}$ **8.** $\begin{bmatrix} 5 & -8 \\ 3 & 6 \end{bmatrix}$

In Exercises 9 and 10, determine optimal strategies for R for the games whose payoff matrices are given.

9. $\begin{bmatrix} 3 & 5 & -1 \\ 4 & -1 & 6 \end{bmatrix}$ **10.** $\begin{bmatrix} -2 & 1 & 0 \\ 2 & 0 & 1 \end{bmatrix}$

In Exercises 11 and 12, determine optimal strategies for C for the games whose payoff matrices are given.

11. $\begin{bmatrix} -3 & 1 \\ 4 & -1 \\ 1 & 0 \end{bmatrix}$ **12.** $\begin{bmatrix} 0 & 2 \\ 2 & -1 \\ 1 & 0 \end{bmatrix}$

13. Two players, Renée and Carlos, play a game with payoff matrix

$$\begin{bmatrix} 5 & -3 \\ -3 & 1 \end{bmatrix}.$$

Is the game strictly determined? Determine the optimal mixed strategy for each player. What is the value of the game? Explain.

14. Determine the optimal mixed strategy for each player, given the payoff matrix

$$\begin{bmatrix} 4 & -2 \\ -3 & 1 \end{bmatrix}.$$

Give the value of the game.

15. Smuggler's Strategy A rumrunner attempts to smuggle rum into a country having two ports. Each day the coast guard is able to patrol only one of the ports. If the rumrunner enters via an unpatrolled port, he will be able to sell his rum for a profit of $7000. If he enters the first port and it is patrolled that day, he is certain to be caught and will have his rum (worth $1000) confiscated and be fined $1000. If he enters the second port (which is big and crowded) and it is patrolled that day, he will have time to jettison his cargo and thereby escape a fine.

(a) What is the optimal strategy for the rumrunner?

(b) What is the optimal strategy for the coast guard?

(c) How profitable is rumrunning? That is, what is the value of the game?

16. Which Hand? Ralph puts a coin in one of his hands and Carl tries to guess which hand holds the coin. If Carl guesses incorrectly, he must pay Ralph $2. If Carl guesses correctly, then Ralph must pay him $3 if the coin was in the left hand and $1 if it was in the right.

(a) What is the optimal strategy for Ralph?

(b) What is the optimal strategy for Carl?

(c) Whom does this game favor?

17. Advertising Strategies The Carter Company can choose between two advertising strategies (I and II). Its most important competitor, Rosedale Associates, has a choice of three advertising strategies (a, b, c). The estimated payoff to Rosedale Associates away from the Carter Company is given by the payoff matrix

$$\begin{array}{c c} & \begin{array}{cc} \text{I} & \text{II} \end{array} \\ \begin{array}{c} a \\ b \\ c \end{array} & \begin{bmatrix} -2 & 1 \\ 2 & -3 \\ 1 & -2 \end{bmatrix}, \end{array}$$

where the entries represent thousands of dollars per week. Determine the optimal strategies for each company.

Solutions to Practice Problems 9.3

1. The associated linear programming problem is: Maximize $z_1 + z_2$ subject to the constraints

$$\begin{cases} z_1 \geq 0, \quad z_2 \geq 0. \\ 2z_1 + 14z_2 \leq 1 \\ 6z_1 + 12z_2 \leq 1 \\ 8z_1 + 6z_2 \leq 1. \end{cases}$$

In Fig. 2 we have sketched the feasible set and evaluated the objective function at each vertex. The maximum value of $z_1 + z_2$ is $\frac{4}{30}$, which is achieved at the vertex $\left(\frac{3}{30}, \frac{1}{30}\right)$. Therefore,

$$v = \frac{1}{z_1 + z_2} = \frac{1}{\frac{4}{30}} = \frac{30}{4}$$

$$c_1 = v \cdot z_1 = \frac{30}{4} \cdot \frac{3}{30} = \frac{3}{4}$$

$$c_2 = v \cdot z_2 = \frac{30}{4} \cdot \frac{1}{30} = \frac{1}{4}.$$

That is, the optimal strategy for C is $\begin{bmatrix} \frac{3}{4} \\ \frac{1}{4} \end{bmatrix}$.

2. (a) $\begin{bmatrix} \frac{3}{4} \\ \frac{1}{4} \end{bmatrix}$. If we add 2 to each entry, we obtain the payoff matrix of Problem 1, so these two games have the same optimal strategies.

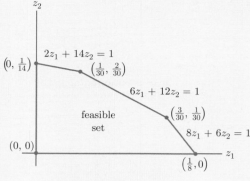

Vertex	$z_1 + z_2$
$(0,0)$	0
$\left(0, \frac{1}{14}\right)$	$\frac{1}{14}$
$\left(\frac{1}{30}, \frac{2}{30}\right)$	$\frac{3}{30}$
$\left(\frac{3}{30}, \frac{1}{30}\right)$	$\frac{4}{30}$
$\left(\frac{1}{8}, 0\right)$	$\frac{1}{8}$

Figure 2

(b) Always play column 2. This game is strictly determined and has the entry 3 as saddle point. It is a good idea always to check for a saddle point before looking for a mixed strategy.

CHAPTER SUMMARY

1. A *zero-sum* game is one in which a payoff to one player results in a loss of the same amount to the other player.

2. The entry in the ith row and jth column of a payoff matrix gives the payoff to the row player (equivalently, the loss to the column player) when the row player chooses row i and the column player chooses column j.

3. A *pure strategy* is one in which the player consistently chooses the same row or column. Strategies involving varied moves are called *mixed strategies*.

4. The *optimal pure strategy* for the row player is to choose the row whose least element is maximal. The optimal pure strategy for the column player is to choose the column whose greatest element is minimal.

5. A *saddle point* is an entry in a payoff matrix that is simultaneously the least element of its row and the greatest element of its column. A game need not have a saddle point. If a game has more than one saddle

point, then the saddle points are equal.

6. A game with a saddle point is called a *strictly determined game*. In a strictly determined game, the optimal pure strategy for each player is to choose a row or column containing a saddle point.

7. In a strictly determined game, if both players use optimal pure strategies, then the saddle point gives the payoff to the row player. The value of the saddle point is called the *value of the game*.

8. If a game is not strictly determined, then the players should use mixed strategies. A *mixed strategy* for the row player is a row matrix whose ith entry is the probability that the row player will choose row i on any repetition of the game. A mixed strategy for the column player is a column matrix whose jth entry is the probability that the column player will choose column j on any repetition of the game.

9. The expected value of a pair of mixed strategies

$$R = \begin{bmatrix} r_1 & r_2 & \cdots & r_m \end{bmatrix} \quad \text{and} \quad C = \begin{bmatrix} c_1 \\ c_2 \\ \vdots \\ c_n \end{bmatrix}$$

is the average payoff per game to the row player if these mixed strategies are used. The expected value of the pair R, C of mixed strategies is found by computing the product RAC, where A is the payoff matrix for the game.

10. An *optimal mixed strategy* for the row player is one for which the column player's best counterstrategy results in the greatest possible expected value. Similarly, an optimal mixed strategy for the column player is one for which the row player's best counterstrategy results in the least possible expected value. Optimal mixed strategies for each player are found by solving a pair of dual linear programming problems, as described on pages 455–456.

REVIEW OF FUNDAMENTAL CONCEPTS

1. What do the individual entries of a payoff matrix represent?

2. What is the difference between a pure strategy and a mixed strategy?

3. What is a zero-sum game?

4. Describe the optimal pure strategies for R and for C.

5. When is an entry of a payoff matrix a saddle point?

6. What is a strictly determined game and what is its value?

7. What is the expected value of a pair of mixed strategies, and how is it computed?

8. What is meant by the optimal mixed strategies of R and C, and how are they computed?

KEY FORMULAS

Optimal Pure Strategy for R:

1. For each row of the payoff matrix, determine the least element.

2. Choose the row for which this is as large as possible.

Optimal Pure Strategy for C:

1. For each column of the payoff matrix, determine the largest element.

2. Choose the column for which this is as small as possible.

Value of a Game: If the game is strictly determined, there is a saddle point and the saddle point is $v =$ value of the game.

Let

$$A = \begin{bmatrix} a_{11} & a_{12} & \cdots & a_{1n} \\ a_{21} & a_{22} & \cdots & a_{2n} \\ \vdots & \vdots & & \vdots \\ a_{m1} & a_{m2} & \cdots & a_{mn} \end{bmatrix}$$

be the payoff matrix of a game.

Expected Value of a Game with Mixed Strategies

$$R = \begin{bmatrix} r_1 & r_2 & \cdots & r_m \end{bmatrix} \quad \text{and} \quad C = \begin{bmatrix} c_1 \\ c_2 \\ \vdots \\ c_n \end{bmatrix} :$$

$$\begin{bmatrix} e \end{bmatrix} = RAC$$

In the linear programming form of the mixed strategy problem for a game with payoff matrix A, if the solution is $y_1, y_2, \ldots, y_m$ for the minimization problem, then the value

$$v = \frac{1}{y_1 + y_2 + \cdots + y_m}$$

and the optimal strategy for R is $r_1 = vy_1$, $r_2 = vy_2$, $\ldots, r_m = vy_m$.

If the solution is $z_1, z_2, \ldots, z_n$ for the maximization problem, then the value

$$v = \frac{1}{z_1 + z_2 + \cdots + z_n}$$

and the optimal strategy for C is $c_1 = vz_1$, $c_2 = vz_2$, $\ldots, c_n = vz_n$.

SUPPLEMENTARY EXERCISES

In Exercises 1–4, state whether or not the games having the given payoff matrices are strictly determined. If so, give the optimal pure strategies and the values of the strategies.

1. $\begin{bmatrix} 5 & -1 & 1 \\ -3 & 5 & 1 \\ 4 & 3 & 2 \end{bmatrix}$ **2.** $\begin{bmatrix} 1 & 2 & 3 \\ 3 & 2 & 1 \end{bmatrix}$

3. $\begin{bmatrix} 0 & 1 \\ 1 & 0 \\ 2 & -1 \end{bmatrix}$ **4.** $\begin{bmatrix} 2 & 1 & 2 \\ -1 & 0 & 3 \\ 4 & 1 & -4 \end{bmatrix}$

In Exercises 5–8, determine the expected value of each pair of mixed strategies for the given payoff matrix.

5. $\begin{bmatrix} \frac{3}{4} & \frac{1}{4} \end{bmatrix}$, $\begin{bmatrix} \frac{1}{3} \\ \frac{2}{3} \end{bmatrix}$; $\begin{bmatrix} 0 & 24 \\ 12 & -36 \end{bmatrix}$

6. $\begin{bmatrix} \frac{1}{2} & \frac{1}{2} \end{bmatrix}$, $\begin{bmatrix} \frac{1}{3} \\ \frac{1}{3} \\ \frac{1}{3} \end{bmatrix}$; $\begin{bmatrix} -6 & 6 & 0 \\ 0 & -12 & 24 \end{bmatrix}$

7. $\begin{bmatrix} .2 & .3 & .5 \end{bmatrix}$, $\begin{bmatrix} .4 \\ .6 \end{bmatrix}$; $\begin{bmatrix} 1 & 0 \\ -3 & 1 \\ 0 & 5 \end{bmatrix}$

8. $\begin{bmatrix} .1 & .1 & .8 \end{bmatrix}$, $\begin{bmatrix} .4 \\ .3 \\ .3 \end{bmatrix}$; $\begin{bmatrix} 0 & 1 & 3 \\ -1 & 0 & 2 \\ -3 & -2 & 0 \end{bmatrix}$

Determine the optimal strategies for R and for C for the games with the payoff matrices of Exercises 9 and 10.

9. $\begin{bmatrix} -3 & 4 \\ 2 & -2 \end{bmatrix}$ **10.** $\begin{bmatrix} 3 & -6 \\ -4 & 4 \end{bmatrix}$

11. Determine the optimal strategy for R for the game with payoff matrix
$$\begin{bmatrix} 5 & -2 & 0 \\ 1 & 4 & 1 \end{bmatrix}.$$

12. Determine the optimal strategy for C for the game with payoff matrix
$$\begin{bmatrix} 1 & 3 \\ 3 & 1 \\ 4 & 2 \end{bmatrix}.$$

13. A Card Matching Game Ruth and Carol play the following game. Both have two cards, a two and a six. Each puts one of her cards on the table. If both put down the same denomination, Ruth pays Carol $3. Otherwise, Carol pays Ruth as many dollars as the denomination of Carol's card.

(a) Find the optimal strategies for Ruth and Carol.

(b) Whom does this game favor?

14. Investment Strategy An investor is considering purchasing one of three stocks. Stock A is regarded as conservative, stock B as speculative, and stock C as highly risky. If the economic growth during the coming year is strong, then stock A should increase in value by $3000, stock B by $6000, and stock C by $15,000. If the economic growth during the next year is average, then stock A should increase in value by $2000, stock B by $2000, and stock C by $1000. If the economic growth is weak, then stock A should increase in value by $1000 and stocks B and C decrease in value by $3000 and $10,000, respectively.

(a) Set up the 3×3 payoff matrix showing the investing gains for the possible stock purchases and levels of economic growth.

(b) What is the investor's optimal strategy?

Conceptual Exercises

15. Show that in a two-person game with payoff matrix
$$\begin{bmatrix} a_{11} & a_{12} \\ a_{21} & a_{22} \end{bmatrix}$$
the only games that are *not* strictly determined are those for which either
$$a_{11} > a_{12}, \quad a_{11} > a_{21}, \quad a_{21} < a_{22}, \quad a_{12} < a_{22}$$
or
$$a_{11} < a_{12}, \quad a_{11} < a_{21}, \quad a_{21} > a_{22}, \quad a_{12} > a_{22}$$

16. In Practice Problem 1 in Section 9.3, we determined the optimal strategy for C in a game with payoff matrix
$$\begin{bmatrix} 2 & 14 \\ 6 & 12 \\ 8 & 6 \end{bmatrix}$$
to be
$$\begin{bmatrix} 3/4 \\ 1/4 \end{bmatrix}.$$
Consider the effect of changing the entry in the first row, first column of the payoff matrix to $2 + h$, where h is any positive integer. For what values of h does the optimal strategy for C remain the same?

17. Assume the payoff matrix for a two-person game is given by
$$\begin{bmatrix} a_{11} & a_{12} \\ a_{21} & a_{22} \end{bmatrix}.$$
Then assume that R uses a strategy $\begin{bmatrix} r & 1-r \end{bmatrix}$. If C chooses column 1, then R can expect a return of $a_{11}r + a_{21}(1 - r)$. If C chooses column 2, then R can expect a return of $a_{12}r + a_{22}(1 - r)$.

(a) Explain why the intersection of the lines

$$y = a_{11}r + a_{21}(1 - r)$$

and

$$y = a_{12}r + a_{22}(1 - r)$$

gives the value of r that is best for R.

(b) How would you find the best strategy for C using a comparable argument?

18. Using the technique of Exercise 17, find a general formula for the best strategy for R in terms of the entries in the payoff matrix.

CHAPTER TEST

1. Consider a game with payoff matrix $\begin{bmatrix} 5 & -1 & 6 \\ -2 & 5 & -8 \\ 8 & -10 & 5 \end{bmatrix}$.

   (a) What is the meaning of the entry 6 in the upper right?

   (b) What is the meaning of the entry -10 in the bottom row?

   (c) Is this game strictly determined? Why or why not?

2. Describe the difference between a pure strategy and a mixed strategy.

3. Each of the following is a payoff matrix for a strictly determined game. Give the value of the game and the optimal pure strategies for each player.

   (a) $\begin{bmatrix} -1 & 0 \\ 2 & -2 \\ 3 & 2 \end{bmatrix}$

   (b) $\begin{bmatrix} 0 & 2 & 4 \\ -4 & 0 & 3 \\ -2 & -3 & 0 \end{bmatrix}$

4. **A Numbers Game** Consider the following game. Each player chooses a number from 1 to 5. If the row player's number is higher, then he wins. If the column player's number is higher or if the two numbers match, then the column player wins. The loser must pay the winner as many dollars as the number chosen by the row player. Construct a payoff matrix for this game. Is the game strictly determined? If so, what is the value of the game? Which player would you rather be?

5. Suppose a game has payoff matrix $\begin{bmatrix} 2 & -2 & 3 \\ -1 & 1 & -3 \end{bmatrix}$.

   (a) Suppose the row player uses the mixed strategy $R = \begin{bmatrix} .4 & .6 \end{bmatrix}$ and the column player uses the mixed strategy $C = \begin{bmatrix} .3 \\ .5 \\ .2 \end{bmatrix}$. Calculate and interpret the expected value for this pair of mixed strategies.

   (b) If the row player uses the mixed strategy from part (a), then is the column player better off using the mixed strategy from part (a) or the mixed strategy $C = \begin{bmatrix} .4 \\ .1 \\ .5 \end{bmatrix}$?

6. Consider a game with payoff matrix $\begin{bmatrix} 0 & -1 \\ -4 & 5 \end{bmatrix}$.

   (a) Determine optimal mixed strategies for each player.

   (b) Whom does this game favor?

CHAPTER 9 | PROJECT

Simulating the Outcomes of Mixed-Strategy Games

A mixed strategy requires the use of a device that will randomly select a row (or column) of the payoff matrix subject to a specified probability. For instance, if the strategy for R is $\begin{bmatrix} .6 & .4 \end{bmatrix}$, the device should select the first row 60% of the time and select the second row 40% of the time. The TI-83/84 Plus calculator is well-suited to handle this task using the *randInt* function along with the *relational operators*.

Each time **randInt(1,10)** in MATH PRB menu is called, an integer between 1 and 10 is generated. See Fig. 1. A relational operator (found in 2nd [TEST]), often an inequality statement, returns the value 1 when true and the value 0 when false. See Fig. 2. The instructions in Fig. 3 are used to select a row from a matrix with two rows.

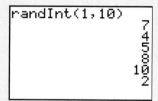

Figure 1

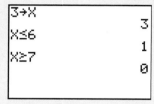

Figure 2

Figure 3

1. Explain why 60% of the time the instructions in Fig. 3 return a 1 and 40% of the time they return a 2. Type the instructions into your calculator, press the ENTER key twenty times, and count the number of 1's and 2's. Are there approximately twelve 1's and eight 2's?

2. Explain why the instructions in Fig. 3 should not be replaced with

$$(\texttt{randInt(1,10)} \leq 6)1 + (\texttt{randInt(1,10)} \geq 7)2$$

Type this line into your calculator and press the ENTER key several times to convince yourself that it does not always produce 1's and 2's.

In part 1 you pressed the ENTER key repeatedly and manually kept track of the outcomes. The TI-83/84 Plus can carry out the instructions many times, store the outcomes in a list, and analyze the list. The first instruction in Fig. 4 generates 100 random numbers between 1 and 10 and places them in the list L_1. The second instruction of Fig. 4 converts each number in the list L_1 to a row number using the strategy $\begin{bmatrix} .6 & .4 \end{bmatrix}$ and places the 100 row choices into the list L_3. Figure 6 uses the window settings shown in Fig. 5 to display the histogram for L_3. We see that the second row was selected 39 times out of 100 times. This is very close to the expected 40%.

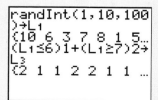

Figure 4

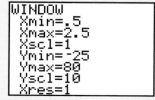

Figure 5

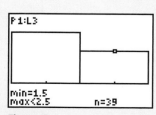

Figure 6

3. Simulate 100 column selections using the strategy $\begin{bmatrix} .2 \\ .8 \end{bmatrix}$ and create a histogram showing the number of times each column was selected. How many times was the second column selected?

In Section 9.3, the optimal mixed strategies for the payoff matrix $\begin{bmatrix} 5 & 3 \\ 1 & 4 \end{bmatrix}$ were found to be $\begin{bmatrix} .6 & .4 \end{bmatrix}$ for R and $\begin{bmatrix} .2 \\ .8 \end{bmatrix}$ for C and the value of the game was found to be $\frac{17}{5}$. In Figs. 7 and 8, 100 games are simulated and the payoffs for the games are stored in the list L_3. Fig. 10 shows the histogram for L_3 using the window settings in Fig. 9. For instance, we see that a payoff of 3 occurred in 50 of the 100 games. Fig. 11 shows that the average of the 100 payoffs, 3.35, is very close to the value of the game, 3.4.

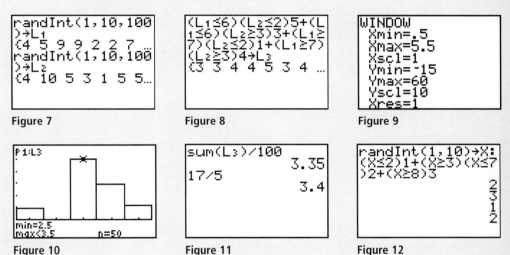

Figure 7   Figure 8   Figure 9

Figure 10   Figure 11   Figure 12

4. Explain in detail what is being calculated in Fig. 8.

5. Create a list of the payoffs for playing 100 games with the payoff matrix $\begin{bmatrix} 5 & 3 \\ 1 & 4 \end{bmatrix}$ using the strategies $\begin{bmatrix} .5 & .5 \end{bmatrix}$ for R and $\begin{bmatrix} .3 \\ .7 \end{bmatrix}$ for C, and compute the average of the payoffs.

6. Suppose a payoff matrix has three rows and that R's strategy is $\begin{bmatrix} .2 & .5 & .3 \end{bmatrix}$. Explain why Fig. 12 simulates the selection of a row by R. Type the instructions into your calculator, press the ENTER key forty times, and count the number of 1's, 2's, and 3's. Are there approximately eight 1's, twenty 2's, and twelve 3's?

7. Consider the 3×2 matrix in the first practice problem of Section 9.3. Suppose the strategies for R and C are $\begin{bmatrix} .2 & .5 & .3 \end{bmatrix}$ and $\begin{bmatrix} .75 \\ .25 \end{bmatrix}$, respectively. Simulate the payoffs for 100 games, display the histogram for the payoffs, and calculate the average value of the payoffs.

APPENDICES

APPENDIX A
Areas Under the Standard Normal Curve

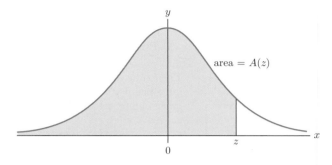

TABLE 1	Areas under the standard normal curve								
z	$A(z)$	z	$A(z)$	z	$A(z)$	z	$A(z)$	z	$A(z)$
−3.50	.0002	−2.00	.0228	−.50	.3085	1.00	.8413	2.45	.9929
−3.45	.0003	−1.95	.0256	−.45	.3264	1.05	.8531	2.50	.9938
−3.40	.0003	−1.90	.0287	−.40	.3446	1.10	.8643	2.55	.9946
−3.35	.0004	−1.85	.0322	−.35	.3632	1.15	.8749	2.60	.9953
−3.30	.0005	−1.80	.0359	−.30	.3821	1.20	.8849	2.65	.9960
−3.25	.0006	−1.75	.0401	−.25	.4013	1.25	.8944	2.70	.9965
−3.20	.0007	−1.70	.0446	−.20	.4207	1.2813	.9000	2.75	.9970
−3.15	.0008	−1.65	.0495	−.15	.4404	1.30	.9032	2.80	.9974
−3.10	.0010	−1.60	.0548	−.10	.4602	1.35	.9115	2.85	.9978
−3.05	.0011	−1.55	.0606	−.05	.4801	1.40	.9192	2.90	.9981
−3.00	.0013	−1.50	.0668	.00	.5000	1.45	.9265	2.95	.9984
−2.95	.0016	−1.45	.0735	.05	.5199	1.50	.9332	3.00	.9987
−2.90	.0019	−1.40	.0808	.10	.5398	1.55	.9394	3.05	.9989
−2.85	.0022	−1.35	.0885	.15	.5596	1.60	.9452	3.10	.9990
−2.80	.0026	−1.30	.0968	.20	.5793	1.65	.9505	3.15	.9992
−2.75	.0030	−1.25	.1056	.25	.5987	1.70	.9554	3.20	.9993
−2.70	.0035	−1.20	.1151	.30	.6179	1.75	.9599	3.25	.9994
−2.65	.0040	−1.15	.1251	.35	.6368	1.80	.9641	3.30	.9995
−2.60	.0047	−1.10	.1357	.40	.6554	1.85	.9678	3.35	.9996
−2.55	.0054	−1.05	.1469	.45	.6736	1.90	.9713	3.40	.9997
−2.50	.0062	−1.00	.1587	.50	.6915	1.95	.9744	3.45	.9997
−2.45	.0071	−.95	.1711	.55	.7088	2.00	.9772	3.50	.9998
−2.40	.0082	−.90	.1841	.60	.7257	2.05	.9798		
−2.35	.0094	−.85	.1977	.65	.7422	2.10	.9821		
−2.30	.0107	−.80	.2119	.70	.7580	2.15	.9842		
−2.25	.0122	−.75	.2266	.75	.7734	2.20	.9861		
−2.20	.0139	−.70	.2420	.80	.7881	2.25	.9878		
−2.15	.0158	−.65	.2578	.85	.8023	2.30	.9893		
−2.10	.0179	−.60	.2743	.90	.8159	2.35	.9906		
−2.05	.0202	−.55	.2912	.95	.8289	2.40	.9918		

APPENDIX B
Using the TI-83/84 Plus Graphing Calculators

Functions

Functions are graphed in a rectangular window like the one shown in Fig. 1. The numbers on the x-axis range from **Xmin** to **Xmax**, and the numbers on the y-axis range from **Ymin** to **Ymax**. The distances between tick marks are **Xscl** and **Yscl** on the x- and y-axes, respectively. To specify these quantities, press WINDOW and type in the values of the six variables. Figure 2 gives the settings associated with the window in Fig. 4. The axis ranges corresponding to this setting are often denoted by $[-4, 4]$ by $[-5, 8]$. (*Note*: To enter a negative number, use the (−) key on the bottom row of the calculator.)

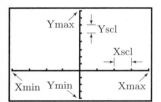

Figure 1 settings — WINDOW
```
WINDOW
 Xmin=-4
 Xmax=4
 Xscl=1
 Ymin=-5
 Ymax=8
 Yscl=1
 Xres=1
```

Figure 1. Typical window

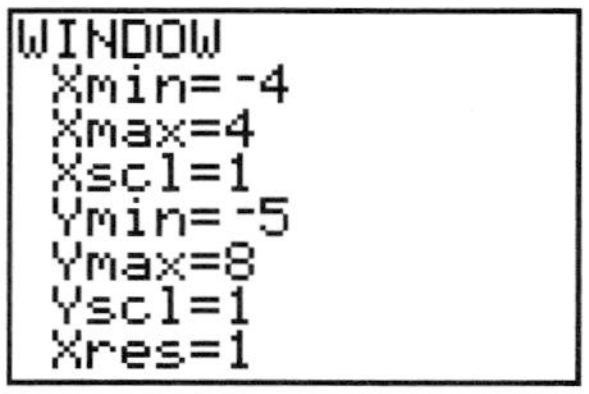

Figure 2. Settings for Fig. 4

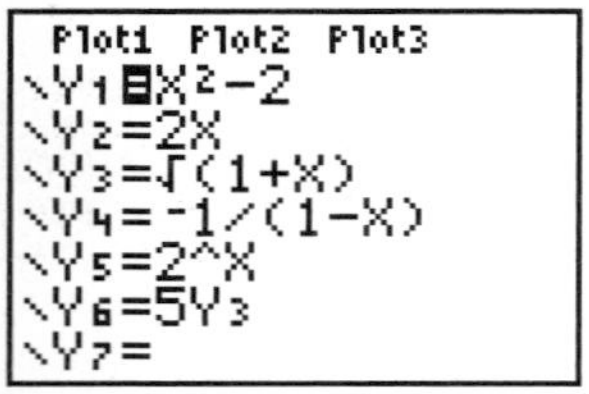

```
Plot1  Plot2  Plot3
\Y1■X²-2
\Y2=2X
\Y3=√(1+X)
\Y4=-1/(1-X)
\Y5=2^X
\Y6=5Y3
\Y7=
```

Figure 3. Function declarations

To specify functions, press the Y= key and type expressions next to the function names $Y_1, Y_2, \ldots$. (*Note*: To erase an expression, use the arrow keys to move the cursor anywhere on the expression, and press CLEAR.) In the screen of Fig. 3, called the "**Y=** editor," several functions have been specified. The expressions were produced with the following keystrokes:

Y₁: X,T,θ,n   x²   −   2

Y₂: 2   X,T,θ,n   (Notice that a multiplication sign is not needed.)

Y₃: 2nd   [√]   1   +   X,T,θ,n   )

Y₄: (−)   1   ÷   (1   −   X,T,θ,n   )

Y₅: 2   ^   X,T,θ,n   (^ is the symbol for exponentiation.)

Y₆: 5   VARS   ▶   1   3   (The standard method for entering a function.)

Notice that in Fig. 3 the equal sign in Y_1 is highlighted, whereas the other equal signs are not highlighted. This highlighting can be toggled by moving the cursor to an equal sign and pressing ENTER. Functions with highlighted equal signs are said to be *selected*. Pressing the GRAPH key instructs the calculator to graph all selected functions. (*Note*: The words **Plot1 Plot2 Plot3** on the first row are used for statistical plots. The backslash symbol preceding each function is used to specify one of seven possible styles for the graph of the function.)

Press GRAPH to obtain Fig. 4. Then press TRACE and press ▶, the right-arrow, 29 times to obtain Fig. 5. Each time a right- or left-arrow key is pressed, the trace cursor moves along the curve and the coordinates of the trace cursor are displayed.

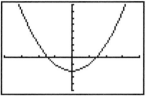

Figure 4

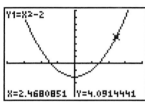

Figure 5

To approximate the function value for a specific value of x, move the trace cursor as close as possible to the value of x and read the y-coordinate of the point. For a more precise function value, press 2nd [CALC] **1**, type in a value for **X** (such as 2.5), and press ENTER. See Fig. 6. Alternately, you can just enter 2.5 without first pressing 2nd [CALC] **1**.

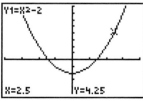

Figure 6

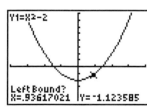

Figure 7

A point where the graph crosses the x-axis is called an *x-intercept*. The coordinates of an x-intercept can be approximated by tracing. The x-coordinate of an x-intercept of the function Y_1 is called a *zero* of Y_1 or a *root* of the equation $Y_1 = 0$. Figure 4 shows that Y_1 has a zero between 1 and 2 and the value of the zero is about 1.5. For a precise value of the zero, press 2nd [CALC] **2** and answer the questions. See Fig. 7. Reply to **"Left Bound?"** by moving the trace cursor to a point whose x-coordinate is less than the root and pressing ENTER. Reply to **"Right Bound?"** by moving the trace cursor to a point whose x-coordinate is greater than the root and pressing ENTER. See Fig. 8. Reply to **"Guess?"** by moving the trace cursor near the x-intercept and pressing ENTER. Figure 9 shows the resulting display. An alternate way to find a zero of a function is to reply to the questions by entering appropriate numbers. For instance, after pressing 2nd [CALC] **2**, respond to **"Left Bound?"** by typing in the number 1 and pressing ENTER, respond to **"Right Bound?"** by typing in the number 2 and pressing ENTER, and respond to **"Guess?"** by typing in the number 1.5 and pressing ENTER. The final screen will be identical to Fig. 9.

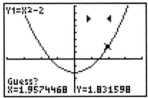

Figure 8

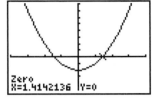

Figure 9

So far, all operations were carried out while looking at the graph of a function. These same operations also can be carried out in the home screen, which is invoked by pressing 2nd [QUIT]. For instance, the function **Y₁** can be evaluated at 4 by entering $Y_1(4)$ and pressing ENTER.

Return to the **Y=** editor by pressing Y= and then select **Y₂** so that now both **Y₁** and **Y₂** are selected. Press GRAPH to obtain the graphs of the two functions. Press TRACE and then press the right-arrow key several times. Now press the down-arrow key several times. Each time the down-arrow key is pressed, the trace cursor moves from one curve to the other. The identity of the function containing the cursor is given in the upper left part of the screen. Move the cursor as close as possible to the point of intersection of the two curves to approximate the coordinates of the intersection point. For more precise values, press 2nd [CALC] **5** and answer the questions. Reply to **"First curve?"** by moving the trace cursor to one of the curves and pressing ENTER. Reply to **"Second curve?"** by moving the trace cursor to the other curve and pressing ENTER. Reply to **"Guess?"** by either moving the trace cursor near the point of intersection or typing in a number close to the x-coordinate of the point and pressing ENTER. Figure 10 shows the resulting display.

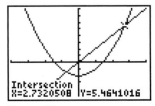

Figure 10

Tables

When you press 2nd [TABLE], a table of function values is displayed with a column for each selected function. (If more than two functions are selected, you must press the right-arrow key to see the third and later functions.) Prior to invoking a table, you should press 2nd [TBLSET] to specify certain properties of the table. See Fig. 11. The values for **X** will begin with the setting of **TblStart** and increase by the setting of **ΔTbl**. For our purposes, the settings for **Indpnt** and **Depend** should always be **Auto**. After you press 2nd [TABLE] to display the table (see Fig. 12), you can use the up- and down-arrow keys to generate further values.

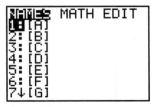

Figure 11   **Figure 12**

Matrices

The TI-83/84 Plus can store up to 10 matrices referred to as **[A]**, **[B]**, **[C]**, ... Pressing 2nd [MATRX] or 2nd [MATRIX] produces the screen in Fig. 13 with the three menus **NAMES**, **MATH**, and **EDIT**. The **NAMES** menu is used to display the name of a matrix on the home screen, the **MATH** menu is used to perform certain operations on a single matrix, and the **EDIT** menu is used to define a new matrix or alter an existing matrix.

Figure 13

To create a new matrix   Press 2nd [MATRX] ◄ to call up the **MATRIX EDIT** menu, and then press a number corresponding to one of the unused matrix names to obtain a matrix-entry screen. Type in the number of rows, press ENTER, type in the number of columns, and press ENTER to specify the size of the matrix. Then type in the first entry of the matrix, press ENTER, type in the next entry of the matrix, press ENTER, and so on until all entries have been entered. See Fig. 14 on the next page.

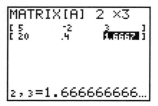

Figure 14

To alter an existing matrix Press $\boxed{\text{2nd}}$ [MATRX] $\boxed{\blacktriangleleft}$ to call up the matrix **EDIT** menu, and then press a number corresponding to the name of the matrix to be altered. Move the cursor to any entry you want to change, type in the new number, and press $\boxed{\text{ENTER}}$. You can change as many entries as you like, even the number of rows and columns.

To delete a matrix Press $\boxed{\text{2nd}}$ [MEM] **2 5** to obtain a list of all matrices that have been created. Use the down-arrow key to select the desired matrix, and then press $\boxed{\text{ENTER}}$ $\boxed{\text{DEL}}$ **2**.

To display the name of a matrix on the home screen Press $\boxed{\text{2nd}}$ [MATRX] to obtain a list of all matrix names. Use the down-arrow key to select the desired matrix, and then press $\boxed{\text{ENTER}}$. Alternately, from the matrix **NAMES** menu, type the number associated with the matrix.

Lists

A list can be thought of as a sequence or an ordered set of up to 999 numbers. Although lists can have custom names, we will use the built-in names $L_1, L_2, \ldots, L_6$ that are found above the numeric keys. To display L_1 on the home screen, press $\boxed{\text{2nd}}$ [L_1]. The elements of list L_1 can be referred to as $L_1(1), L_1(2), L_1(3), \ldots$. A set of numbers can be placed into a list by enclosing them with set braces and storing them in the list. However, often the stat list editor provides the best way to place numbers into lists and to view lists.

To invoke the stat list editor, press $\boxed{\text{STAT}}$ 1. Initially, the stat list editor has columns labeled L_1, L_2, and L_3. See Fig. 15. Three more columns for lists are off the screen.

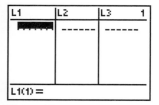

Figure 15

To place a number into a list in the stat list editor Move the cursor to the dashed line, type in the number, and press either the down-arrow key or the $\boxed{\text{ENTER}}$ key.

To remove a number from a list in the stat list editor Move the cursor to the number and press $\boxed{\text{DEL}}$.

To delete all numbers in a list from the stat list editor Move the cursor to the list name at the top of the screen and press $\boxed{\text{CLEAR}}$ $\boxed{\text{ENTER}}$.

To create a scatterplot of a set of points whose x-coordinates are in L_1 and whose y-coordinates are in L_2 Press $\boxed{\text{2nd}}$ [STAT PLOT] **1**, create the screen in Fig. 16, and press $\boxed{\text{GRAPH}}$. (*Note*: Check that the window settings are adequate for displaying the points.)

Figure 16

Histograms

The following steps display a frequency histogram with rectangles centered above the integers $a, a + 1, \ldots, b$.

- Press $\boxed{\text{STAT}}$ 1 to invoke the list editing screen shown in Fig. 15.
- Enter each number from a to b having nonzero frequency in the L_1 column and its associated frequency to its right in the L_2 column. Or, ignore the L_2 column and place each number (repeated according to its frequency) in the L_1 column.
- Press $\boxed{\text{2nd}}$ [STAT PLOT] **1** to invoke a screen similar to Fig. 16.
- Select "On" in the second line, the histogram icon in the Type line, and L_1 in the Xlist line. If you ignored the L_2 column in the second step, place 1 in the Freq line; otherwise, place L_2 in the Freq line.
- Press $\boxed{\text{WINDOW}}$ to invoke the window screen in Fig. 2.
- Set Xmin $= a - .5$, Xmax $= b + .5$, Xscl $= 1$, Ymin $\approx -.3*$(greatest frequency), Ymax $\approx 1.2*$(greatest frequency), Yscl $\approx .1*$(greatest frequency). *Note*: These Y settings allow ample space for the display of values while tracing.
- Press $\boxed{\text{GRAPH}}$ to view the histogram.
- To view the height of a rectangle, press $\boxed{\text{TRACE}}$ and use the arrow keys to move the cursor to the top center of the rectangle. The values of *min*, *max*, and *n* will be the x-coordinate of the left side of the rectangle, the x-coordinate of the right side of the rectangle, and the height of the rectangle, respectively.

A relative frequency histogram can be displayed by placing the relative frequencies in the L_2 column of the list editor. If so, the *greatest relative frequency* should be used in place of the *greatest frequency* when setting the values of Ymin, Ymax, and Yscl.

TVM Solver

TVM stands for "Time Value of Money." TVM Solver is a powerful calculating tool than can compute the values discussed in Chapter 10, "The Mathematics of Finance." Compound interest problems, annuities, and mortgages involve five numbers: duration, interest rate, periodic payment (0 for compound interest problems), present value, and future value. Once four of the five numbers are known, TVM Solver can be used to calculate the fifth number. The TVM Solver screen, shown in Fig. 17, is invoked by pressing APPS ENTER ENTER.

Figure 17   **Figure 18**

The eight lines of TVM Solver hold the following information:

N: The duration in terms of interest periods.

I%: The annual interest rate given as a percent; such as 6 or 4.5. In Chapter 10 its value would be $100r$.

PV: The present value. It is the principal of a compound interest problem, and the loan amount of a mortgage. It has the value 0 for an increasing annuity.

PMT: The periodic payment. It is the rent of an annuity or mortgage, and has value 0 in a compound interest problem.

FV: The future value. It is the balance in a compound interest problem and an annuity. It has the value 0 for a mortgage.

P/Y: The number of payments per year. For our purposes, it is the same as C/Y.

C/Y: The number of times interest is compounded per year. That is, 1, 2, 4, 12, 52, or 365.

PMT: When payments are paid—the *end* or *beginning* of each interest period. For our purposes, it will always be set to END.

Note: Amounts paid to the bank, such as the principal in a compound interest problem or the rent of a mortgage, are given as negative numbers.

To use TVM Solver.

- Enter all information except for one of the top five values, the value to be calculated.
- Move the cursor to the line containing the value to be calculated.
- Press ALPHA [SOLVE]. (*Note*: The green word SOLVE is located above the ENTER key.) A small square will appear to the left of the line and the calculated value will appear in the line.

Fig. 18 shows that the interest rate required for a deposit of $100 to double to $200 in 10 years with interest compounded quarterly is almost 7%. (The value entered for PV is negative since it represents money paid to the bank.)

Finance Functions

In addition to containing TVM Solver, the finance menu contains several functions. The two functions most valuable to us, Eff and Nom, calculate effective and nominal interest rates. (To display one of these functions on the home screen, press APPS ENTER, scroll to the function, and press ENTER.) If interest rate r compounded m times per year is a nominal rate, then $r_{eff} = $ **Eff(100r,m)/100**. For instance, the effective rate .037 found in Example 7 of Section 10.1 can be calculated as **Eff(3.65,4)/100**.

Similarly, the value of **Nom(100r_{eff},m)/100** is the corresponding nominal rate. For instance, the value of **Nom(3.7,4)/100** is approximately 3.65%. *Note*: The values for effective and nominal rates calculated with Eff and Nom will differ slightly from those calculated in Section 10.1 due to rounding errors.

APPENDIX C
Spreadsheet Fundamentals

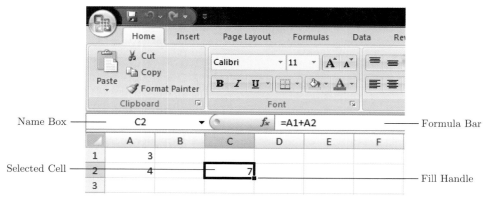

Figure 1.   Upper-left corner of a Microsoft Excel spreadsheet.

Cell

A *cell* is a small rectangle located at the intersection of a column and a row. Its *address* or *reference* (also known as its *relative address* or *relative reference*) consists of its column letter followed by its row number. When you click on a cell, its border thickens and its address is displayed in the Name box. Such a cell is said to be *selected* or *active*. After you type text, a number, or a formula into an active cell and press the Enter key, the text, number, or the value of the formula is displayed in the cell. The exact information you typed (known as the *content* of the cell) is displayed in the Formula bar whenever you reselect the cell.

Range

A *range of cells* or *range* is a rectangular array of more than one cell. The *address* or *reference* of a range consists of the address of the cell in the upper-left corner of the range, a colon (:), and then the address of the cell in the lower-right corner. To *select* a range, hold down the left mouse button while you drag the cursor from the upper-left cell to the lower-right cell. You can fill a range by entering information into each cell individually. However, often you fill an entire range with a single formula. If so, you should press Ctrl+Shift+Enter (instead of just Enter) after typing in the formula. Such a formula, called a *range formula* or an *array formula*, is automatically displayed in the Formula bar surrounded by braces.

Moving a Cell or Range

You can move a selected cell or range by dragging its border, or by pressing Ctrl+X, clicking on the new location, and pressing Ctrl+V. If the content of the original cell or range uses relative addresses, these addresses automatically change to reflect the new position of the cell or range. (You can prevent an address from changing by preceding its column letter and row number with dollar signs. Such an address is called an *absolute address*.)

Naming a Cell or Range

As an alternative to identifying cells or ranges with addresses, you can give a *name* to a cell or range. To specify a name, select the cell or range, click on the Name box, type in the name, and press the Enter key. (*Note:* The name will not be registered if you forget to press the Enter key.) Names can contain up to 255 characters (no spaces), must begin with a letter or underscore character, and cannot look like addresses. Deleting the contents of a cell or range does not delete its name. To delete a name with Excel 2007, click Name Manager in the Defined Names group on the Formulas tab, click on the name that you want to change in the Name Manager dialog box, press the Delete key, and then click OK to confirm the deletion. To delete a name in Excel 97-2003, click on Name in the Insert menu, click on Define, click on the name in the list of names that appears, click the Delete button, and click the OK button.

Entering a Formula

Formulas are what make a spreadsheet a spreadsheet. To specify that the entry typed into a selected cell or range is a formula, you first type an equal sign (=). The equal sign is followed by a expression containing numbers, addresses, names, functions, and operators such as +, −, *, /, and ^ (exponentiation).

Copying a Formula

Select the cell or range whose content is the original formula. There are two methods to copy the formula. (*Note*: With both methods, all relative addresses will be altered appropriately.)

First method: Press Ctrl+C, select the location(s) to hold the copy or copies, and press Ctrl+V.

Second method: Hover the mouse pointer over the cell's fill handle until the pointer becomes a crosshair (+). Drag the pointer vertically or horizontally along the cells that are to hold the copy or copies.

Installing Add-Ins

Two Excel tools that we use in this book are called *Solver* and *Data Analysis*. Solver is used to find solutions to systems of linear equations and to linear programming problems. Data Analysis is used to analyze data. To see if these tools have been installed with Excel 2007, look in the Analysis group on the Data tab. If they are not present, click the round Microsoft Office button, click Excel Options, click Add-Ins, select Excel Add-ins in the Manager box, click Go, select Analysis ToolPak and Solver Add-in in the Add-ins window, and click OK. To see if these tools have been installed with Excel 97-2003, click the Tools button on the menu bar and see if the tools are listed. If not, click on Add-Ins in the Tools menu, check the boxes next to Analysis ToolPak and Solver, and then click on the OK button. In some cases, they will not become available until you exit Excel and reinvoke it. Also, you might be instructed to insert your Microsoft Office DVD and run the setup routine to install them.

Entering a Formula by Pointing

Instead of typing the address of a cell into a formula manually, just click on the cell. A dotted rectangle will surround the cell, the cell's name or address will appear in the formula, and the word *Point* will appear in the status bar below the spreadsheet. To enter the address of a range, click on the upper-left cell of the range and drag the mouse cursor to the lower-right cell of the range. A dotted line will surround the range. When you release the mouse, the range's name or address will appear in the formula.

Converting Formulas to Values

Sometimes the formulas that were used to fill a cell or range are no longer needed. To replace their contents with the formulas' values, select the cell or range, and press Ctrl+C. With Excel 2007, click Paste in the Clipboard group on the Home tab, and then click Paste Values. With Excel 97-2003, click on *Paste Special* in the Edit menu, click on the Values circle, and click on the OK button.

Summing a Column or Row of Numbers

Click on the top number in the column or row, drag the mouse pointer to one or more cells beyond the column or row of numbers, and click on *AutoSum*. (In Excel 2007, "Σ AutoSum" is found in the Editing group on the Home tab. In Excel 97-2003, the AutoSum button (Σ) is located in the Standard toolbar.) The contents of the last cell will be a formula containing the SUM function and the value of the cell will be the sum of the numbers in the column or row.

Simulating a Random Sample from a Probability Distribution

The following steps use Excel's Data Analysis tool to create a random sample from a discrete probability distribution. The sample numbers will be displayed in a range of m rows and n columns.

- Place the probability table in the first two columns of the spreadsheet. That is, column A should contain the possible outcomes (which must be numeric) and column B should contain the associated probabilities.
- Click on Data Analysis. (With Excel 2007, Data Analysis is in the Analysis group on the Data tab. With Excel 97-2003, Data Analysis is in the Tools menu.)
- Double-click on Random Number Generation in the Data Analysis dropdown list.
- Enter the number of columns (n) of random numbers into the "Number of Variables" box.
- Enter the number of random numbers (m) that you would like to generate in each column into the Number of Random Numbers box.
- Select "Discrete" as the Distribution.
- Place the address of the range containing the probability distribution in the "Value and Probability Input Range" box. This can be accomplished by placing the cursor in the box, clearing the box if necessary, dragging the mouse pointer from cell A1 to the lower-right corner of the probability table, and releasing the mouse button.
- Click on the Output Range circle, and enter the address of an $m \times n$ array of cells.
- Click on the OK button to generate the desired random sample.

Creating a Frequency Distribution Table and Histogram for the Random Sample Generated Above

The following steps use Excel's Data Analysis tool to create a frequency distribution and optionally a histogram for a range of cells containing the random numbers generated above.

- Click on Data Analysis.

- Double-click on Histogram in the Data Analysis list.
- Place into the Input Range box the address of the range of cells containing the random sample.
- Place into the Bin Range box the address of the range of possible outcomes; that is, the first column of the probability table.
- Click the Output Range circle and key in the address of any cell to the right of the cells already filled.
- If you would like also to display a histogram, click the small rectangle to the left of Chart Output.
- Click the OK button to see the frequency distribution table and possibly the histogram. (*Note*: The word More and the number 0 appear in the last row of the table and in the histogram. To delete them, select the row, click the right mouse button, click Delete, select "Shift cells up", and click OK.)

Using Goal Seek to Solve an Equation Having One Unknown

Suppose the contents of cell B1 contains a formula whose value depends on the value of A1, and you know the value you would like B1 to have. Then the *Goal Seek* tool can be used to determine the value of A1 that will produce the sought-after value in B1. For example, you can use Goal Seek to find the interest rate (compounded annually) for which $100 will grow to $146 after 11 years. Enter `=100*(1+A1)^11` into cell B1 and click on the Goal Seek tool. (In Excel 2007, you locate Goal Seek by clicking on What-If Analysis in the Data Tools group on the Data tab. In Excel 97-2003, Goal Seek is in the Tools menu.) A Goal Seek window will appear. Fill in the window as shown in Fig. 2, and then click the OK button. The

solution, $\approx .0035$ (that is, 3.50%), will appear in cell A1 of the spreadsheet. *Note*: Using the Goal Seek tool is sometimes referred to as *backsolving*.

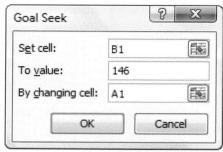

Figure 2

Using the Insert Function Dialog Box

To invoke the Insert Function dialog box, click on the Insert Function button located next to the Formula bar. The dialog box allows you to display the more than 300 available functions and descriptions of their arguments and what they do. When you select a function and click on OK (or double-click on the function), a Function Arguments dialog box appears to help you specify the arguments of the function. You can fill in each argument box by typing or pointing. To assist you when using the pointing method, you can click on the icon at the right side of an argument box to temporarily collapse the dialog box and thereby make more of the spreadsheet visible. After you have filled the boxes for all the arguments, press OK (or the Enter key) to fill a single cell with the value of the function, or press Ctrl+Shift+Enter to fill a range of cells.

Using Excel's Financial Functions

The five most important financial functions for our purposes are shown in Table 1.

The values of these functions and their parameters are signed according to their flows. Money received by you is given a positive value, and money paid by you is given a negative value. For instance, the values of savings account deposits and loan payments are negative, and the values of savings account withdrawals and loan amounts are positive. Table 2 shows how to use these functions to solve some examples from the text.

Table 3 contains some other useful financial functions. Example 5 of Section 10.3 can be solved by keying

$$=\textbf{IPMT(0.75\%,A1,360,112475,0)}$$
$$-\textbf{PPMT(0.75\%,A1,360,112475,0)}$$

into B1 and using Goal Seek to set cell B1 to the value 0 by changing cell A1.

TABLE 1		
Function	**Used to calculate**	**Function and required arguments**
FV	future value	FV(rate, nper, pmt, pv)
PV	present value	PV(rate, nper, pmt, fv)
PMT	periodic payment	PMT(rate, nper, pv, fv)
NPER	number of interest periods	NPER(rate, pmt, pv, fv)
EFFECT	effective rate of interest	EFFECT(nominal_rate, nper)

TABLE 2		
Section	**Example**	**Function and required arguments**
10.1	3	FV(1%, 4, 0, −100)
10.1	5	PV(0.5%, 104, 0, 10000)
10.1	7	EFFECT(3.65%, 4)
10.2	1	FV(0.5%, 60, −100, 0)
10.2	3	PMT(2%, 16, 0, 300000)
10.2	4	PV(1.5%, 8, 3000, 0)
10.2	5	PMT(0.5%, 12, −10000, 0)
10.2	6	NPER(0.5%, −100, 0, 10000)
10.3	2(a)	PMT(0.75%, 360, 112475, 0)
10.3	4	PV(2%, 12, 200, 1000)

TABLE 3		
Function	**Used to calculate**	**Function and required arguments**
RATE	interest rate per period	RATE(nper, pmt, pv, fv)
IPMT	interest portion of loan payment number *per*	IPMT(rate, per, nper, pv, fv)
PPMT	principal reduction portion of loan payment number *per*	PPMT(rate, per, nper, pv, fv)
NOMINAL	nominal rate of interest	NOMINAL(effective_rate, nper)

APPENDIX D
Using the TI-89 Graphing Calculator

Functions

Functions are graphed in rectangular windows like the one shown in Fig. 1. The numbers on the x-axis range from **xmin** to **xmax**, and the numbers on the y-axis range from **ymin** to **ymax**. The distance between the tick marks are **xscl** and **yscl** on the x- and y-axes, respectively. To specify these quantities, press ◆ [WINDOW] and type in the values of these variables. Figure 2 shows the settings associated with the windows in Figs. 1 and 4. The axis ranges associated with this setting are often written $[-4, 4]$ *by* $[-5, 8]$. (*Note*: To enter a negative number you must use the $\boxed{(-)}$ key on the bottom row of the calculator.)

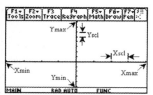

Figure 1. Typical window

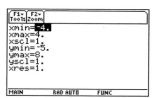

Figure 2. Settings for Figs. 1 and 4

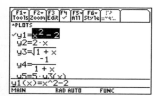

Figure 3. Function declarations

To input functions, press ◆ [Y=] and type expressions next to the function names **y1**, **y2**, ... (*Note*: To erase an expression, use the arrow keys to move to that function and press $\boxed{\text{CLEAR}}$ or $\boxed{\leftarrow}$. To edit an expression once it has been entered, use the arrow keys to highlight the expression and press $\boxed{\text{F3}}$.) In the screen of Fig. 3, called the "**Y=** editor", several functions have been specified. The expressions were input with the following keystrokes:

y1: $\boxed{\text{X}}$ $\boxed{\wedge}$ $\boxed{2}$ $\boxed{-}$ $\boxed{2}$ ($\wedge$ is the symbol for exponentiation.)

y2: $\boxed{2}$ $\boxed{\text{X}}$ (Notice that a multiplication symbol is not necessary.)

y3: $\boxed{\text{2ND}}$ $\boxed{\sqrt{\ }}$ $\boxed{1}$ $\boxed{+}$ $\boxed{\text{X}}$ $\boxed{)}$

y4: $\boxed{(-)}$ $\boxed{1}$ $\boxed{\div}$ $\boxed{(}$ $\boxed{1}$ $\boxed{+}$ $\boxed{\text{X}}$ $\boxed{)}$

y5: $\boxed{5}$ $\boxed{\text{Y}}$ $\boxed{3}$ $\boxed{(}$ $\boxed{\text{X}}$ $\boxed{)}$

Notice that in Fig. 3 there is a check mark in front of **y1** while the other functions do not have check marks in front of them. The check mark can be toggled with the $\boxed{\text{F4}}$ button. Functions with a check mark are said to be

selected. Pressing ◆ [GRAPH] instructs the calculator to graph all selected functions. *Note*: Arrowing up from **y1** shows **Plot1**, **Plot2**, (up to **Plot9**) which are used for statistical plots. There are eight possible styles for the graph of a function found in the STYLE menu accessed by $\boxed{\text{2ND}}$ [F6].

Press ◆ [GRAPH] to obtain Fig. 4. Then press $\boxed{\text{F3}}$ to trace and press $\boxed{\blacktriangleright}$, the right arrow, 49 times to obtain Fig. 5. Each time a right- or left-arrow key is pressed, the trace cursor moves along the curve and the coordinates of the trace cursor are displayed below the graph.

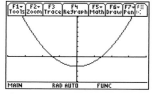

Figure 4

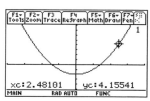

Figure 5

To approximate the function value for a specific value of x, move the cursor as close as possible to the value of x and read the y-coordinate of the point. For a more precise function value, there are two options. While using the trace cursor, input the value of x and press $\boxed{\text{ENTER}}$. Alternatively, press $\boxed{\text{F5}}$, for the Math menu, then **1**, then type in the value of x (such as 2.5), and press $\boxed{\text{ENTER}}$. See Fig. 6.

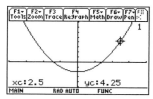

Figure 6

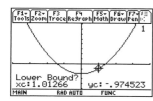

Figure 7

A point where the graph crosses the x-axis is called an x-*intercept*. Tracing can approximate the coordinates of an x-intercept. The x-coordinate of an x-intercept of the function **y1** is called a *zero* of **y1** or a *root* of the equation **y1=0**. Figure 4 shows that **y1** has a zero between 1 and 2 and the value is about 1.5. For a more precise value of the zero, press $\boxed{\text{F5}}$ **2** and answer the questions. See Fig. 7. Reply to "**Lower Bound?**" by either moving the trace cursor to a point whose x-coordinate is less than the root and pressing $\boxed{\text{ENTER}}$ or by simply typing in a value for the x-coordinate which is less than the root (say 1) and pressing $\boxed{\text{ENTER}}$. See Fig. 8. Reply to "**Upper Bound?**" by either moving the trace cursor to a point whose x-coordinate is greater than the root and pressing $\boxed{\text{ENTER}}$ or by simply typing in a value for the x-coordinate which is greater than the root (say 2) and pressing ENTER. Figure 9 shows the resulting display.

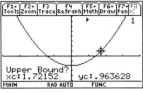

Figure 8

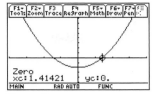

Figure 9

Many operations can be carried out using the home screen, which is invoked by pressing HOME. For instance, the function **y1** can be evaluated at -2 by entering **y1(-2)** and pressing ENTER.

Return to the **Y=** editor by pressing ♦[Y=] and then select **y2** so that both **y1** and **y2** are selected. Press ♦ [GRAPH] to obtain the graphs of both functions. Press F3 to trace and then press the right-arrow key several times. Now press the down-arrow key several times. Notice that each time the down-arrow key is pressed, the trace cursor moves from one curve to the other. The identity of the function containing the cursor is indicated in the upper right hand part of the screen. Move the cursor as close as possible to the point of intersection to approximate the coordinates of the point of intersection. For more precise values, press F5 5 and answer the questions. Reply to "**1st Curve?**" by moving the trace cursor to one of the curves and pressing ENTER. Reply to "**2nd Curve?**" by moving the trace cursor to the other curve and pressing ENTER. Reply to "**Lower Bound?**" by either moving the trace cursor to the left of the point of intersection or typing in a number less than the x-coordinate of the point and pressing ENTER. Reply to "**Upper Bound?**" by either moving the trace cursor to the right of the point of intersection or typing in a number greater than the x-coordinate of the point and pressing ENTER. Figure 10 shows the resulting display.

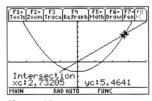

Figure 10

Tables

When ♦ [TABLE] is pressed, a table of function values is displayed showing a column for each selected function. (If more than three functions are selected, use the right-arrow key to see the fourth and later functions.) Prior to invoking a table, press ♦ [TBLSET] to specify certain properties of the table. See Fig. 11. The values for **x** will

begin with the setting of **tblStart** and increase by the setting of **Δtbl**. For our purposes, the setting for **Graph <-> Table** should be **OFF** and the setting for **Independent** should be **AUTO**. After the table is displayed by pressing ♦ [TABLE] (see Fig. 12), use the up- and down-arrow keys to generate further values.

Figure 11

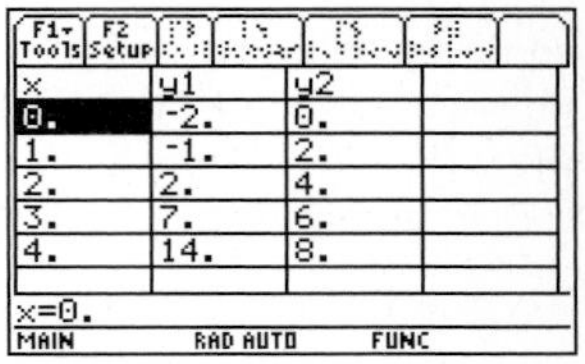

Figure 12

Matrices

Although matrices can be created directly on the home screen, it is usually better to use the Data/Matrix Editor

To create a new matrix   Press APPS, move the cursor to Data/Matrix Editor, and press ENTER followed by **3** to open a **New** matrix. Press ▶ **2** to set the **Type** to **Matrix**. Suppose we want to input a 2×3 matrix. Arrow down to **Variable** and type in a name for the matrix (say **a**). Next input the **Row dimension** (2) and the **Col dimension** (3). See Fig. 13. Then press ENTER twice to obtain the matrix-entry screen. Finally, type in the first entry of the matrix, press ENTER, type in the next entry of the matrix, press ENTER, and so on until all entries have been entered. See Fig. 14.

Figure 13

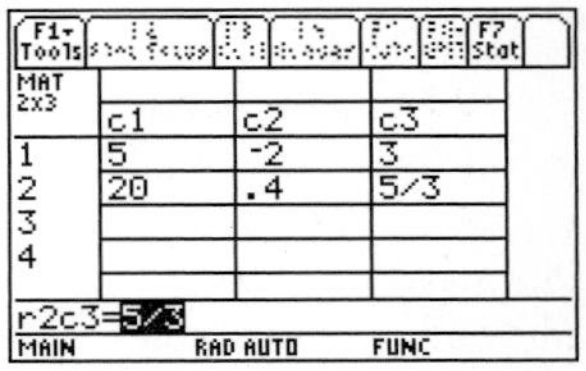

Figure 14

To alter an existing matrix   Press APPS, move the cursor to Data/Matrix Editor, and press ENTER followed by **2** to **Open** an existing matrix. Press ▶ **2** to set the **Type** to **Matrix**. Arrow down to **Variable** and press ▶ to view a list of all saved matrices. Use the down-arrow key to select the matrix you wish to change and press ENTER. Press ENTER again to obtain the matrix-entry screen. Use the arrow keys to highlight the entry to be altered, type the new value, and press ENTER. Change as many entries as needed. If an extra row or column needs to be added, press 2ND [F6] **1**, and then press **2** to insert a new row above the current row or press **3** to insert a new column to the left of the current column. If a row or column needs to be deleted, press 2ND [F6] **2**, and then press **2** to remove the current row or press **3** to remove the current column. The matrix can also be directly resized by pressing 2ND [F6] **6** and then inputting the new row and column dimensions.

To delete a matrix Press 2ND [Var-Link] to view a list of all variables that have been saved including matrices. Use the down-arrow key to highlight the matrix to be deleted, and then press ←. A screen appears asking for confirmation; press ENTER to delete. If there are multiple matrices to be deleted, highlight each matrix in turn and press F4 each time, then press ←. The confirmation screen will appear; press ENTER to delete.

To display the name of a matrix on the home screen To display a matrix on the home screen, simply type its name on the entry line and press ENTER. Alternately, press 2ND [Var-Link] to view a list of all variables that have been saved including matrices. Use the down-arrow key to highlight the matrix to be displayed, press ENTER to place the matrix name on the entry line, and press ENTER again to see the matrix displayed on the home screen.

To carry out elementary row operations The three elementary row operations are carried out with the following commands from the MATH/Matrix/Row ops menu.

Interchange *rowA* and *rowB* of *matrix*

   `rowSwap(matrix, rowA, rowB)`

Multiply *rowA* by *value*

   `mRow(value, matrix, rowA)`

Add *value·rowA* to *rowB*

   `mRowAdd(value, matrix, rowA, rowB)`

   When one of these commands is carried out, the resulting matrix is displayed but the stored matrix is not changed. Therefore, when a sequence of commands is executed to carry out the Gauss–Jordan elimination method, each command should be followed with STO ▶ *matrix* to change the stored matrix. For instance, if in Example 5 of Section 2.1 the original matrix is named *a*, then the first three row operations are carried out with

   `mRow(1/3,a,1)` STO ▶ a

   `mRowAdd(-4,a,1,2)` STO ▶ a

   `mRowAdd(2,a,1,3)` STO ▶ a

Lists

A list can be thought of as a sequence or an ordered set of up to 999 numbers. There are two basic ways to create a list. In the home screen, a set of numbers can be placed into a list by enclosing the numbers with braces and storing in a variable. See Fig. 15. Lists can also be created in the Data/Matrix Editor by pressing APPS, selecting the Data/Matrix editor, and pressing ENTER followed by **3** to open a new **List**. Press ▶ **3** to set the **Type** to **List**.

Then type in a name for the **Variable**. Press ENTER twice to open the list editor. Type the numbers into the first column that is labeled **c1**. (*Note:* There are 99 columns available.) See Fig. 16.

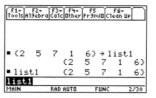
Figure 15

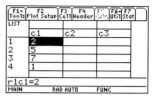
Figure 16

To place a number into a list in the list editor Type in the number, and press either an arrow key or the ENTER key.

To remove a number from a list in the list editor Move the cursor to the number and press ←.

To remove all numbers in a list in the list editor Move the cursor to the column, then press 2ND [F6] **5** to clear the entire column.

To create a scatter plot of a set of points whose *x*-coordinates are in c1 and whose *y*-coordinates are in c2 First note that when a second column is added, the variable type automatically changes from **List** to **Data**. From the list/data editor press F2 F1 to see Fig. 17. Change the **Plot Type** to **Scatter**, and change the **Mark** to **Dot** (or **Box** or **Cross** or **Plus** or **Square**). Set **x** to **c1** and **y** to **c2**. Leave **Use Freq and Categories?** set to **NO**. See Fig. 18. Press ENTER to save the plot definitions. To view the scatter plot, first set the window to the appropriate ranges and then press ◆ [GRAPH] or type F2 **9** (ZoomData) to have the calculator automatically set the ranges to the data values and graph the scatter plot. (*Note:* Make sure all functions have been deselected before you graph the scatter plot.)

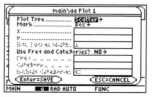
Figure 17

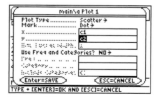
Figure 18

Histograms

The following steps display a frequency histogram with rectangles centered above the integers $a, a + 1, \ldots, b$.

* Press APPS, move the cursor to Data/Matrix Editor, and press ENTER followed by **3** to open a **New** data screen. Then type in a name for the variable. Press ENTER twice to open a data editing screen similar to that in Fig. 16.

- Enter each number from a to b having nonzero frequency in the **c1** column and its associated frequency to its right in the **c2** column. Or, ignore the **c2** column and place each number (repeated according to its frequency) in the **c1** column.
- Press F2 F1 to invoke a screen similar to Fig. 17. Or, press ♦ [Y=], select **Plot1**, and press F3 to invoke a screen similar to Fig. 17. (*Note*: Make sure to uncheck any other functions defined in the **Y=** editor.)
- Press ▶ 4 to set the **Plot Type** to **Histogram**. Set **x** to **c1**, set **Hist. Bucket Width** to 1. If the frequencies are in **c2**, set **Use Freq and Categories?** to **YES** by pressing ▶ 2 and then type **c2** in the **Freq** box. If only **c1** is used, leave **Use Freq and Categories?** set to **NO**. Press ENTER to save the plot definitions.
- Press ♦ [WINDOW] to invoke a window screen similar to Fig. 2.
- Set **xmin** $= a - .5$, **xmax** $= b + .5$, **xscl** $= 1$, **ymin** $\approx -.3*$(greatest frequency), **ymax** $\approx 1.2*$(greatest frequency), **yscl** $\approx .1*$(greatest frequency). (*Note*: These y settings will allow ample space for the display of values while tracing.)
- Press ♦ [GRAPH] to display the histogram.
- To view the height of each rectangle, press F3 and use the arrow keys to move the cursor to the top center of the rectangles. The value of **min** is the x-coordinate of the left edge of the rectangle, the value of **max** is the x-coordinate of the right edge of the rectangle, and the value of **n** is the height of the rectangle.

A relative frequency histogram can be displayed by placing the relative frequencies in the **c2** column of the data editor. If so, the *greatest relative frequency* should be used in place of the *greatest frequency* when setting **ymin**, **ymax**, and **yscl**.

Least-Squares Line

The following steps find the straight line that minimizes the least-squares error for the points $(1, 4)$, $(2, 5)$, and $(3, 8)$.

- Use APPS to display the Data/Matrix editor.
- Press **3** to display a New dialog box.
- Press ▼ ▼ and give a name to the variable, such as **dat**.
- Press ENTER twice to display a spreadsheet.
- Enter the three x-values (1, 2, and 3) into the first column.

- Enter the three y-values (4, 5, and 8) into the second column.
- Press F5 to invoke a Calculate dialog box.
- Set **Calculation Type** to **LinReg**; that is, press **5**.
- Set **x** to **c1**, and set **y** to **c2**.
- Set **Store RegEQ** to **y1(x)**.
- Press ENTER to invoke a STAT VARS window displaying $y = a \cdot x + b$, $a = 2$, $b = 1.666667$, $corr = .960769$, $R^2 = .923077$. (*Note*: $\frac{5}{3} \approx 1.666667$.) The expression $2 \cdot x + 1.6666666666667$ will be assigned to **y1(x)** in the **Y=** editor.)
- Press ENTER or ESC to return to the spreadsheet.
- Press F2 to invoke the Plot window.
- Press F1 to invoke the dialog box for setting Plot1.
- Set **Plot Type** to **Scatter**, set **Mark** to **Box**, set **x** to **c1**, set **y** to **c2**, and then press ENTER.
- Press ♦ F2 and set the window to $[-4, 4]$ by $[-4, 9]$.
- Press ♦ F3 to produce the graph. (*Note*: The point plotting feature can be suspended by going to the **Y=** window, moving the cursor to Plot1 and pressing F4. Pressing F5 instead, clears the value assigned to Plot1.)

Statistics

The following steps find the mean and standard deviation for a sample.

- Invoke the Data/Matrix editor from the APPS menu.
- Select **3** to set up a new data variable dialog box.
- Set **Type** to **Data**, and give the variable a name such as **s**.
- Press ENTER twice to invoke a spreadsheet.
- Place the numbers from the left column of the frequency table in the **c1** column and the frequency figures in the **c2** column.
- Press F5 to bring up the Calculate dialog box.
- Set **Calculation Type** to **OneVar**, set **x** to **c1**, set **Use Freq and Categories** to **YES**, and set **Freq** to **c2**.
- Press ENTER twice to bring up a STAT VARS window. The sample mean and the sample standard deviation appear denoted by $\bar{x}$ and **Sx**. *Note*: The population standard deviation, σ_X, can be displayed on the home screen. From the home screen, press 2ND [CHAR] **1**, arrow down to σ, press ENTER, press X, and press ENTER.

ANSWERS SECTION

From *Brief Calculus & Its Applications*, Twelfth Edition by Larry J. Goldstein, David C. Lay, David I. Schneider, and Nakhlé H. Asmar ISBN: 0321568567

CHAPTER 7

Exercises 7.1, page 352

1. $f(5,0) = 25$, $f(5,-2) = 51$, $f(a,b) = a^2 - 3ab - b^2$ **3.** $g(2,3,4) = -2$, $g(7,46,44) = \frac{7}{2}$
7. $C(x,y,z) = 6xy + 10xz + 10yz$ **9.** $f(8,1) = 40$, $f(1,27) = 180$, $f(8,27) = 360$ **11.** $\approx \$50$. $50 invested
at 5% continuously compounded interest will yield $100 in 13.8 years **13. (a)** \$1875 **(b)** \$2250; yes
15. **17.** **19.** $f(x,y) = y - 3x$ **21.** They correspond to the points

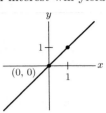

having the same altitude above sea level. **23.** d **25.** c

Exercises 7.2, page 361

1. $5y$, $5x$ **3.** $4xe^y$, $2x^2e^y$ **5.** $\dfrac{1}{y} - \dfrac{y}{x^2}$; $\dfrac{-x}{y^2} + \dfrac{1}{x}$ **7.** $4(2x - y + 5)$, $-2(2x - y + 5)$ **9.** $(2xe^{3x} + 3x^2e^{3x}) \ln y$,

x^2e^{3x}/y **11.** $\dfrac{2y}{(x+y)^2}$, $-\dfrac{2x}{(x+y)^2}$ **13.** $\dfrac{3}{2}\sqrt{\dfrac{K}{L}}$ **15.** $\dfrac{2xy}{z}$, $\dfrac{x^2}{z}$, $-\dfrac{1+x^2y}{z^2}$ **17.** ze^{yz}, xz^2e^{yz}, $x(yz+1)e^{yz}$

19. 1, 3 **21.** -12 **23.** $\dfrac{\partial f}{\partial x} = 3x^2y + 2y^2$, $\dfrac{\partial^2 f}{\partial x^2} = 6xy$, $\dfrac{\partial f}{\partial y} = x^3 + 4xy$, $\dfrac{\partial^2 f}{\partial y^2} = 4x$, $\dfrac{\partial^2 f}{\partial y \partial x} = \dfrac{\partial^2 f}{\partial x \partial y} = 3x^2 + 4y$

25. (a) Marginal productivity of labor $= 480$; of capital $= 40$ **(b)** $480h$ **(c)** Production decreases by 240
units. **27.** If the price of a bus ride increases and the price of a train ticket remains constant, fewer people will
ride the bus. An increase in train-ticket prices coupled with constant bus fare should cause more people to ride
the bus. **29.** If the average price of DVDs increases and the average price of a DVD player remains constant,
people will purchase fewer DVDs. An increase in average DVD player prices coupled with constant DVD prices
should cause a decline in the number of DVD players purchased. **31.** $\dfrac{\partial V}{\partial P}(20,300) = -.06$, $\dfrac{\partial V}{\partial T}(20,300) = .004$

33. $\dfrac{\partial f}{\partial r} > 0$, $\dfrac{\partial f}{\partial m} > 0$, $\dfrac{\partial f}{\partial p} < 0$ **35.** $\dfrac{\partial^2 f}{\partial x^2} = -\dfrac{45}{4}x^{-5/4}y^{1/4}$. Marginal productivity of labor is decreasing.

Exercises 7.3, page 369

1. $(-2,1)$ **3.** $(26,11)$ **5.** $(1,-3)$, $(-1,-3)$ **7.** $(\sqrt{5},1)$, $(\sqrt{5},-1)$, $(-\sqrt{5},1)$, $(-\sqrt{5},-1)$ **9.** $\left(\frac{1}{3},\frac{4}{3}\right)$
11. Relative minimum; neither relative maximum nor relative minimum **13.** Relative maximum; neither
relative maximum nor relative minimum; relative maximum **15.** Neither relative maximum nor relative
minimum **17.** $(0,0)$ min **19.** $(-1,-4)$ max **21.** $(0,-1)$ min **23.** $(-1,2)$ max; $(1,2)$ neither max nor
min **25.** $\left(\frac{1}{4},2\right)$ min; $\left(\frac{1}{4},-2\right)$ neither max nor min **27.** $\left(\frac{1}{2},\frac{1}{6},\frac{1}{2}\right)$ **29.** 14 in. × 14 in. × 28 in.
31. $x = 120$, $y = 80$

Exercises 7.4, page 377

1. 58 at $x = 6$, $y = 2$, $\lambda = 12$ **3.** 13 at $x = 8$, $y = -3$, $\lambda = 13$ **5.** $x = \frac{1}{2}$, $y = 2$ **7.** 5, 5 **9.** Base 10 in.,
height 5 in. **11.** $F(x,y,\lambda) = 4xy + \lambda(1 - x^2 - y^2)$; $\dfrac{\sqrt{2}}{2} \times \dfrac{\sqrt{2}}{2}$
13. $F(x,y,\lambda) = 3x + 4y + \lambda(18{,}000 - 9x^2 - 4y^2)$; $x = 20$, $y = 60$
15. (a) $F(x,y,\lambda) = 96x + 162y + \lambda(3456 - 64x^{3/4}y^{1/4})$; $x = 81$, $y = 16$ **(b)** $\lambda = 3$ **17.** $x = 12$, $y = 2$, $z = 4$
19. $x = 2$, $y = 3$, $z = 1$ **21.** $F(x,y,z,\lambda) = 3xy + 2xz + 2yz + \lambda(12 - xyz)$; $x = 2$, $y = 2$, $z = 3$
23. $F(x,y,z,\lambda) = xy + 2xz + 2yz + \lambda(32 - xyz)$; $x = y = 4$, $z = 2$

Exercises 7.5, page 384

1. $E = 6.7$ **3.** $E = (2A + B - 6)^2 + (5A + B - 10)^2 + (9A + B - 15)^2$ **5.** $y = 4.5x - 3$ **7.** $y = -2x + 11.5$
9. $y = -1.4x + 8.5$ **11. (a)** $y = .2073x + 2.7$ **(b)** \$4773 **(c)** 2006 **13. (a)** $y = .497x + 11.2$
(b) 22.6 percent **(c)** 2002 **15. (a)** $y = -4.24x + 22.01$ **(b)** $y = 8.442$ degrees Celsius

Exercises 7.6, page 390

1. $e^2 - 2e + 1$ **3.** $2 - e^{-2} - e^2$ **5.** $309\frac{3}{8}$ **7.** $\frac{5}{3}$ **9.** $\frac{38}{3}$ **11.** $e^{-5} + e^{-2} - e^{-3} - e^{-4}$ **13.** $9\frac{1}{3}$

Chapter 7: Supplementary Exercises, page 391

1. $2, \frac{5}{6}, 0$ **3.** ≈ 19.94. Ten dollars increases to 20 dollars in 11.5 y.   **5.** $6x + y, x + 10y$ **7.** $\frac{1}{y}e^{x/y}$, $-\frac{x}{y^2}e^{x/y}$ **9.** $3x^2, -z^2, -2yz$ **11.** $6, 1$ **13.** $20x^3 - 12xy, 6y^2, -6x^2, -6x^2$ **15.** $-201, 5.5$. At the level $p = 25$, $t = 10,000$, an increase in price of \$1 will result in a loss in sales of approximately 201 calculators, and an increase in advertising of \$1 will result in the sale of approximately 5.5 additional calculators.   **17.** $(3, 2)$ **19.** $(0, 1), (-2, 1)$ **21.** Min at $(2, 3)$ **23.** Min at $(1, 4)$; neither max nor min at $(-1, 4)$ **25.** 20; $x = 3$, $y = -1$ **27.** $x = \frac{1}{2}, y = \frac{3}{2}, z = 2$ **29.** $F(x, y, \lambda) = xy + \lambda(40 - 2x - y)$; $x = 10$, $y = 20$ **31.** $y = \frac{5}{2}x - \frac{5}{3}$ **33.** $y = -2x + 1$ **35.** 5160 **37.** 40

ANSWERS SECTION

From *Finite Mathematics & Its Applications,* Tenth Edition by Larry J. Goldstein, David I. Schneider, and Martha J. Siegel ISBN: 0321571894

ANSWERS

CHAPTER 1

Exercises 1.1, page 7

1., 3., 5.

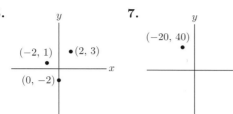

$(-2, 1)$ $\bullet (2, 3)$ $(0, -2)$

7.

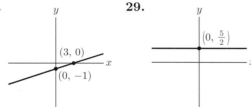

$(-20, 40)$

9. e **11.** Yes **13.** No **15.** $m = 5, b = 8$
17. $m = 0, b = 3$ **19.** $y = -2x + 3$
21. $x = \frac{5}{3}$ **23.** $(2, 0), (0, 8)$ **25.** $(7, 0)$, none

27.

$(3, 0)$ $(0, -1)$

29.

$\left(0, \frac{5}{2}\right)$

31.

$(0, 6)$ $(8, 0)$

33.

$\left(-\frac{5}{2}, 0\right)$

35. a, b, c, e **37.** (a) L_3 (b) L_1 (c) L_2 **41.** (a)
39. (a) Water at a temperature of $72°$F was
placed in the kettle. (b) $162°$F
(c) $4\frac{2}{3}$ minutes, or 4 minutes, 40 seconds

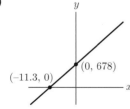

$\left(-33\frac{1}{3}, 0\right)$ $(0, 2.5)$

(b) In 1960, 2.5 trillion
cigarettes were sold.
(c) 1980
(d) 7 trillion

43. (a)

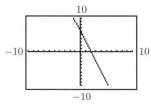

$(0, 678)$ $(-11.3, 0)$

(b) In 1997 the yearly insurance rate for a small car was \$678.
(c) \$858 (d) The year 2012
45. (a) In 2000, 10% of college freshmen smoked. (b) 6.3% (c) 2007
47. $y = -1.5x + .9$ **49.** $y = 0$ **51.** $y = b$ **53.** $2x - y = -3$
55. $1 \cdot x + 0 \cdot y = -3$ **57.** $2x + 3y = -15$ **61.** $y = x - 9$
63. $y = x + 7$ **65.** $y = x + 2$ **67.** $y = x + 9$

69. (a)

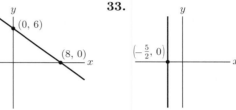

(b) 0
(c) $(2, 0), (0, 6)$

71. (a)

(b) $\frac{13}{3}$
(c) $(-4.5, 0), (0, 3)$

73. $[-10, 110]$ by $[-10, 60]$

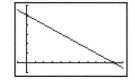

Exercises 1.2, page 16

1. False   **3.** True   **5.** $x \geq 4$ **7.** $x \geq 3$ **9.** $y \leq -2x + 5$ **11.** $y \geq 15x - 18$ **13.** $x \geq -\frac{3}{4}$ **15.** Yes   **17.** No
19. Yes   **21.** Yes   **23.** 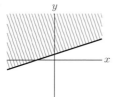   **25.** 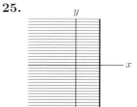   **27.**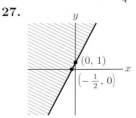

29. 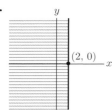   **31.** 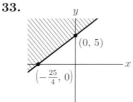   **33.** 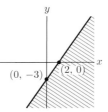   **35.**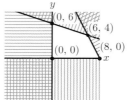

37. 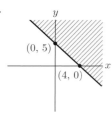   **39.** 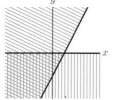   **41.** 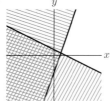   **43.**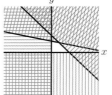

45. Yes   **47.** No   **49.** Below   **61.**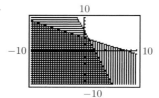
51. Above
53. $\begin{cases} y \geq 2x - 1 \\ y \leq 2x \end{cases}$
55. d   **57.** e
59. (a) $(6, 2.5)$ **(b)** Above

Exercises 1.3, page 22

1. $(2, 3)$ **3.** $(2, 1)$ **5.** $(12, 3)$ **17.** 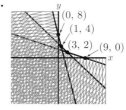   **19.**   **21.**
7. Yes   **9.** $x = \frac{10}{3}, y = \frac{1}{3}$
11. $x = -\frac{7}{9}, y = -\frac{22}{9}$
13. $A = (3, 4), B = (6, 2)$
15. $A = (0, 0), B = (2, 4),$
$C = \left(5, \frac{11}{2}\right), D = (5, 0)$

23. (a) \$2.00 **(b)** \$.05 or less   **25.** 29,500 units; \$3.00   **27.** 180; \$13.60   **29.** $(18, 63)$; Both plans cost 63 cents for 18 minute calls.   **31.** d   **33.** $(1.69, 3.38)$ **35.** $(1, 1)$

37. (a) 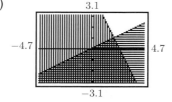   **(b)** $(2, 1)$ **(c)**   **(d)** Yes

Exercises 1.4, page 30

1. $\frac{2}{3}$ **5.** $m = \frac{5}{4}$ **7.** $m = \frac{4}{5}$ **9.** Undefined   **11.**   **13.**

3. 5

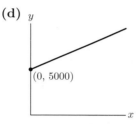

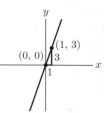

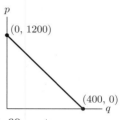

15. $y = -2x + 7$ **17.** $y = -2x + 4$ **19.** $y = \frac{1}{4}x + \frac{3}{2}$ **21.** $y = -x$ **23.** $y = 3$ **25.** $(0, 3)$ **27.** Each unit sold yields a commission of \$5. In addition, she receives \$60 per week base pay.

29. **(a)** $(0, 1200)$; at \$1200 no one will buy the item.

(b) $(400, 0)$; even if the item is given away, only 400 will be taken.

(c) -3; to sell an additional item, the price must be reduced by \$3.

(d) \$150   **(e)** 300 items

(f)

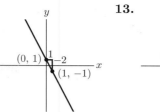

31. **(a)** $y = 90x + 5000$ **(d)**

(b) \$5000   **(c)** \$90

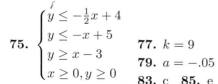

33. **(a)** \$30,000   **(b)** 60 coats

(c) $(0, 0)$; if no coats are sold, there is no revenue.

(d) 100; each additional coat yields an additional \$100 in revenue.

35. **(a)**

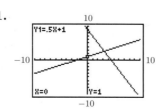

(b) 17,600 gallons

(c) 12,000 gallons

(d) $(0, 30,000)$; the tank holds 30,000 gallons.

(e) $(75, 0)$; the tank is empty after 75 days.

37. **(a)** $y = .1x + 220$ **(b)** \$420   **(c)** \$3200

39. $y = 3x - 1$ **41.** $y = x + 1$ **43.** $y = -7x + 35$

45. $y = 4$ **47.** $y = \frac{1}{2}x$ **49.** $y = -2x$ **51.** $5; 1; -1$

53. $-\frac{5}{4}; -\frac{3}{2}; -\frac{3}{4}$ **55.** **(a)** (C)   **(b)** (B)   **(c)** (D)

(d) (A)   **57.** $y = x + 1$ **59.** $y = 5$ **61.** $y = -\frac{2}{3}x$

63. $F = \frac{9}{5}C + 32$ **65.** $y = \frac{2837}{11}x + 2848$; \$4137.55

67. $y = -\frac{1}{2}x + 25$; 21 mpg   **69.** 341,001

71. $y = .1x + 1.9$; \$2.6 million   **73.** $y \geq 4x + 3$

75. $\begin{cases} y \leq -\frac{1}{2}x + 4 \\ y \leq -x + 5 \\ y \geq x - 3 \\ x \geq 0, y \geq 0 \end{cases}$ **77.** $k = 9$ **91.**

79. $a = -.05$

83. c   **85.** e

87. c   **89.** d

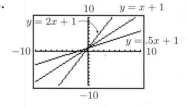

93.

Exercises 1.5, page 41

1. 4   **3.** 6.70   **5.** $m = -1.4, b = 8.5$ **7.** $y = 4.5x - 3$ **9.** $y = -2x + 11.5$ **11.** **(a)** $y = .338x + 21.6$

(b) About 393   **13.** **(a)** $y = .419x + 17.1$ **(b)** About 26.7%   **(c)** 2011 (or late 2010)

15. **(a)** $y = .153x + 73.5$ **(b)** 78.09   **(c)** 81.15   **(d)** 87.27 This is an example of a fit that is not capable of extrapolating beyond the given data.   **17.** **(a)** $y = .048x + 2.89$ **(b)** \$3.18   **(c)** 2013   **19.** $y = -.5x + 6.5$

Chapter 1: Supplementary Exercises, page 46

1. $x = 0$ **2.**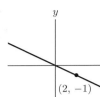
$(2, -1)$

3. $\left(2, -\frac{4}{5}\right)$
4. $\frac{3}{4}$
5. $y = -\frac{1}{2}x + 5$

6.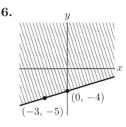
$(0, -4)$
$(-3, -5)$

7. Yes   **8.** $(3, 5)$ **9.** $y = \frac{1}{5}x + 13$
10. 10   **11.** $(5, 0)$

12.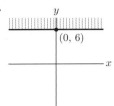
$(0, 6)$

13. $(7, 10)$ **14.**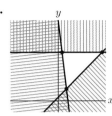

15. $(0, 7)$
16. The rate is \$35 per hour plus a flat fee of \$20.   **17.** No   **18.** $y = \frac{2}{3}x - 2$ **19.** d
20. $y \le \frac{2}{3}x + \frac{3}{2}$ **21.** $y \ge 2.4x - 5.8$
22. $x = -.3$, $y = .4$ **23.** $y = -\frac{2}{5}x + \frac{7}{5}$
24. $x \ge \frac{6}{5}$

25. $m = -2$;
y-intercept: $(0, 8)$;
x-intercept: $(4, 0)$;

$(0, 8)$
$(4, 0)$

26. No
28. (a) (C)   (b) (A)   (c) (B)   (d) (D)
29. (a) L_3 (b) L_1 (c) L_2 **30.** $\begin{cases} y \le -\frac{7}{8}x + 5 \\ y \ge \frac{8}{7}x - \frac{43}{14} \\ x \ge 0, y \ge 0 \end{cases}$; $\left(\frac{43}{16}, 0\right)$

31. 300 units; \$2
32. $(0, 0)$, $(10, 0)$, $(9, 5)$, $(6, 7)$, $(0, 4)$
33. (a) In 2000, 8.8% of entering college freshmen intended to eventually obtain a degree in a medical field.   (b) 9.6%   (c) 2004

34. (a) $y = 10x - 6000$ (c)
(b) x-intercept: $(600, 0)$,
y-intercept: $(0, -6000)$
$(600, 0)$
$(0, -6000)$

35. (a) A: $y = .1x + 50$,   **37.**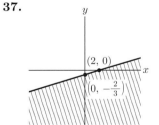
B: $y = .2x + 40$
(b) B   (c) A
(d) 100 miles
36. (a) $y = .031x + .69$
(b) 2000
$(2, 0)$
$\left(0, -\frac{2}{3}\right)$

38. \$5000   **39.** $\begin{cases} y \le \frac{5}{4}x + 5 \\ y \le -\frac{2}{5}x + 2 \\ y \ge \frac{3}{5}x - 3 \\ y \ge -\frac{5}{2}x - 5 \end{cases}$ **40.** $\begin{cases} y \le -\frac{2}{3}x + 2 \\ y \ge -3 \\ x \ge -2 \\ x \le 4 \end{cases}$ **41.** $y = 14{,}800x + 417{,}000$; 505,800   **42.** 106,286

43. 18.1%   **44.** (a) $y = 1.06x + 1.71$ (b) 71.2   (c) 91.0   **45.** (a) $y = .18x + 3.06$ (b) 4.68%   (c) 2013
46. (a) $y = .152x - 3.063$ (b) About 21   (c) About 165 grams   **47.** Up   **48.** Counterclockwise   **51.** No; no

Chapter 1: Chapter Test, page 49

1.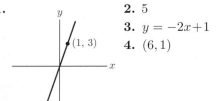
$(1, 3)$

2. 5
3. $y = -2x + 1$
4. $(6, 1)$

6.
$(0, 8)$
$(8, 0)$

7. $y = 2x - \frac{71}{11}$
8. $(16, 0)$; $(25, 0)$; $(13, 36)$; $(2, 14)$
9. Less than \$2500; greater than \$2500
10. (a) $y = .033x + .819$ (b) \$0.98
(c) 2012

CHAPTER 2

Exercises 2.1, page 60

1. $\xrightarrow{2R_1}$ $\begin{cases} x - 6y = 4 \\ 5x + 4y = 1 \end{cases}$ **3.** $\xrightarrow{R_2 + 5R_1}$ $\begin{cases} x + 2y = 3 \\ 14y = 16 \end{cases}$ **5.** $\xrightarrow{R_3 + (-4)R_1}$ $\begin{cases} x - 2y + z = 0 \\ y - 2z = 4 \\ 9y - z = 5 \end{cases}$

7. $\xrightarrow{R_1 + \frac{1}{2}R_2}$ $\begin{bmatrix} 1 & 0 & | & 5 \\ 0 & 1 & | & 4 \end{bmatrix}$ **9.** $\begin{bmatrix} -3 & 4 & | & -2 \\ 1 & -7 & | & 8 \end{bmatrix}$ **11.** $\begin{bmatrix} 1 & 13 & -2 & | & 0 \\ 2 & 0 & -1 & | & 3 \\ 0 & 1 & 0 & | & 5 \end{bmatrix}$ **13.** $\begin{cases} -2y = 3 \\ x + 7y = -4 \end{cases}$

15. $\begin{cases} 3x + 2y = -3 \\ y - 6z = 4 \\ -5x - y + 7z = 0 \end{cases}$ **17.** Multiply the second row of the matrix by $\frac{1}{3}$. **19.** Change the first row of the

matrix by adding to it 3 times the second row. **21.** Interchange rows 2 and 3. **23.** $\begin{bmatrix} 1 & 2 & | & 0 \\ 0 & 10 & | & 5 \end{bmatrix}$

25. $\begin{bmatrix} 1 & 2 & | & 3 \\ 3 & -2 & | & 0 \end{bmatrix}$ **27.** $\begin{bmatrix} 1 & 3 & | & -5 \\ 0 & 1 & | & 7 \end{bmatrix}$ **29.** $R_2 + 2R_1$ **31.** $R_1 + (-2)R_2$ **33.** $R_1 \leftrightarrow R_2$ or $R_1 \leftrightarrow R_3$

35. $R_1 + (-3)R_3$ **37.** $x = -1, y = 1$ **39.** $x = -\frac{8}{7}, y = -\frac{9}{7}, z = -\frac{3}{7}$ **41.** $x = -1, y = 1$ **43.** $x = 1, y = 2,$
$z = -1$ **45.** $x = -2.5, y = 15$ **47.** $x = 1, y = -6, z = 2$ **49.** $x = -1, y = -2, z = 5$ **51.** b **53.** d **55.** 150
short sleeve, 200 long sleeve **57.** 262 adults, 88 children **59.** $x = \$25,000, y = \$50,000, z = \$25,000$ **61.** $23\frac{1}{3}$
pounds of first type, 85 pounds of second type, $201\frac{2}{3}$ pounds of third type **67.** $x = 1, y = -6, z = 2$

Exercises 2.2, page 69

1. $\begin{bmatrix} 1 & -2 & | & 3 \\ 0 & 13 & | & -8 \end{bmatrix}$ **3.** $\begin{bmatrix} 9 & -1 & 0 & | & -7 \\ -\frac{1}{2} & \frac{1}{2} & 1 & | & 3 \\ 5 & -1 & 0 & | & -3 \end{bmatrix}$ **5.** $\begin{bmatrix} 1 & \frac{3}{2} \\ 0 & -9 \\ 0 & \frac{7}{2} \end{bmatrix}$ **7.** $\begin{bmatrix} 4 & 3 & 0 \\ 1 & 1 & 0 \\ \frac{1}{6} & \frac{1}{2} & 1 \end{bmatrix}$ **9.** $y =$ any value, $x = 3 + 2y$

11. $x = 1, y = 2$ **13.** No solution **15.** $z =$ any value, $x = -6 - z, y = 5$ **17.** No solution **19.** $z =$ any value,
$w =$ any value, $x = 2z + w, y = 5 - 3w$ **21.** $x = 5, y = 7$ **23.** Possible answers: $z = 0, x = -13, y = 9; z = 1,$
$x = -8, y = 6; z = 2, x = -3, y = 3$ **25.** Possible answers: $y = 0, x = 23, z = 5; y = 1, x = 16, z = 5; y = 2,$
$x = 9, z = 5$ **27.** $x =$ food 1, $y =$ food 2, $z =$ food 3; $z =$ any amount, $x = 300 - z, y = 100 - z$ $(0 \le z \le 100)$
29. 6 floral squares, the other 90 any mix of solid green and solid blue **31.** $x = \pm 1, y = \pm 2, z = \pm 3$ **33.** No
solution if $k \ne -12$. Infinitely many if $k = -12$. **35.** b **37.** One; $x = 7, y = 3$ **39.** No solution

Exercises 2.3, page 81

1. 2×3 **3.** 1×3, row matrix **5.** 2×2, square matrix **7.** $-4; 0$ **9.** $i = 1, j = 3$ **11.** $\begin{bmatrix} 9 & 3 \\ 7 & -1 \end{bmatrix}$

13. $\begin{bmatrix} 1 & 3 \\ 1 & 2 \\ 4 & -2 \end{bmatrix}$ **15.** $[11]$ **17.** $[10]$ **19.** Yes; 3×5 **21.** No **23.** Yes; 3×1 **25.** $\begin{bmatrix} 6 & 17 \\ 6 & 10 \end{bmatrix}$ **27.** $\begin{bmatrix} 21 \\ -4 \\ 8 \end{bmatrix}$

29. $\begin{bmatrix} 5 & 6 \\ 7 & 8 \end{bmatrix}$ **31.** $\begin{bmatrix} .48 & .39 \\ .52 & .61 \end{bmatrix}$ **33.** $\begin{bmatrix} 25 & 17 & 2 \\ 3 & -1 & 2 \\ 1 & 1 & 4 \end{bmatrix}$ **35.** $\begin{cases} 2x + 3y = 6 \\ 4x + 5y = 7 \end{cases}$ **37.** $\begin{cases} x + 2y + 3z = 10 \\ 4x + 5y + 6z = 11 \\ 7x + 8y + 9z = 12 \end{cases}$

39. $\begin{bmatrix} 3 & 2 \\ 7 & -1 \end{bmatrix} \begin{bmatrix} x \\ y \end{bmatrix} = \begin{bmatrix} -1 \\ 2 \end{bmatrix}$ **41.** $\begin{bmatrix} 1 & -2 & 3 \\ 0 & 1 & 1 \\ 0 & 0 & 1 \end{bmatrix} \begin{bmatrix} x \\ y \\ z \end{bmatrix} = \begin{bmatrix} 5 \\ 6 \\ 2 \end{bmatrix}$ **47. (a)** $\begin{bmatrix} 340 \\ 265 \end{bmatrix}$ **(b)** Mike's clothes cost \$340;

Don's clothes cost \$265. **49. (a)** $[2282.50 \quad 2322.50 \quad 3550.50]$, total cost for the plain, milk chocolate-covered,

and dark chocolate-covered items **(b)** $\begin{bmatrix} 3138.00 \\ 3337.50 \\ 6772.50 \end{bmatrix}$, total revenue from peanuts, raisins, and espresso beans

51. (a) I: 2.75, II: 2, III: 1.3   **(b)** A: 74, B: 112, C: 128, D: 64, F: 22   **53.** 10,100 voting Democratic, 7900 voting Republican   **55.** Carpenters: \$1000, bricklayers: \$1050, plumbers: \$600   **57. (a)** $\begin{bmatrix} 162 & 150 & 143 \end{bmatrix}$, number of units of each nutrient consumed at breakfast   **(b)** $\begin{bmatrix} 186 & 200 & 239 \end{bmatrix}$, number of units of each nutrient consumed at lunch   **(c)** $\begin{bmatrix} 288 & 300 & 344 \end{bmatrix}$, number of units of each nutrient consumed at dinner   **(d)** $\begin{bmatrix} 5 & 8 \end{bmatrix}$, total number of ounces of each food that Mikey eats during a day   **(e)** $\begin{bmatrix} 636 & 650 & 726 \end{bmatrix}$, number of units of each nutrient consumed per day   **59. (a)** $\begin{bmatrix} 720 \\ 646 \end{bmatrix}$ **(b)** \$720

61. (a) $T = \begin{bmatrix} 30 & 45 \\ 30 & 50 \\ 15 & 10 \end{bmatrix} \begin{matrix} \text{Preparation} \\ \text{Baking} \\ \text{Finishing} \end{matrix}$ (columns: Boston cream pie, Carrot cake)

(b) $S = \begin{bmatrix} 20 \\ 8 \end{bmatrix} \begin{matrix} \text{Boston cream pie} \\ \text{Carrot cake} \end{matrix}$; $TS = \begin{bmatrix} 960 \\ 1000 \\ 380 \end{bmatrix} \begin{matrix} \text{Preparation} \\ \text{Baking} \\ \text{Finishing} \end{matrix}$ **(c)** Total baking time: 1000 minutes or 16 2/3 hours; total finishing time: 380 minutes or 6 1/3 hours

63. (a) $T = \begin{bmatrix} 2 & 3 & 2 \\ 1.5 & 2 & 1 \end{bmatrix} \begin{matrix} \text{Huge One} \\ \text{Regular Joe} \end{matrix}$ (columns: Cutting, Sewing, Finishing)   **(b)** $S = \begin{bmatrix} 32 \\ 24 \end{bmatrix} \begin{matrix} \text{Huge One} \\ \text{Regular Joe} \end{matrix}$

(c) $A = \begin{bmatrix} 27 & 56 \end{bmatrix}$ (columns: Huge One, Regular Joe); $AT = \begin{bmatrix} 138 & 193 & 110 \end{bmatrix}$ (columns: Cutting, Sewing, Finishing); $AS = \begin{bmatrix} 2208 \end{bmatrix}$ **(d)** 193 hours

(e) \$2208   **67.** $\begin{bmatrix} 3 & -2 & 1 \\ -5 & 6 & 7 \end{bmatrix}$ **69.** 4×4 **71.** $\begin{bmatrix} 7998 & 56{,}685 & 96{,}158 \end{bmatrix} \begin{bmatrix} 15.1 \\ 15.2 \\ 12.6 \end{bmatrix}$

73. $\begin{bmatrix} 27.9 & 130.6 & -69.88 \\ 106.75 & -149.44 & 26.1 \\ -47.5 & 336.2 & -18.7 \end{bmatrix}$ **75.** $\begin{bmatrix} -69.14 & 147.9 & -43.26 \\ 158.05 & -3.69 & 33.46 \\ -176.1 & 259.5 & 59.3 \end{bmatrix}$ **77.** $\begin{bmatrix} 160.16 & -26.7 & 4 \\ 2.7 & 150.85 & -53 \\ 187.4 & -35.5 & 48.6 \end{bmatrix}$
79. They match.

Exercises 2.4, page 94

1. $x = 2$, $y = 0$ **3.** $\begin{bmatrix} 1 & -2 \\ -3 & 7 \end{bmatrix}$ **5.** $\begin{bmatrix} 1 & -1 \\ -\frac{5}{2} & 3 \end{bmatrix}$ **7.** $\begin{bmatrix} 1.6 & -.4 \\ -.6 & 1.4 \end{bmatrix}$ **9.** $\begin{bmatrix} \frac{1}{3} \end{bmatrix}$ **11.** $x = 4$, $y = -\frac{1}{2}$ **13.** $x = 32$, $y = -6$ **15. (a)** $\begin{bmatrix} .8 & .3 \\ .2 & .7 \end{bmatrix} \begin{bmatrix} x \\ y \end{bmatrix} = \begin{bmatrix} m \\ s \end{bmatrix}$ **(b)** $\begin{bmatrix} x \\ y \end{bmatrix} = \begin{bmatrix} 1.4 & -.6 \\ -.4 & 1.6 \end{bmatrix} \begin{bmatrix} m \\ s \end{bmatrix}$ **(c)** 110,000 married; 40,000 single

(d) 130,000 married; 20,000 single   **17. (a)** $\begin{bmatrix} .7 & .1 \\ .3 & .9 \end{bmatrix} \begin{bmatrix} x \\ y \end{bmatrix} = \begin{bmatrix} u \\ v \end{bmatrix}$ **(b)** $\begin{bmatrix} x \\ y \end{bmatrix} = \begin{bmatrix} \frac{3}{2} & -\frac{1}{6} \\ -\frac{1}{2} & \frac{7}{6} \end{bmatrix} \begin{bmatrix} u \\ v \end{bmatrix}$ **(c)** 8500;

4500   **19.** $x = 9$, $y = -2$, $z = -2$ **21.** $x = 1$, $y = 5$, $z = -4$, $w = 9$ **25. (a)** $\begin{bmatrix} 1 & 2 \\ .9 & 0 \end{bmatrix} \begin{bmatrix} x \\ y \end{bmatrix} = \begin{bmatrix} a \\ b \end{bmatrix}$ **(b)** After 1 year: 1,170,000 in group I and 405,000 in group II. After 2 years: 1,980,000 in group I and 1,053,000 in group II.   **(c)** 700,000 in group I and 55,000 in group II.   **29.** One possible answer is $\begin{bmatrix} 1 & 1 \\ 1 & 1 \end{bmatrix} \begin{bmatrix} x \\ y \end{bmatrix} = \begin{bmatrix} 2 \\ 3 \end{bmatrix}$.

31. $\begin{bmatrix} -\frac{10}{73} & \frac{75}{292} \\ \frac{25}{73} & -\frac{5}{292} \end{bmatrix}$ **33.** $\begin{bmatrix} \frac{1020}{8887} & \frac{2910}{8887} & -\frac{500}{8887} \\ \frac{3050}{8887} & \frac{860}{8887} & \frac{1990}{8887} \\ \frac{125}{8887} & \frac{618}{8887} & \frac{810}{8887} \end{bmatrix}$ **35.** $x = -\frac{4}{5}$, $y = \frac{28}{5}$, $z = 5$ **37.** $x = 0$, $y = 2$, $z = 0$, $w = 2$
39. Displays ERR:SINGULAR MAT.

Exercises 2.5, page 101

1. $\begin{bmatrix} -2 & 3 \\ 5 & -7 \end{bmatrix}$ **3.** $\begin{bmatrix} \frac{7}{2} & \frac{3}{2} \\ -2 & -1 \end{bmatrix}$ **5.** No inverse   **7.** $\begin{bmatrix} -1 & 2 & -4 \\ 1 & -1 & 3 \\ 0 & 0 & 1 \end{bmatrix}$ **9.** No inverse   **11.** $\begin{bmatrix} -5 & 6 & 0 & 0 \\ 1 & -1 & 0 & 0 \\ 0 & 0 & -\frac{1}{46} & \frac{1}{46} \\ 0 & 0 & \frac{25}{46} & -\frac{1}{23} \end{bmatrix}$

13. $x = 2$, $y = -3$, $z = 2$ **15.** $x = 4$, $y = -4$, $z = 3$, $w = -1$ **17.** $\begin{bmatrix} -3 & 7 \\ 1 & -2 \end{bmatrix}$ **19.** $\begin{bmatrix} -3 & 5 \\ 10 & -16 \end{bmatrix}$

Exercises 2.6, page 107

1. 20 cents   **3.** Energy sector   **5.** Coal: \$8.84 billion, steel: \$3.725 billion, electricity: \$9.895 billion

7. Computers: \$354 million, semiconductors: \$172 million   **11. (a)** $A = \begin{bmatrix} .25 & .30 \\ .20 & .15 \end{bmatrix} \begin{matrix} T \\ E \end{matrix}$ with column headers $T\ \ E$

(b) $\begin{bmatrix} 1.47 & .52 \\ .35 & 1.30 \end{bmatrix}$ **(c)** Transportation: \$8.91 billion, energy: \$5.65 billion.   **13.** Plastics: \$955,000, industrial equipment: \$590,000   **15.** Manufacturing: \$398 million, transportation: \$313 million, agriculture: \$452 million   **19.** $\begin{bmatrix} 10.25 \\ 13.82 \\ 8.65 \end{bmatrix}$

Chapter 2: Supplementary Exercises, page 110

1. $\begin{bmatrix} 1 & -2 & \frac{1}{3} \\ 0 & 8 & \frac{16}{3} \end{bmatrix}$ **2.** $\begin{bmatrix} 1 & 0 & 1 \\ 2 & 1 & 0 \\ -12 & 0 & 7 \end{bmatrix}$ **3.** $x = 4$, $y = 5$ **4.** $x = 50$, $y = 2$, $z = -12$ **5.** $x = -1$, $y = \frac{2}{3}$, $z = \frac{1}{3}$

6. No solution   **7.** $z =$ any value, $x = 1 - 3z$, $y = 4z$, $w = 5$ **8.** $x = 7$, $y = 3$ **9.** $\begin{bmatrix} 5 \\ 3 \\ 7 \end{bmatrix}$ **10.** $\begin{bmatrix} 6 & 17 \\ 12 & 26 \end{bmatrix}$

11. $x = -2$, $y = 3$ **12. (a)** $x = 13$, $y = 23$, $z = 19$ **(b)** $x = -4$, $y = 13$, $z = 14$ **13.** $\begin{bmatrix} -1 & 3 \\ \frac{1}{2} & -1 \end{bmatrix}$

14. $\begin{bmatrix} 5 & -1 & -1 \\ -3 & 1 & 0 \\ -1 & 0 & 1 \end{bmatrix}$ **15.** Corn: 500 acres; Wheat: 0 acres; Soybeans: 500 acres   **16. (a)** $\begin{bmatrix} 5455 \\ 5275 \end{bmatrix}$; total

month's costs for each store   **(b)** $\begin{bmatrix} 6600 \\ 6360 \end{bmatrix}$; total month's revenue for each store   **(c)** $\begin{bmatrix} 35 \\ 15 \\ 40 \end{bmatrix}$; profit for each

piece of equipment   **(d)** $\begin{bmatrix} 1145 \\ 1085 \end{bmatrix}$; total month's profit for each store   **17. (a)** $\begin{bmatrix} 10,100 & 8230 & 4670 \end{bmatrix}$; total amount invested in bonds, stocks, and the conservative fixed income fund, respectively   **(b)** $\begin{bmatrix} 522.40 & 1807.30 \end{bmatrix}$; total returns on the investments for one year and five years, respectively   **(c)** \$8230 is the total amount invested in stocks.   **(d)** \$522.40 is the total return after one year.

18. (a) $\begin{bmatrix} 238 \\ 246 \\ 233 \\ 236 \end{bmatrix}$; total amount earned by each person for the week   **(b)** Most: Quinn; least: Tamia

(c) Quinn and Zack each earn \$239.   **(d)** 30 hours   **19.** 4 apples, 9 bananas, 5 oranges   **20. (a)** A: 9400, 8980; B: 7300, 7510   **(b)** A: 10,857, 12,082; B: 6571, 5959   **21.** Industry I: 20; industry II: 20   **22.** a
23. (a) True   **(b)** False   **(c)** True   **25.** No

Chapter 2: Chapter Test, page 112

1. $x = 2$, $y = 4$, $z = -5$ **2. (a)** $x = 4$, $y = -3$, $z = 6$ **(b)** $x = 2$, $y = 3$, $z = 5$ **(c)** No solution
(d) $z =$ any value; $x = z + 2$, $y = -2z + 2$ **(e)** $y =$ any value; $x = -2y$, $z = 0$ **3.** $w = 1$, $z = 2$, $x = 3$, $y = 5$
4. (1) $z = 0$, $y = 6$, $x = 9$; **(2)** $z = 1$, $y = 2$, $x = 15$; **(3)** $z = -1$, $y = 10$, $x = 3$ **5.** Not defined; $\begin{bmatrix} 2 & 2 & 2 \\ 2 & 3 & 2 \end{bmatrix}$;

$\begin{bmatrix} -2 & 3 \\ -2 & 4 \end{bmatrix}$; not defined; $\begin{bmatrix} -1 & 0 & -1 \\ -1 & 1 & 1 \\ 1 & 0 & 1 \end{bmatrix}$ **6. (a)** $.5x + y + z = m$; $3x + 2.5y + 2z = v$; $4x + 3y + 2z = p$

(b) $\begin{bmatrix} .5 & 1 & 1 \\ 3 & 2.5 & 2 \\ 4 & 3 & 2 \end{bmatrix} \cdot \begin{bmatrix} x \\ y \\ z \end{bmatrix} = \begin{bmatrix} m \\ v \\ p \end{bmatrix}$ **(c)** 550 hours molding time, 1450 hours oven time, 1700 hours painting time

7. $\begin{bmatrix} \frac{1}{2} & -\frac{1}{2} & \frac{1}{2} \\ \frac{1}{2} & -\frac{1}{2} & -\frac{1}{2} \\ -\frac{1}{2} & \frac{3}{2} & \frac{1}{2} \end{bmatrix}$ **8.** 400 students   **9.** Wood: \$1.98, steel: \$7.39, coal: \$3.87

CHAPTER 3

Exercises 3.1, page 121

1. Yes   **3.** No   **5. (a)**

	A	**B**	**Truck capacity**
Volume	4 cubic feet	3 cubic feet	300 cubic feet
Weight	100 pounds	200 pounds	10,000 pounds
Earnings	\$13	\$9	

(b) $4x + 3y \leq 300$; $100x + 200y \leq 10{,}000$
(c) $y \leq 2x$, $x \geq 0$, $y \geq 0$
(d) $13x + 9y$

(e)

7. (a)

	Essay questions	**Short-answer questions**	**Available**
Time to answer	10 minutes	2 minutes	90 minutes
Quantity	10	50	
Required	3	10	
Worth	20 points	5 points	

(b) $10x + 2y \leq 90$ **(c)** $x \geq 3$, $x \leq 10$, $y \geq 10$, $y \leq 50$ **(d)** $20x + 5y$

(e)

9. (a)

	Alfalfa	**Corn**	**Requirements**
Protein	.13 pound	.065 pound	4550 pounds
TDN	.48 pound	.96 pound	26,880 pounds
Vitamin A	2.16 IUs	0 IUs	43,200 IUs
Cost/lb	\$0.01	\$0.016	

(b) $.13x + .065y \geq 4550$;
$.48x + .96y \geq 26{,}880$;
$2.16x \geq 43{,}200$; $y \geq 0$

(c)

(d) $.01x + .016y$

Exercises 3.2, page 130

1. $(20, 0)$ **3.** $(6, 0)$ **5.** $(0, 5)$ **7.** $(3, 3)$ **9.** $(0, 7)$ **11.** $(2, 1)$ **13.** Ship 75 crates of cargo A and no crates of cargo B. **15.** Answer 3 essay questions and 30 short-answer questions. **17.** The minimum cost of $504 is achieved by buying 28,000 pounds of alfalfa and 14,000 pounds of corn. **19.** Make 16 chairs and no sofas.
21. The minimum value is 30 and occurs at $(2, 6)$. **23.** The maximum value is 49 and occurs at $(2, 9)$.
25. The maximum value is 6600 and occurs at $(12, 36)$. **27.** The minimum value is 40 and occurs at $(4, 3)$.
29. Produce 9 hockey games and 8 soccer games each day. **31.** Supply 6 tubes of food A and 6 tubes of food B.
33. Make 400 cans of Fruit Delight and 500 cans of Heavenly Punch. **35.** The farmer should plant $83\frac{1}{3}$ acres of oats and $16\frac{2}{3}$ acres of corn to make a profit of $6933.33. **37. (b)** The farmer should plant 78 acres of oats and 22 acres of corn to make a profit of $7040. Yes, it provides more profit. **39.** Produce 49 regular bags and 14 deluxe bags. **41.** The feasible set contains no points. **43.** The maximum value is 84 and occurs at $(12, 0)$.

Exercises 3.3, page 143

1. (a) $y = -\frac{3}{2}x + \frac{c}{14}$ **(b)** Up **(c)** B **3.** Possible answer: $5x + y$ **5.** Possible answer: $2x + y$ **7.** Possible answer: $x + 5y$ **9.** Possible answer: $2x + 3y$ **11.** C **13.** D **15.** D **17.** C **19.** $\frac{1}{4} \le k \le 3$ **21.** Feed 1 can of brand A and 3 cans of brand B. **23.** Mr. Jones should invest $2000 in low-risk stocks, $3000 in medium-risk stocks, and $4000 in high-risk stocks. **25.** Let (a, b) correspond to a cars shipped from Baltimore to Philadelphia, b cars shipped from Baltimore to Trenton, $4 - a$ cars shipped from NY to Philadelphia, and $7 - b$ cars shipped from NY to Trenton. Then the minimum cost of $990 is achieved at $(0, 5)$, $(4, 1)$, or anywhere on the line segment connecting these two points. **27.** Produce 90,000 gallons of gasoline, 5000 gallons of jet fuel, and 5000 gallons of diesel fuel. **29.** Buy 9 high-capacity trucks and 21 low-capacity trucks. **31.** Ship 400 pounds of coffee from Seattle to Salt Lake City and 350 pounds from San José to Reno. **33.** Create 22 of Kit I, 10 of Kit II, and 12 of Kit III. **35.** rice: $[9.33, 42]$; soybeans: $[7, 31.5]$

Chapter 3: Supplementary Exercises, page 146

1. Use 10 type A planes and 3 type B planes. **2.** Use 2 ounces of wheat germ and 1 ounce of enriched oat flour.
3. Produce 9 hardtops and 16 sports cars. **4.** Make 500 boxes of mixture A and 200 boxes of mixture B.
5. Publish 60 elementary books, 8 intermediate books, and 4 advanced books. **6.** Transport 80 computers from Rochester and 45 computers from Queens. **7.** Transport no computers from warehouse A to outlet I, 200 computers from warehouse A to outlet II, 200 computers from warehouse B to outlet I, and 100 computers from warehouse B to outlet II. **8.** Invest $2000 in the CD, $0 in mutual funds, and $8000 in stocks. **9.** Yes; No
10. Yes; No

Chapter 3: Chapter Test, page 147

1. Step 1: Translate the problem into mathematical language. Identify variables and write the inequalities and objective function.
Step 2: Graph the feasible set.
Step 3: Determine the vertices of the feasible set.
Step 4: Evaluate the objective function at each vertex. Determine the optimal point.
2. (a) Minimize $70x + 90y$ subject to $\begin{cases} 20x + 30y \ge 300 \\ 10x + 20y \ge 200 \\ x \ge 0, y \ge 0 \end{cases}$

(b) Maximize $.07x + .06y + .045z$ subject to $\begin{cases} y \ge 150,000 \\ z \le 200,000 \\ x + y + z \le 500,000 \\ x \ge .5y \\ x \ge 0, y \ge 0, z \ge 0 \end{cases}$

3. (a)

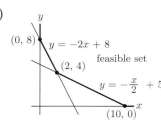

(b) No **4.** $(0, 10)$; $(7, 5)$; $(9, 3)$; $(9, 0)$; $(0, 0)$

5. (a) $x = 10$, $y = 0$ **(b)** $x = 3$, $y = 6$

6. (a) $y = -\frac{8}{5}x + 640$ **(b)** $y = -\frac{8}{5}x + \frac{c}{5}$ **(c)** down **(d)** E

7. C

8. 8 bears and 6 wreaths

FEASIBLE SETS FOR CHAPTER 3

Exercises 3.2

21.

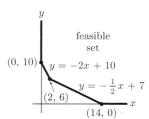

23.

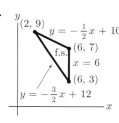

25.

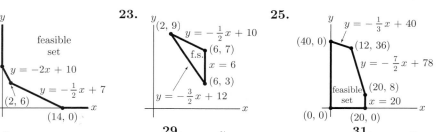

27.

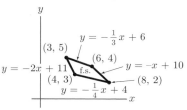

29.

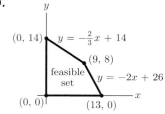

31.

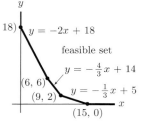

33.

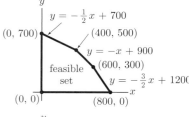

35.

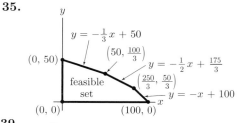

37.

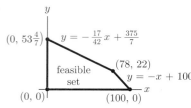

39.

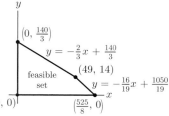

Exercises 3.3

21.

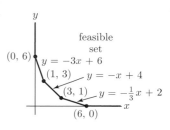

23.

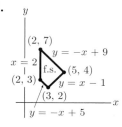

25.

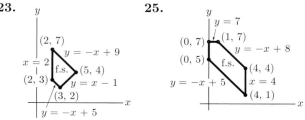

27.

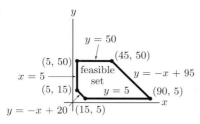

29.

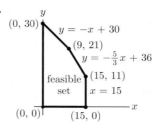

31.

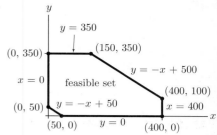

33.

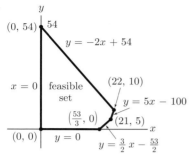

Chapter 3: Supplementary Exercises

1.

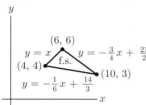

2.

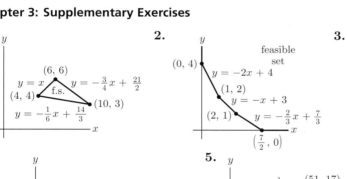

3.

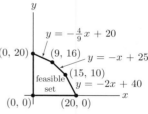

4.

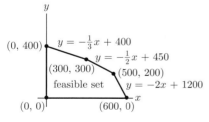

5.

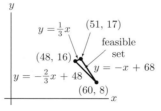

6.

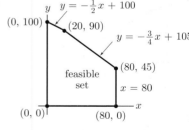

7.

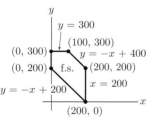

8.

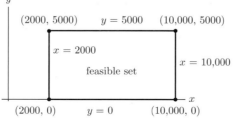

CHAPTER 4

Exercises 4.1, page 159

1. $\begin{cases} 20x + 30y + u \qquad\qquad = 3500 \\ 50x + 10y \qquad + v \qquad = 5000 \\ -8x - 13y \qquad\qquad + M = 0 \end{cases}$ Maximize M given $x \geq 0,\ y \geq 0,\ u \geq 0,\ v \geq 0$.

3.
$$\begin{cases} x + y + z + u & = 100 \\ 3x \quad + z \quad + v & = 200 \\ 5x + 10y \quad + w & = 100 \\ -x - 2y + 3z \quad + M & = 0 \end{cases}$$
Maximize M given $x \geq 0$, $y \geq 0$, $z \geq 0$, $u \geq 0$, $v \geq 0$, $w \geq 0$.

5.
$$\begin{cases} 4x + 6y - 7z + u & = 16 \\ 3x + 2y \quad + v & = 11 \\ 9y + 3z \quad + w & = 21 \\ -3x - 5y - 12z \quad + M = 0 \end{cases}$$
Maximize M given $x \geq 0$, $y \geq 0$, $z \geq 0$, $u \geq 0$, $v \geq 0$, $w \geq 0$.

7. (a)

	x	y	t	u	v	w	M	
	3	2	1	0	0	0	0	10
	1	0	0	1	0	0	0	15
	0	1	0	0	1	0	0	3
	1	1	0	0	0	1	0	5
	-1	-15	0	0	0	0	1	0

(b) $x = 0$, $y = 0$, $t = 10$, $u = 15$, $v = 3$, $w = 5$, $M = 0$

9. (a)

	x	y	u	v	w	M	
	1	3	1	0	0	0	24
	0	1	0	1	0	0	5
	1	7	0	0	1	0	10
	-2	-1	0	0	0	1	50

(b) $x = 0$, $y = 0$, $u = 24$, $v = 5$, $w = 10$, $M = 50$

11. $x = 15$, $y = 0$, $u = 10$, $v = 0$, $M = 20$ **13.** $x = 10$, $y = 0$, $z = 15$, $u = 23$, $v = 0$, $w = 0$, $M = -11$

15. (a)

	x	y	u	v	M	
	1	$\frac{3}{2}$	$\frac{1}{2}$	0	0	6
	0	$-\frac{1}{2}$	$-\frac{1}{2}$	1	0	4
	0	-5	5	0	1	60

$x = 6$, $y = 0$, $u = 0$, $v = 4$, $M = 60$

(b)

	x	y	u	v	M	
	$\frac{2}{3}$	1	$\frac{1}{3}$	0	0	4
	$\frac{1}{3}$	0	$-\frac{1}{3}$	1	0	6
	$\frac{10}{3}$	0	$\frac{20}{3}$	0	1	80

$x = 0$, $y = 4$, $u = 0$, $v = 6$, $M = 80$

(c)

	x	y	u	v	M	
	0	1	1	-2	0	-8
	1	1	0	1	0	10
	0	-10	0	10	1	100

$x = 10$, $y = 0$, $u = -8$, $v = 0$, $M = 100$

(d)

	x	y	u	v	M	
	-1	0	1	-3	0	-18
	1	1	0	1	0	10
	10	0	0	20	1	200

$x = 0$, $y = 10$, $u = -18$, $v = 0$, $M = 200$

17. d   **19. (a)** Group I: x, y; Group II: u, v, M **(b)** (i) feasible; I: y, u; II: x, v, M (ii) feasible; I: x, u; II: y, v, M (iii) not feasible; I: y, v; II: x, u, M (iv) not feasible; I; x, v; II: u, y, M **(c)** Operation (i)

Exercises 4.2, page 169

1. (a) 3   **(b)**

	x	y	u	v	M	
u	$\frac{16}{3}$	0	1	$-\frac{2}{3}$	0	6
y	$\frac{1}{3}$	1	0	$\frac{1}{3}$	0	2
M	0	0	0	4	1	24

(c) $x = 0, y = 2, u = 6, v = 0$; $M = 24$

3. (a) 10   **(b)**

	x	y	u	v	M	
u	-13	0	1	$-\frac{6}{5}$	0	6
y	$\frac{3}{2}$	1	0	$\frac{1}{10}$	0	$\frac{1}{2}$
M	7	0	0	$\frac{1}{5}$	1	1

(c) $x = 0$, $y = \frac{1}{2}$, $u = 6$, $v = 0$, $M = 1$

5. $x = 0$, $y = 5$; $M = 15$ **7.** $x = 12$, $y = 20$; $M = 88$ **9.** $x = 0$, $y = \frac{19}{3}$, $z = 5$; $M = 44$ **11.** $x = 0$, $y = 30$; $M = 90$ **13.** $x = 50$, $y = 100$; $M = 1300$ **15.** 24 basketballs, 224 footballs   **17.** 98 chairs, 4 sofas, 21 tables   **19.** 11 hours bicycling, 4 hours swimming, 15 hours jogging; 3 pounds   **21.** 65 type A restaurants and 5 type C restaurants   **23.** 100 bags of mix B and 25 bags of mix C   **25.** $x = 100$, $y = 50$; $M = 45{,}000$ **27.** $x = \frac{8}{5}$, $y = \frac{3}{5}$; $M = 10$ **29.** $x = 5$, $y = 0$, $z = 0$; $M = 80$

Exercises 4.3, page 178

1. $x = \frac{3}{5}$, $y = \frac{22}{5}$; 156   **3.** $x = \frac{5}{2}$, $y = \frac{1}{2}$; 8   **5.** $x = 3$, $y = 5$; 59   **7.** $x = 5$, $y = 4$; 38   **9.** 1 serving of food A, 3 servings of food B   **11.** Stock 100 of brand A, 50 of brand B, and 450 of brand C.   **13.** Supply all computers from Chicago at a cost of \$8800.   **15.** $x = 1$, $y = 1$; $M = -1$

Exercises 4.4, page 187

1. $x = 4$, $y = 22$; profit $= \$122$ **3.** $x = 25$, $y = 25$; cost $= \$250$ **5.** $-400 \le h \le \frac{400}{3}$ **7.** $\begin{bmatrix} 9 & 1 & 1 \\ 4 & 8 & -3 \end{bmatrix}$

9. $\begin{bmatrix} 7 \\ 6 \\ 5 \\ 1 \end{bmatrix}$ **11.** Yes   **13.** Minimize $\begin{bmatrix} 7 & 5 & 4 \end{bmatrix} \begin{bmatrix} x \\ y \\ z \end{bmatrix}$ subject to the constraints $\begin{bmatrix} 3 & 8 & 9 \\ 1 & 2 & 5 \\ 4 & 1 & 7 \end{bmatrix} \begin{bmatrix} x \\ y \\ z \end{bmatrix} \ge \begin{bmatrix} 75 \\ 80 \\ 67 \end{bmatrix}$ and

$\begin{bmatrix} x \\ y \\ z \end{bmatrix} \ge \begin{bmatrix} 0 \\ 0 \\ 0 \end{bmatrix}$.   **15.** Maximize $\begin{bmatrix} 3 & 5 \end{bmatrix} \begin{bmatrix} x \\ y \end{bmatrix}$ subject to the constraints $\begin{bmatrix} 3 & 6 \\ 7 & 5 \\ 4 & 3 \end{bmatrix} \begin{bmatrix} x \\ y \end{bmatrix} \le \begin{bmatrix} 90 \\ 138 \\ 120 \end{bmatrix}$ and $\begin{bmatrix} x \\ y \end{bmatrix} \ge \begin{bmatrix} 0 \\ 0 \end{bmatrix}$.

17. Minimize $2x + 3y$ subject to the constraints $\begin{cases} 7x + 4y \ge 33 \\ 5x + 8y \ge 44 \\ x + 3y \ge 55 \\ x \ge 0,\ y \ge 0 \end{cases}$ **19.** -2; $[25, 55]$

Exercises 4.5, page 198

1. Minimize $80u + 76v$ subject to the constraints $\begin{cases} 5u + 3v \ge 4 \\ u + 2v \ge 2 \\ u \ge 0,\ v \ge 0 \end{cases}$ **3.** Maximize $u + 2v + w$ subject to the

constraints $\begin{cases} u - v + 2w \le 10 \\ 2u + v + 3w \le 12 \\ u \ge 0,\ v \ge 0,\ w \ge 0 \end{cases}$ **5.** Maximize $-7u + 10v$ subject to the constraints $\begin{cases} -2u + 8v \le 3 \\ 4u + v \le 5 \\ 6u + 9v \le 1 \\ u \ge 0,\ v \ge 0 \end{cases}$

7. $x = 12$, $y = 20$, $M = 88$; $u = \frac{2}{7}$, $v = \frac{6}{7}$, $M = 88$ **9.** $x = 0$, $y = 2$, $M = 24$; $u = 0$, $v = 12$, $w = 0$, $M = 24$

11. Maximize $3u + 5v$ subject to the constraints $\begin{cases} u + 2v \le 3 \\ u \quad \le 1 \\ u \ge 0,\ v \ge 0 \end{cases}$ $x = \frac{5}{2}$, $y = \frac{1}{2}$, minimum $= 8$; $u = 1$, $v = 1$,

maximum $= 8$ **13.** Minimize $6u + 9v + 12w$ subject to the constraints $\begin{cases} u + 3v \ge 10 \\ -2u + w \ge 12 \\ v + 3w \ge 10 \\ u \ge 0,\ v \ge 0,\ w \ge 0 \end{cases}$

$x = 3$, $y = 12$, $z = 0$, maximum $= 174$; $u = 0$, $v = \frac{10}{3}$, $w = 12$, minimum $= 174$ **15.** Suppose we can hire workers out at a profit of u dollars per hour, sell the steel at a profit of v dollars per unit, and sell the wood at a profit of w dollars per unit. To find the minimum profit at which that should be done, minimize

$90u + 138v + 120w$ subject to the constraints $\begin{cases} 3u + 7v + 4w \geq 3 \\ 6u + 5v + 3w \geq 5 \\ u \geq 0, \ v \geq 0, \ w \geq 0. \end{cases}$ **17.** Suppose we can buy anthracite at u dollars per ton, ordinary coal at v dollars per ton, and bituminous coal at w dollars per ton. To find the maximum cost at which this should be done, maximize $80u + 60v + 75w$ subject to the constraints $\begin{cases} 4u + 4v + 7w \leq 150 \\ 10u + 5v + 5w \leq 200 \\ u \geq 0, \ v \geq 0, \ w \geq 0. \end{cases}$ **19.** \$3.63   **21.** $x = 2$, $y = 1$, maximum $= 74$

Chapter 4: Supplementary Exercises, page 200

1. $x = 2$, $y = 3$, max. $= 18$ **2.** $x = 0$, $y = 7$, max. $= 35$ **3.** $x = 4$, $y = 5$, max. $= 23$ **4.** $x = 2$, $y = 4$, max. $= 34$ **5.** $x = 5$, $y = 1$, min. $= 6$ **6.** $x = 0$, $y = 6$, min. $= 12$ **7.** $x = 4$, $y = 1$, min. $= 110$ **8.** $x = 4$, $y = 3$, min. $= 41$ **9.** $x = 1$, $y = 6$, $z = 8$, max. $= 884$ **10.** $x = 60$, $y = 8$, $z = 20$, $w = 0$, max. $= 312$

11. Minimize $14u + 9v + 24w$ subject to the constraints $\begin{cases} u + v + 3w \geq 2 \\ 2u + v + 2w \geq 3 \\ u \geq 0, \ v \geq 0, \ w \geq 0 \end{cases}$ **12.** Maximize $8u + 5v + 7w$ subject to the constraints $\begin{cases} u + v + 2w \leq 20 \\ 4u + v + w \leq 30 \\ u \geq 0, \ v \geq 0, \ w \geq 0 \end{cases}$ **13.** Primal: $x = 4$, $y = 5$, max. $= 23$; Dual: $u = 1$, $v = 1$, $w = 0$, min. $= 23$ **14.** Primal: $x = 4$, $y = 1$, min. $= 110$; Dual: $u = \frac{10}{3}$, $v = \frac{50}{3}$, $w = 0$, max. $= 110$

15. $A = \begin{bmatrix} 1 & 2 \\ 1 & 1 \\ 3 & 2 \end{bmatrix}$, $B = \begin{bmatrix} 14 \\ 9 \\ 24 \end{bmatrix}$, $C = \begin{bmatrix} 2 & 3 \end{bmatrix}$, $X = \begin{bmatrix} x \\ y \end{bmatrix}$ Primal: Maximize CX subject to $AX \leq B, X \geq \mathbf{0}$.

Dual: $U = \begin{bmatrix} u \\ v \\ w \end{bmatrix}$ Minimize $B^T U$ subject to $A^T U \geq C^T, U \geq \mathbf{0}$.   **16.** $A = \begin{bmatrix} 1 & 4 \\ 1 & 1 \\ 2 & 1 \end{bmatrix}$, $B = \begin{bmatrix} 8 \\ 5 \\ 7 \end{bmatrix}$, $C = \begin{bmatrix} 20 & 30 \end{bmatrix}$,

$X = \begin{bmatrix} x \\ y \end{bmatrix}$ Primal: Minimize CX subject to $AX \geq B, X \geq \mathbf{0}$. Dual: $U = \begin{bmatrix} u \\ v \\ w \end{bmatrix}$ Maximize $B^T U$ subject to

$A^T U \leq C^T, U \geq \mathbf{0}$.   **17. (a)** 30 attack sticks, 40 defense sticks   **(b)** \$22   **18.** \$210

Chapter 4: Chapter Test, page 201

1.
$$\begin{array}{c} \begin{matrix} x & \ y & \ \ z & \ \ u & \ v & \ w & \ M \end{matrix} \\ \left[\begin{array}{ccccccc|c} 1 & 1 & -2 & 1 & 0 & 0 & 0 & 10 \\ 2 & -1 & 3 & 0 & 1 & 0 & 0 & 18 \\ 1 & 3 & 1 & 0 & 0 & 1 & 0 & 21 \\ \hline -2 & -1 & 3 & 0 & 0 & 0 & 1 & 0 \end{array}\right] \end{array}$$
2. $x = 35$, $y = 0$, $z = 30$, $u = 0$, $v = 0$, $w = 42$, $M = 560$ Dual:

$x = 0$, $y = 14$, $z = 0$, $u = 0$, $v = \frac{7}{2}$, $w = 0$, $M = 560$ **3.** Maximize $3x - 4y$ subject to $\begin{cases} 6x + 7y \leq 120 \\ 15x + 5y \leq 195 \ ; \\ x \geq 0, \ y \geq 0 \end{cases}$

$x = 13$, $y = 0$, $u = 42$, $v = 0$, $M = 39$ **4.** $x = 2$, $y = 4$, $u = 0$, $v = 4$, $w = 0$, $M = 44$.   **5.** Maximize $6u + 3v$

subject to $\begin{cases} u + 2v \leq 3 \\ u - v \leq 2 \\ u \geq 0, \ v \geq 0 \end{cases}$ **6. (a)** Maximize $\begin{bmatrix} .50 & .35 \end{bmatrix} \begin{bmatrix} x \\ y \end{bmatrix}$ subject to the constraints $\begin{bmatrix} 2 & 1 \\ 2 & 3 \end{bmatrix} \begin{bmatrix} x \\ y \end{bmatrix} \leq \begin{bmatrix} 6000 \\ 9600 \end{bmatrix}$ and

$\begin{bmatrix} x \\ y \end{bmatrix} \geq \begin{bmatrix} 0 \\ 0 \end{bmatrix}$.   **(b)** Minimize $\begin{bmatrix} 6000 & 9600 \end{bmatrix} \begin{bmatrix} u \\ v \end{bmatrix}$ subject to the constraints $\begin{bmatrix} 2 & 2 \\ 1 & 3 \end{bmatrix} \begin{bmatrix} u \\ v \end{bmatrix} \geq \begin{bmatrix} .50 \\ .35 \end{bmatrix}$ and $\begin{bmatrix} u \\ v \end{bmatrix} \geq \begin{bmatrix} 0 \\ 0 \end{bmatrix}$.

(c) Minimize $6000u + 9600v$ subject to the constraints $\begin{cases} 2u + 2v \geq .50 \\ u + 3v \geq .35 \\ u \geq 0, \ v \geq 0 \end{cases}$ where u is a measure of the value of a pound of paper and v is a measure of the value of a minute of labor.   **(d)** The dual gives the minimum acceptable profit that can be achieved by selling the paper and hiring out the workers.

CHAPTER 5

Exercises 5.1, page 210

1. (a) $\{5,6,7\}$ **(b)** $\{1,2,3,4,5,7\}$ **(c)** $\{1,3\}$ **(d)** $\{5,7\}$ **3. (a)** $\{a,b,c,d,e,f\}$ **(b)** $\{c\}$ **(c)** $\varnothing$
5. $\varnothing, \{1\}, \{2\}, \{1,2\}$ **7. (a)** {all male college students who like football}   **(b)** {all female college students}
(c) {all female college students who don't like football}   **(d)** {all male college students or all college students who like football}   **9. (a)** $S = \{1983, 1984, 1987, 1999, 2003, 2006\}$
(b) $T = \{1980, 1983, 1985, 1989, 1991, 1995, 1996, 1997, 1998, 1999, 2003\}$ **(c)** $S \cap T = \{1983, 1999, 2003\}$
(d) $S \cup T = \{1980, 1983, 1984, 1985, 1987, 1989, 1991, 1995, 1996, 1997, 1998, 1999, 2003, 2006\}$
(e) $S' \cap T = \{1980, 1985, 1989, 1991, 1995, 1996, 1997, 1998\}$ **(f)** $S \cap T' = \{1984, 1987, 2006\}$ **11.** From 1980 to 2007, during only three years did the Standard and Poor's Index increase by 2% or more during the first five days and not increase by 16% or more for that year.   **13. (a)** $\{d, f\}$ **(b)** $\{a, b, c, e, f\}$ **(c)** $\varnothing$ **(d)** $\{a, c\}$
(e) $\{e\}$ **(f)** $\{a, c, e, f\}$ **(g)** $\{a, b, c, e\}$ **(h)** $\{a, c\}$ **(i)** $\{d\}$ **15.** S **17.** U **19.** $\varnothing$ **21.** $L \cup T$
23. $L \cap P$ **25.** $P \cap L \cap T$ **27.** S' **29.** $S \cup A \cup D$ **31.** $(A \cap S)' \cap D$ **33.** {male students at Mount College}
35. {people who are both teachers and students at Mount College}   **37.** {males or students at Mount College}
39. {females at Mount College}   **41.** S' **43.** $(V \cup C) \cap S'$ **45.** $(V \cup C)'$ **47. (a)** $\{B, C, D, E\}$
(b) $\{C, D, E, F\}$ **(c)** $\{A, D, E, F\}$ **(d)** $\{A, C, D, E, F\}$ **(e)** $\{A, F\}$ **(f)** $\{D, E\}$ **49.** Possible answer:
$\{2\}$ **51.** $S \subseteq T$ **53.** True   **55.** True   **57.** False   **59.** True

Exercises 5.2, page 217

1. 7   **3.** 0   **5.** 11
7. $S \subseteq T$ **9.** 19 million
11. 10   **13.** 452

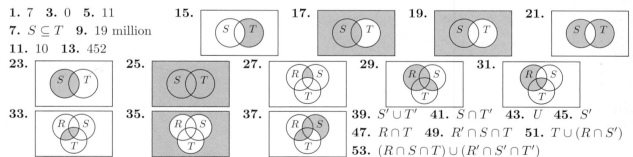

39. $S' \cup T'$ **41.** $S \cap T'$ **43.** U **45.** S'
47. $R \cap T$ **49.** $R' \cap S \cap T$ **51.** $T \cup (R \cap S')$
53. $(R \cap S \cap T) \cup (R' \cap S' \cap T')$

55. People who are not illegal aliens or everyone over the age of 18 who is employed   **57.** Everyone over the age of 18 who is unemployed   **59.** Noncitizens or legal aliens who are unemployed

Exercises 5.3, page 222

1. 11   **3.** 46   **5.** 11   **11.**
7. 75   **9.** 30

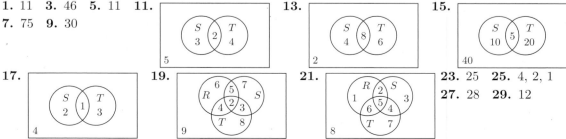

23. 25   **25.** 4, 2, 1
27. 28   **29.** 12

31. (a)

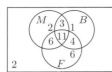

(b) 2   **33.** 190   **35.** 180   **37.** 210   **39.** d   **41.** 450   **43.** 3750   **45.** 30   **47.** 4
(c) 5   **49.** 40   **51.** 27   **53.** 20   **55.** 90   **57.** 6   **59.** 140   **61.** 30   **63.** 35   **65.** 3

Exercises 5.4, page 228

1. 15   **3.** 676   **5.** 380   **7.** 20   **9.** 120   **11.** 64   **13.** 6840   **15.** 870   **17.** 24   **19.** 32   **21.** 360,000
23. (a) 2401   **(b)** 840   **(c)** 343   **(d)** 240   **25. (a)** 362,880   **(b)** 40,320   **(c)** 720   **27.** 256   **29.** 729
31. 168   **33.** 175,760,000   **35.** 160   **37.** 145   **39.** 972   **41.** 1,048,576   **43.** 16   **45.** d   **47.** 24   **49.** 7755
51. 33   **53.** 324   **55.** 1512   **57.** 999,999,999   **59.** 16   **61.** 48   **63.** 48; 1152   **65.** 900

Exercises 5.5, page 235

1. 12   **3.** 120   **5.** 120   **7.** 5   **9.** 7   **11.** n **13.** 1   **15.** $\dfrac{n(n-1)}{2}$ **17.** 720   **19.** 72   **21.** 24   **23.** 36
25. 2730   **27.** 210   **29.** 210   **31.** 120   **33.** 28   **35.** 30,240   **37.** 252   **39.** 38,955,840   **41.** 161,700; 35
43. 15,600   **45.** 75,287,520   **47.** 2,598,960   **49.** 1287   **51.** 1140   **53.** 120   **55.** 70   **57.** Yes; Moe: 36; Joe: 35
59. 479,001,600   **61.** 14,400   **63.** 840   **65.** 10,080   **67.** 120   **69.** 379,236   **71.** 96,875   **73.** 10   **75.** 680
77. b   **79.** 56   **81.** semester system   **83. (a)** 1,221,759   **(b)** 3,921,225   **(c)** first lottery   **(d)** second
lottery

Exercises 5.6, page 242

1. (a) 64   **(b)** 20   **(c)** 22   **(d)** 57   **3.** 126   **5. (a)** 120   **(b)** 56   **(c)** 64   **7.** $\approx 7.14 \cdot 10^{44}$ **9.** 60
11. 67,800,320   **13.** 80   **15.** 3,527,160   **17.** 3528   **19.** 225,225   **21.** 165,765,600   **23.** 210   **25.** 30,240
27. 870,912,000   **29.** 24   **31.** 24   **33.** 3744   **35.** 3050   **37.** 369   **39.** 1500   **41.** 3,628,800   **43.** 64   **45.** 16
47. 262,495   **49.** .264%   **51.** Four aces

Exercises 5.7, page 248

1. 15   **3.** 8   **5.** 153   **7.** 1   **9.** 1   **11.** n **13.** 1   **15.** $n!$ **17.** 64   **19.** $x^{10}, 10x^9y, 45x^8y^2$ **21.** $105x^2y^{13},$
$15xy^{14}, y^{15}$ **23.** $184,756x^{10}y^{10}$ **25.** 330   **27.** 64   **29.** 16   **31.** 32   **33.** 255   **35.** 196,608   **37.** 120   **39.** 16
41. 247   **43.** 4096   **47.** 3696   **49.** $2835x^3$ **51.** 32,767

Exercises 5.8, page 253

1. 20   **3.** 180   **5.** 210   **7.** 34,650   **9.** 166,320   **11.** 1,401,400   **13.** 2,858,856   **15.** 99,768,240
17. 2,546,168,625   **19.** 488,864,376   **21.** 12   **23.** 135,135   **25.** 126   **27.** 115,166,175,166,136,334,240

Chapter 5: Supplementary Exercises, page 256

1. $\varnothing, \{a\}, \{b\}, \{a, b\}$ **2.**

3. 120   **5.**

6. $x^{12}, 12x^{11}y, 66x^{10}y^2$ **7.** 840
4. 240   **8.** 15   **9.** 35   **10.** 13,860   **11.** 0
12. 136   **13.** 6   **14.** 49   **15.** 47
16. 11   **17.** 46   **18.** 58   **19.** 22   **20.** 23   **21.** 126   **22.** 2^{40} **23.** 550   **24.** 480   **25.** 20   **26.** 450,000
27. 8,100,000,000   **28.** 146,813,779,479,510   **29.** 390,625; 325,089   **30.** 792   **31.** $C(100, 14)$ **32.** 27,500
33. 59,049   **34.** $C(60, 10)$ **35.** 9,765,625   **36.** 85,766,121   **37.** 210   **38.** 66,512,160   **39.** 14!   **40.** $\dfrac{1}{5!} \cdot \dfrac{100!}{(20!)^5}$
41. $\dfrac{80}{99} \cdot \dfrac{1}{5!} \cdot \dfrac{100!}{(20!)^5}$ **42.** 135   **43.** $C(n, 2) - n$ or $\dfrac{n(n-3)}{2}$ **44.** 48   **45.** 34,560   **46.** 95,040   **47.** 5148
48. 648   **49.** 243   **50.** 4512   **51.** 12,696   **52.** 6   **53.** 72   **54.** 12   **55.** 45; 35   **56.** Second teacher   **57.** 4200
58. 5   **59.** 5040   **60. (a)** 14,520   **(b)** 25,344   **61.** 29   **62.** 70   **63.** 36,504   **64.** 12   **65.** 16,360,143,800
66. (a) 224,640,000   **(b)** There are 20 times as many plates in (a).

Chapter 5: Chapter Test, page 259

1. (a) 24 **(b)** 210 **(c)** 153 **(d)** 1 **(e)** 30 **2. (a)** True **(b)** True **(c)** False **3. (a)** {a, e} **(b)** Ø
4. $C \cap E$ represents the set of certified public accountants who are self-employed. $C \cup E'$ represents the set of people who are either certified public accountants or are not self-employed.

5.

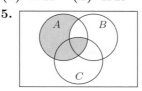

6. 10 **7.** 5 **8.** 60
9. (a) 2,209,413,024 **(b)** 210
10. 210 **11.** 144 **12.** 136,800
13. 792 **14.** 128 **15.** 2520

CHAPTER 6

Exercises 6.2, page 270

1. (a) {RS, RT, RU, RV, ST, SU, SV, TU, TV, UV} **(b)** {RS, RT, RU, RV} **(c)** {TU, TV, UV}
3. (a) {HH, HT, TH, TT} **(b)** {HH, HT} **5. (a)** {(I, red), (I, white), (II, red), (II, white)}
(b) {(I, red), (I, white)} **7. (a)** $S = $ {All positive numbers of minutes} **(b)** "More than 5 minutes but less than 8 minutes," Ø, "5 minutes or less," "8 minutes or more," "5 minutes or less," "Less than 4 minutes," S
9. (a) {(Fr, Lib), (Fr, Con), (So, Lib), (So, Con), (Jr, Lib), (Jr, Con), (Sr, Lib), (Sr, Con)} **(b)** {(Fr, Con), (So, Con), (Jr, Con), (Sr, Con)} **(c)** {(Jr, Lib)} **(d)** {(So, Lib), (Jr, Lib), (Sr, Lib)} **11. (a)** No
(b) Yes **13.** Ø, {a}, {b}, {c}, {a, b}, {a, c}, {b, c}, S **15.** Yes **17. (a)** {0, 1, 2, 3, 4, 5, 6, 7, 8, 9, 10} **(b)** {6, 7, 8, 9, 10} **19. (a)** No **(b)** Yes **(c)** Yes **21.** The set of integers from 0 to 8 **23.** (7, 4); 81
25. {2, 6, 9, 10}; 1.7% **27.** {Colonel Mustard, Miss Scarlet, Professor Plum, Mrs. White, Mr. Green, Mrs. Peacock} **(a)** 324 **(b)** "The murder occurred in the library with a gun." **(c)** "Either the murder occurred in the library or it was done with a gun."

Exercises 6.3, page 281

1. (a) $\frac{46,277}{774,746}$ **(b)** $\frac{48,132}{774,746}$ **(c)** $\frac{726,614}{774,746}$ **3. (a)** $\frac{5}{36}$ **(b)** $\frac{1}{6}$ **5.** $\frac{1}{19}$ **7. (a)** $\frac{1}{6}$ **(b)** 1 to 5 **9. (a)** .7
(b) .7 **11. (a)** $\frac{10}{11}$ **(b)** $\frac{1}{3}$ **(c)** $\frac{4}{9}$ **13.** 9 to 91 **15.** $\frac{11}{18}; \frac{7}{18}$ **17. (a)** .7 **(b)** .2 **19.** .9 **21.** .6
23. (a) .7 **25.**

Number of Colleges Applied to	Probability
1	.17
2	.12
3	.14
4	.16
5 to 20	.41

(b) 7000

27. (a) .15, .55, .20, .10 **(b)** .30
29. (a) Some categories are left out—people who use a computer for both school and work, for example. **(b)** .83 **31.** 41 to 9

33. (a) $\frac{3}{8}, \frac{1}{4}, \frac{2}{5}, \frac{1}{5}$ **(b)** $\frac{49}{40}$, which is greater than 1 **(c)** Bookies have to make a living. The payoffs are a little lower than they should be; thus allowing the bookie to make a profit. **35.** 1 **37.** 0

Exercises 6.4, page 288

1. (a) $\frac{1}{9}$ **(b)** $\frac{2}{9}$ **3. (a)** $\frac{7}{13}$ **(b)** $\frac{6}{13}$ **(c)** $\frac{4}{13}$ **(d)** $\frac{9}{13}$ **5. (a)** $\frac{2}{429}$ **(b)** $\frac{7}{429}$ **(c)** $\frac{427}{429}$ **7.** $\frac{11}{12}$ **9.** $\frac{5}{6}$
11. $\frac{16}{17}$ **13.** $\frac{5}{7106}$ **15.** $\frac{47}{250}$ **17.** $\frac{13}{49}$ **19. (a)** .25 **(b)** .75 **(c)** .8 **21.** 0 **23.** $\frac{1}{11}$ **25.** $\frac{2}{5}$ **27. (a)** $\frac{15}{28}$
(b) $\frac{15}{56}$ **(c)** $\frac{9}{56}$ **(d)** $\frac{9}{14}$ **29.** $\frac{5}{6}$ **31.** $\frac{5}{16}$ **33.** $\frac{1}{1,919,190}$ **35.** .90055 **37.** .066 **39. (a)** .119 **(b)** .152
41. .625 **43. (a)** 1 to 146,107,961 **(b)** $\frac{1}{146,107,962}$ **45.** $\frac{5}{7}$ **47.** $\frac{8815}{499422} \approx .01765$ **49.** $\frac{12}{25}$ **51.** .729
53. (a) .00144 **(b)** .0211 **55. (a)** .1054 **(b)** .2155 **57.** 13 **59. (a)** 4 **(b)** .2139 **61.** 27 **63.** 6

Exercises 6.5, page 299

1. $\frac{1}{3}, \frac{1}{5}$ **3.** $\frac{4}{7}$ **5.** No **7. (a)** .36 **(b)** .81 **9.** .7967 **11.** $\frac{3}{4}, \frac{1}{2}$ **13. (a)** .4 **(b)** .6 **(c)** .75 **15.** $\frac{1}{4}$
17. .94 **19.** No **21.** .009975 **23.** .2401 **27.** .4, .24, .36 **31. (a)** $\frac{1}{10}$ **(b)** 100 per 1000 **(c)** $\frac{1}{20}$
33. (a) .28 **(b)** .07 **(c)** .6065 **35. (a)** .16 **(b)** .64 **(c)** .36 **(d)** .42 **(e)** .64 **(f)** .31

37. (a) .2686 (b) .4239 (c) .5749 (d) .0297 **39.** (a) .40 (b) .56 (c) .18 (d) .70 (e) .45
(f) .67 **41.** (a) .7599 (b) .0642 (c) .7348 **45.** $\frac{10}{143}$; $\frac{25}{286}$ **47.** $\frac{1}{6}$; $\frac{1}{3}$ **49.** .0986 **51.** $\frac{1}{1717}$ **53.** Yes
55. $\frac{1}{16}$ **57.** (a) $1000p$ (b) $1000p - 499{,}500p^2$ **59.** .24; .24; Toss the coin twice. If HT comes up, let the
home team kick off. If TH comes up, let the visiting team kick off. If HH or TT comes up, repeat the coin toss
until one of each face occurs. **61.** No **63.** Not independent **65.** (a) 3.69×10^{-6} (b) 6.16×10^{-7} (c) a

Exercises 6.6, page 309

1. **3.** **5.** .08 **11.**
7. .295
9. $\frac{7}{12}$

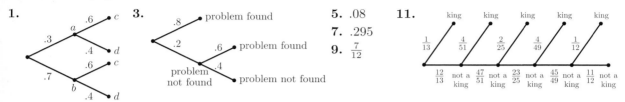

$\frac{1201}{5525} \approx .22$ **13.** .14 **15.** $\frac{25}{27}$ **17.** .86 **19.** $\frac{4}{7}$ **21.** (a) .60 (b) .75 **23.** $1 - (.9999)^n$ **25.** Same shape;
probability of winning card game is greater. **27.** (a) $\frac{1}{4}$; $\frac{3}{4}$ (b) .7 **29.** $\frac{6}{11}$ **31.** .999996 **33.** $\frac{25}{26}$ **35.** $\frac{3}{8}$
37. .66 **39.** (a) .99 (b) .0180 Oliver is almost certain to win each game. However, he is almost certain to
lose the 400-game match. **41.** .92

Exercises 6.7, page 315

1. $\frac{8}{53}$ **3.** $\frac{3}{7}$ **5.** .075 **7.** $\frac{8}{9}$ **9.** (a) .1325 (b) $\frac{12}{53} \approx .23$ **11.** $\frac{5}{103} \approx .049$ **13.** (a) .01 (b) $\frac{33}{34} \approx .971$
15. $\frac{31}{37} \approx .838$ **17.** (a) $\frac{1}{4}$ (b) $\frac{13}{17} \approx .765$ (c) .130 **19.** (a) $\frac{5}{9}$ (b) 11%

Chapter 6: Supplementary Exercises, page 325

1. $\frac{31}{32}$ **2.** No **3.** $\frac{4}{9}$ **4.** $\frac{1}{12}$ **5.** $\frac{2}{5}$ **6.** $\frac{2}{11}$ **7.** $\frac{1}{5}$ **8.** $\frac{1}{5}$ **9.** .4667 **10.** .3333 **11.** $\frac{7}{15}$ **12.** (a) $\frac{1}{10}$ (b) $\frac{2}{5}$
13. (a) $\frac{2}{15}$ (b) $\frac{1}{3}$ **14.** (a) $\left(\frac{1}{36}\right)^3$ (b) $\left(\frac{1}{10}\right)^4$ (c) $\frac{167}{500}$ (d) $\left(\frac{13}{18}\right)^3\left(\frac{1}{2}\right)^4$ **15.** (a) $\frac{1}{12}$ (b) $\frac{1}{2}$ **16.** $\frac{7}{12}$
17. $\frac{1}{21}$ **18.** $\frac{2}{3}$ **19.** No **20.** $\frac{2}{3}$ **21.** $\frac{1}{3}$ **22.** $\frac{19}{49}$ **23.** $\frac{1}{6}$ **24.** $\frac{1}{21}$ **25.** $\frac{2}{3}$ **26.** Switch **27.** $\frac{13}{25}$ **28.** 13 to 37
29. $\frac{1}{120{,}960}$ **30.** $\frac{1}{6}$ **31.** $\frac{5}{16}$ **32.** $\frac{1}{3}$ **33.** $\frac{4}{25}$ **34.** $\frac{1}{8}$ **35.** $\frac{138}{301}$ **36.** e **37.** a **38.** $\frac{6}{7}$ **39.** $\frac{5}{324}$ **40.** $\frac{95}{1827}$
41. (a) $\frac{1}{2197}$ (b) $\frac{469}{2197}$ **42.** 65,535 to 1 **43.** $\frac{1}{3}$ **44.** .5 **45.** 5 to 13 **46.** .02695 **47.** 421 **49.** Theoretical
probability: $\frac{5}{32}$

Chapter 6: Chapter Test, page 328

1. (a) $S = \{$PN, PD, PQ, PH, ND, NQ, NH, DQ, DH, QH$\}$ (b) $E = \{$PN, PQ, NQ, DH$\}$ **2.** (a) $\frac{3}{8}$
(b) $\frac{1{,}000{,}000}{1{,}000{,}001}$ **3.** (a) 2 to 3 (b) 7 to 3 **4.** (a) A male junior is elected. (b) A female junior is not
elected. (c) A male or a junior is elected. **5.** $\frac{15}{16}$ **6.** .9612 **7.** (a) $\frac{5}{8}$ (b) $\frac{3}{4}$ (c) $\frac{2}{3}$ (d) No (e) No
8. .6513; .3874 **9.** (a) $\frac{1}{3}$ (b) $\frac{7}{13}$ (c) No; No (d) $\frac{1}{3}$ **10.** (a) .50 (b) .50 **11.** (a) $\frac{18}{25}$ (b) $\frac{7}{13}$

CHAPTER 7

Exercises 7.1, page 337

1. **3.** **5.** **7.** b

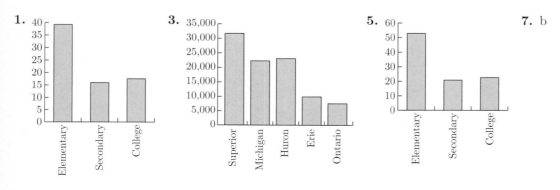

9.

Ontario 8.0%
Erie 10.5%
Superior 33.5%
Huron 24.4%
Michigan 23.6%

11. .602 **13.**

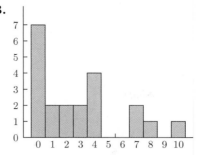

15. c

17.

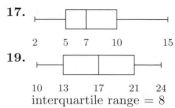

2 5 7 10 15

19.

10 13 17 21 24
interquartile range = 8

21.

20 28 42 52.5 56
interquartile range = 24.5

23. (A)–(c), (B)–(d), (C)–(a), (D)–(b)

25. (a) min = 200, Q_1 = 400, Q_2 = 600, Q_3 = 700, max = 800 **(b)** 25% **(c)** 25%
(d) 50% **(e)** 75%

27.

.200 .229 .2835 .317 .350

.091 .175 .270 .325 .359

Exercises 7.2, page 347

1.

Grade	Relative frequency
0	.08
1	.12
2	.40
3	.24
4	.16

3.

Number of calls during minute	Relative frequency
20	.05
21	.05
22	0
23	.10
24	.30
25	.20
26	0
27	.15
28	.10
29	.05

5.

Number of heads	Probability
0	$\frac{1}{8}$
1	$\frac{3}{8}$
2	$\frac{3}{8}$
3	$\frac{1}{8}$

7.

Number of red balls	Probability
0	$\frac{4}{35}$
1	$\frac{18}{35}$
2	$\frac{12}{35}$
3	$\frac{1}{35}$

9.

Number of red balls	Player's earnings	Probability
2	\$5	$\frac{1}{15}$
1	\$1	$\frac{8}{15}$
0	−\$1	$\frac{6}{15}$

11. .6 **13.**

k	$\Pr(X^2 = k)$
0	.1
1	.2
4	.3
9	.2
16	.2

15.

k	$\Pr(X-1=k)$
-1	.1
0	.2
1	.3
2	.2
3	.2

17.

k	$\Pr(\frac{1}{5}Y=k)$
1	.3
2	.4
3	.1
4	.1
5	.1

19.

k	$\Pr((X+1)^2=k)$
1	.1
4	.2
9	.3
16	.2
25	.2

21.

Grade	Relative frequency 9 AM class	Relative frequency 10 AM class
F	.17	.16
D	.25	.23
C	.33	.15
B	.17	.21
A	.08	.25

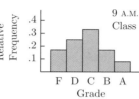

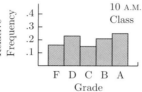

The 9 A.M. class has the distribution centered on the C grade with relatively few A's. The 10 A.M. class has a large percentage of A's and D's with fewer C's.

23. 80% **25.**

(a) 25%

(b) 60%

(c)

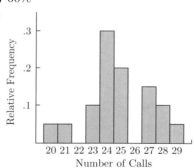

(d) ≈ 25

27. (a) 59

(b) 5%

(c) 54

(d) 35%

(e) ≈ 54

29. (a) $\Pr(U=4)=\frac{1}{15}$

(b) $\frac{2}{3}$ **(c)** $\frac{14}{15}$ **(d)** $\frac{1}{3}$

(e)

Exercises 7.3, page 354

1. $\frac{25}{216}$

3. $\frac{3}{64}$

5. .3174

7. .1488

9. .8507

11. .2007

13. .2618

15.

k	$\Pr(X=k)$
0	.0168
1	.0896
2	.2090
3	.2787
4	.2322
5	.1239
6	.0413
7	.0079
8	.0007

17. d **19.** .5583 **21.** .0820

23. $\frac{20}{27}$ **25.** 9 **27.** .20736

29. (a) .375 **(b)** .5

(c) .125 **31.** a **33.** .5

35. .102

37. (a) .2898 **(b)** 21 games

39. (a) .0003976 **(b)** .02624

41. (a) .0290

(b)

k	$\Pr(X=k)$
0	.0105
1	.0524
2	.1258
3	.1929
4	.2122
5	.1782
6	.1188

(c) .0047

43. 178

Exercises 7.4, page 364

1. 2.35 **3. (a)** 2.9 **(b)**

Grade	Relative Frequency
4	.3
3	.4
2	.2
1	.1

(c) 2.9
5. $\bar{x}_A = 1.5$, $\bar{x}_B = 1.6$;
Group A had fewer cavities.

7.

Earnings	Probability
−$1	$\frac{37}{38}$
$35	$\frac{1}{38}$

$E(X) \approx -5.26¢$

9.

Earnings	Probability
−50¢	$\frac{1}{3}$
0¢	$\frac{4}{15}$
50¢	$\frac{1}{5}$
$1	$\frac{2}{15}$
$1.50	$\frac{1}{15}$

$E(X) \approx 16.67¢$

11. $1000 **13.** 4.47 **15.** 10 **17.** Three free throws
19. Many possible answers **21.** 58.5° **23.** d **25.** b
27. c **29.** d **31.** b **33.** a **35.** a

Exercises 7.5, page 373

1. 1.4 **3.** B **5. (a)** $\mu_A = 15$, $\sigma_A^2 = 160$, $\mu_B = 13$, $\sigma_B^2 = 141$ **(b)** A **(c)** B **7. (a)** $\mu_A = 103$, $\sigma_A^2 = 4.6$,
$\mu_B = 104$, $\sigma_B^2 = 3.4$ **(b)** B **(c)** B **9.** 6, ≈ 1.732 **11.** 3, ≈ 1.719 **13. (a)** $\geq .75$ **(b)** $\geq .89$ **(c)** $\geq .31$
15. ≥ 4688 **17.** 8 **19. (a)** $\mu = 7$, $\sigma^2 = \frac{35}{6}$ **(b)** $\frac{5}{6}$ **(c)** $\geq \frac{19}{54}$ **21.** 2 **25.** $\mu = 50,334.75$, $\sigma \approx 2364.08$
27. $\mu = 4.72$, $\sigma \approx 1.40$

Exercises 7.6, page 387

1. .8944 **3.** .4013 **5.** .2417 **7.** .6170 **9.** 1.75 **11.** .75 **13.** ≈ 1.28 **15.** $\mu = 6$, $\sigma = 2$ **17.** $\mu = 9$, $\sigma = 1$
19. $-\frac{8}{3}$ **21.** a **23.** .9772 **25.** .6247 **27.** .9544 **29.** .5 **31.** .0002 **33.** .9876 **35.** .0122 **37. (a)** 616
(b) Between 396 and 644 **(c)** 674 **39.** 19,750 miles **41. (a)** 5.35 ounces **(b)** 4.76 ounces **43.** The
normal curve is translated to the right. **45.** .2358

Exercises 7.7, page 393

1. (a) .1974 **(b)** .7888 **(c)** .9878 **3.** .0062 **5.** .2743 **7.** .0013 **9.** .6368 **11.** .1056 **13.** 2, .1469
15. .7498 **17.** .61 **19.** Exact: .2356; normal approximation: .2358 **21.** Exact: .0812; normal approximation:
.0813

Chapter 7: Supplementary Exercises, page 397

1.

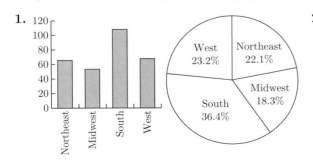

2.

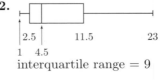

interquartile range = 9

3. (a)

k	$\Pr(X = k)$
0	$\frac{8}{27}$
1	$\frac{12}{27}$
2	$\frac{6}{27}$
3	$\frac{1}{27}$

(b) $\mu = 1$, $\sigma^2 = \frac{2}{3}$

4. .2266 **5.** .2857 **6.** .2646
7. $\geq \frac{8}{9}$ **8.** $\mu = 4.8$, $\sigma^2 = 19.76$
9. 10.56%

10.

k	$\Pr(X = k)$
0	$\frac{1}{70}$
1	$\frac{16}{70}$
2	$\frac{36}{70}$
3	$\frac{16}{70}$
4	$\frac{1}{70}$

$\mu = 2$, $\sigma^2 = \frac{4}{7}$

11. .0122 **12.** .84 **13.** 22.5 **14.** $-.75$
15. (a) 1.39% (b) 124.75
16. 52; choose true for all the questions.
21. Yes **22.** Yes

Chapter 7: Chapter Test, page 398

1. .58 **2.**

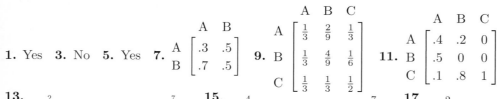

20 26 30 37 42
interquartile range = 11

3. (a)

Number of Heads, k	$\Pr(X = k)$
0	.25
1	.50
2	.25

(b)

k	$\Pr(2X + 5 = k)$
5	.25
7	.50
9	.25

4. (a) .296 (b) .619 (c) 2 **5.** .4, 3.24, 1.8 **6.** Lucy; ≈ 11 cents per roll **7.** (a) .8413 (b) .9878
(c) .7162 **8.** (a) .1587 (b) .7745 (c) 99 mg/100 ml, 113 mg/100 ml **9.** (a) .3983 (b) .0118; .0092;
difference is .0026 (c) .9962; .9878; difference is .0084

CHAPTER 8

Exercises 8.1, page 409

1. Yes **3.** No **5.** Yes **7.** $\begin{array}{c} \\ A \\ B \end{array}\begin{array}{cc} A & B \\ \begin{bmatrix} .3 & .5 \\ .7 & .5 \end{bmatrix} \end{array}$ **9.** $\begin{array}{c} \\ A \\ B \\ C \end{array}\begin{array}{ccc} A & B & C \\ \begin{bmatrix} \frac{1}{3} & \frac{2}{9} & \frac{1}{3} \\ \frac{1}{3} & \frac{4}{9} & \frac{1}{6} \\ \frac{1}{3} & \frac{1}{3} & \frac{1}{2} \end{bmatrix} \end{array}$ **11.** $\begin{array}{c} \\ A \\ B \\ C \end{array}\begin{array}{ccc} A & B & C \\ \begin{bmatrix} .4 & .2 & 0 \\ .5 & 0 & 0 \\ .1 & .8 & 1 \end{bmatrix} \end{array}$

13. **15.** **17.**

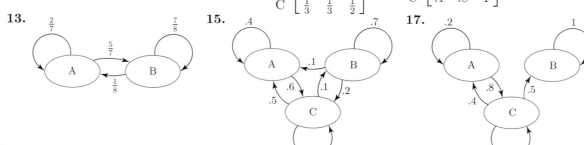

19. 53.5%, 56.75% **21.** 40% will be in zone I, 40% will be in zone II, and 20% will be in zone III.

23. (a) $\begin{array}{c} \\ S \\ O \end{array}\begin{array}{cc} S & O \\ \begin{bmatrix} .992 & .007 \\ .008 & .993 \end{bmatrix} \end{array}$ (b) 36.17%, 36.33% **25.** (a) $\begin{array}{c} \\ L \\ R \end{array}\begin{array}{cc} L & R \\ \begin{bmatrix} .9 & .7 \\ .1 & .3 \end{bmatrix} \end{array}$ (b) $\begin{bmatrix} .88 & .84 \\ .12 & .16 \end{bmatrix}$ (c) $\begin{bmatrix} .8 \\ .2 \end{bmatrix}_1, \begin{bmatrix} .86 \\ .14 \end{bmatrix}_2$
(d) 87.5% **27.** (a) 4% (b) 96% of the freshmen who held middle-of-the-road political views continued to
hold those views as sophomores.

$$\begin{array}{c} \\ \\ \begin{array}{c}U\\S\\R\end{array}\end{array}\begin{array}{ccc}U & S & R\\\end{array}$$

(c)

(d) 43.88%; 44.68%   **29. (a)** $\begin{array}{c}U\\S\\R\end{array}\begin{bmatrix}.86 & .05 & .03\\.08 & .86 & .05\\.06 & .09 & .92\end{bmatrix}$ **(b)** 11.4%

31. (a) $\begin{array}{c}V\\C\end{array}\begin{array}{cc}V & C\end{array}$ $\begin{array}{c}V\\C\end{array}\begin{bmatrix}.128 & .663\\.872 & .337\end{bmatrix}$ **(b)** .59452   **33.** $\begin{bmatrix}.44\\.56\end{bmatrix}_3,\begin{bmatrix}.44\\.56\end{bmatrix}_4,$

35. All powers are $\begin{bmatrix}\frac{1}{3} & \frac{1}{3}\\\frac{2}{3} & \frac{2}{3}\end{bmatrix}.$

37. $\begin{bmatrix}.1 & .3\\.9 & .7\end{bmatrix};\begin{bmatrix}.28 & .24\\.72 & .76\end{bmatrix};\begin{bmatrix}.24 & .25\\.76 & .75\end{bmatrix};\begin{bmatrix}.25 & .25\\.75 & .75\end{bmatrix};\begin{bmatrix}.25 & .25\\.75 & .75\end{bmatrix}$ **39.** No   **41. (a)** $\begin{bmatrix}.35\\.65\end{bmatrix};\begin{bmatrix}.425\\.575\end{bmatrix};\begin{bmatrix}.3875\\.6125\end{bmatrix};$

$\begin{bmatrix}.40625\\.59375\end{bmatrix}$ **43.** $\begin{bmatrix}.4\\.6\end{bmatrix}$ **45.** $\begin{bmatrix}.4 & .4\\.6 & .6\end{bmatrix}$

Exercises 8.2, page 420

1. Yes   **3.** Yes   **5.** Yes   **7.** $\begin{bmatrix}\frac{1}{6}\\\frac{5}{6}\end{bmatrix}$ **9.** $\begin{bmatrix}.6\\.4\end{bmatrix}$ **11.** $\begin{bmatrix}\frac{5}{14}\\\frac{3}{7}\\\frac{3}{14}\end{bmatrix}$ **13.** 87.5%   **15.** 20%   **17.** 40%

19. (a) $\begin{array}{c}A\\B\\C\end{array}\begin{array}{ccc}A & B & C\end{array}$ $\begin{array}{c}A\\B\\C\end{array}\begin{bmatrix}.7 & .1 & .1\\.2 & .8 & .3\\.1 & .1 & .6\end{bmatrix}$ **(b)** 34%; 30.4%   **(c)** $\frac{1}{4}$ at location A, $\frac{11}{20}$ at location B, $\frac{1}{5}$ at location C   **21.** 25%

23. $\begin{bmatrix}.5\\.5\end{bmatrix}$ is a stable distribution for the matrix $A=\begin{bmatrix}0 & 1\\1 & 0\end{bmatrix}$ because $.5+.5=1$ and $\begin{bmatrix}0 & 1\\1 & 0\end{bmatrix}\begin{bmatrix}.5\\.5\end{bmatrix}=\begin{bmatrix}.5\\.5\end{bmatrix}.$ However,

given an arbitrary initial distribution $\begin{bmatrix}\\\end{bmatrix}_0\neq\begin{bmatrix}.5\\.5\end{bmatrix},A^n\begin{bmatrix}\\\end{bmatrix}_0$ will not approach $\begin{bmatrix}.5\\.5\end{bmatrix}$ as n gets large, so the

existence of a stable distribution for A does not contradict the main premise of this section.   **25.** $\begin{bmatrix}.7 & .7\\.3 & .3\end{bmatrix};\begin{bmatrix}.7\\.3\end{bmatrix}$

27. $\begin{bmatrix}\frac{8}{35} & \frac{8}{35} & \frac{8}{35}\\\frac{3}{7} & \frac{3}{7} & \frac{3}{7}\\\frac{12}{35} & \frac{12}{35} & \frac{12}{35}\end{bmatrix};\begin{bmatrix}\frac{8}{35}\\\frac{3}{7}\\\frac{12}{35}\end{bmatrix}$

Exercises 8.3, page 430

1. Yes   **3.** No   **5.** No   **7.** Yes   **9.** $\begin{array}{c}B\\A\\C\end{array}\begin{array}{ccc}B & A & C\end{array}$ $\begin{array}{c}B\\A\\C\end{array}\begin{bmatrix}1 & .3 & .4\\0 & .2 & .5\\0 & .5 & .1\end{bmatrix}$ **11.** $\begin{array}{c}D\\A\\B\\C\end{array}\begin{array}{cccc}D & A & B & C\end{array}$ $\begin{array}{c}D\\A\\B\\C\end{array}\begin{bmatrix}1 & .4 & 0 & .1\\0 & .1 & 1 & .6\\0 & .2 & 0 & .1\\0 & .3 & 0 & .2\end{bmatrix}$ **13.** $R=[.5]; S=\begin{bmatrix}.3\\.2\end{bmatrix};$

$F=[2];\begin{bmatrix}1 & 0 & .6\\0 & 1 & .4\\0 & 0 & 0\end{bmatrix}$ **15.** $R=\begin{bmatrix}.3 & .6\\.1 & .2\end{bmatrix}; S=\begin{bmatrix}.1 & 0\\.5 & .2\end{bmatrix}; F=\begin{bmatrix}1.6 & 1.2\\.2 & 1.4\end{bmatrix};\begin{bmatrix}1 & 0 & .16 & .12\\0 & 1 & .84 & .88\\0 & 0 & 0 & 0\\0 & 0 & 0 & 0\end{bmatrix}$ **17.** $R=\begin{bmatrix}.5 & 0\\.1 & .6\end{bmatrix};$

$$S = \begin{bmatrix} .1 & .2 \\ .3 & 0 \\ 0 & .2 \end{bmatrix}; \quad F = \begin{bmatrix} 2 & 0 \\ .5 & 2.5 \end{bmatrix}; \quad \begin{bmatrix} 1 & 0 & 0 & .3 & .5 \\ 0 & 1 & 0 & .6 & 0 \\ 0 & 0 & 1 & .1 & .5 \\ 0 & 0 & 0 & 0 & 0 \\ 0 & 0 & 0 & 0 & 0 \end{bmatrix}$$

19. If the gambler begins with \$2, he should have \$1 for an expected number of .79 plays.

21. (a)

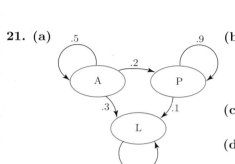

(b)

	L	A	P
L	1	.3	.1
A	0	.5	0
P	0	.2	.9

(c)

	L	A	P
L	1	1	1
A	0	0	0
P	0	0	0

(d) 6

23. (a)

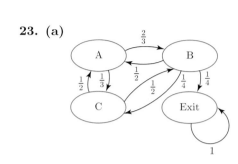

(b)

	E	A	B	C
E	1	0	$\frac{1}{4}$	0
A	0	0	$\frac{1}{2}$	$\frac{1}{2}$
B	0	$\frac{2}{3}$	0	$\frac{1}{2}$
C	0	$\frac{1}{3}$	$\frac{1}{4}$	0

(c)

	E	A	B	C
E	1	1	1	1
A	0	0	0	0
B	0	0	0	0
C	0	0	0	0

(d) 10.6 minutes

(b)

	D	G	F	S
D	1	0	.28	.1
G	0	1	.72	.9
F	0	0	0	0
S	0	0	0	0

(c) .72   **(d)** 1.8 years

25. (a)

	D	G	F	S
D	1	0	.2	.1
G	0	1	0	.9
F	0	0	0	0
S	0	0	.8	0

27. (a) $\frac{13}{14}$; $\frac{11}{14}$ **(b)** $\frac{20}{7}$ months   **(c)** \$5786; \$1214

29. (a) $\frac{3}{4}$; $\frac{1}{2}$; $\frac{1}{4}$ **(b)** 4   **31.** $\frac{50}{81}$; $5\frac{1}{2}$

Chapter 8: Supplementary Exercises, page 434

1. Stochastic, neither   **2.** Stochastic, regular   **3.** Stochastic, regular   **4.** Stochastic, absorbing   **5.** Not stochastic   **6.** Stochastic, absorbing   **7.** $\begin{bmatrix} \frac{5}{9} \\ \frac{4}{9} \end{bmatrix}$

8. $\begin{bmatrix} 1 & 0 & 0 & \frac{1}{2} & \frac{1}{2} \\ 0 & 1 & 0 & \frac{1}{4} & \frac{1}{8} \\ 0 & 0 & 1 & \frac{1}{4} & \frac{3}{8} \\ 0 & 0 & 0 & 0 & 0 \\ 0 & 0 & 0 & 0 & 0 \end{bmatrix}$

9. (a)

	H	M	L
H	.5	.4	.3
M	.4	.3	.5
L	.1	.3	.2

;   **(b)** 38%   **(c)** $\frac{19}{97}$

10. (a)

	P	N
P	.8	.3
N	.2	.7

(b) 30%   **(c)** 60%

11. $\begin{bmatrix} 1 & 0 & \frac{11}{12} & 1 & \frac{1}{2} \\ 0 & 1 & \frac{1}{12} & 0 & \frac{1}{2} \\ 0 & 0 & 0 & 0 & 0 \\ 0 & 0 & 0 & 0 & 0 \\ 0 & 0 & 0 & 0 & 0 \end{bmatrix}$

12. (a)

	I	II	III	IV
I	1	0	0	$\frac{1}{4}$
II	0	1	$\frac{1}{3}$	$\frac{1}{4}$
III	0	0	0	$\frac{1}{2}$
IV	0	0	$\frac{2}{3}$	0

(b) $\frac{5}{12}$ **(c)** $\frac{5}{8}$ **(d)** $2\frac{1}{2}$ minutes   **13.** c   **14.** 58.5%   **15. (a)** If the traffic is Moderate on a particular day, then for the next day the probability of Light is .2, the probability of Moderate is .75, and the probability of

Heavy is .05.   **(b)** About 37.0%, Light; 47.8%, Moderate; 15.2%, Heavy   **(c)** About 3 days   **16.** State G:

≈ 1.48 months; state S: ≈ 1.83 months.   **17. (a)** $\begin{bmatrix} \frac{122}{1683} \\ \frac{23}{99} \\ \frac{4}{9} \\ \frac{422}{1683} \end{bmatrix}$; In the long run, the probability of having 1, 2, 3, or 4

units of water in the reservoir at any given time will be $\frac{122}{1683}$, $\frac{23}{99}$, $\frac{4}{9}$, or $\frac{422}{1683}$, respectively.   **(b)** About \$6881

Chapter 8: Chapter Test, page 436

1. (a) stochastic   **(b)** not stochastic   **(c)** not stochastic   **(d)** stochastic   **2. (a)** not regular   **(b)** regular

(c) regular   **3.** b   **4.** $\begin{bmatrix} \frac{3}{7} \\ \frac{4}{7} \end{bmatrix}$; $\begin{bmatrix} \frac{3}{7} & \frac{3}{7} \\ \frac{4}{7} & \frac{4}{7} \end{bmatrix}$ **5. (a)** $\begin{bmatrix} .70 & .60 \\ .30 & .40 \end{bmatrix}$ **(b)** $\begin{bmatrix} .50 \\ .50 \end{bmatrix}$ **(c)** 66.5%

(d) $\begin{bmatrix} .70 & .60 \\ .30 & .40 \end{bmatrix} \begin{bmatrix} \frac{2}{3} \\ \frac{1}{3} \end{bmatrix} = \begin{bmatrix} \frac{2}{3} \\ \frac{1}{3} \end{bmatrix}$ **6. (a)** absorbing   **(b)** not absorbing   **(c)** absorbing

7. (a)
	PC	Apple	None
PC	1	0	.3
Apple	0	1	.1
None	0	0	.6

(b) $\begin{bmatrix} 1 & 0 & \frac{3}{4} \\ 0 & 1 & \frac{1}{4} \\ 0 & 0 & 0 \end{bmatrix}$ **(c)** 25%   **(d)** 2.5 years

CHAPTER 9

Exercises 9.1, page 445

1. R: row 2; C: column 1   **3.** R: row 2; C: column 1   **5.** R: row 1; C: column 1   **7. (a)** row 1, column 2

(b) 0   **9.** $\begin{array}{c c} & \begin{array}{cc} H & T \end{array} \\ \begin{array}{c} H \\ T \end{array} & \begin{bmatrix} 2 & -1 \\ -1 & -4 \end{bmatrix} \end{array}$; strictly determined; R shows heads, C shows tails

11. $\begin{array}{c c} & \begin{array}{ccc} F & A & N \end{array} \\ \begin{array}{c} F \\ A \\ N \end{array} & \begin{bmatrix} 8000 & -1000 & 1000 \\ -7000 & 4000 & -2000 \\ 3000 & 3000 & 2000 \end{bmatrix} \end{array}$; strictly determined; both should be neutral   **13.** $\begin{array}{c c} & \begin{array}{ccc} 6 & 7 & 8 \end{array} \\ \begin{array}{c} 5 \\ 10 \end{array} & \begin{bmatrix} 1 & -5 & -5 \\ -6 & 3 & 2 \end{bmatrix} \end{array}$; not

strictly determined

Exercises 9.2, page 451

1. (a) 0   **(b)** 1   **(c)** -1.12 **(d)** .5 [b is most advantageous to R]   **3.** \$29,200   **5.** 0   **7.** No, no saddle

point, yes, $\begin{bmatrix} \frac{11}{16} \\ \frac{5}{16} \end{bmatrix}$ **9.** No, no saddle point, yes, $\begin{bmatrix} \frac{1}{30} \\ \frac{29}{30} \end{bmatrix}$ **11.** Yes, Renée row 1, Carlos column 1; value = 1; no

Exercises 9.3, page 461

1. Minimize $y_1 + y_2$ subject to $\begin{cases} y_1 + 4y_2 \geq 1 \\ 6y_1 + 3y_2 \geq 1 \\ y_1 \geq 0, \ y_2 \geq 0 \end{cases}$ **3.** $\begin{bmatrix} \frac{1}{2} & \frac{1}{2} \end{bmatrix}$; $\begin{bmatrix} \frac{1}{4} \\ \frac{3}{4} \end{bmatrix}$ **5.** $\begin{bmatrix} \frac{1}{2} & \frac{1}{2} \end{bmatrix}$; $\begin{bmatrix} \frac{5}{9} \\ \frac{4}{9} \end{bmatrix}$ **7.** $\begin{bmatrix} \frac{2}{5} & \frac{3}{5} \end{bmatrix}$; $\begin{bmatrix} \frac{3}{5} \\ \frac{2}{5} \end{bmatrix}$

9. $\begin{bmatrix} \frac{7}{13} & \frac{6}{13} \end{bmatrix}$ **11.** $\begin{bmatrix} \frac{1}{5} \\ \frac{4}{5} \end{bmatrix}$ **13.** No, Carlos: $\begin{bmatrix} \frac{1}{3} \\ \frac{2}{3} \end{bmatrix}$, Renée: $\begin{bmatrix} \frac{1}{3} \\ \frac{2}{3} \end{bmatrix}$, $v = -\frac{1}{3}$ **15. (a)** $\begin{bmatrix} \frac{8}{17} & \frac{9}{17} \end{bmatrix}$ **(b)** $\begin{bmatrix} \frac{8}{17} \\ \frac{9}{17} \end{bmatrix}$

(c) about \$2765   **17.** $\begin{bmatrix} \frac{5}{8} & \frac{3}{8} & 0 \end{bmatrix}$; $\begin{bmatrix} \frac{1}{2} \\ \frac{1}{2} \end{bmatrix}$

Chapter 9: Supplementary Exercises, page 464

1. Strictly determined; $R\,3$, $C\,3$; 2   **2.** Not strictly determined   **3.** Not strictly determined   **4.** Strictly determined; $R\,1$, $C\,2$; 1   **5.** 7   **6.** 2   **7.** 1.4   **8.** -1.3 **9.** $\begin{bmatrix} \frac{4}{11} & \frac{7}{11} \end{bmatrix}$; $\begin{bmatrix} \frac{6}{11} \\ \frac{5}{11} \end{bmatrix}$ **10.** $\begin{bmatrix} \frac{8}{17} & \frac{9}{17} \end{bmatrix}$; $\begin{bmatrix} \frac{10}{17} \\ \frac{7}{17} \end{bmatrix}$ **11.** $\begin{bmatrix} 0 & 1 \end{bmatrix}$

12. $\begin{bmatrix} \frac{1}{4} \\ \frac{3}{4} \end{bmatrix}$ **13. (a)** Carol should play the two $\frac{9}{14}$ of the time and the six $\frac{5}{14}$ of the time. Ruth should play the two $\frac{5}{14}$ of the time and the six $\frac{9}{14}$ of the time.   **(b)** Ruth   **14. (a)**

$$\begin{array}{c} \\ A \\ B \\ C \end{array} \begin{array}{ccc} S & A & W \\ \begin{bmatrix} 3000 & 2000 & 1000 \\ 6000 & 2000 & -3000 \\ 15{,}000 & 1000 & -10{,}000 \end{bmatrix} \end{array}$$

(b) Buy stock A   **15.** Consider the optimal strategies using the maxima/minima technique.   **16.** $h < 4$

Chapter 9: Chapter Test, page 465

1. (a) A move R_1 by R and C_3 by C results in a payoff of 6 to R.   **(b)** A move R_3 by R and C_2 by C results in a payoff of 10 to C.   **(c)** No   **3. (a)** row 3, column 2, value $= 2$ **(b)** row 1, column 1, value $= 0$

4.
$$\begin{array}{c} \\ 1 \\ 2 \\ 3 \\ 4 \\ 5 \end{array} \begin{array}{ccccc} 1 & 2 & 3 & 4 & 5 \\ \begin{bmatrix} -1 & -1 & -1 & -1 & -1 \\ 2 & -2 & -2 & -2 & -2 \\ 3 & 3 & -3 & -3 & -3 \\ 4 & 4 & 4 & -4 & -4 \\ 5 & 5 & 5 & 5 & -5 \end{bmatrix} \end{array}$$; Yes; -1; C **5. (a)** On average, C gains .16 every time the game is played.

(b) $C = \begin{bmatrix} .4 \\ .1 \\ .5 \end{bmatrix}$ **6. (a)** $C = \begin{bmatrix} \frac{3}{5} \\ \frac{2}{5} \end{bmatrix}$; $R = \begin{bmatrix} \frac{9}{10} & \frac{1}{10} \end{bmatrix}$ **(b)** C

CHAPTER 10

Exercises 10.1, page 477

1. (a) $i = .01$, $n = 24$ **(b)** $i = .02$, $n = 20$ **(c)** $i = .05$, $n = 40$ **3. (a)** $i = .06$, $n = 4$, $P = \$500$, $F = \$631.24$ **(b)** $i = .005$, $n = 120$, $P = \$800$, $F = \$1455.52$ **(c)** $i = .02$, $n = 19$, $P = \$6177.88$, $F = \$9000$
5. \$1127.16   **7.** \$22,396.57   **9.** \$7180.08; \$1180.08   **11.** \$34.19   **13.** \$10,000   **15. (a)** \$3548.74   **(b)** \$451.26
(c)

Month	Interest	Balance
0		\$3548.74
1	\$17.74	\$3566.48
2	\$17.83	\$3584.31
3	\$17.92	\$3602.23

17. \$12,824.32   **19.** \$8874.49   **21. (a)** 6%   **(b)** \$5.05; \$1015.08   **(c)** \$5.61; \$1127.16   **23.** \$1700 in 9 years   **25.** Better   **27.** \$8874.49   **29. (a)** $r = .04$, $n = \frac{1}{2}$, $P = \$500$, $F = \$510$ **(b)** $r = .05$, $n = 2$, $P = \$500$, $F = \$550$ **31.** \$1150   **33.** \$2500   **35.** 4.08%   **37.** 10   **39.** 20 years   **41.** $P = \dfrac{F}{1 + nr}$ **43.** a   **45.** \$104.06; 4.06%   **47.** 4.04%   **49.** 4.49%   **51.** 4%   **53.** 18 yrs.   **55.** d   **57.** $\approx 4.9\%$ **59.** 4.6   **61.** \$1065; \$1134.23; \$1207.95; 8; 12   **63.** 30 years   **65.** 11

Exercises 10.2, page 487

1. (a) $i = .005$, $n = 120$, $R = \$50$, $F = \$8193.97$ **(b)** $i = .02$, $n = 20$, $R = \$8231.34$, $F = \$200{,}000$

3. $23,123.67   **5.** $4698.97   **7. (a)** $27,048.92   **(b)** $3048.92   **(c)**

Month	Interest	Balance
1		500
2	2.50	1002.50
3	5.01	1507.51

9. $305.06; $10,982.16, $1017.84   **11.** $200 each month; $343.75   **13.** $24,649.92   **15.** $2.5 billion   **17.** No; $277,151.11   **19.** $43,839.83   **21.** $877.91   **23.** $1000 at the end of each month   **25.** $7239.32   **27.** $17,584.62   **29.** $1800   **31.** a   **33.** $24,000   **35.** $4339.35   **37.** $591,898.46   **39.** $5600.40   **41. (a)** $1269.67   **(b)** $65,134.88   **43.** $B_{\text{new}} = (1 + i)B_{\text{previous}} - R$ **45.** $2050, $3152.50, $4310.13; 19; 26   **47.** After 33 weeks   **49.** $4734.59

Exercises 10.3, page 496

1. $193.33   **3.** $11,469.92   **5. (a)** $583.31   **(b)** $16.69   **(c)** $58,314.31   **(d)** $26,973.02   **(e)** $4188.65   **(f)** $269.73   **7. (a)** $265.71   **(b)** $9565.56   **(c)** $1565.56   **(d)** $5644.58   **(e)** $2990.59   **(f)** $534.53   **9.** $8950   **11.** $14,042.36

(g)

Payment number	Amount	Interest	Applied to principal	Unpaid balance
1	$265.71	$80.00	$185.71	$7814.29
2	265.71	78.14	187.57	7626.72
3	265.71	76.27	189.44	7437.28
4	265.71	74.37	191.34	7245.94

13.

Payment number	Amount	Interest	Applied to principal	Unpaid balance
1	$256.28	$10.00	$246.28	$753.72
2	256.28	7.54	248.74	504.98
3	256.28	5.05	251.23	253.74
4	256.28	2.54	253.74	0.00

15. $1856.92   **17.** $119,161.62   **19.** $1196.68   **21.** a   **23. (a)** $183,927.96   **(b)** $24,989.92   **(c)** $105,266.63   **25. (a)** $722.22   **(b)** $760.55   **(c)** a   **27.** 26.56%   **29.** $346.81   **31. (d)** $101, $102.01   **33.** $2105.33, $2021.12, $1936.28, 24 months   **35.** $4258.21; after 46 months   **37.** 261   **39. (a)** $871.11   **(b)** $869.69   **(c)** b

Exercises 10.4, page 513

1. deferred   **3.** $165,000   **5.** $1,641,407.11   **7.** $1,641,407.11   **9. (a)** $412,330.96   **(b)** $357,362.60   **(c)** Larry   **(d)** Earl   **11.** $366.67   **13.** $105.83   **15.** 2.73%   **17.** 3.17%   **19. (a)** $41.67   **(b)** $41.07; the monthly payment is less.   **21.** False   **23.** False   **25.** False   **27.** d   **29.** a   **31.** a   **33.** c   **35.** 12*RATE(240, -573.14, 77600, 0); 12*RATE(120, -573.14, 77600, -51624.70)
37. $(((1 + i)^{180} - 1)/(i(1 + i)^{180})) \cdot 1217.12 = 118800; 1217.12 - i \cdot 96081.51 = (1217.12 - i \cdot 118800)(1 + i)^{60}$
39. The salesman should compare the present value of the loan payments with the $1000.   **41.** $1150; $2311.87   **43. (a)** $1610.75   **(b)** $224,829.73   **(c)** $1729.63   **45. (a)** $219,418.04   **(b)** $2181.80   **(c)** $1850.70   **(d)** $1865.05   **(e)** $219,432.39   **47.** 11.08%   **49.** 6.83%   **51.** 7.08%   **53.** 87.72 months   **55.** 128.63 months

Chapter 10: Supplementary Exercises, page 518

1. (d)   **2.** $1464.49   **3.** $101,497   **4.** $53.79   **5.** 10% compounded annually   **6.** $13,954.01   **7. (a)** $2400.34   **(b)** $167,304.95   **8.** $43,665.52   **9.** $27,481.64   **10.** $13,050.08   **11.** $211.37   **12.** $12,050.34   **13.** $782.92   **14.** $6872.11   **15.** $100,451.50   **16.** $139,401.04   **17.** Investment A   **18.** Yes, it is a bargain since the present value is $879.57.   **19.** 10.25%   **20.** 19.56%   **21.** $146,861.85

22.

Payment number	Amount	Interest	Applied to principal	Unpaid balance
1	$304.22	$50.00	$254.22	$9745.78
2	304.22	48.73	255.49	9490.29
3	304.22	47.45	256.77	9233.52
4	304.22	46.17	258.05	8975.47
5	304.22	44.88	259.34	8716.13
6	304.22	43.58	260.64	8455.49

23. $151,843.34   **24.** $5799.84   **25.** $1206.93
26. (a) $21,000   **(b)** $26,095.40
27. (a) $30,000   **(b)** $40,146.77   **28.** 4.82%
29. Consumer Loan A, The monthly payment for loan B is $265.00.   **30.** $P = 88,200$, $n = 180$, $R = 759.47$ **31.** $P = 97,000$, $m = 72$, $R = 716.43$; $B = 81,298.32$ **32.** $i = .035/12$, $R = 63.15$, $P = 2000$ **35.** $2185; $3394.34
36. (a) $1458.08   **(b)** $198,690.34   **(c)** $1582.46   **37.** Higher   **38.** No   **39.** No   **40.** Decrease; increase

Chapter 10: Chapter Test, page 520

1. $524.38   **2.** $4464.29   **3.** $1189.77; $164.77   **4.** $11,263.09   **5.** $72,704.68   **6.** $21,290.16   **7.** $1095.92
8. $2533.52   **9.** $3086.04   **10.** $2187.43   **11. (a)** $166.07   **(b)** $60   **(c)** $7893.93   **(d)** $1899.00
12. $225,686.46   **13. (a)** $405,610.82   **(b)** $368,198.99   **14.** $144.44   **16. (a)** It will decrease because the cost of the points will be spread over a longer period of time.   **(b)** Increasing the number of points will increase the effective cost of the loan, therefore, increasing its interest rate.   **17.** If there are no points, or the mortgage is not terminated early.   **18.** $3250; $4120.18

CHAPTER 11

Exercises 11.1, page 531

1. $4, -6; 2$ **3.** $-\frac{1}{2}, 0; 0$ **5.** $-\frac{2}{3}, 15; 9$

7. (a) $10, 4, 1, -\frac{1}{2}, -\frac{5}{4}$ **(b)**

(c) $y_n = -2 + 12 \left(\frac{1}{2}\right)^n$

9. (a) $3.5, 4, 5, 7, 11$ **(b)**

(c) $y_n = 3 + (.5)2^n$

11. (a) $17.5, 0, 7, 4.2, 5.32$ **(b)**

(c) $y_n = 5 + 12.5(-.4)^n$

13. (a) 15, 14, 12, 8, 0   **(b)**

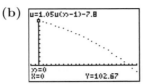

(c) $y_n = 16 - 2^n$ **15.** 1, 5, 5.8, 5.96, 5.992
17. $y_n = 1.05y_{n-1}, y_0 = 1000$
19. $y_n = .99y_{n-1} - 1,000,000, y_0 = 70,000,000$
21. (a) 1, 3, 5, 7, 9   **(b)** The points lie on a straight line.   **(c)** $a = 1$, so the denominator of $\frac{b}{1-a}$ is zero.   **23.** $30

25. (a) $y_n = 1.04y_{n-1} + 250; y_0 = 800$ **(b)** $y_n = -6250 + 7050(1.04)^n$ **(c)** about $3027.32
27. (a) $y_n = .85y_{n-1}, y_0 = 20,000$ **(b)** $y_n = 20,000(.85)^n$ **(c)** $8,874.11

29. (a)

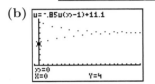

(b)

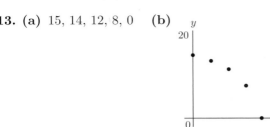

(c) 50.41; 22   **31. (a)**

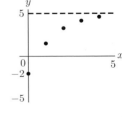

(b)

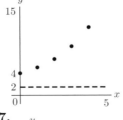

(c) 5.715516; $n \geq 19$ **33. (a)**

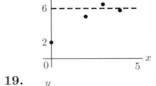

(b)

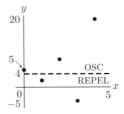

(c) 4.831059; $n \geq 20$

Exercises 11.2, page 537

1. $y_n = 1 + 5n$ **3.** $80(1.0075)^{60}$ **5.** $80\left(1 + \frac{1}{365}\right)^{1825}$ **7.** 108   **9. (a)** $1.40   **(b)** $1.44   **(c)** $1.46
11. (a) 10, 10, 10, 10, 10; points lie on a horizontal line   **(b)** 11, 12, 14, 18, 26; points curve upward   **(c)** 9, 8, 6, 2, −6; points curve downward   **13.** $y_n = 5 + 2(.4)^n$; y_n approaches 5   **15.** $y_n = 2(-5)^n$; y_n gets arbitrarily large, alternating between being positive and negative.   **17.** $y_n = 1.0055y_{n-1} - 1600, y_0 = 250,525$
19. $y_n = y_{n-1} - 2000, y_0 = 50,000$; $y_n = 50,000 - 2000n$ **21.** b   **23.** c   **25.** c   **27.** c   **29.** $1195.62; $8\frac{1}{2}$ years; 47   **31.** $245; 12 years; 23   **33.** 22   **35.** 60

Exercises 11.3, page 546

1. a, b, d, f, h
3. b, d, e, f
5. b, d, e, f
7. a, c, h, possibly g

9. Possible answer:

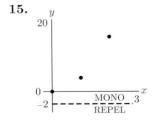

11. Possible answer:

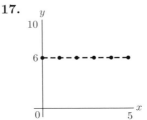

13. Possible answer:

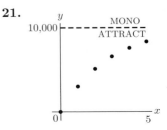

15.

17.

19.

21.

23.

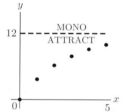

25. less than $60,000   **27. (a)** $y_n = 1.06y_{n-1} - 120$ **(b)** at least $2000
29. less than $30,000   **31.** Possible answer: $y_n = .5y_{n-1} + 4$, $y_0 = 1$
33. Possible answer: $y_n = 2y_{n-1}$, $y_0 = 1$
35. Possible answer: $y_n = -2y_{n-1}$, $y_0 = 5$

Exercises 11.4, page 552

1. $y_n = 1.0075y_{n-1} - 261.50$, $y_0 = 32,500$ **3.** $y_n = 1.015y_{n-1} + 200$, $y_0 = 4000$ **5.** $46,002.34   **7.** $11,035.68
9. $28.55   **11.** $132.86   **13.** $39.205 million; 30   **15.** $505.03; $1022.80; $1553.65; 30; 37

Exercises 11.5, page 556

1. $y_n = 1.02y_{n-1}$, $y_0 = 100$ million   **3.** $y_n = .75y_{n-1}$ **5.** $y_n = .92y_{n-1} + 8$, $y_0 = 0$

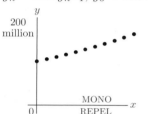

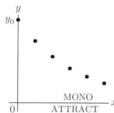

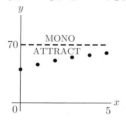

7. $y_n = .7y_{n-1} + 3.6$, $y_0 = 0$ **9.** $y_n = 1.05y_{n-1} - 1000$, $y_0 = 30,000$ **11.** $y_n = .8y_{n-1} + 14$, $y_0 = 40$

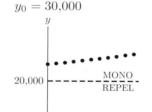

13. $p_n = -.5p_{n-1} + 21$, $p_0 = 4.54$ **15.** b   **17.** 5.38 million; 2022; 2056   **19.** $y_n = .87y_{n-1}$, $y_0 = 130$;

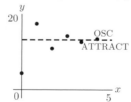

$y_n = 130(.87)^n$; 5 hours; 4.6 mg

Chapter 11: Supplementary Exercises, page 560

1. (a) 5; -7; 29   **(b)** $y_n = 2 - (-3)^n$ **(c)** -79 **2. (a)** $\frac{17}{2}$; 7; $\frac{11}{2}$ **(b)** $y_n = 10 - \frac{3}{2}n$ **(c)** 1   **3.** $2000.00
4. $1109.54   **5.**   **6.**   **7. (a)** $y_n = 1.03y_{n-1} - 600$, $y_0 = 120,000$
(b) 200,611   **8. (a)** $y_n = 1.01y_{n-1} - 360$, $y_0 = 35,000$ **(b)** $33,693.28   **9.** $20.22
10. $237.14   **11.** $22,492.53   **12.** $2,704.89

13. $y_n = .9y_{n-1} + 100{,}000$, $y_0 = 0$ **14.** $y_n = .92y_{n-1}$, $y_0 = 100$

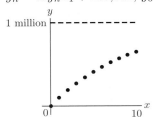   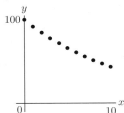

Chapter 11: Chapter Test, page 561

1. (a) $2, 4, 5$ (b) $y_n = 6 - 8\left(\frac{1}{2}\right)^n$ (c) 5.5 **2.** (a) $110, 160, 210$ (b) $y_n = 60 + 50n$ (c) 260
3. (a)   (b)   **4.** $.3$ ppm   **5.** (a) $\$31{,}726$ (b) 8%
(c) $\$3000$ (d) $\$29{,}360.52$
6. (a) $\$454.15$ (b) 12.5%
(c) $\$9{,}245.85$; $\$8{,}526.44$; $\$361.57$
7. $\$119{,}161.62$
8. (a) $y_n = 1.06y_{n-1} + 500$; $y_0 = 0$
(b) $\$14{,}106.44$ **9.** $\$122.04$
10. $y_n = .9y_{n-1} + .05$; $y_0 = 0$. The graph begins at the origin, increases monotonically, and approaches the line $y = .5$.

CHAPTER 12

Exercises 12.1, page 567

1. Statement   **3.** Statement   **5.** Not a statement   **7.** Not a statement   **9.** Statement   **11.** Not a statement
13. Not a statement   **15.** Statement   **17.** p: The Phelps Library is in New York.
q: The Phelps Library is in Dallas.
$p \vee q$
19. p: The Smithsonian Museum of Natural History has displays of rocks.
q: The Smithsonian Museum of Natural History has displays of bugs.
$p \wedge q$
21. p: Amtrak trains go to Chicago.
q: Amtrak trains go to Cincinnati.
$\sim p \wedge \sim q$ or $\sim(p \vee q)$
23. (a) Ozone is opaque to ultraviolet light, and life on earth requires ozone.   (b) Ozone is not opaque to ultraviolet light, or life on earth requires ozone.   (c) Ozone is not opaque to ultraviolet light, or life on earth does not require ozone.   (d) It is not the case that life on earth does not require ozone.   **25.** (a) $p \vee q$
(b) $p \wedge \sim q$ (c) $q \wedge \sim p$ (d) $\sim p \wedge \sim q$

Exercises 12.2, page 575

5.

p	q	$p \wedge \sim q$
T	T	**F** F
T	F	**T** T
F	T	**F** F
F	F	**F** T

7.

p	q	$(p \vee \sim q)$	$\vee$	$\sim p$
T	T	T F	**T**	F
T	F	T T	**T**	F
F	T	F F	**T**	T
F	F	T T	**T**	T

9.

p	q	$\sim$	$((p \vee q)$	$\wedge$	$(p \wedge q))$
T	T	**F**	T	T	T
T	F	**T**	T	F	F
F	T	**T**	T	F	F
F	F	**T**	F	F	F

11.

p	q	p ⊕ (~p ∨ q)
T	T	T **F** F T T
T	F	T **T** F F F
F	T	F **T** T T T
F	F	F **T** T T F

13.

p	q	r	(p ∧ ~r) ∨ q
T	T	T	T
T	T	F	T
T	F	T	F
T	F	F	T
F	T	T	T
F	T	F	T
F	F	T	F
F	F	F	F

15.

p	q	r	~[(p ∧ r) ∨ q]
T	T	T	F
T	T	F	F
T	F	T	F
T	F	F	T
F	T	T	F
F	T	F	F
F	F	T	T
F	F	F	T

17.

p	p ∨ ~p
T	T
F	T

19.

p	q	r	p ⊕ (q ∨ r)
T	T	T	F
T	T	F	F
T	F	T	F
T	F	F	T
F	T	T	T
F	T	F	T
F	F	T	T
F	F	F	F

21.

p	q	r	(p ∨ q) ∧ (p ∨ r)
T	T	T	T
T	T	F	T
T	F	T	T
T	F	F	T
F	T	T	T
F	T	F	F
F	F	T	F
F	F	F	F

23.

p	q	(p ∨ q) ∧ ~(p ∨ q)
T	T	F
T	F	F
F	T	F
F	F	F

25.

p	q	r	~(p ∨ q) ∧ r
T	T	T	F
T	T	F	F
T	F	T	F
T	F	F	F
F	T	T	F
F	T	F	F
F	F	T	T
F	F	F	F

27.

p	q	r	~p ∨ (q ∧ r)
T	T	T	T
T	T	F	F
T	F	T	F
T	F	F	F
F	T	T	T
F	T	F	T
F	F	T	T
F	F	F	T

29. They are identical.   **31.** They are identical.   **33.** (p ∧ q) ∨ r is T and p ∧ (q ∨ r) is F when p is F and r is T. Otherwise, the tables are identical.   **35. (a)**

p	p|p
T	F
F	T

(b)

p	q	(p|p)|(q|q)
T	T	T
T	F	T
F	T	T
F	F	F

(c)

p	q	(p|q)|(p|q)
T	T	T
T	F	F
F	T	F
F	F	F

(d)

p	q	p|((p|q)|q)
T	T	F
T	F	F
F	T	T
F	F	T

37. (a) T **(b)** F **(c)** T **(d)** F **(e)** F **(f)** F **39. (a)** F **(b)** F **(c)** F

(d) F **41.** (p ⊕ q) ∧ r   **43.** (p ∨ q) ∧ (p ∨ ~r)   **45.** 0 **47. (a)** T **(b)** T **49. (a)** T **(b)** F

51.

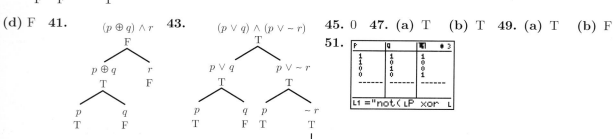

Exercises 12.3, page 582

1.

p	q	$p \to\, \sim q$
T	T	F
T	F	T
F	T	T
F	F	T

3.

p	q	$(p \oplus q) \to q$
T	T	T
T	F	F
F	T	T
F	F	T

5.

p	q	r	$(\sim p \wedge q) \to r$
T	T	T	T
T	T	F	T
T	F	T	T
T	F	F	T
F	T	T	T
F	T	F	F
F	F	T	T
F	F	F	T

7.

p	q	$(p \to q) \leftrightarrow (\sim p \vee q)$
T	T	T
T	F	T
F	T	T
F	F	T

9.

p	q	r	$(p \to q) \to r$
T	T	T	T
T	T	F	F
T	F	T	T
T	F	F	T
F	T	T	T
F	T	F	F
F	F	T	T
F	F	F	F

11.

p	q	r	$\sim (p \vee q) \to (\sim p \wedge r)$
T	T	T	T
T	T	F	T
T	F	T	T
T	F	F	T
F	T	T	T
F	T	F	T
F	F	T	T
F	F	F	F

13.

p	q	$(p \vee q) \leftrightarrow (p \wedge q)$
T	T	T
T	F	F
F	T	F
F	F	T

15.

p	q	r	$[p \wedge (q \vee r)] \leftrightarrow [(p \wedge q) \vee (p \wedge r)]$
T	T	T	T
T	T	F	T
T	F	T	T
T	F	F	T
F	T	T	T
F	T	F	T
F	F	T	T
F	F	F	T

17. $((\sim p) \wedge (\sim q)) \to ((\sim p) \wedge q)$ **19.** $(((\sim p) \wedge (\sim q)) \vee r) \to ((\sim q) \wedge r)$ **21.** T **23.** T **25.** T **27.** F **29.** T
31. $p \leftrightarrow q$ **33.** $q \to p$; hyp: q; con: p **35.** $q \to p$; hyp: q; con: p **37.** $\sim p \to\, \sim q$; hyp: $\sim p$; con: $\sim q$
39. $\sim p \to\, \sim q$; hyp: $\sim p$; con: $\sim q$; TRUE **41.** $\sim q \to\, \sim p$; hyp: $\sim q$; con: $\sim p$; TRUE **43. (a)** hyp: A person is healthy. con: The person lives a long life. **(b)** hyp: The train stops at the station. con: A passenger requests the stop. **(c)** hyp: The azalea grows. con: The azalea is exposed to sunlight. **(d)** hyp: I will go to the store. con: Jane goes to the store. **45. (a)** If City Sanitation collects the garbage, then the mayor calls.
(b) The price of beans goes down if there is no drought. **(c)** Goldfish swim in Lake Erie if Lake Erie is fresh water. **(d)** Tap water is not salted if it boils slowly. **47. (a)** 4 **(b)** 4 **(c)** 4 **(d)** 4 **(e)** 6 **(f)** 6
49. (a) 7 **(b)** 7 **(c)** 0 **(d)** 7 **(e)** 0 **(f)** 0 **51. (a)** 6 **(b)** -12 **(c)** 0 **(d)** 0 **(e)** 28 **(f)** 0
53. (a) 3 **(b)** 3 **(c)** -37 **(d)** -7 **(e)** 43 **(f)** -7

Exercises 12.4, page 590

5. (d) $p|(q|q)$ **(e)** $\sim (p \wedge q)$ **7.**

p	q	c	$(p \to q) \leftrightarrow [(p \wedge \sim q) \to c]$
T	T	F	T
T	F	F	T
F	T	F	T
F	F	F	T

9. False

11. $\sim [\sim (p \vee q) \vee \sim (\sim p \vee \sim q)]$ **13.** $\sim(p \vee q) \vee (q \wedge \sim r)$ **15.** $(p \wedge \sim q) \vee (p \vee \sim r)$ **17. (a)** Arizona does not border California, or Arizona does not border Nevada. **(b)** There are no tickets available, and the agency cannot get tickets. **(c)** The killer's hat was neither white nor gray. **19.** $\sim p \wedge q \wedge \sim r$ **21. (a)** Jeremy does not take 12 credits and Jeremy does not take 15 credits this semester. **(b)** Sandra did not receive a gift from

Sally or Sandra did not receive a gift from Sacha.   **23. (a)** "The Old Man and the Sea" was written by Ernest Hemingway or "The Old Man and the Sea" was written by Jack London. "The Old Man and the Sea" was not written by Ernest Hemingway and not written by Jack London.   **(b)** "H. M. S. Pinafore" was written by Gilbert and "H. M. S. Pinafore" was written by Sullivan. "H. M. S. Pinafore" was not written by Gilbert or not written by Sullivan.   **25. (a)** I have a ticket to the theater, and I did not spend a lot of money.
(b) Basketball is played on an indoor court, and the players do not wear sneakers.   **(c)** The stock market is going up, and interest rates are not going down.   **(d)** Humans have enough water, and humans are not staying healthy.   **27. (a)** If the number of odd numbers in a sum is even, then the sum is even. (T)   **(b)** If K is next to W, then the computer keyboard is not standard. (T)   **29. (a)** Contrapositive: If a bird is not a hummingbird, then it is not small. (F) Converse: If a bird is a hummingbird, then it is small. (T)
(b) Contrapositive: If two nonvertical lines are not parallel, they do not have the same slope. (T) Converse: If two nonvertical lines are parallel, they have the same slope. (T)   **(c)** Contrapositive: If we are not in France, then we are not in Paris. (T) Converse: If we are in France, we must be in Paris. (F)   **(d)** Contrapositive: If you can legally make a U-turn, then the road is not one-way. (T) Converse: If you cannot legally make a U-turn, then the road is one-way. (F)   **31.** Ask either guard, "If I asked you whether your door was the door to freedom, would you say yes?"   **33.**

p	q	r	$(p \to q)$	$\wedge$	$(q \to r)$	$\implies$	$(p \to r)$
T	T	T	T	T	T	**T**	T
T	T	F	T	F	F	**T**	F
T	F	T	F	F	T	**T**	T
T	F	F	F	F	T	**T**	F
F	T	T	T	T	T	**T**	T
F	T	F	T	F	F	**T**	T
F	F	T	T	T	T	**T**	T
F	F	F	T	T	T	**T**	T

Exercises 12.5, page 597

1. $m =$ "Sue goes to the movies."
$r =$ "Sue reads."

1.	$m \vee r$	hyp.
2.	$\sim m$	hyp.
3.	r	disj. syll. (1, 2)

3. $a =$ "My allowance comes this week."
$p =$ "I pay the rent."
$b =$ "My bank account will be in the black."
$e =$ "I will be evicted."

1.	$(a \wedge p) \to b$	hyp.
2.	$\sim p \to e$	hyp.
3.	$\sim e \wedge a$	hyp.
4.	$\sim e$	subtr. (3)
5.	p	mod. tollens (2, 4)
6.	a	subtr. (3)
7.	b	mod. ponens (5, 6, 1)

5. $p =$ "The price of oil increases."
$a =$ "The OPEC countries are in agreement."
$d =$ "There is a U.N. debate."

1.	$p \to a$	hyp.
2.	$\sim d \to p$	hyp.
3.	$\sim a$	hyp.
4.	$\sim p$	mod. tollens (1, 3)
5.	d	mod. tollens (2, 4)

7. $g =$ "The germ is present."
$r =$ "The rash is present."
$f =$ "The fever is present."

1.	$g \to (r \wedge f)$	hyp.
2.	f	hyp.
3.	$\sim r$	hyp.
4.	$\sim r \vee \sim f$	addition (3)
5.	$\sim (r \wedge f)$	De Morgan (4)
6.	$\sim g$	mod. tollens (1, 5)

9. c = "The material is cotton."
r = "The material is rayon."
d = "The material can be made into a dress."

1.	$(c \vee r) \to d$	hyp.
2.	$\sim d$	hyp.
3.	$\sim (c \vee r)$	mod. tollens (1, 2)
4.	$\sim c \wedge \sim r$	De Morgan (3)
5.	$\sim r$	subtraction (4)

11. Invalid **13.** Valid **15.** Valid **17.** Invalid **19.** Invalid

21. s = "Sam goes to the store."
m = "Sam needs milk."
$H_1 = s \to m$
$H_2 = \sim m$
$C = \sim s$

1.	s	$\sim C$
2.	$s \to m$	H_1
3.	m	$\sim H_2$; mod. ponens (1, 2)

23. n = "The newspaper reports the crime."
t = "Television reports the crime."
s = "The crime is serious."
k = "A person is killed."
$H_1 = (n \wedge t) \to s$
$H_2 = k \to n$
$H_3 = k$
$H_4 = t$
$C = s$

1.	$\sim s$	$\sim C$
2.	$(n \wedge t) \to s$	H_1
3.	$\sim (n \wedge t)$	mod. tollens (1, 2)
4.	$\sim n \vee \sim t$	De Morgan (3)
5.	t	H_4
6.	$\sim n$	disj. syllogism (4, 5)
7.	$k \to n$	H_2
8.	$\sim k$	$\sim H_3$; mod. tollens (6, 7)

25. j = "Jimmy finds his keys."
h = "He does his homework."

Direct proof

1.	$\sim j \to h$	H_1
2.	$\sim h$	H_2
3.	j	mod. tollens (1, 2)

Indirect proof

1.	$\sim j$	$\sim C$
2.	$\sim j \to h$	H_1
3.	h	mod. ponens (1, 2)
4.	$\sim h$	H_2

$\}$ contradiction

27. m = "Marissa goes to the movies."
k = "Marissa is in a knitting class."
i = "Marissa is idle."

1.	$\sim m \to \sim i$	H_1
2.	$\sim k \to i$	H_2
3.	$\sim k$	H_3
4.	i	mod. ponens (2, 3)
5.	m	mod. tollens (1, 4)

Exercises 12.6, page 605

1. (a) F **(b)** T **(c)** T **(d)** T **(e)** F **3. (a)** $\forall x\, p(x)$ **(b)** $\sim [\forall x\, p(x)]$ **(c)** $\forall x \sim p(x)$ **(d)** (c) implies (b) **5.** $\forall x \sim p(x)$, or $\sim [\exists x\, p(x)]$. This is FALSE. Abby meant to say, "Not all men cheat on their wives." **7. (a)** $\forall x\, p(x)$ **(b)** $\exists x \sim p(x)$ **(c)** $\exists x\, p(x)$ **(d)** $\sim [\forall x\, p(x)]$ **(e)** $\forall x \sim p(x)$ **(f)** $\sim [\exists x\, p(x)]$ **(g)** (b) and (d); (e) and (f) **9. (a)** T **(b)** F **11. (a)** T **(b)** F **(c)** T **(d)** F **(e)** F **(f)** T **(g)** F **(h)** T **13. (a)** Not every dog has his day. **(b)** No men fight wars. **(c)** Some mothers are unmarried. **(d)** There exists a pot without a cover. **(e)** All children have pets. **(f)** Every month has 30 days. **15. (a)** "The sum of any two nonnegative integers is greater than 12." FALSE: let $x = 1$, $y = 2$. "There exist two nonnegative integers whose sum is not greater than 12." **(b)** "For any nonnegative integer, there is another nonnegative integer that, added to the first, makes a sum greater than 12." TRUE. **(c)** "There is a nonnegative integer that, added to any other nonnegative integer, makes a sum greater than 12." TRUE. **(d)** "There are two nonnegative integers the sum of which is greater than 12." TRUE. **17. (a)** FALSE: let $x = 2, y = 3$. **(b)** TRUE: for any x, let $y = x$. **(c)** TRUE: let $x = 1$. **(d)** FALSE: no y is divisible by every x. **(e)** TRUE: for any y, let $x = y$. **(f)** TRUE: any x divides itself. **19. (a)** $\forall x[x \geq 8 \to x \leq 10]$ **(b)** No; consider $x = 11$. **21.** $S = \{2, 4, 6, 8\}, T = \{1, 2, 3, 4, 6, 8\}$. So $\forall x[x \in S \to x \in T]$.

23. The solutions to $(x-8)(x-3) = 0$ are 8 and 3. The solutions to $x^2 = 9$ are -3 and 3. Therefore, $S = T = \{3\}$. So, $\forall x(x \in S \leftrightarrow x \in T)$.

Exercises 12.7, page 610

1. $(p \vee q) \wedge (p \vee \sim q)$ **3.** $((p \wedge q) \wedge \sim r) \wedge (\sim q \vee r)$ **5.** p ————————— ; 1

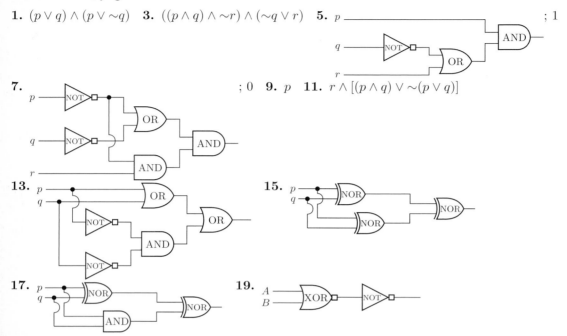

7. ; 0   **9.** p **11.** $r \wedge [(p \wedge q) \vee \sim(p \vee q)]$

13. **15.**

17. **19.**

Chapter 12: Supplementary Exercises, page 614

1. (a) Statement   **(b)** Not a statement   **(c)** Statement   **(d)** Not a statement   **(e)** Statement   **2. (a)** If two lines are perpendicular, then their slopes are negative reciprocals of each other.   **(b)** If goldfish can live in a fishbowl, then the water is aerated.   **(c)** If it rains, then Jane uses her umbrella.   **(d)** If Sally gives Morris a treat, then he ate all his food.   **3. (a)** Contrapositive: If the Yankees are not playing in Yankee Stadium, then they are not in New York City; Converse: If the Yankees are playing in Yankee Stadium, then they are in New York City.   **(b)** Contrapositive: If the earthquake is not considered major, then the Richter scale does not indicate the quake is a 7; Converse: If the earthquake is considered major, then the Richter scale indicates the quake is a 7.   **(c)** Contrapositive: If the coat is not warm, then it is not made of fur; Converse: If the coat is warm, then it is made of fur.   **(d)** Contrapositive: If Jane is not in Moscow, then she is not in Russia; Converse: If Jane is in Moscow, then she is in Russia.   **4. (a)** Two triangles are similar but their sides are unequal.   **(b)** For every real number x, $x^2 \neq 5$.   **(c)** There exists a positive integer n such that n is even and n^2 is not even.   **(d)** For every real number x, $x^2 + 4 \neq 0$.   **5. (a)** Tautology   **(b)** Tautology   **(c)** Not a tautology   **(d)** Not a tautology   **6. (a)**

p	q	r	$p \to (\sim q \vee r)$
T	T	T	T
T	T	F	F
T	F	T	T
T	F	F	T
F	T	T	T
F	T	F	T
F	F	T	T
F	F	F	T

(b)

p	q	r	$p \wedge (q \leftrightarrow (r \wedge p))$
T	T	T	T
T	T	F	F
T	F	T	F
T	F	F	T
F	T	T	F
F	T	F	F
F	F	T	F
F	F	F	F

7. (a) True   **(b)** False   **8. (a)** True   **(b)** False   **9. (a)** False   **(b)** True   **10. (a)** 17   **(b)** 100   **(c)** 100   **(d)** 100   **11. (a)** 50   **(b)** -25 **(c)** -15 **(d)** 10   **12. (a)** Cannot be determined   **(b)** TRUE

(c) TRUE   **(d)** Cannot be determined   **(e)** Cannot be determined   **13. (a)** Cannot be determined
(b) Cannot be determined   **(c)** TRUE   **14. (a)** TRUE   **(b)** FALSE   **(c)** TRUE   **15. (a)** Cannot be
determined   **(b)** Cannot be determined   **(c)** TRUE

16. $t =$ "Taxes go up."

$s =$ "I sell the house."	1. $t \rightarrow (s \wedge m)$	hyp.
$m =$ "I move to India."	2. $\sim m$	hyp.
	3. $\sim s \vee \sim m$	addition (2)
	4. $\sim (s \wedge m)$	De Morgan (3)
	5. $\sim t$	mod. tollens (1, 4)

17. $m =$ "I study mathematics."

$b =$ "I study business."	1. $m \wedge b$	hyp.
$p =$ "I can write poetry."	2. $b \rightarrow (\sim p \vee \sim m)$	hyp.
	3. b	subtraction (1)
	4. $\sim p \vee \sim m$	mod. ponens (2, 3)
	5. m	subtraction (1)
	6. $\sim p$	disj. syllogism (4, 5)

18. $d =$ "I shop for a dress."

$h =$ "I wear high heels."	1. $d \rightarrow h$	hyp.
$s =$ "I have a sore foot."	2. $s \rightarrow \sim h$	hyp.
	3. d	hyp.
	4. h	mod. ponens (1, 3)
	5. $\sim s$	mod. tollens (2, 4)

19. $a =$ "Asters grow in the garden."

$d =$ "Dahlias grow in the garden."	1. $a \vee d$	hyp.
$s =$ "It is spring."	2. $s \rightarrow \sim a$	hyp.
	3. s	hyp.
	4. $\sim a$	mod. ponens (2, 3)
	5. d	disj. syllogism (1, 4)

20. $t =$ "The professor gives a test."

$h =$ "Nancy studies hard."	1. $\sim h$	$\sim$C
$d =$ "Nancy has a date."	2. $t \rightarrow h$	H_1
$s =$ "Nancy takes a shower."	3. $\sim t$	mod. tollens (1, 2)
$H_1 = t \rightarrow h$	4. $\sim t \rightarrow \sim s$	H_3
$H_2 = d \rightarrow s$	5. $\sim s$	mod. ponens (3, 4)
$H_3 = \sim t \rightarrow \sim s$	6. $d \rightarrow s$	H_2
$H_4 = d$	7. $\sim d$	$\sim H_4$; mod tollens (5, 6)
$C = h$		

21.

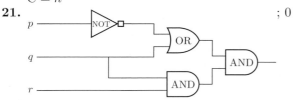

; 0

22. $p \wedge \sim q \wedge r$ **23.** $(p$ NOR $q)$ NOR $(p$ AND $q)$

24.

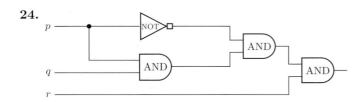

25.

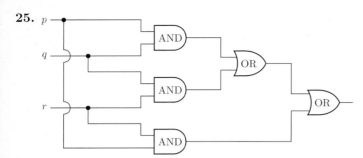

Chapter 12: Chapter Test, page 615

1.

p	q	$(p \wedge \sim q) \to q$
T	T	T
T	F	F
F	T	T
F	F	T

2. (a) Statement   **(b)** Not a Statement   **(c)** Statement   **(d)** Statement
(e) Not a Statement   **3.** If the coach does not buy Bob ice cream, then Bob did not hit a triple or a home run.
4. Every integer is either even or greater than 8.   **5.** False; True   **6. (a)** Neither   **(b)** Tautology
(c) Contradiction   **7. (a)** True   **(b)** False   **(c)** True   **(d)** False   **8.** The argument is valid.
9. (a) Every English dictionary contains the word "Internet."   **(b)** There is a student at the university who
does not listen to jazz.   **(c)** There is a floor at which the elevator does not stop.   **10. (a)** $p \to q$
(b) $q \to p$ **(c)** $p \to q$ **(d)** $p \to q$ **(e)** $q \to p$ **11. (a)** -19 **(b)** 0   **(c)** 180   **(d)** 0   **12. (a)** False
(b) True   **13.**   **14.**   ; 0

INDEX